INTERNATIONAL SERIES OF MONOGRAPHS ON PURE AND APPLIED BIOLOGY

Division: ZOOLOGY

General Editor: G. A. Kerkut

Volume 16

THE EVOLUTION OF THE METAZOA

OTHER TITLES IN THE ZOOLOGY DIVISION

GENERAL EDITOR G. A. KERKUT

Vol. 1. RAVEN — *An Outline of Developmental Physiology*
Vol. 2. RAVEN — *Morphogenesis: The Analysis of Molluscan Development*
Vol. 3. SAVORY — *Instinctive Living*
Vol. 4. KERKUT — *Implications of Evolution*
Vol. 5. TARTAR — *Biology of Stentor*
Vol. 6. JENKINS — *Animal Hormones*
Vol. 7. CORLISS — *The Ciliated Protozoa*
Vol. 8. GEORGE — *The Brain as a Computer*
Vol. 9. ARTHUR — *Ticks and Disease*
Vol. 10. RAVEN — *Oogenesis*
Vol. 11. MANN — *Leeches*
Vol. 12. SLEIGH — *The Biology of Cilia and Flagella*
Vol. 13. PITELKA — *Electron-Microscopic Structure of Protozoa*
Vol. 14. FINGERMAN — *The Control of Chromatophores*
Vol. 15. LAVERACK — *The Physiology of Earthworms*

OTHER DIVISIONS IN THE SERIES ON PURE AND APPLIED BIOLOGY

BIOCHEMISTRY

BOTANY

MODERN TRENDS
IN PHYSIOLOGICAL SCIENCES

PLANT PHYSIOLOGY

THE EVOLUTION
OF THE
METAZOA

PROFESSOR JOVAN HADŽI
Slovenska Akademija Znanosti in Umetnosti
Ljubljana

A Pergamon Press Book

THE MACMILLAN COMPANY
NEW YORK
1963

THE MACMILLAN COMPANY
60 Fifth Avenue
New York 11, N. Y.

This book is distributed by
THE MACMILLAN COMPANY
pursuant to a special arrangement with
PERGAMON PRESS LIMITED
Oxford, England

Library of Congress Card Number 63-10129

Made in Great Britain

CONTENTS

Preface vii
Introduction x

Chapter 1. Cnidaria as the Only Coelenterata 1
The systematic position of the Spongiae 1
The systematic position of the Ctenophora 8
Cnidaria as the only Coelenterata 23
Something about the methods that can be used in connection with the construction of the natural animal system 28
The significance of the sessile way of life 47
The role of the polymerization and of subsequent oligomerization during the phylogeny 52
The validity of Watson's rule for the Invertebrates 68

Chapter 2. The Previous Interpretations of Cnidaria 73
The origin of Cnidaria 87
The right sequence of the Cnidaria groups 95
Why is there no medusa form in Anthozoa? 103
The primarily solitary polyps appear in Anthozoa only 106
Polymorphism has reached its climax in Hydrozoa 109
The regressive development of the intermediate layer in Cnidaria 112
The morphologic proofs of the new interpretation of the phylogeny of Cnidaria 114
Muscular tisue 114
The nervous system 124
The emunctory-excretory organ 137
The genital system 145
The alternation of generations in Cnidaria 153
The digestive system 163
The skin and cnidae 190
Ontogeny (The development of the embryo) 204
Asexual reproduction and the regeneration 213
The endosymbiotic mononuclear algae 222

Chapter 3. The Consequences of the New Interpretation of Cnidaria 226
The new system of the Cnidaria 229
The rank and the position of Cnidaria in the animal system .. 243
Discussion of the new interpretation of the evolution of Cnidaria 245
The probable origin of Cnidaria 248
The larvae of Cnidaria 259
A comparison of Cnidaria larvae with other larvae 266
The origin of the Turbellaria 269
The origin of the acoelous Turbellaria 273

The relationship between conjugation and copulation 280
The point of separation of the evolutions of Infusoria and Eumetazoa 298
The origin of the complex, hypercellular individualities 305
Is the plasmodial state of the Acoela a primary element? 314
An attempt to reconstruct the initial state of the Eumetazoa... 319
The origin of the middle body layer of the so-called mesoderm 321
Two difficulties of the theory of polykaryonts 329
Can cleavage be really considered as a proof of the colonial theory? 335
The basic principles that should be used in a reform of the whole animal system 337
Evolution generally had a progressive trend 346

CHAPTER 4. THE CLASSIFICATION OF THE ANIMAL WORLD AND THE NEW GENEALOGICAL TREE 352
General premises 352
The limit between the plant and the animal worlds 352
The system of the Protozoa 357
The transition from the Protozoa to the metazoan state 361
There are no well-warranted Mesozoa 366
The classification of Metazoa 368
The Parazoa as an independent subregnum 368
The Eumetazoa and their subdivisions 372
The elimination of the terms Coelenterata-Coelomata 372
The Coelomata as a taxonomic unit 384
The first phylum of the Eumetazoa: The Ameria 391
The transition from the amerous to the polymerous state 397
The problem of justification of the high taxons: Protostomia-Deuterostomia 407
The classes of the Polymeria 411
The phylum Oligomeria and its classes 421
The sphere of the phylum Oligomeria 423
The problem of the inclusion of the Sipunculida into the phylum Oligomeria 431
The Oligomeria as the initial form for the evolution of the Chordonia 437
The fourth and the last phylum of the Eumetazoa: Chordonia 441
The probable origin of the Chordonia 447
A comparison of the present attempt to derive the Chordonia from the ancestral form resembling the present day Enteropneusta with the similar attempt made by Hans Steiner 452
The genealogical tree of the Chordonia 455
The genealogical tree of the entire animal world 457
An attempt to unify the animal system 461

BIBLIOGRAPHY 467

INDEX 483

PREFACE

It was with great pleasure that I accepted the invitation of the Editor of the Pergamon Press Zoological Series to publish in book form and in English, as an international language, the results of my research on the Cnidaria, the interpretations of this research, and the final effects of these interpretations. I was all the more pleased with this invitation because my first general study of this problem appeared 17 years ago during the turmoils of the Second World War, when I tried to save the existence of the Slovene Academy of Arts and Sciences at Ljubljana which was threatened by the occupying powers.

My book, *The Turbellarian Theory of the Cnidaria ; The Phylogeny of the Cnidaria and Their Position in the Animal System* was published in a Slav language, in the language of the small yet progressive nation of Slovenes. Added to this text was a detailed summary written in an international language which could help various scholars to get acquainted with the contents of the book. The summary was written in German because I myself completed my studies at Vienna University.

Since the publication of this book many new elements have become known in the field of biology, and above all in zoology. Neither have I ceased with my studies: a whole series of special papers have been written by me in the meantime which are closely connected with problems that had only been touched on in the book. In the international literature there were a number of reactions to my book and to my subsequent shorter publications; this was especcially true for my article which appeared in the American review, *Systematic Zoology*. The publication of this article was made possible due to the generous help of an excellent translator, Professor A. Petrunkewitch. American and the English zoologists have shown particularly great interest in my interpretations and ideas. I have, therefore, now a welcome chance to answer all the critical observations that have so far been made as regards my suggestions.

The present volume must not be simply considered as a second revised edition of the first volume even if I deal in both these books with the same or at least similar problems. This book is a completely new work: the foundations only of the two books have remained the same.

To these few words of preface I wish to add a few more words dictated by my feelings of indebtedness. Above all, I wish to thank all those critics of my earlier studies who have helped me to clarify many points that had previously been not clear. They must excuse me if I have occasionally used too vehement words that have been dictated "by the heat of the struggle." My wish has always been to convince them. I can not accept the suggestion made by a prominent scholar that such revolutionary novelties have to wait the till present generation dies out and the next generation becomes convinced of the correctness of the new concept.

My special thanks go to my dear friend, Professor Dr. Otto Steinböck (Innsbruck, Austria). He has not only critically read my manuscript; he has also always excelled as a noble colleague. Without any previous knowledge of our researches, we both came to the same conclusions regarding the origin of the Eumetazoa. Each of us has made his researches in his special group of animals: Professor Steinböck has mainly worked on the Turbellaria, and I myself mainly on the Cnidaria. Otto Steinböck came to the conclusion that the Turbellaria, i.e. the acoelous Turbellaria, must be the most primitive Eumetazoa, even before I was able to formulate the results of my studies. As a consequence of this discovery, Steinböck had correctly made important conclusions especially as regards the way the Eumetazoa had evolved, and as regards the previously firmly held theory of the germ layers. He did not, however, succeed in publishing the results of his research and his ideas. Just before the outbreak of the Second World War, Steinböck gave a lecture on this subject at the International Congress of Cytology at Stockholm. Only the title of this lecture has ever been published. This is how it happened that I was the first scholar to publish these ideas, in spite of the fact that I developed the same ideas later than Professor Steinböck: this has been due to various circumstances, among others, also to the outbreak of the Second World War. This fact, however, is not ultimately so important for the progress of the science itself; it is much more important that two researchers have reached quite independently the same conclusions; and that they continue to collaborate in a friendly way to prepare the way for the final reception of their ideas. It is unimportant that we differ in several unessential points; it seems that we will soon reach an agreement even on these points. The difficulties we have to overcome are great; we must struggle against interpretations and ideas which were considered inviolate since the days of the struggle for the victory of Darwinism and which were supported by such an authority as Haeckel, and by many other most prominent names. We must struggle against interpretations which have been considered as laws, i.e. as truths, and replace them by new suggestions.

I also wish to express my warmest thanks to the distinguished publishing house of Pergamon Press which has made possible the publication of this book in such a full presentation. I am also grateful to Dr. Janez Stanonik, the translator of the present text, the original of which was written in German; he has completed his task, which has certainly not been easy, to my full satisfaction.

JOVAN HADŽI

INTRODUCTION

It was in 1903, 58 years ago, that I, then a young man who had just left the classical grammar school at Zagreb, went to Vienna to study Natural Sciences and above all my beloved Zoology at Vienna University. For this study I was well prepared. Whilst at school, I had made a large collection of zoological objects. I had learnt the richness of forms and the ways of life of the animal world through my diligent study of Brehm's work on the Lives of Animals as well as through my field studies. At Vienna my teachers were the two professors of zoology, Carl Grobben and Berthold Hatschek, particularly the latter under whose guidance I also worked on my dissertation thesis.

During my second year at university, a public aquarium was purchased in Prater by some young Austrian biologists supported by their prosperous parents; in it they established a modern biological research institute—The Prater Biological Experimental Testing Station (Die biologische Versuchsanstalt im Prater)—and I applied as one of the first to this place to learn there the methods of scientific research. Dr. Hans Przibram, then Privatdocent, was the head of the department; he is the author of the well known synoptic work on Experimental Zoology. *Hydra* was my first object of study. There were numerous green *Hydra* in a half-darkened concrete basin; their exterior looked rather pale. This induced me to transfer the same *Hydra* into a completely darkened place. When these *Hydra* began to procreate I could observe what I had actually expected: their ova were without the symbiotic green algae so that finally there were at least some colourless "green" *Hydra*. Other tests and researches were made in the same place. In 1906 my first results were published in Roux's *Archiv für Entwicklungsmechanik*.

From here I went to the Zoological Institute of Vienna University which was at that time headed by the famous zoologist, Councillor Prof. Dr. Berthold Hatschek. Besides him there were also on the staff Prof. Dr. Karl Camillo Schneider, a well known comparative histologist of Invertebrata, Prof. Dr. Heinrich Joseph, a comparative cytologist, and Dr. R. Zwicklitzer who worked as assistant. I remained faithful to *Hydra* and so I chose "The Nervous System of *Hydra*" as my theme for the doctoral thesis. I succeeded in using methylene blue as an *intra-vitam* colouring of the complete nervous system of *Hydra*. In spring 1908, when I was in the eighth semester of my studies, I became a Doctor of Philosophy. In 1909 the results of my thesis were published in the Institute's journal *Arbeiten der zoologischen Institute Wien und Triest*. This work has never been surpassed by any other study in the same field, it has been quoted everywhere, and the pictures published in it have often been reproduced. Because of the early appearance of this work and because of the other works written by me on *Hydra* and other hydroids (gemmation, migration of nematocysts, etc.) that soon followed, it was not strange that after a lapse of years I have been looked upon at various congresses of zoologists and other meetings as being a son or even a grandson of the "Old Hydra—Hadži."

After the completion of my studies and after I had passed in 1907 the state examination, I returned to my country (Zagreb in Croatia, now Yugoslavia). Here I came, after a short stay at the local Zoological Museum, to the University Institute of Comparative Anatomy, headed by Prof. Dr. Lazar Car. I still continued to remain faithful to hydroids as well as to other Cnidaria and Coelenterata. It was only when I was called, at the end of the First World War, to the newly founded Ljubljana University (Slovenia, Yugoslavia) that I extended the sphere of my interest to some groups of land Arthropoda (Chelicerata), particularly those which inhabit underground caves.

For more than 40 years I have collected experience and knowledge about Cnidaria and Coelenterata, constantly thinking about their real nature. Though dogmas are characteristic for religious systems, yet the same can also be found in science. One such dogma was, and it still is, the belief in the primary simplicity of *Hydra*, and even more so of Hydrozoa, and so too with Cnidaria and Coelenterata. It is well known how difficult it is to fight against dogmas, particularly when they have been accepted for so long, when they have been supported by renowned scholars, and when they appear to be well founded. My initial researches have shown that *Hydra* is in no way so simply organized as the simple structure of its body would seem to indicate when considered from a crudely anatomical point of view. Soon I saw the first pillar of the proud structture of Coelenterata collapse. It has been almost generally accepted that *Hydra* and its closest relatives are not primarily solitary animals but that, instead, they are derived from ancestors that were able to form cormi. Naturally, this discovery alone could not suffice to make all Hydrozoa the secondarily simplified Eumetazoa. Nevertheless, with this a good beginning was made.

CHAPTER 1

CNIDARIA AS THE ONLY COELENTERATA

The Systematic Position of the Spongiae

The next step, apparently without connection with the former, was made when some well-known researchers especially Sollas and Delage, came to the conclusion that the Spongiae must not only be placed far from the immediate vicinity of Cnidaria, but also that they must be completely separated from the Coelenterata and even from all the remaining real Metazoa, the Eumetazoa; they must appear completely isolated as an independent type, as Parazoa or Enantiozoa. We must consider this separation as being definite, and, in my opinion, nothing can be changed in this respects by recent attempts made particularly by Miss O. Tuzet and her collaborators.

On the basis of works of older investigators, especially the researchers into the ontogeny of Spongiae (Metschnikoff, Delage, etc.) it is no longer necessary to defer d the special position that the Spongiae have as Parazoa (Sollas) in the animal classification. Recently, however, a tendency has arisen which aims at a revision of this point of view and tries to bring Spongiae back amongst the other Metazoa. The French school in particular, which created the term Enantiozoa (Delage), attempts to cancel out the progress that has been achieved; Tuzet points in this connection mainly to the following evidence: (1) According to her School, the Spongiae have a nervous system; (2) the choanocytes are found in the other Metazoa; (3) the stretching out and the pulling in of a part of the blastoderm observed in the embryos of Spongiae is not a completely isolated case *(Volvox)*. On the basis of all this, Tuzet comes to the conclusion that Spongiae are genuine Coelenterata, and are thus Eumetazoa and not Parazoa. In this she is followed by many zoologists, even by scholars who are not French (Remane, Jägersten, Alvarado).

Considered critically, one can see that the arguments proposed by Tuzet in favour of the old thesis which holds that Spongiae are Coelenterates, have a rather weak foundation. The existence of a nervous system is in no way proved for Spongiae, yet it is of great importance in this connection and Tuzet tries hard to prove the contrary. The pictures of thin sections that have been shown by Tuzet and her collaborators, have been seen by many investigators and I, too, have able been to see them. Yet no one—with one exception that will be mentioned later—has classified these cells of the central stratum with plasmatic processes, as genuine ganglion-cells or even nerve cells. They have always been identified as simple cells of the connective tissue from the central stratum which is filled up with jelly. In all probability these cells are as much, or perhaps slightly more, irritable and able to conduct excitement much as any other animal cell. In order to prove that these cells, or at least some of them, really have a nervous character it would be necessary to apply successfully special selective stains, as for example methylene blue which colours the nerve cells selectivily *intra-vitam*. If this has not been done, then at least it would be necessary to carry out some neurophysiological experiments, and achieve a positive result.

The general behaviour of Spongiae as well as the kind of reactions they show to various stimuli, make it completely improbable that Spongiae could possess a real net of nerves, let alone sensory nerves, as these can with certainty be considered to exist, e.g. in *Hydra*. Some time ago, von Lendenfeld sketched such nerve cells in pictures published by him, yet nobody believed his allegations or his beautiful pictures. And even, if there were some of these cells that exist—not that they do!—they would be a *lucus a non lucendo*, since they would be physiologically meaningless.

Lévi (1956) made, after the publications of the school of Tuzet had become known, an extensive and critical histological study of Spongiae, and did not report any finding of a nervous system or of nerve cells in Spongiae. Neither could such a finding be confirmed by others, e.g. G. Eberl (Eberl, 1950), an excellent histologist from Vienna who used numerous staining techniques in her work. Yet in spite of all this the propositions as well as pictures published by Tuzet have found acceptance in many schoolbooks, especially in France.

Neither did Miss Tuzet succeed with her—it can be truly said—attempt to disprove the law of the supposedly inversed sequence of body layers in Spongiae. As is well known, Metschnikoff and many other famous zoologists after him, among them particularly Yves Delage, have shown that in the ontogenies of Spongiae, the early morphogeny proceeds along very particular lines. We get the impression that during the morphogeny of Spongiae a process takes place that is opposite to the process which can be observed in Eumetazoa. The primitive "ectoderm," i.e. the foremost part of the spongula, develops into the definite "entoderm," and the primitive "entoderm" into skin, this into the "ectoderm." For this reason Spongiae have been called Enantiozoa (i.e. animals with the two strata of body inversed) by Delage. Naturally, this inversed character is relative only i.e. in comparison to the development that can be observed in Eumetazoa. In fact, we have here a particular characteristic of Spongiae which has been developed during the course of their own phylogeny. It is therefore better not to speak in connection with Spongiae about an ecto- or an entoderm but rather to use special names, e.g. *pinacoderm* and *choanoderm*. The facts themselves cannot be changed. Yet Tuzet gives a description of an isolated case among Calcispongiae where the extroversion of the spongula blastoderms can be observed. A comparison with the only slightly similar case in the ontogeny of *Volvox*, is in this connection completely out of place. *Volvox*, is in fact a real alga in spite of its slight resemblance to an animal (its spheric form, free swimming ability). The very rare appearance of an organelle in some Eumetazoa which resembles more or less the "collar" of the choanocytes in Spongiae is too insignificant to be used as a proof to support the thesis that Spongiae are really Coelenterata, and it can be explained by the fact that both Parazoa as well as Eumetazoa arise from the ancestors of Flagellata (i.e. the scattered appearance of similar genes).

Disregarding the fact that the arguments brought forward by Tuzet cannot be considered sound, we must emphasize that the principal mistake in this kind of reasoning lies in the wrong belief that individual morphological or morphogenetic features and characteristics can represent the special type of organisation of Spongiae; in reality, this is represented by their special "nature," so as to say by the whole spirit of the organisation of Spongiae, and by their way of life. Again and again it is necessary to point out that the Spongiae have neither a digestive canal nor an oral opening. To this one could remark that in this respect Spongiae do not represent a unique case; even among the genuine Eumetazoa there are some in which we can find neither an oral opening nor a digestive canal, e.g. among the extreme endoparasites, or in the strongly aberrant *Pogonophora*. Nevertheless, there is a basic difference between Spongiae and these cases observed in Eumetazoa. It is beyond any doubt that in the case of the parasitic Eumetazoa and the freely living Pogonophora the absence of the oral opening and of the digestive canal is nothing but a secondary phenomenon. Spongiae, on the other hand, indubitably have primarily neither an oral opening nor a digestive canal, and this is a consequence of their special organisation. The feeding system with its numerous pores, the canal system with layers of choanocytes in chambers separated from each other that serve to maintain the flow of water, the larger aperture for the discharge of surplus water, and many other things, all this is unparalleled in other animals. In addition to this comes the special kind of ontogeny.

Finally, when we study attempts to construct the phylogeny of Spongiae as if they had the nature of Coelenterata (Remane, Jägersten)—these attempts must be considered as quite unsuccessful—then it actually becomes clear that Spongiae are really something "exceptional," and that they have developed independently from Protozoa, most probably out of Choanoflagellata. (Hadži, 1917). Yet even here it remains impossible to get ahead without a grain of imagination; we must use it to construct the phylogenetic processes of sponge evolution since it is completely hopeless to expect that we will ever run into any new documents which will help us to construct an actual phylogeny of Spongiae. Naturally enough, such an artificial construction, too, must be based on the actual facts that are now accessible. The scheme must be as close as possible to reality.

Since the Spongiae with their structure, their way of life, and their individual development represent something different from all other Metazoa, it must be expected, and actually reckoned with, that their phylogenetic evolution, too, was a special one. It is therefore quite improbable that the ancestors of Spongiae could be similar to gastraea. Here we run into very great difficulties when we try to construct the origin of Spongiae. We cannot expect any palaeontological evidence. We must limit ourselves to comparative morphology where, too, we are completely unable to make any progress without some imagination. Nevertheless, our scientific imagination—let us call it so, though it is usually called speculation—must be kept in check and within the limits of probability. The reconstruction must correspond to the factual material that is available.

On the basis of my studies on Spongiae (Hadži, 1917) I constructed a phylogeny of Spongiae and submitted this to the International Congress of Zoologists at Budapest in Hungary (Hadži, 1929). This construction was later somewhat improved and is reproduced in the present volume (Fig. 1). According to this hypothesis the evolution of Spongiae progressed completely independent from that of Eumetazoa. The starting point was probably the freely swimming colonies of Mastigophora of the subtype Choanoflagellata. The subindividuals were

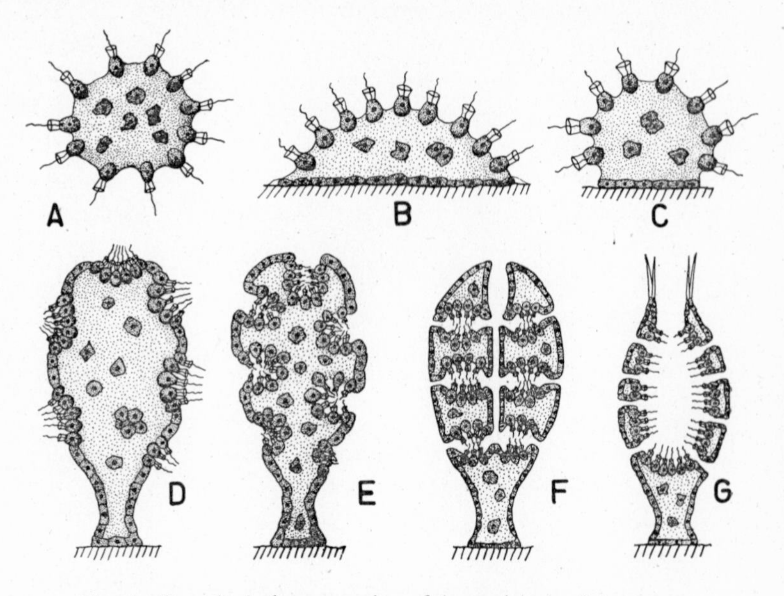

Fig. 1. Hypothetical construction of the evolution of the sponges. A, free swimming phase resembling *Proterospongia* sp.; B—C, the beginning of the sessile phase; D—E, erect phase with the formation of chambers; F, primitive phase of the heterocoelic state; G, homocoelic phase. (After Hadži, somewhat altered.)

kept together by means of a richly secreted jelly in a way which can even now be observed among Choanoflagellata in the genus *Proterospongia*. The existence of this form of Choanoflagellata, which was first described by Saville Kent, was disbelieved and it was considered that we did not have here an independent animal but rather a surviving fragment of a real sponge. In the meantime, another species of the same genus has been described, so that now we have not only the old species *Proterospongia haeckelii* S. Kent, (Gröntved, 1956; Lackey,

1959). In this way the existence of freely living colonies of Choanoflagellata can no longer be doubted. Of course, this can only be an example in our attempt to reconstruct the phylogeny of Spongiae. When an organism which was similar to *Proterospongia* changed to a sessile way of life, the duty to stick to the floor of the sea was taken over by a small number of basal choanocytes losing their character as choanocytes. Later, some of the surface cells that could stretch out freely into water took over the form of flattened amoebocytes and the latter developed the peculiarities of pinacocytes. Depressions developed in several parts of the surface when groups of choanocytes sank deeper into the jelly. It was probably in this way that several chambers with pores developed on the surface; the remaining surface was covered with pinacocytes. The pore of the highest placed chamber developed into an osculum when the internal connection of chambers was evolved. The water flow through individual chambers was united into a common draining system. The amoebocytes in the jelly developed partly into the skeleton cells and partly into the primitive sex cells.

As a result of such an interpretation we find that the homocoelous type of Spongiae, the Ascon or Olynthus according to Haeckel, cannot be primordial but rather a result of a secondary development due to a secondary union of chambers. This makes it clear that ascon cannot be a gastraea. The freely living larva, the spongula, which is characteristic for Spongiae and which actually has a very manifold structure, developed independently and thus it cannot be considered to be a recapitulated form. There were no primitive Spongiae whose form and structure resembled those of the spongulae. The adoption of a freely living, usually planktonic juvenile stage of Spongiae, and, herewith, their prolonged ontogeny, corresponds to a general phenomenon and is a consequence of the transition to the sessile way of life by the adult form. The sexual stage together with the development (cleavage, etc.) which follows fertilization cannot be considered as a proof of the common derivation of all Metazoa from the colonies of Flagellata. The former has been inherited from the protozoic ancestors, the latter corresponds to a disposition which is common to all metabionts including metaphytes to develop a multicellular organism from a zygote (see the conditions in *Volvox*, a green alga).

In this way the second pillar of the old concept about Coelenterata collapsed with the definite removal of Spongiae from the relationship with Coelenterata. This was initially made by Leuckart (1859). The first pillar was the removal of *Hydra* from the basis of Hydrozoa.

The Position of Ctenophora in the Animal Classification

It was comparatively easy to show that the removal of Spongiae from the vicinity of Cnidaria could be convincingly upheld; such was their isolation (as Parazoa) from all other Metazoa. The great differences that exist between Spongiae and the remaining Coelenterata—the latter taken in the old sense of the word—are evident since they are both considerable as well as numerous. As has been already emphasized, we have here two completely different "spirits of organization" which force us to consider a different origin. It is clear that though there are some similarities between Spongiae and Cnidaria, that these similarities are purely external and can be mostly traced back to a sessile way of life and to a generally low stage of organisation.

Considerably greater difficulties have to be overcome if we try to exclude Ctenophora from the triangle Spongiae–Cnidaria–Ctenophora. It is clear that Ctenophora stand much closer to Cnidaria. Both are animals whose digestive organs have reached the aproctous stage of development; they have one opening only, the oral opening. In both, the digestive tract shows an inclination to the formation of the so-called gastrovascular system. Due to their life as plankton, a similarity of forms developed, particularly in medusae and Ctenophora, with a rich development of a jelly-like intermediate substance. Though cnidae are, on the whole, developed in Cnidaria only, they have nevertheless been found also in a genuine ctenophore, in *Euchlora rubra*. Furthermore, a coelenterate has been described which has been considered as an intermediate form between the two subtypes of Coelenterata *(Hydroctena salenskii* Dawydoff). Finally, not without significance is the discovery of ctenophores which, though genuine, have begun to resemble Turbellaria due to their transition to a benthonic way of life; they have been explained as a transition form to Turbellaria, and in this way a connection of Colenterata with "higher forms" has been won.

All these facts have helped to support zoologists in their belief that Ctenophora are real Coelenterata and as such the closest relatives of Cnidaria. It is surprising to see how the numerous and fundamental differences that actually exist between the two groups of animals and touch not only their structures but even their ontogenies, make no deep impression on the majority of zoologists. At the most, the absence of cnidae in Ctenophora has been considered as an important mark of difference and for this reason they have been called Acnidaria. In our discussion we will limit ourselves to the essential points only; we shall try to show that Cnidaria are basically different from Ctenophora and that this difference is due to the fact that both these types of animals have a different origin, even if these origins are not widely separated from each other. For this reason we will base our discussion on selected properties that can be observed in Ctenophora.

One of the principal characteristics of Ctenophora is their bisymmetry. This quality pervades the whole organization of Ctenophora to such an extent that it can be observed already in the fine structure of their ovum and also in their ontogeny. Something identical—or even anything similar—cannot be found in any medusa. The basically quadri-radial symmetry which can be secondarily multiplied through the process of polymerization is typical for medusae. On the other hand one can observe a development towards a secondary oligomerization of individual pairs of antimeres or of individual antimeres so that finally we see either a single pair preserved, or a marginal tentacle only, or even none whatever. In this way a purely external similarity with Ctenophora can naturally develop. One such case was formerly described by Ernst Haeckel who called an Anthomedusa with one pair only of marginal tentacles, *Ctenaria ctenophora* (see Fig. 2); by this he wished to express the palpable similarity that exists with a typical Ctenophora and in this way point to the possibility that Ctenophora had perhaps developed from Hydromedusae. For some time this comparison had a very great influence upon zoologists; a more precise comparison, however, has finally shown that these are inessential external similarities only. *Ctenaria* remains a typical Anthomedusa and it does not stand in the slightest degree closer to Ctenophora than any other Hydromedusa. The symmetry of the body is not a property which can be considered unchangeable. On the contrary, it shows comparatively rapid changes, e.g. when the sessile way of life has been adopted, or, vice versa, during the transition from a sessile way of life to that of a free movement. Many instances could be mentioned in this connection yet it should suffice to point to the case of echinoderms only. We shall later return to this question to discuss it in greater details.

It is in no way difficult to show how the bisymmetry has been developed in Ctenophora. It is a result of the transition from a benthonic to a pelagic way of life; during this transition the difference between the ventral and dorsal sides has disappeared. Thus we have here a combination of bilateral and radial symmetries. The internal organs remained true to the original bilateral symmetry while those situated on the periphery leaned towards the radial symmetry.

The second main difference between Ctenophora and Cnidaria is in their tentacles. It is well known that both a majority of Cnidaria as well as Ctenophora possess tentacles which are strongly contractile and serve mainly for the capture of the living prey. In those cases where there are no tentacles it seems more probable that their absence is a secondary phenomenon. The fact is noteworthy that Ctenophora never form more than one pair of tentacles, and that they show no leaning to polymerization which nevertheless can be observed to have

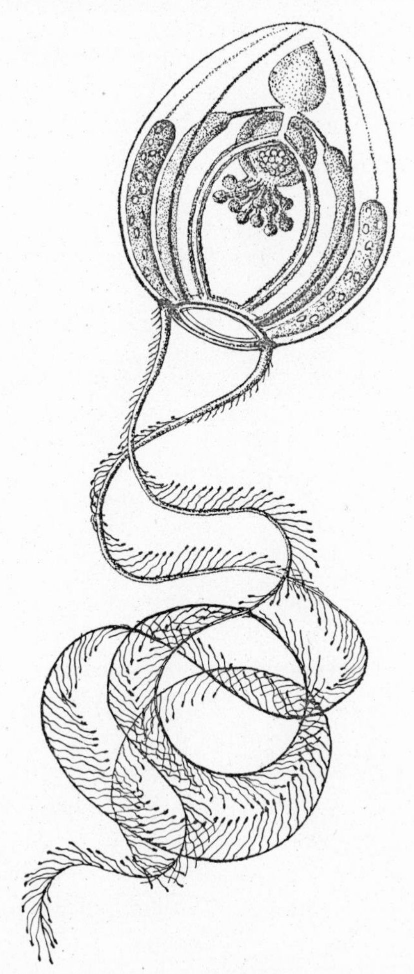

Fig. 2. An anthomedusa species: *Ctenaria ctenophora* Haeckel. (After Haeckel.)

taken place in several other organs (intestinal diverticulum, swimming plates).

In both groups we find their tentacles equipped with particular specialized monocellular gland cells; on one hand with colloblasts, and on the other with cnidae. The two forms are so widely different from each other that they cannot be considered to have developed one from the other. It seems, however, as if *Euchlora rubra*, a ctenophore, stood in apparent contradiction to these observations. This ctenophore can rarely be observed and it does not have colloblasts in its two tentacles, but instead genuine cnidae; these are not only "drawn up" (i.e. ready to be used) but also kept in reserve, as is the case with medusae which are genuine Cnidaria. A detailed analysis of this case (Hadži, 1951, 1959, 1959a), however, has shown that we do not have here a real exception, but that instead this phenomenon is not limited to *Euchlora* only. In all probability this is a case of the so-called *kleptocnidae*, i. e. cnidae that have remained alive and that have been stolen by the predator from prey which had been devoured. Taku Komai (1935, 1951), a well-known Japanese zoologist, who has recently had the good luck to be able to make a detailed study of *Euchlora* and who in his work first expressed his opinion that these cnidae actually belong to the animal, has later become convinced that we really have here a case of kleptocnidae. *Euchlora* subsists mainly on Narcomedusae and it seems that it has become so specialized that it has ceased to produce colloblasts, its original weapons, and instead "works" exclusively with cnidae taken over from its usual prey. This certainly is a very interesting case and it is at the same time at least one more fact which supports our thesis that the Ctenophora cannot be directly related to Cnidaria.

Besides the differences which have been already mentioned, between the tentacles of Ctenophora and medusae, there is one more which makes it completely impossible—in spite of their great external similarities—to consider the two organs as homologous or descending from the same origin, or even to be brought forward as a proof of the direct relationship between Ctenophora and Cnidaria. The tentacles of medusae have always and without exception, an intestinal diverticulum in their axes, i.e. a continuation of the intestine with an entodermal coat and with an intestinal lumen. It is not rare for the intestinal lumen to be secondarily obliterated. In this case the entoderm forms a solid entodermal axis which is not unlike a *rouleau* of money or a primitive *chorda dorsalis*. In this way the entodermal axis develops into an internal skeleton. The structure of the tentacles of Cnidaria is usually described as if they were composed of an ectoderm and of an entoderm only. Later we shall try to show in more detail and in connection with the whole body of Cnidaria that the intermediate layer of the body participates also in the structure of the tentacles. This layer usually bears the unsuitable name of a mesoderm or mesogloea which again creates the impression that we have here something different from the intermedial layer of the body of other Eumetazoa. I have therefore proposed for it the name *mesohyl*. It is better to speak about the mesoderm only in connection with early ontogenies.

A typical feature of all Ctenophora is the fact that their tentacles never have an intestinal diverticulum or any entoderm whatever. As important as this difference is, it is, however, by no means the only one. Even the way that these tentacles grow is completely different in the two cases. In Ctenophora the tentacles actually grow constantly during their whole life time; their growth continually takes place at the considerably thickened bases deeply sunk into a cutaneous follicle, while at the same time the free ends slowly break away. In connection with this we find in Ctenophora the base is organized in a completely different way from that of Cnidaria. Without finding it necessary to enter into further details we have the full right to maintain and conclude on the basis of what has already been mentioned, that the tentacles of Ctenophora and Cnidaria do not have the same origin and that we have here a case of functionally similar, and therefore analogous, organs.

The difference between the tentacles of Ctenophora and Cnidaria would be perfectly clear if we could show the origin of tentacles in Ctenophora as well as in Cnidaria. In both cases the tentacles are, in all probability, not completely new formations. We presuppose that in both cases the tentacles have developed out of paired excrescences at the anterior part of the body (at the "head") of their turbellarian ancestors and that on both occasions this development was independent from each other. It should be mentioned in this connection that paired organs of touch (this in connection with the bilateral symmetry of the animals) can already be found among Turbellaria, once with the inclusion of the intestinal diverticulum, another time without it. Cnidaria must therefore have descended from those turbellarian ancestors whose palpi had an intestinal diverticulum, and Ctenophora from those whose palpi had none. We can see that in Temnocephala, i.e. in Turbellaria which have adopted a half-sessile way of life, the polymerization of these excrescences has already taken place; this has become even more developed in Cnidaria which have similarly adopted first a half-sessile and later a completely sessile way of life. Ctenophora, however, as freely moving animals, retained the original paired system of tentacles which became specialized in another direction. In the first case (Cnidaria) the turbellarian ancestors belonged to a rhabdocoelian subtype while in the second case (Ctenophora) they belonged to the subtype of Polycladida, and especially to their larvae that became neotenic and remained in the plankton during the whole of their life.

In this connection I would like to point to the fact that in the course of phylogeny, tentacles have been repeatedly evolved and have either a horseshoe-shaped (the younger phyletic stage) or crown-shaped form. This pattern has always stood in connection with the transition to a sessile way of life (Entoprocta among the Ameria, in nearly all Oligomeria, and even in the "lower" Chordata: in Tunicata).

The third peculiarity and at the same time the third point in which Ctenophora differ sharply from the Cnidarian medusae is their combined aboral sensory organ (see Fig. 3). Anything identical or even similar is completely absent in medusae. *Hydroctena* has been mentioned again and again as if it was an exception and at the same time an intermediate link between those Cnidaria which resemble Narcomedusae and Ctenophora.

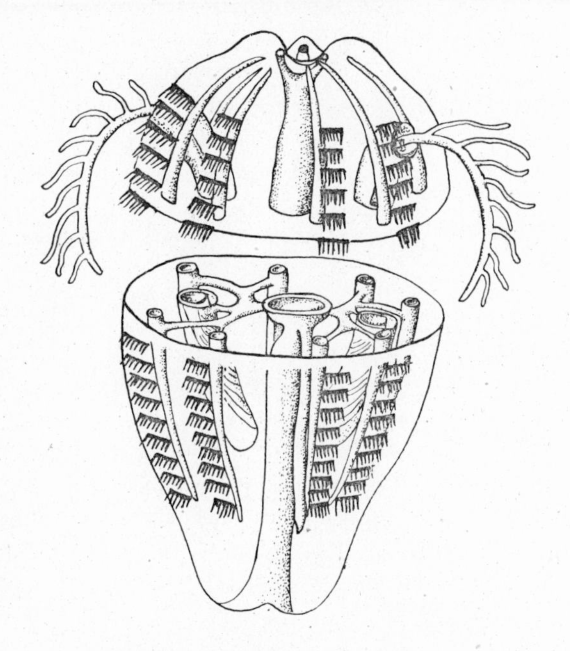

Fig. 3. Diagram of the Ctenophore organization. (After Hertwig and Kaestner.)

Hydroctena, however, as this will be shown in the ensuing pages of the present study, cannot be considered to have such a role. The absence of a static organ in the exumbrella of medusae is not a mere chance. Its absence in medusae and its presence in Ctenophora can be easily and convincingly explained.

We shall later see how the part of the body which is turned upwards in a ctenophore that is freely poised in water corresponds to its anterior part. In Turbellaria, a static organ situated close under the skin and in the centre of their central nervous system has been developed in the same place. This organ has been inherited by the Ctenophora from their turbellarian ancestors, and during the transition it came completely to the surface. This agrees perfectly with the orientation as well as with the way of life of Ctenophora. We must not forget in this connection that the Ctenophora must in all probability be considered to have evolved by means of neoteny from the organizationally simpler planktonic larvae. Naturally, evolution has proceeded until the present forms of Ctenophora have been reached. The oral opening was transplaced from the vicinity of the aboral pole (first the anterior pole, and in Ctenophora the upper pole) to the vegetative pole (in the creeping Turbellaria the posterior pole, and in Ctenophora which are poised in water the lower pole) (see Fig. 2).

Medusae, too, regardless of whether they are Hydromedusae or Scyphomedusae, live as planktonic animals poised in water, not with their "head turned upwards" as in the case with Ctenophora, but rather with their "head turned downwards," i.e. with their vegetative pole turned upwards. Thus the oral opening of medusae is turned downwards; its place corresponds to that of the animal pole since they have developed from polyps either by means of gemmation budding, (Hydromedusae), or by means of transverse fission (Scyphomedusae), or secondarily, directly from ova. The polyp, the initial form of Cnidaria, "stands" upright and is attached with its vegetative or posterior pole to the floor of the sea. The medusa, which has evolved from the oral part of the polyp, underwent a reversion when it became a freely-swimming animal and turned its originally anterior part upwards. Yet this uppermost part of the medusa is no longer a part of its head as it has remained in the ancestors of polyps, but instead the oral part has been removed and is now, so to speak, only at the end of a stem. We find therefore the surface of the so-called exumbrella turned upwards when the animal rests, and forward when the animal moves. The exumbrella is genetically and morphogenetically empty because it is covered with one layer only of the ectoderm and it is not able to form—even if this were useful—a nerve centre, a brain ganglion, or even a sensory organ of the type of statocyst. The facts show that this is really so; it becomes particularly clear in those cases—which are by no means rare—where a secondary, the so-called hypogenetic development takes place, i.e. where the original generation of polyps is left out so that the form of medusa develops as the only type from the egg, and where, in spite of all this, the

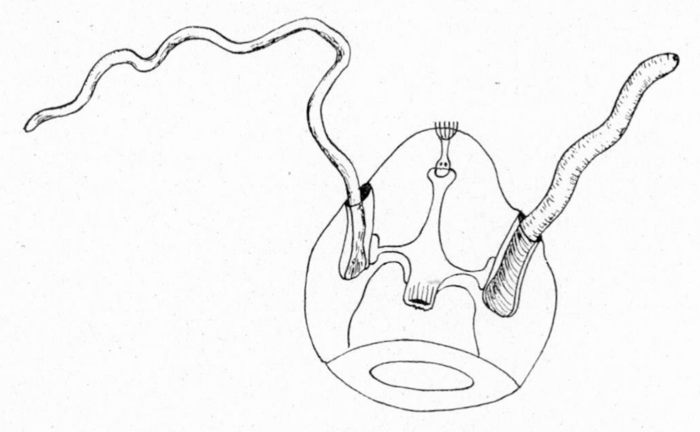

Fig. 4. *Hydroctena salenskii* Dawydoff. (After Dawydoff.)

exumbrella remains empty and does not possess a vertical sensory organ. This can be understood only if we take into consideration the fact that in medusae their physiological anterior pole is not their vertical pole, as is, on the other hand, the case with Ctenophora.

We will now pass to *Hydroctena salenskii* which has been discussed by C. Dawydoff. The name itself of this remarkable animal shows that it was considered as an intermediate link between medusae and Ctenophora. *Hydroctena* has been observed once and in three specimens only; these were neither sexually ripe nor, as it seems, particularly well preserved. It has been thought that it represents a mixture of elements characteristic for Ctenophora and Hydromedusae, that is Hydromedusae of the type of Narcomedusae (see Fig. 4). Various authors proposed different opinions regarding *Hydroctena*. Some have thought it to be an aberrant type of Narcomedusae, others have considered that it is a ctenophore yet without the swimming apparatus in the form of eight meridional bands of plates which is so characteristic for Ctenophora; the least accepted interpretation has been that it represents a transition form. I have tried to submit all the known factual data (which are very incomplete) to a renewed scrutiny (Hadži, 1958 b). In this way I have come to the conclusion that in all probability we have here ctenophores which have developed crippled forms because their embryos had been damaged by an external event (storm). In this connection I have referred to observations, especially those made by C. Chun, according to which the damaged embryos of Ctenophora continued to develop into partial forms because of the strong determinism in their ontogeny. Dawydoff maintained that *Hydroctena* had no colloblasts on its tentacles and that instead cnidae had been found much as can be observed in Narcomedusae. On the basis of this I have proposed that the supposed *Hydroctena* could have developed from the embryos of *Haeckelia rubra*. I have therefore suggested that *Hydroctena* should be set aside.

In the meantime C. Dawydoff has published a short notice where, on the basis of serial sections of *Hydroctena* made by another zoologist, he comes to the conclusion that we have here a genuine Narcomedusan. The vertical sensory organ, which was the main point in this revision, has been explained as a form *sui generis* that has nothing in common with the aboral sensory organ in Ctenophora, but instead corresponds to a pair of club-shaped marginal sensory organs of Narcomedusae: this was first transplaced to the vertex of the umbrella and later sunk into the interior of the same. This interpretation seems to me completely improbable and at the same time incompatible with the original description of the structure of the supposed *Hydroctena* as it had been given by the same author (cf. the conditions of tentacles and of the so-called gastrovascular system). I consider that I am justified in deciding my interpretation as the more probable.

Many other arguments and evidence could be given to support the thesis that the Ctenophora cannot be directly related to Cnidaria. The ontogenies of the two groups in particular are completely different from each other. It may be useful to mention the so-called ciliary rosettes in Ctenophora for which there is no homologue in Cnidaria. I think that these ciliary rosettes developed out of the terminal organs of the protonephridial system in Turbellaria. The examples which have been given so far should suffice to prove that there are important differences between Ctenophora and Cnidaria; yet at the same time there are also some similarities which are such that they make it probable that the two groups did not develop one from the other, but instead independently from two ancestors that had been closely related to each other and that had evolved from the same primitive form. This interpretation could perhaps be also expressed with the dictum: *si duo faciunt idem—non est idem*. In both of them the evolution took a new direction: it was the same in both cases and it tried to adopt the characteristics of animals living a pure planktonic life. In the case of medusae, the evolution proceeded from a bilateral symmetric and mobile stage, through a second stage which was radial symmetric and sessile, to a third stage which was radial symmetric and planktonic. In Ctenophora the development went from a bilateral symmetric and mobile stage through that of a planktonic larva influenced by the neoteny into the final planktonic stage. In both cases the ancestors were bilateral symmetric Turbellaria, but they belonged to two different subgroups (see Fig. 5).

To the best of my knowledge no hypothesis that is more probable, and therefore better, has been proposed to explain the origin of Ctenophora which takes into consideration so many of the numerous peculiarities of this small and now isolated animal group, and which would make it possible to understand them. Yet even if we do not bother about this

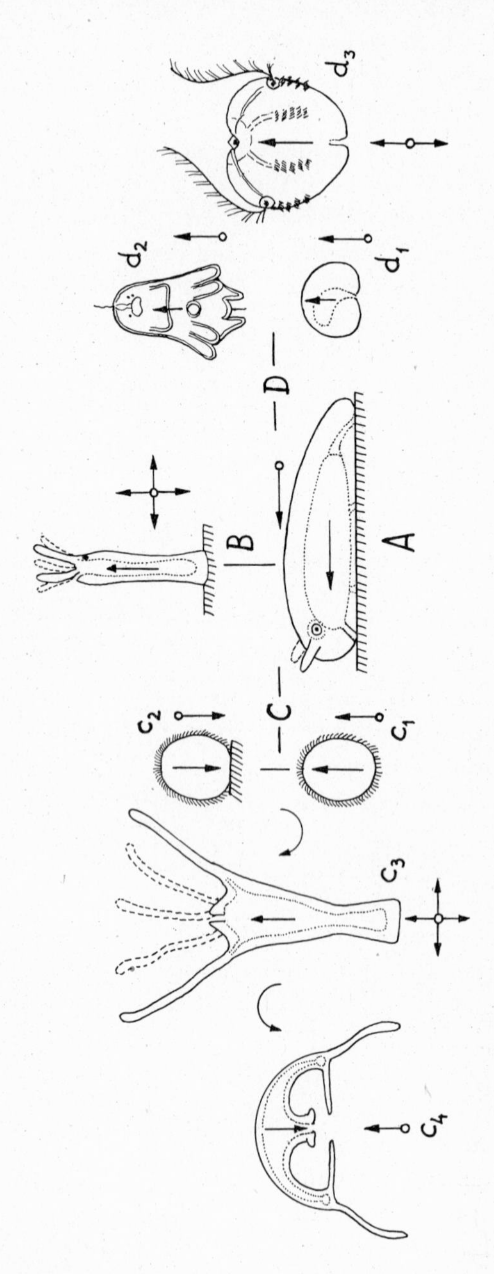

Fig. 5. Schematic illustration of the evolution of the Temnocephala (B), Cnidaria (C) and Ctenophora (D) from the rhabdocoeloid turbellarian (A); ← the orientation of the body axis; ←o the direction of movement. (After Hadži, somewhat altered.)

origin of Ctenophora which has now been accepted by numerous zoologists, e.g. Sir Gavin de Beer (1954 a), it has now become completely clear that Ctenophora cannot be simply considered as Coelenterata that have no cnidae (Acnidaria). Nevertheless, such an interpretation can be frequently encountered. The Ctenophora are not Coelenterata and they are not directly related to Cnidaria even if there is some relationship between the two. Later we shall try to show in more detail that the Turbellaria, the original form out of which all Eumetazoa have developed, are also the starting point of many other Ameria (lower invertebrates), even of molluscs. All these groups represent independent units as is true also for Cnidaria and Ctenophora. Yet it will not do to establish special phyla for these groups; the highest systematic category (taxon) must be reserved for large groups that are basically different from each other. I will return to the discussion of this problem later in the present study.

It should be remarked in passing that unknown to me, I was not the only person who tried to derive Ctenophora by way of neoteny from the planktonic polyclad larvae. A similar interpretation of the origin of Ctenophora has been proposed by W. Garstang (cf. J. I. Brooks, 1954) at approximately the same time that my thesis was published. Yet the form in which that interpretation appeared is somewhat unusual for a scientist: it was in a poem (Comic Verses) which was first published in 1951 by A. C. Hardy (1954). Nevertheless, this does not change the fact that an idea has been conceived according to which the origin of Ctenophora must be sought in Müller's larvae that remain in the plankton and whose evolution is influenced by neoteny.

It has been now generally accepted by all zoologists that the Spongiae represent a blind side branch of the animal kingdom, which means that no other higher type of animal has been developed from them. We have, therefore, no further interest in the Spongiae. We shall return to discuss them only when we deal with the problem of the origin of Metazoa. On the other hand, however, attempts have been made to see in the Ctenophora an initial stage for a higher development. This was suggested in connection with the discovery of certain species of Ctenophora which do not live in the plankton as is typical for Ctenophora but rather on the sea bottom, and for this reason have been correspondingly changed, especially in their external forms *(Platyctenea)*. They have been thought in this connection as a possible transition to Turbellaria: but the specialists have been able to show that these are genuine, though specialized, Ctenophora. In this way, the Ctenophora, too, as the third element of the old group of Coelenterata represent a blind side branch of the animal kingdom: no higher type of animals has been developed out of them. Though there are some connections between Ctenophora and Turbellaria, these connections are in my opinion exactly opposite to those as viewed by the old interpretation. The Ctenophora should be considered to have evolved out of a turbellarian form due to their transition from a life on the bottom of the sea, when they had a pure bilateral symmetry, to a life in the plankton, with a change of their symmetrical structure to that of bisymmetry. A detailed comparison of Ctenophora and Turbellaria brings to light a large number of common characteristics and peculiarities, particularly if in connection with the latter we take into consideration the planktonic larvae of Polycladida. The difference, however, can be explained on one hand as a result of the neoteny, and, on the other, as being due to the adoption of a freely moving life in water. This latter specialization makes it particularly impossible to regard the Turbellaria as having evolved from the Ctenophora. A small but welcome contribution which supports my hypothesis of the development of the Ctenophora from the Turbellaria has been the recently proposed theory (Hadži, 1955) which tries to find the origin of the so-called ciliary rosette organs of Ctenophora in the turbellarian protonephridia. There are present-day zoologists who have assumed a critical attitude towards all attempts which try to explain the formation of new animal types by way of neoteny. This scepticism, does not seem to be justified in spite of the fact that not all such attempts can be considered to have been very successful. New animal forms—and not only new animal types—have in numerous cases been developed by way of neoteny (cf. de Beer, 1958).

Cnidaria as the Only Coelenterata

Now that we have succeeded in isolating the Cnidaria, the concept of the Coelenterata which has been so widely used during the last hundred years has been reduced to one group only. In this connection the question arises whether it is still wise to continue to use this concept as well as the name Coelenterata as opposed to Coelomata. The fact that we have reduced the contents of the Coelenterata to a single group, can certainly not be considered as sufficient to allow us to question its existence. As a matter of fact, classifications can occasionally be found where "Coelenterata" appear in which Coelenterata are represented by the Cnidaria only. It can be easily imagined that Coelenterata—considered as a necessary stage in the evolution—are represented by one subtype only, by Cnidaria. Yet in this case it would be necessary to make it probable, if not proved, that the Cnidaria have developed as the first Eumetazoa from the Protozoa; a supposition which again, if taken alone, could not be sufficient because it would be necessary to show further that the next higher animal group which, according to the present opinion, are Tubellaria, have developed from the Cnidaria.

I will try now to prove or to show it more probable that the Cnidaria are neither the first (i.e. the lowermost) Eumetazoa, nor the ancestors of the next higher developed Eumetazoa, the Turbellaria. Since 1944, I have defended this thesis and supported it in numerous articles (Hadži, 1946–1959.). The fact that my book appeared during the Second World War and in Slovene, a language of a small though progressive

Slavic nation, has been of considerable disadvantage even though the Slovene text appeared together with an extensive German summary. This book was followed by later publications in international languages. The thesis has become best known and discussed through an article published in the United States in the journal *Systematic Zoology;* the article was beautifully translated into English by Professor A. Petrunkevitch for whose translation I wish to express here my warmest thanks. There was no visible reaction to my short lecture given at the Fourteenth International Congress of Zoologists held at Paris. A further essential contribution to the propagation of my ideas was made by Sir Gavin de Beer's *Evolution as a Process* which contained an article written from a sympathetic point of view by G. S. Carter (1949, 1954.), and in the German-speaking area by Professors Ferdinand Pax, (1954) Dr. Otto Steinböck, and by the palaeontologist Müller (1958), among others. An important contribution to the development of my ideas has been made by Hanson (1958) who discussed the consequences my theory would have for the estimation of the true nature of Cnidaria. It had been expected as well as desired that there would be several critics of my thesis (among them some well-known scholars, e.g. Beklemischew [1958], Laubenfels [1955], Carter [1949, 1954], A. Remane [1957], L. H. Hyman [1940—1958]). No criticism has yet been published which I consider to the point and which I would be forced to accept; there have been no critiques which have weakened my conviction or even forced me to abandon my theory. The majority of remarks do not even touch the core of my concept, i. e. my hypothesis about the origin and the position of Cnidaria in the system of the animal classification, but instead they discuss the numerous and important consequences of this hypothesis. These consequences undermine the basic pillars of the old concept. It is, therefore, not surprising that they have provoked sharp and occasionally even agressive criticism.

The three types of Metazoa, Spongiaria, Cnidaria, and Ctenophora, have not been united into the higher unit of Coelenterata not only for the reason that they lack a secondary body cavity, the coelom (I prefer to call it *perigastrocoel)*, since there are many other groups of lower Coelomata where the same coelom is absent; but rather because they represent with their general organization a lower stage of development. This, however, does not suffice, as has been demonstrated, to unite them all into one group. The organizations of all these animal groups are different from each other. The thing above all which has to be done if we wish to place them into one common higher systematic category, would be to prove a common origin of all these three groups. This was not necessary in the days of Leuckart. After the general acceptance of the Theory of Evolution the problem was solved first by E. Haeckel, and later by numerous other zoologists (E. Metschnikoff, B. Hatschek, C. Claus, L. v. Graff, the two brothers Hertwig, R. Lankester, A. Balfour, and many other zoologist up to the present day for example, A. Sachwatkin, A. Remane, L. H. Hyman, etc.), in a very simple and quite obvious, way. There was a simply-built primitive form which, though variously called (gastraea according to Haeckel, placula according to v. Graff, parenchymella according to Metschnikoff, and planula according to Lankester), and differing in details from one another, is, nevertheless, essentially the same. This primitive form has been used in connection with the ontogenetic stages and declared to be the common primitive form of the recapitulation theory as it appears in the "fundamental biogenetic law" proposed by Haeckel. According to this theory three different types of animals have been developed from the one polarized bistratal being which resembled a gastrula. The development diverged in three different directions, and as a result of it we have the Spongiae and Cnidaria which have adopted a sessile way of life, and the Turbellaria which creep over the surface of the sea bottom. The Ctenophora, however, have been usually considered—as it has been already mentioned—to have evolved from the Cnidaria, and not directly from the blastea. The Tubellaria, finally, have been thought to have developed from the Ctenophora. The main idea has been to derive the lowest Metazoa from a ciliated gastrula-like primitive form, which itself has been supposed to go back to an organism resembling a blastula, and this finally to a colony of Flagellata. Even nowadays this same theory is proposed with an admirable ardour by A. A. Sachwatkin (1956) on the basis of Metschnikoff's parenchymella theory.

Since in a classification which should be natural, i.e. phylogenetically founded, a similar or even identical level of organization cannot be considered sufficient to bring together several groups into a higher unit; it is also necessary to prove that they have descended from the same ancestral form. In the case of the Coelenterata it has been attempted to prove again and again—or at least to make it seem probable—that they have a common origin. These attempts, however, cannot be considered to have been successful. The completely artificial constructions such as those proposed by Remane (1950) and by those who followed him, e.g. by Alvarado and Jägersten—to mention three recent attempts only—have been completely unconvincing.

The isolation of Cnidaria alone, after the withdrawal of Spongiae and Ctenophora, would not suffice to cause the abandonment of the higher category of Coelenterata. It would now be necessary to prove that there is a basic difference between Cnidaria and the animal groups that stand closest to them, and, then, all other animal groups (the so-called Coelomata, or, according to Ray Lankester, Coelocoela), as has been the case with Spongiae. This difference was believed to have been found in the fact that Cnidaria are real "Gastraeadae," i.e. animals with their body built of two body layers. For this reason they have been called Diblastica, Didermique, etc. Furthermore, and in connection with this, the Cnidaria have no coelom cavities and in particular no perigastrocoel. Later I will show that the assertion according to which Cnidaria are built of two body layers does not agree with actual fact. The true coelom, which I call perigastrocoel, and which alone would allow us to call the bearer of such a coelom, a coelomate, does not occur earlier than in Annelida, the lowest subgroup of Polymeria.

Even if the Cnidaria remain, on the basis of their actual situation and not on that of a hypothesis, isolated from the two other supposed members of Coelenterata (Spongiae and Ctenophora), they are not yet distinguished from other lower invertebrates, i.e. from my Ameria or from the primarily unsegmented animals. We must search for their connection downwards, i.e. for the point where they have branched off; that is, we must search for it among the freely moving bilaterally symmetric ancestors, that lived on the bottom of the sea and whose organization shows a somewhat higher development. This must be proved, or at least made probable, and it will be my duty to try to do this in the present study.

A detailed comparison of Cnidaria with Ctenophora shows that these two groups of animals, which for a long time have been grouped together with Spongiae into the phylum Coelenterata, do not even stand in a direct mutual relationship. In my opinion they have evolved independently, each from its own ancestor. In this way Cnidaria are the only animals that remain in the large group of Coelenterata.

Yet before we begin to tackle our main problem, to try to identify the origin and the true nature of Cnidaria, it may be useful to discuss first those methods which have been used in connection with the solution of our problem.

Something About the Methods That Can Be Used in Connection with the Construction of the Natural Animal System

It should first be mentioned that we are discussing here a phylogenetic construction which should form a basis of an attempted reform of the system. This touches the very roots of the concepts that have so far prevailed with regard to classification, and the consequences can be of considerable importance. Furthermore, it should be mentioned, even if it seems superfluous, that I base my work constantly on the neo-Darwinian principles of evolution. I find any idealistic morphology, or any system based on it, and any purely idealistic taxonomy, unacceptable; they are both out of date as well as unscientific. Modern zoologists are endeavouring to construct a natural animal classification which, in agreement with this, must be based on the supposed phylogenetic development. The results, for better or worse as they are achieved, depend above all on our present positive knowledge—which is an objective element—and, naturally, to a certain extent on the scientific worker—which is an unavoidable subjective element. We can make no progress either with agnosticism or with an ultraconservatism, if it is linked with a complete absence of the creative imagination. It is therefore necessary to form a realistic concept even in those cases where the obstacles we have to overcome are due to our present insufficient knowledge. In this connection we must not be afraid to dare to conjecture or to use our imagination. Yet at the same time we have to be aware of the fact that these are hypothetical constructions only. They have not been made for all eternity.

It would be detrimental to our progress is we reject on principle and without discussion, any more or less daring construction; if we declare any work of this kind to be a pure waste of time; and if we look upon it disparagingly as is frequently the case. The numerous and mutually different attempts to construct the animal system that we have met even in the present day, prove that we are still far from the ideal solution. Many difficulties arise from this situation, especially in the field of teaching. I tried to seek a redress to this situation at the Fourteenth International Congress of Zoologists which was held at Copenhagen, and I proposed to find a unified or compromissary animal classification which could serve our practical purposes (Hadži, 1956 a). Due to my proposition a committee and president have been elected, as yet without any further results. It is possible that this attempt was made too early, or that it was discarded because it was considered as being impracticable.

Fortunately enough, the interest in the problem of phylogeny and, in connection with this, of the construction of a truly natural animal classification has been recently reawakened. As an illustration I can mention the reaction which occurred when my article appeared in *Systematic Zoology* (Hadži, 1953). It is perfectly natural that such reactions were not always favourable, or, even constructive in regard to the new proposition. It is not easy to convince those zoologists who have been trained in long established concepts which they firmly accept, that these old concepts are actually untenable. Max Planck, if I am not mistaken, once stated that one is more likely to see the defenders of the old concepts die out before becoming converted to new interpretations. It is now time for the new generation, one free of tradition, to proceed critically and make the decision.

Some progress has nevertheless been made in the field of phylogeny; this can be seen in the fact that the "variation width" of hypotheses and theories, and thus of concepts, has finally become somewhat narrower. An objective, even if sharp, discussion can always be useful.

In my opinion, in this area of biology one can arrive at a new concept, at a new evaluation which has a synthetic character, mainly along two lines. Either we succeed in making a new discovery, a discovery of a brand new fact, e.g. of a new fossil or of a living animal which has been unknown so far ("a living fossil"), or we succeed in establishing new facts—facts which had not been known previously—through our study of the structure and of the ontogeny of a known animal species. The new fact must throw a new light on our present concepts. The second way that can be taken which, even if harder, is in reality much less dependent on a mere chance, is that of a profounder comparison or of a juxtaposition of facts that are already known. It enables us to discover new relationships. Frequently we find this second way to be connected with the discovery of mistakes made by earlier authors when they had formulated their final conclusions or in relation to methods which they had incorrectly used. This second way has been pursued in our investigations.

In our case, that is in the study of the origin of Cnidaria, it is impossible to expect that we will be able either to find the corresponding fossil-material or to make direct observations; and so it is clear that we must rely on the comparative method as applied to the present living species. The fossil documents that have been found belong exclusively to the skeleton-building Cnidaria: with a few exceptions they are all impressions of fully-developed medusae. We can see, however, that even in those cases where a much richer fossil-material stands at our disposal (e.g. in Vertebrata) and where we are able, on the basis of the fossil-remains of skeletons, to make far-reaching conclusions with regard to the structure of the "soft" parts of their bodies, that even here we must use the comparative method in its full extent in order to be able to make correct interpretations of facts i.e. to reconstruct the way the evolution had taken.

It should be mentioned in passing that only humble results have been achieved so far by means of the biochemical method in our study of the degrees of relationship, even if considerable expectations had been originally placed in this method. The chemical processes in question are certainly very complicated and the special serum methods that have been used till now are not yet fully developed. In the future we can with certainty expect more important results from this method. My invitation to biochemists to check, by means of the serum method, my hypothesis of the closer relationship between Cnidaria and Turbellaria has remained, to the best of my knowledge, so far without any response in the international literature on the subject.

It has been already mentioned that we cannot expect to find fossil remains of the early stages in the evolution of Cnidaria, since possibly no species belonging to them had existed at that time which could have left some fossilized traces. Yet even those traces which go back to more recent times are not unimportant for our purposes. Somewhat doubtful kinds of remains belonging to Cnidaria are known, that date from the Middle Cambrian. They belong to the now extinct Tetracoralla. No remains that can with certainty be attributed to Hydrozoa can be found earlier than in the Upper Triassic; some partly uncertain forms that resemble the present-day Campanulariae date from the Silurian. Impressions of Scyphomedusae that can be easily identified go back to the Middle Cambrian.

According to Schindewolf (1950), who in his studies paid special attention to the evolution of corals, the earliest remains that can with certainty be attributed to Madreporaria, and thus to Anthozoa, belong to the Upper Ordovician (which was formerly usually called Silurian). They evolved rapidly and differentiated into numerous species, some lived a solitary life (this is very important in our connection!), and some which formed colonies or cormi and which began to build coral reefs. Similar earlier reefs had been built by the Archaeocyathidae, which are now considered to have been a kind of silicious sponges. Fortunately enough, we find sclerosepta even in the earliest stone-corals; this enables us to study their internal structures, i.e. the distribution of the sarcosepta. It has even been possible to trace the ontogenetical development of their septal apparatus. In this way Schindewolf has been able to prove not only that in pterocorals the distribution of septa is bilaterally symmetric, but also that even the first anlage of the septal apparatus was bilateral ("the six protosepta show a distinct bilaterally symmetric development" Schindewolf, 1950, p. 179). Later, a secondary radial (hexamerous) symmetry has been developed from the former. It must be emphasized that according to Schindewolf (1950, p. 181–2) "the Palaeozoic pterocorals form the ancestral forms of the now living stone-corals. Together with the latter they must be included in the order of Madreporaria which had been previously limited to the recent forms only."

The fact is established by Schindewolf that this orthogenetic course of evolution which goes from an internal bilateral symmetry to a full cyclomeric radial symmetry has not been completely carried through even in the present-day Madreporaria. It will be later seen that this has been first achieved in Scyphozoa, and particularly perfectly in Hydrozoa. Here we meet with a phenomenon which is especially important to a phylogenist: it enables him to make well-founded conclusions about to the interrelationships on the basis of a comparison of recent forms only.

Again it can be stated that fortunately enough for phylogenists, the phyletic evolution of animals did not take such a course that it evolved along a single progressively advancing front so that the present day fauna would consist of the most advanced vertebrata only, actually of only one species: man. Even now we can find, so to say, in one and the same pool, various forms living together: Flagellata, amoebae, Turbellaria, snails, Annelida, insects, Bryozoa, fishes, frogs, etc. Thus we have old types which themselves have undergone further development and which in this way have become more differentiated, together with new types which are constantly emerging yet which are not necessarily always the more progressive forms. The primitive characteristics have not been preserved in the older types of structures only, but also in structures of some younger forms. These latter forms are particularly interesting to a phylogenist. It is only necessary to identify these primitive characteristics which had been typical also for their ancestors, and to interpret them correctly. Comparative morphology leads us to find these true homologies.

In our morphological comparisons we take into consideration above all the stages reached by the grown-up animals. This is a point that has been accepted by all morphologists. In Protista we consider the so-called vegetative stage in their cycles of development to correspond to the grown-up stage in metabionts. Secondarily, we have to take into consideration the succeeding stages in the individual, or ontogenetic, development, starting with the zygote (the fertilized egg) or even with gametes and with the gametogenesis. The comparison can be made either between various grown-up forms, or between various stages of its development, or, finally, between the grown-up forms and their stages of development. Naturally the latter kind of comparison is to be preferred.

Here, however, we meet with a problem which has been widely discussed and which has provoked the sharpest controversies among the zoologists. This is the question of the relation between ontogenies and phylogenies. The way we understand this relationship will be decisive to a large extent for the kind of conclusions we shall reach in individual cases. Here we cannot possibly start to discuss this whole problem; it should suffice to refer to the book by Sir Gavin de Beer, *Embryos and Ancestors.* Purely as a result of my own research in Cnidaria, and not as a result of the study of the corresponding literature, I came to the conclusion that the now prevailing concept of this relationship which finds its culmination in the well-known "fundamental biogenetic law" as it has been proposed by Ernst Haeckel, must be basically wrong. The facts that can be established on the basis of a study of the structure as well as of the individual development of Cnidaria disprove decisively the very spirit of this rule (it is better not to speak about laws within the field of biology) which wishes to see a recapitulation of the phyletic stages (i.e. the characteristics of the grown-up forms) in the ontogenies of their descendants, i.e. of the recent animal species. Garstang, was the first scholar to make it clear that the ontogenetic morphogeneses which are constantly repeated in each succeeding generation are also constantly changing.

The changes in the ontogenetic process, whether the introduction of new characteristics or the loss of characteristics and peculiarities which had previously existed, cannot possibly be considered to originate in an adult stage. It is only if we accept the standpoint of Lamarckism, that we could take a possible recapitulation of characteristics of the grown up individual into consideration.

In this way, and to the great regret of the comparative morphologists, the recapitulations which can take place during the ontogenies will be found to be limited, even if not completely eliminated. It is not true when it is said—as this can be frequently heard—"that Haeckel's law is not generally valid but that instead its validity is only limited;" in reality this supposed law is basically wrong. Nevertheless, there are recapitulations in ontogenies and these recapitulations are such that they can be of good use and service to a phylogenist. It is necessary to proceed very cautiously when in search of these recapitulations. One must be constantly aware of the fact that these are really ontogenetic characteristics that are recapitulated. This, however, does not exclude the possibility that these same characteristics eventually appeared in the grown up stages of their ancestors. These characteristics remain, even if they can be observed only under special circumstances of morphogeny, in spite of the fact that they had long been lost in their grown-up stages because of suppression due to the natural selection. In this way the phylogenist is fully justified in using those characteristics that have developed during ontogeny for his conclusions regarding the interrelationships between such animal types which he wishes to compare; but this must be done *cum grano salis.*

Even those peculiarities of different ontogenetic stages for which the unsuitable name of *Caenogeneses* (foreign or tampered peculiarities) has been invented by Haeckel, could be profitably used. Yet in this connection it is necessary to be even more cautious. I think that at this point morphologists have gone much too far, especially when they tried to develop the classification of animal types into large units on the basis of similarities that can only be observed during the earlier ontogenetic stages, e.g. during the segmentation of the egg, during the formation of the entoderm, etc. To demonstrate the above statement we may take the systematic category of Spiralia. A special type of cleavage, of the formation of the blastomere—the spiral type—is common to all animal types (this of course is not without exceptions) even if they show great varieties in their structures. Will this type of cleavage prove the common origin of all the animal species in which it appears, and should we therefore in a natural system combine all of them into one large group? I completely agree with Steinböck's suggestion to look upon these types of division from the point of view of the evolutionary mechanics (I like to speak in this connection about an "ontogenetic technique"). The type of cleavage usually depends on the quantity of the reserve food and so it appears in various forms within the narrow frame of a systematic category. Sacarão (1952) has described many examples in this connection which he explained in the same way. The phylogenist finds it useless to speak about Spiralia because among these there are whole groups that are no "Spiralia" whatever.

A special treatment is needed in the case of those ontogenetic stages that live freely and—as larvae—have had a progressive development which has been, say, in other surroundings and with another way of life than the corresponding grown-up forms. These cases are important for phylogenetic purposes.

The situation is usually such that the grown-up animal types—actually with widely different kinds of structure—live on the floor of the sea, lead a benthonic life, while at the same time their embryos have developed into planktonic larvae. The way that this case is presented here shows that we consider the life on the floor of the sea to be primary, and that in the open water, i.e. in the plankton, to be a secondary result of the development. In fact, *the larval stage represents a prolongation of the ontogeny*. In no way can we consider these larvae to be ancestors of any recent animals that live on the floor of the sea. We have no recapitulation of some stage reached by their ancestors, as is the case with some other stages in ontogeny In spite of this the larval stages can be of good use in our study of phylogeny. Larvae of some animal groups, e.g. those of Crustacea, have very characteristic forms and structures (in this instance the so-called *nauplius)*. These forms are so firmly established in the whole that they are present even when the grown-up forms had been much changed so that they can hardly be identified—whether this change be due to an adaptation of the benthonic way of life or to a strong parasitism. A similar case can be observed in Tunicata (Kowalevski). In such cases it is our right to consider larvae as evidence that species do belong together whose larvae have the same forms and structures. It would, however, be completely wrong to conclude on the basis of these facts that an ancestral form is being recapitulated in a nauplius. The example of Crustacea itself shows that it is not impossible that the larval stage, the nauplius, disappears. In the transition from the sea to fresh water, the free larval stage—the nauplius—becomes embryonalized. Frequently, this change is hardly noticeable. The free living stage of ontogeny had possibly originated in various levels which the evolution of the animal had reached, and it can also depart more or less from the "normal" type. Not infrequently (e.g. in insects) we find the main part of the individual existence transferred to the larval stage. In these instances the life of the adult stage can become very short: particularly in the case of male animals, so short that it just suffices for propagation. In these instances, the differences between a larva and its imago have become so considerable, both with regard to their structures as well as their ways of life (the type of feeding, the sphere within which the animal lives) that finally a great crisis occurs and the ontogeny which can only be overcome by way of an extremely radical method i.e. that of the total metamorphosis. These instances have the character of true catastrophies which, however, can fortunately enough be mastered. In the case of strongly developed parasitism we can frequently observe that a larva which has preserved a free mode of life, reaches a higher level of development than its grown-up form.

Beginning with Turbellaria and ending with Amphibia among the Vertebrata, larvae have had an important role during the levels reached in evolution. It is therefore not surprising that attempts have been made to use larvae as a basic element in the construction of a natural (i.e. evolutionistic) animal system. This is particularly true for those zoologists who came under the influence of the supposed "fundamental biogenetic law" as it had been formulated by Haeckel. It was all too easy to accept the possibility that in larvae, an ancestral form is being recapitulated and that for this reason all smaller groups whose larvae show a certain degree of similarity must have (1) a common ancestor, and (2) the form of this common ancestor must have been basically the same as that of the recent larva. In spite of the fact that these theses have been found to be essentially untrue, they have proved useful in the struggle for the recognition of the theory of evolution. This particularly in the sense that they have numerous well-known zoologists to make "embryological" studies of such species and groups of animals where natural relationships are not clear. It had been hoped that the better known ontogenies could prove useful in attempts to unravel these connections. The facts which have been discovered in this way have had an enduring value in spite of the fact that they have been arrived at by way of some wrong initial presumptions.

It was soon found that the larval stages, as well as complete ontogenies, proved useful for the construction of the natural system even if one did not employ the "fundamental biogenetic law;" it is only necessary to change the basis of such comparisons and to make these comparisons exclusively between various stages of development, even if the results reached in this way seem to be less important and certain. We can now state—and this with considerable certainty—that in a comparison of ontogenetic stages the chances of success are the greater, when the older stages are compared. It must be initially expected that in comparison to the primitive forms, the greatest changes will be observed in the youngest or initial stages of the ontogeny, since these are not only phyletically the oldest but also in their organization, the simplest stages. Here *Caenogeneses* may often take place. This is particularly true in the case of those animals whose development occurs from the very beginning in free water. It is therefore better to omit the early phases of ontogenesis from phyletic constructions, or, as is frequently heard, from our speculations.

Let us bypass the intermediate ontogenetic phases and discuss the phyletically oldest larvae. The planula of Cnidaria has generally been considered to be such a larva partly because the Cnidaria are believed to be the oldest Eumetazoa and partly because the planula has the simplest structure, i.e. it corresponds to Haeckel's gastraea. It consists of two layers only and it has neither an intestine nor an oral opening. The next form which follows the planula is the famous trochophore. This development frequently takes place by way of an intermediate form of protrochophora.

Because of its simplicity the planula has given rise to conjectures regarding the primitive form of all Metazoa. The planula has generally been considered as a very primitive form even if it does not have a feeding or a digestive system and even if it lives for a while on the reserve food it had obtained from its maternal organism. The structure, however, of this planula is not quite so simple even if it does not yet possess organs; it is well differentiated both histologically and cytologically. The tissue that can be observed in its interior does not correspond to an anlage of an intestine, to an entoderm; it is rather an "entomesoderm."

The planula, however, is a pure larva and by no means corresponds to a primitive form of the ancestors of Cnidaria; it is impossible to imagine the existence of a freely living Eumetazoa without an active digestive apparatus. As is the case with other animals that live on the floor of the sea, and particularly those that lead a sessile way of life, so it was with Cnidaria when they developed their specific larva which lived in the sea plankton and which was characteristic of them. We can speak here of a metamorphosis in Cnidaria even if it is not a very radical one. In numerous Cnidaria, with the exception of the Scyphozoa, the next higher ontogenetic stage, which is called the actinula, develops from the planula during its free life in the plankton. This can be explained as a case of paedogenesis and here we can see a formerly older phase, which had developed on the floor of the sea, transferred into the larval period. It is my belief that it would be possible to find early stages in the ontogenies of animal groups that stand higher in the animal system, where the same stages would resemble that of the planula in Cnidaria. It would only be necessary to make the effort, though this seems hardly worth while. It is perfectly clear that it would be wrong to make any conclusions about relationships from this. Neither would it be sensible to speak here about some modified planulae.

The same is true for the trochophore, the next higher stage in the ontogenetic development. It is by no means difficult to show that all those stages that have been called trochopphores, are neither identical nor homologous. A modified trochophore can occur only within the limits of an animal group which is uniform both phyletically as well as from the point of view of the comparative morphology. Yet in this case it would be senseless to speak about a modified trochophore. In my opinion we should dispense with special new names for each different larval form and drop those that have been already accepted. These names were given in former days when specimens were found swimming in the sea plankton; the puzzled scholars did not know where these animals belonged and since each child must have its own name, names were given to these specimens as if they were independent organisms. It was later found that these specimens were really larvae of some known or even unknown species. The names, however, have been preserved together with their suggestive influence, particularly in those cases where there is some similarity between several larval forms which have for this reason previously received a common name.

As long as the name trochophore continues to be used it should be limited to the planktonic larvae of Annelida only. Larvae of animal groups that stand either below or above Annelida in the animal system should not be called trochophores even in cases where they resemble the latter; these similarities are due first to analogous ways of life which lead to convergences, and, secondly, to an approximately equally low stage of organization (the unsegmented stage). Even the orientation of animals, e.g. the poised position in free water with its longitudinal axis in the direction of the earth's centre of gravity can lead to a general similarity in the habit of these larvae.

Certainly there won't be many objections if we do not call the planktonic larvae of aproctous animals (Ameria) trochophores, even if they look somewhat similar to the trochophore of *Polygordius* which is considered as the most typical form of all trochophores. These larvae are not numerous. Boas in his excellent *Lehrbuch der Zoologie* which was widely used in his day, had already stated for good reasons that trochophores were convergently developed pelagic larval forms, i.e. they developed independently from each other in completely different animal groups, beginning with *Turbellaria* and continuing up to the very last *Oligomeria*, or close to the very threshold of Chordonia.

Unfortunately, there have been numerous zoologists not only in former days (e.g. Hatschek, Cori) but even, now (e.g. Carter, Marcus) who have been induced to attribute great phyletic significance to these larval forms. This led finally to an unnecessary increase in the number of proposed animal systems. One example should suffice to show how this exaggerated appreciations of similarities between various larvae—in this case between trochophores—led to wrong conclusions. We think here of Mollusca. The veliger larva of Mollusca has been rather generally considered as a kind of trochophore. Because of an external similarity, yet frequently not for this reason only, it has been thought that there is a close relationship between Mollusca and Annelida. According to this interpretation the primitive Mollusca have been believed to have developed from primitive Annelida by way of an omission of their metamerism. In the not very distant past, earnest attempts have been made to find in the ontogeny of Mollusca, in their veliger larva, traces of a former metamerism with the cavity of the former perigastrocoel (eucoelom, as it is called by American authors). It has been thought that these have been found, in the Mollusca, in much the same way that they have been described for the Echiuroidea. The Mollusca, however, are genuine and primary Ameria, i.e. they are from their very beginning unsegmented Eumetazoa, and it can be proved that in their phyletic past they have never been segmented animals. They represent the climax in the progressive development within the phylum of Ameria. They are therefore not directly related to Annelida, either in the sense that we see in Annelida a development from the primitive Mollusca, or, vice versa as a result of a partly regressive development due to a secondary omission of the segmentation.

I am fully convinced that this, my interpretation, is right in spite of a recent discovery of *Neopilina* which has been found by Lemche (1958) to be a segmented animal with five body segments. As in the case of several other Ameria we can observe a partial *polymerization* in a certain number of Mollusca, and therefore not only in *Neopilina* and in the related fossil species. It occurs, however, in *Neopilina* to a stronger and fuller degree than, for example in Tetrabranchia among the Cephalopoda.

As far as is known, no pelagic larvae have been developed by the acoelous Turbellaria in spite of the fact that they live (with a few exceptions in planktonic species) on the sea bottom. Unfortunately, our present knowledge of the ontogeny of Acoela is still very unsatisfactory. Surprisingly enough, we do not find pelagic larvae in Turbellaria earlier than in Polycladida (e.g. Müller's larva). It is aproctous like the grown-up Turbellaria—it has no anal orifice—and for this reason it cannot be compared to a trochophore but rather to a protrochophore, unless as it has even been thought, we consider the aproctous condition to be secondary. This larva has developed its own swimming apparatus in the form of an irregular circle which consists of eight lobular excrescences that are rimmed with cilia. This larva is poised "vertically" in water. It develops gradually and without a real metamorphosis into a polyclad that lives on the sea bottom. It is not my intention to discuss here any other larval groups that live in plankton; the only form I would like to mention is the so-called *pilidium* of Nemertinea. In spite of the fact that Nemertinea stand close to Turbellaria, they have nevertheless become euproctous; there is a very great difference between the pelagic larvae of the two groups which can be observed not only in their external forms. The Pilidium is aproctous—in agreement with its ontogenetic stage—and it has a completely different type of development to the Müller's larva. On the basis of these facts we can come to the conclusion that the two larvae developed independently from each other, and, furthermore, that they are no recapitulation of some grown-up ancestors. In the pilidium the first genuine metamorphosis can be observed: in this "catastrophic" metamorphosis the worm develops out of special and quite separate *Anlagen* and in an entirely different orientation so that finally a considerable part of the body is destroyed, (see Fig. 6).

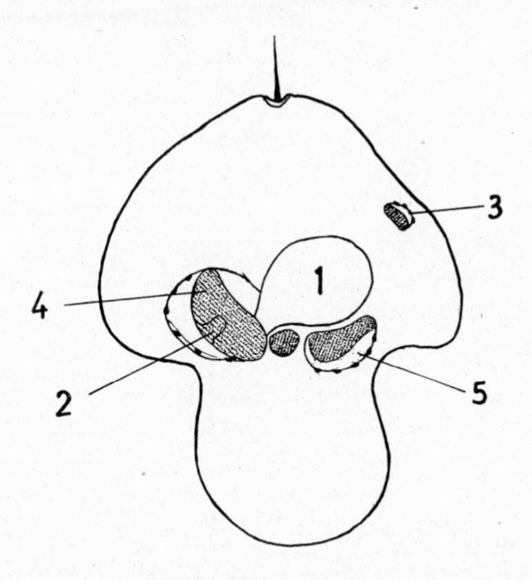

Fig. 6. Nemertinan planktonic larva, called the pilidium; (1), the gut, (2), primordium *(Anlage)* of the proboscis; (3—5), primordia of the "worm-body".

I repeat that comparative morphology which tries to find homologies and evaluate relationship connections on the basis of such homologies can with full right make use of ontogenetic morphogeny and thus the larval stages. Yet, first, it must not seek in these some recapitulation of the morphogeny of their grown-up ancestors, and, secondly, it should not lay too great an emphasis on the ontogenetic facts and on the larval stages. It should not base the whole animal classification on the larval stages or even on the type of cleavage. The main emphasis should be on comparisons of grown-up forms both of the fossil as well as of recent animal species.

I will not enter here into the discussion of phylembryogenetic problems which have been already touched on. However, since we are speaking about larvae, I wish to mention two other extreme cases of such changes because they are important from a methodological point of view. In one case which I have already mentioned, the larval phase is simply omitted; it has been cancelled. It seems that this takes place comparatively rapidly.

The best known condition under which the larval phase has become lost is that of the transition from sea to fresh water (e.g. in *Hydra*, numerous Crustacea, Mollusca). To this should also be added perhaps migration into great depths, and life in the far northern regions with their cold waters (a transition to the nursing of the progeny taking place). Not infrequently, however, traces of a former larval stage can in these cases be observed in the development of the embryo.

The opposite case is represented on one hand by the phenomenon of neoteny and on the other by the complete prevalence of the larval phase. The essential difference between these two cases can be seen in the fact that in the former the adult stage is simply omitted, the development of gonads and maturation are transferred to the larval stage. Dissogeny represents a transition to this stage; this is the double sexual maturation which takes place once during the grown-up stage and once in larva (it has been observed in Ctenophora). This change, too, is connected with a change of the environment, usually in the way that the animal remains in the plankton. Something similar to neoteny can be found in animals with metagenesis (the alternation of generations) when either one or the other generation is preserved as this can be frequantly observed in Cnidaria; here the sexual function which had passed over from the polypoid to the newly formed medusoid generation is later transferred back to the polypoid generation; in case, however, of an omission of the polypoid generation, the sexual function remains with the medusoid generation which is then the only generation preserved (the so-called hypogenetic species). In these cases, too, the changes are connected with a change of the environment.

In the other extreme case, the main role in the life cycle is taken over by the larval phase. The animal feeds during this phase only. It lives in the larval environment for most of its life. The imago stage is limited to a very short period of time; it serves mainly the purpose of propagation and it's digestive organs are frequently lost. Such cases are best known to occur among insects.

In our study of phylogeny and in our attempt to reconstruct the phylogenetic development, we frequently meet with the problem of whether a simple structure can be taken as a sign of primitivism. This leads us to the important problem of the progressivity of evolution. In a not too distant past it could be frequently seen, and sometimes this occurs even now, that a simple structure is taken simply as something primary, primitive. Completely wrong constructions have been made because of this mistake. It will be seen later that it was especially so in the interpretation of the evolution of Cnidaria. It must be confessed that it is not always very easy to differentiate between a primary primitive and a secondary simplicity of a structure. Here one has to proceed very carefully; one must make investigations by means of intensive and extensive comparisons, taking particularly into consideration the way of life and its changes. One must especially have a clear understanding of general conditions. Here it should suffice to state that there certainly are both primary as well as secondary simple phenomena, as has been proved by verified facts. This is due to the fact that the evolution does not always and exclusively show a *progressive tendency*; its tendency can also be in the opposite direction, it can be *regressive*, and this is quite often the case. This regressive development (which is usually and unfortunately called a *degeneration*) does not take place to a minor extent only, i.e. in the lower categories of the animal system. In my opinion, it has to be reckoned with even in the so-called macro-evolution, or in the evolution of the highest categories which are characterized by phyla. The whole phylum of Oligomeria with its numerous subtypes (situated between Polymeria and Chordonia) is in my opinion a product of a generally regressive development. In all probability such a type of development has occured in the Cnidaria, as is also the case of other animal types that have adopted a sessile way of life.

We speak here of circumstances which usually accompany regressive development, or actually cause it. In a sessile way of life Natural Selection favours the *minus mutanta* which gradually reduce and eliminate all those organs and parts of the structure that are causally or functionally connected with the free mobility of the mobile or swimming animal types.

Besides the sessile way of life in which the animal becomes immobile, there is also the parasitic way of life which regularly leads to a regressive development, particularly in the case of internal parasites. It is well known that due to parasitism, characteristic form can be reduced so much that it is past recognition. It should be mentioned that it is often the larval stage, so far as this is preserved, which enables zoologists in cases of a well advanced regression ("degeneration") to determine the history of a species and thus the membership in a certain animal group.

All this is well known and nothing new has really been said here. Nevertheless, it has been necessary to discuss this point because it was in connection with Coelenterata, and also with Cnidaria, that many mistakes have been made. The rule—it is better not to speak about laws in biology—according to which a constantly sessile way of life leads to a simplification of the body structure has been believed to be true in connection with other animal groups; these are by no means few; yet it has not been accepted in connection with Coelenterata, i.e. Cnidaria. Later it will be seen that, due to historical reasons, particularly to our deficient knowledge of the fine structure of Cnidaria, the Cnidaria have been believed to be primarily simple animals which are just on the border between animals and plants (Zoophyta). The conservatism and the authority of prominent scholars, both basically useful to the science, can become detrimental to it and an obstacle to the progress when they exceed all bounds. This has been the case with Cnidaria. The freshwater *Hydra* has for a long time been considered to be the most primitive of all Eumetazoa, and consequently also of Cnidaria. Even at the present time, *Hydra* is often described as a primitive simply built animal, a description which is made for didactic purposes if for no other reason. Finally, when the idea has been accepted that the solitary character of *Hydra* is a secondary phenomenon, and that *Hydra* is without its medusoid generation, progress has stopped here and the scholars did not try to draw the necessary consequences. This situation has continued even after it had been proved by palaeozoologists that the Anthozoa actually have an internal bilaterally symmetric structure.

The Significance of the Sessile Way of Life

In our study of phylogenetic problems we must not be satisfied with an exclusive use of comparative morphology even in those cases where a rich fossil material has been available. We shall completely understand and comprehend a species of animals—and this is true also for a systematic group of animals—when we also know their way of life, and the environment in which they live. Even if this is an old and generally accepted truth one can never emphasize enough its great, and decisive, importance. In this connection mistakes have again been made, with regard to Cnidaria, which persist down to the present day. It is therefore necessary to discuss this problem at some length. All Cnidaria live in water, and all—with a few exceptions—live in the sea; we shall therefore limit ourselves to the study of conditions that prevail in this largest and oldest of all environments in which the life of organisms, and thus also of animals, has been developed.

The first and the most important problem we meet here is which of the two opposite large biotopes of the sea is primary; benthos (the bottom of the sea), or the pelagic zone (the zone of the free water)?

It can soon be found if we make a physicochemical comparison of the sea properties, that it was in all probability the sea bottom where the first life came into being. This was the only place where life was initially able to develop further. It must have been in the shallow water that sunrays could penetrate down to the sea bottom and where the early life of animals could develop and be sustained on algae and on bacteria. Individual types of animals could later get used, by way of special adjustments, to the life on a deeper sea bottom, or they could begin to inhabit as plankton the free water area. It is very probable that the life on the deeper sea bottom of the abyssal zone developed much later than that in the plankton. In the plankton, life reached an exuberant growth and sank as an organic rain to the unproductive sea bottom.

Purely inductive thinking alone allows us to suppose that in free water the animal life began to develop in a similar way. First it was necessary that phytoplankton appeared which synthesized the organic substances and served as a basic food for animal consumers. The substance of a living organism has a greater specific gravity than the sea water (in the remote past this difference was probably even greater than it is now); organisms had therefore to depend on the sea bottom until finally individual small algae—it was easier for these to do so—succeeded in developing mechanisms which helped them to overcome the effects of gravity, i.e. to lower their specific gravity, as was done, for example, by undulipodia (flagella, drops of oil, gelatinous coverings lighter than sea water, excrescences and similar forms of the body that increased the friction between the body and water).

It is certainly not a mere chance that we find the phytoplankton of the sea to be composed exclusively of monocellular small algae and that no higher type of plants had been able to develop in the sea plankton. We can safely maintain that this was so because, *rebus sic stantibus*, it could simply not begin to develop here. It was only in a calm and shallow fresh water where *Volvox*, and Anthophyta like *Lemna*, could begin to develop, either in free water or on its surface, and without a contact with the bottom.

Protozoa were in all probability the first animals that began to live in the water of the free sea and continued to exist in it. They evolved as Zooflagellata out of Phytoflagellata and further continued their evolution into the planktonic Protozoa, i.e. the rhizopodan Radiolaria. It is *a priori* improbable that Metazoa developed out of planktonic Protozoa either such as had formed colonies or those that consisted of several nuclei (polyenergida). The reason is the same which prevented metaphytes from developing in the sea plankton.

The first Metazoa that inhabited the free water of the sea were certainly the freely developing ontogenetic stages of animals that lived on the sea bottom, first, because they had evolved out of eggs that had been left freely swimming in water, secondly, because they were small and light with a comparatively large surface, and thirdly, because they were covered with flagella and cilia which they could use, even if to a smaller degree, as a means of locomotion. Slight vertical streams were sufficient to bring these future larvae into the upper strata of water where they could find a rich food and other conditions of life. This is the way we have to explain the origin of planktonic larvae. It was only later that these larvae were followed by grown-up animal species into these strata of free water, and these again had to make special adaptations to new conditions. Or some larvae which belonged to animals that lived on the sea bottom, remained constantly in the plankton so that they changed by way of neoteny into planktonic animals. The feeding of the first metazoic planktonic animals must have been microphagous; it was only later when animal types developed, that macrophages began to feed on the former (Cephalopoda, Vertebrate).

It is conspicuous that no new animal types have developed in the plankton of the free water zone of the sea. All the major types of animals have developed on the sea bottom. Neither have any of the main types (phyla) developed by way of neoteny.

For methodological reasons and because of its special connection with Cnidaria we must deal here with one more problem. We must differentiate between the two types of relationship that exist between the stage that lives on the sea bottom and the stage that lives in the plankton. On one hand we have the transition which takes place within the frame of one and the same generation. First we have to imagine a case in which the phase of the grown-up form which lives on the sea bottom is primary, and the planktonic phase of a juvenile, usually larval, stage secondary. In another case the form which lives on the sea bottom is primary; naturally, it is able to propagate sexually and it can eventually develop its own juvenile planktonic form; and there is a secondary generation which had developed by way of gemmation or fission—in an asexual way—before the sexual propagation has been adopted by the phase which lives on the sea bottom. The generation which had been created by way of an asexual reproduction evolves into plankton and adopts sexual reproduction while it becomes adjusted to life in the free water. This is the classical case of the alternation of generations, or *metagenesis*, where an originally single phase which was for some time also the main phase becomes, so to speak, degraded and it continues to live a vegetative life only.

The subsequent development can pursue two or three different ways. Either we find the originally primary generation withering away (this is the generation which lives on the sea bottom, in our case the generation of polyps), so that the secondary, planktonic, form remains as the only one that has survived (in our case the form of medusae); or, vice versa we find that the secondary planktonic form and generation, i.e. that of medusae, is withering away, while the primary, benthonic generation, i.e. the generation of polyps, is really the only form which survives. Thus we can return by way of an indirect course to the initial situation. Finally, the generation of medusae as the only form that had survived, can develop into an animal that resembles polyps and lives as such on the sea bottom (*Armohydra* see Fig. 7, *Halammohydra* see Fig. 8, *Otohydra* see Fig. 18.)

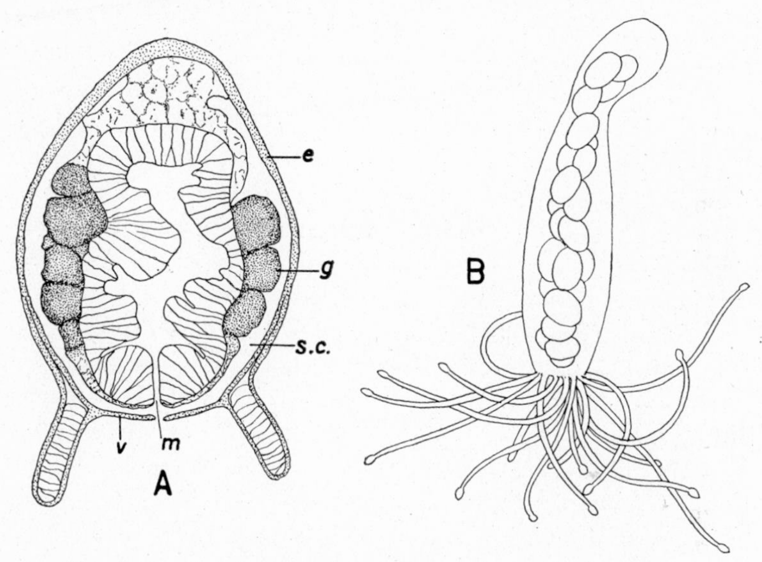

Fig. 7. A reduced trachyline medusa *Armohydra janowiczi* Swedmark & Tesnier; A, longitudinal section; B, habit; g, gonad; e, exumbrella; m, mouth; sc, subumbrellar cavity; v, velum; (after Swedmark and Tesnier).

In connection with all these developments the question necessarily arises how can we in a given case differentiate and correctly interpret the path evolution had taken? A broader and deeper comparison can help us here while we take into consideration on one hand the ecologic conditions and on the other Dollo's rule of the irreversibility of evolution. Many mistakes have been made in this connection. Many zoologists, among them even specialists in Cnidaria, are inclined to see in the planktonic form of medusae the original, the primary, or the main form out of which the polyps can be considered to have evolved. On the other hand, the solitary forms of the Hydrozoa polyps, and of polyps that have no generation of medusae have also been believed to be the primitive forms. Both these interpretations are equally wrong; both of them are based on pre-suppositions that are methodologically wrong.

One more point can be of good service in our phylogenetic studies. This is the relationship between locomotion on one hand and the environment and the kind of feeding on the other. As is well known, three stages in the evolution of the active forms of locomotion must be taken into consideration (cf. the study by L. Zenkewitsch). We disregard two forms that occur in Protozoa: the amoeboid movement and the movement effected by the individual flagella (it is true that in Spongiae the amoeboid type of movement does occur, even if to a small degree only; cf. Hadži, 1917). In the small and primitive groups of Ameria the type of movement corresponds mainly to conditions that can be found among Protozoa, in the Infusoria; this is movement by means of cilia and this type of movement is preserved in planktonic larvae, so to say, right through one classificatory system. The ciliary pulsation produced by animals while they are exposed to the rhythmical swell of waves enables them not only to glide over a firm ground, which is true for the majority of Turbellaria, but also to swim in free water, as can be observed in Infusoria and Rotatoria. The formation of undulipodia (flagella and cilia) by individual cells belongs to a general inventory of all animals. There have been a few specialized animals however, e.g. Nematoda among Ameria and insects among Polymeria, which have completely dispensed with the action of undulipodia because the surface of these animals had been strongly cuticularized.

Undulipodia which cover the free upper surface do not serve the purpose of locomotion only; they can also be transplaced, together with their maternal cells, into the interior of the animal by way of the invagination of the surface stratum of the body. This is how we have to understand the origin of nephridia which serve as excretory and emunctory organs. Another point to be mentioned here is that Dollo's rule does not seem to be valid in connection with the formation of cilia, i.e. even after they had been lost during the phyletic development of

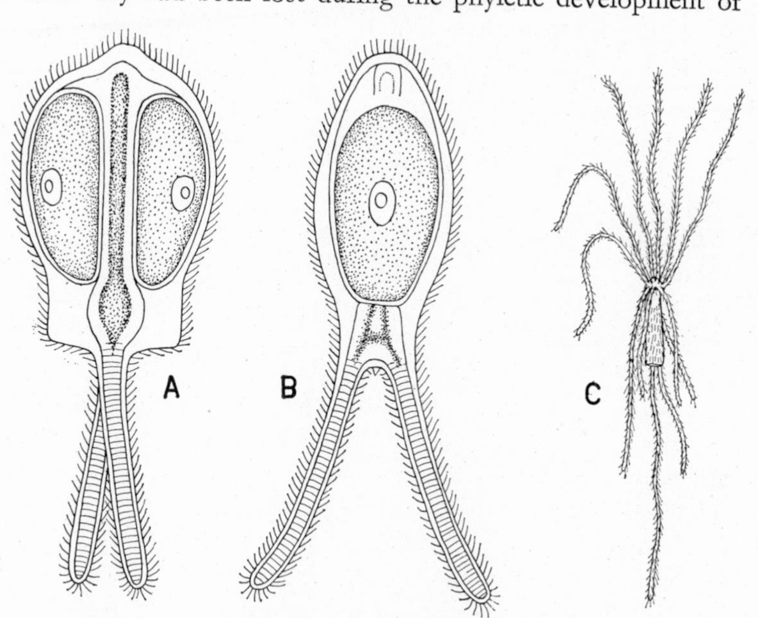

Fig. 8. Secondarily ciliated Hydrozoa; A—B, sporosac of *Dicoryne conferta* Alder (after Allman); C, *Halammohydra octopodides* Remane; (after Remane).

an animal they can be later reintroduced. This can be proved by some clear instances that can be observed among Hydrozoa. It has been known since Allman's days that in the species *Dicoryne conferta* Allman, which belongs to Hydroidea (Athecata), completely retrograded medusoids which lived otherwise as completely immobile forms as its cormus, regain their ability to swim again by means of a secondary development of cilia (the so-called sporosacs, see Fig. 8 A-B). *Halammohydra*, a Hydrozoon which has been recently discovered by A. Remane (1937), and which lives in the sea sand, has a polyp form; its surface is covered with cilia which enable the animal to glide actively and move in this way among small grains of sand (see Fig. 8 C). I have succeeded in showing (Hadži 1959) that *Halammohydra* actually corresponds to a strongly modified Narcomedusa whose muscular swimming apparatus has been much reduced while at the same time secondary cilia have developed. It is certain that something similar could also be found in other animal groups.

The second type of locomotion is based on contractions of muscular fibres which had developed within the cellular cytoplasm. This specialized form of a general ability of the cytoplasm to contract has already been "invented" by Protozoa. Metazoa have inherited it fully developed from their protozoan ancestors. These contractile fibres served first to make possible movement on a fixed spot, bowing, the contraction of stem-shaped forms, the constriction of cavities, e.g. of the peristomial ciliary apparatus in the peritrichous and epitrichial Infusoria (also in sphincters), etc. As a secondary result and parallel to an increase of the size of the body, locomotion by means of cilia is given up, and the muscular movements of the body begin to be used to effect locomotion. This can be observed as early as in the larger flat Turbellaria, particularly in Polycladida. The highest level in the development of the means of locomotion in free water is reached in medusae which possess special transverse stripes in their muscular fibres: in these, movement is effected by means of regular rhythmic contractions which are controlled and led by nerves and which remind us already of the pulsation of the heart (the latter is first developed in Mollusca).

A higher type of locomotion by means of contraction of muscles has been developed with the formation of extremities. Here we are less interested in this type because it has not been developed in Ameria.

The type of locomotion used by an animal is very important and the symmetrical conditions in animals depend on it to a large extent. We meet with this problem immediately when we compare the first opposing pair: the mobility in contact with the firm ground (vagility), and the immobility, the permanent attachment to the ground, and a stronger contractility (sessility). Whenever we see that the free mobility has been abandoned, a phenomenon which can be observed quite often in Protozoa as well as in Metazoa, we can regularly observe how a simultaneous change of the carriage of the animal takes place. The consequences of this change are great. A characteristic property of animals which move or glide over a firm surface is the bilateral symmetry of their bodies. The animal moves forward with its anterior end placed in the direction of the movement; this is the way the head region begins to develop and with it, the great contrast between the anterior and posterior ends of the body. The contacts of the two ends with the environment are widely different. An almost equally great difference can be observed in the contacts of the dorsal and ventral sides and their environments: the flattened ventral side touches the ground over which the animal moves while the slightly vaulted dorsal side has contact with free water only. The contacts of the two lateral sides (the left and the right sides) are basically identical and this is why these two sides are similar. In this way the bilateral organization and form, and thus the bilateral symmetry, have been evolved.

Bilateral symmetry exists in the whole animal world and it must be considered as primitive All the other types of symmetry can be deduced from the bilateral symmetry. The changes in this symmetry are always due to the changes in the relationship between the type of locomotion and the environment; they can all be explained as modifications of the bilateral symmetry.

The most frequent change, which occurs as a more or less distinct disturbance, is that of asymmetry. It is rather rare that we find the assymetry to be conspicuous and characteristic for larger groups of animals. It occurs, for example, in Infusoria when they swim freely but not far from the sea bottom by means of beating of cilia, and among Gastropoda where the origin of their asymmetry is a special problem which cannot be discussed here at any length. In certain groups of fishes the asymmetry is due to their lying constantly on one side of their body, similarly as in the case of *Branchiostoma (Amphioxus)*.

Most frequently, however, we see that a secondary radial symmetry develops out of the primary bilateral symmetry. Always, and without an exception, this change stands in causal relationship to the transition to a secondary, sessile, way of life, i.e. to the fact that the active locomotion had been given up. These changes of symmetrical conditions occur in varying degrees of intensity in all the large groups of the animal world, beginning with Flagellata among Protozoa and continuing up to Chordonia. Radial symmetry can occur even without a trace of the former bilateral symmetry or of the asymmetry; the degree of evolution of this radial symmetry depends on the final structural conditions, the way of life, the type of feeding, as well as on the phyletic age of the transition to a semi-sessile or finally to a fully sedentary way of life. This radial symmetry can be so completely without a trace of the former bilateral symmetry that it was believed, especially by older zoologists (and unfortunately it still is accepted by some modern scholars,) that this radial symmetry is an original property of Metazoa. We cannot blame the idealistically minded pre-Darwinian morphologists that they put together Coelenterata (actually Cnidaria) and Echinodermata, i.e. two animal groups with the most highly developed radial symmetry, and created for them the taxonomic unit of Radiata. Even in the post-Darwinian days there were zoologists—and there are some even now—who, following Cuvier, try to preserve this artificial unit. As a matter of fact, however, Cnidaria are in no way whatever phyletically related to Echinodermata.

As a preliminary stage in the development towards the radial symmetry we can observe first a change in the general carriage of the animal and in connection with this, the disappearance of the difference between the dorsal and ventral sides of its body. As a result of this, the form of the transverse section of the animal becomes circular. In some animal groups, whose body is otherwise completely bilaterally symmetrical, the inclination to accept the radial symmetry can be developed in one part of its body only, e.g. in its anterior part. This depends on how much these organs are used by the animal to stick to the ground or to adhere to it by means of suction. Clear examples of such a development can be seen in Cestoda (scolex) and in Nematoda (the coroniform distribution of various papillae and of sensory organs of the skin) (see Fig. 9.). A complete radial symmetry can only be reached in the aproctous types of animals, e.g. in Cnidaria, or in such euproctous animals where the absence of the anal orifice is a secondary phenomenon in their development (some Echinodermata, especially among the Ophiuroidea). In Infusoria, a complete radial symmetry can rarely, if ever, be observed, even if in these the anal orifice has frequently not developed. This is due to their strong inclination to adopt an asymmetrical structure; the latter has also been inherited in their digestive apparatus by animals that live a sessile way of life (epitrichial Infusoria).

The combination of a primary bilateral symmetry and of a secondary radial symmetry can lead to a bisymmetry. This can be observed in the interior of numerous anthopolyps and of other animals, and it is best and most purely developed in Ctenophora. In my opinion, the origin of this bisymmetry can be explained rationally in one way only if we consider the bilaterally symmetric form as primary, and we presuppose that there had been a development caused by the loss of contact with the firm ground which made the ventral and dorsal sides similar. The two lateral sides preserve their original similarity with each other, yet they are more rounded off and therefore better developed. Moreover, they still continue to be different from the ventral and dorsal sides, though the latter have become similar with each other. In Ctenophora this change of symmetrical conditions occurs in connection with their

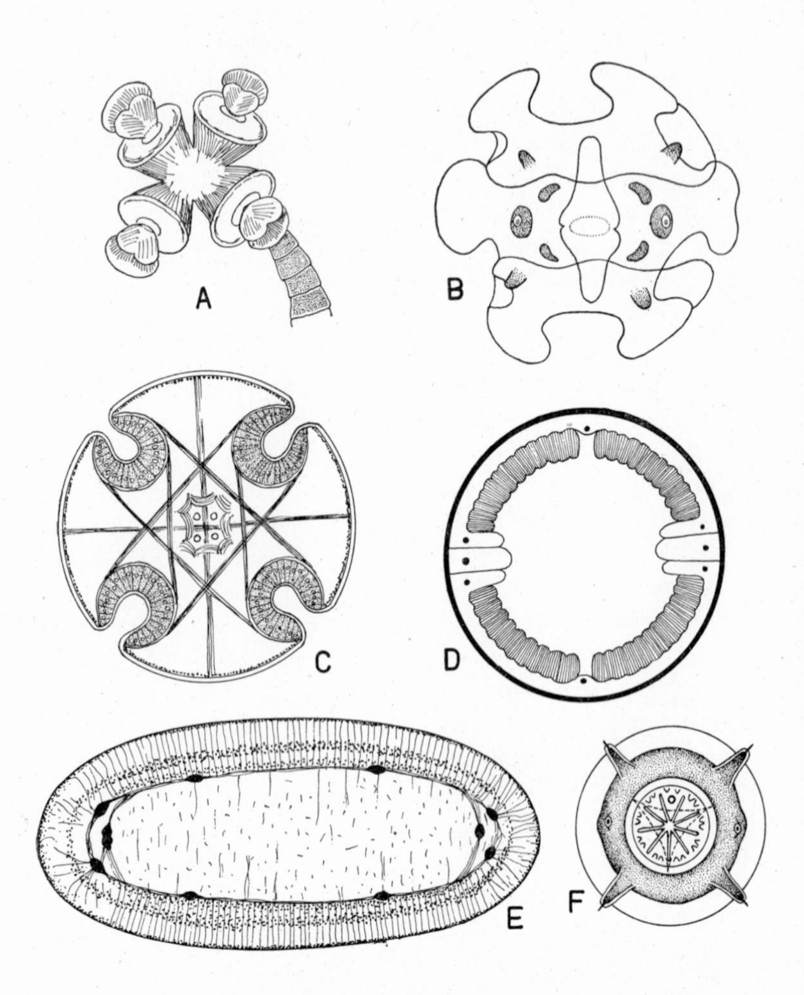

Fig. 9. Some cases of transition from bilateral to radial symmetry of entoparasitic "worms" but only on the "head"; A, scolex of *Carpobothrium* sp., (after Shipley and Hornell); B, anterior view of the nematode *Parabronema* sp., (after Baylis); C, cross-section through the scolex of *Nematobothrium* sp., (after Fuhrmann); D, cross-section of a polymerian nematode (after Filipjev); E, cross-section of a proglottis of *Anoplacephala* sp. (after Becker); F, anterior view of the nematode *Oesophagostomum* sp., (after Goodey).

transition from a life in benthos to a life in the pelagic zone, i.e. to the zone of the free water (see Fig. 10).

In this connection we are able to ascertain a very welcome regularity; it enables us to find out the way along which the change takes place. The rule is that this change occurs first in the peripheral parts of the body of the animal, and only later in its internal organs. The eight "antimeres" or ribs that

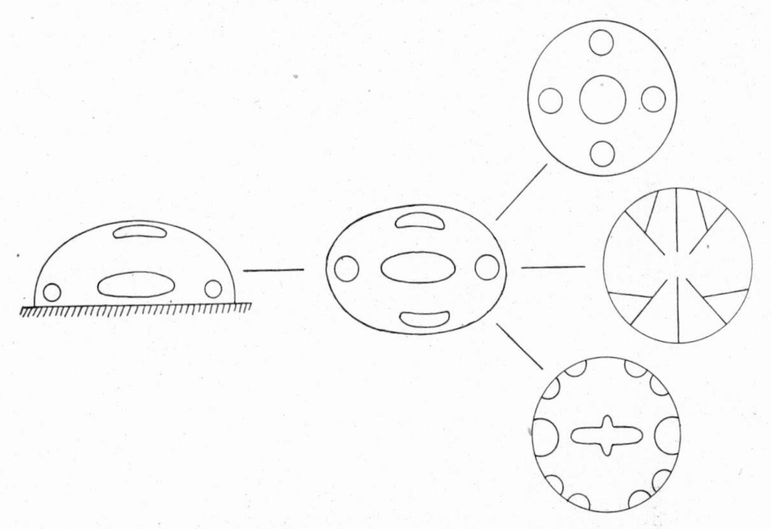

Fig. 10. Scheme illustrating the transition of primarily bilateral symmetry to other symmetries as consequence of a changed way of life.

can be found in an otherwise swivel-round body of Ctenophora show a nearly perfect radially symmetrical distribution, and yet at the same time some well-preserved traces of a former bilateral symmetry can be observed in the central parts of their digestive organs which are frequently called the gastrovascular system (see Fig. 3.). Similar conditions exist in numerous anthozoan polyps as was first noticed by palaeozoologists.

In our study of Ctenophora, we meet with the problem how life in the free zone, i.e. in the pelagic zone, influenced the general form of the body of animals. If we review all the planktonic animals the impression we finally get is that there has been no general regularities in respect. In these animals all possible symmetrical conditions can be found exactly as in the animals that live on the ground. And still there are differences which are due, as we shall see later, to the fact that in free water there is no contact between the firm ground and the animal, i.e. its ventral side. In the Ctenophora we can observe how life in free water promotes the development of radial symmetry; this is due to the similarity of contacts between the milieu and all parts of the animal body. If there is, however, an eventual change of symmetrical conditions, then this change is largely due to the type of movement. In types of animals that move only slowly and mainly by means of cilia or organs which have developed out of these (e.g. the swimming plates in Ctenophora, the circlets of cilia in trochophores), and in types that hang vertically in water, the inclination to adopt the radial symmetry must always be expected, and, as a matter of fact, it will be found in them. Bilateral symmetry, however, remains preserved a long time after the transition from a life in the benthos to a life in the pelagic zone had taken place, if the movement of the animal is more energetic and stronger and if it is effected by means of muscles and particularly by means of limbs. This can be best observed in the case of Chaetognatha. I derive them, in agreement with some other zoologists, from the planktonic larvae of Brachiopoda. These brachiopod larvae hang in water or they move slowly by means of a pulsation of cilia. They are basically bilaterally symmetric animals but they show a clear inclination to adopt radial symmetry. In Chaetognatha, however, which are predatory animals with strong contractions of muscles and with an ability to move rapidly head first, bilateral symmetry had been developed in spite of their life in free water. Radiolaria, an extremely old protozoan group which for a long time has been living exclusively in the pelagic zone or in plankton, contain all possible forms among their very numerous species that live in various depths of the sea, yet they never have a typical bilaterally symmetric form with a difference between ventral and dorsal sides. The impression we get in the face of these immense riches of forms of Radiolaria is that the life in free water is indifferent to the symmetric conditions of basic forms and that it therefore "allows" all kind of forms.

In Cnidaria, as animals that primarily live on the sea bottom, the radial symmetry has already been developed because of their sessile way of life; after their transition, as medusae, to a life in plankton, this radial symmetry becomes considerably intensified. A more or less expressed bisymmetry can be occasionally developed due to a reduction of their tentacles, and in some cases even a state of asymmetry can be approached if only one marginal tentacle has been preserved. The bilaterally symmetric and bisymmetric medusae can be found as medusoids in the cormi of Siphonophora only; it is only here that a polymorphism of medusoids can be observed. The individual swimming medusae have never developed bilateral symmetry in spite of the fact that they are excellent swimmers.

The example of Echinodermata shows how long the old symmetric conditions can be preserved during life in plankton. Echinodermata are considered to have evolved out of some bilaterally symmetrical ancestors that had crept over the surface of the sea bottom. Because of a later adoption of a sessile way of life, these Echinodermata have subsequently developed more or less radially symmetric forms. Their larvae, however, are purely bilaterally symmetric animals in spite of the fact that they still continue to go into free water and that they move slowly and only by means of cilia. This shows that here we have a kind of conservatism; similar to the case of starfishes which have adopted a secondary vagile way of life while at the same time they still preserve an obvious radial symmetry because of the slowness of their movements. On the other hand, sea urchins which burrow in the soft sea bottom have adopted a secondary bilateral symmetry.

The Role of the Polymerization and of the Subsequent Oligomerization During the Phylogeny

A very important and fruitful criterion for the evaluation of phylogenetic problems has been recently discussed at great length by the well-known Russian scholar, the now unfortunately deceased zoologist V. Dogiel. This is the phenomenon of the polymerization of smaller and also of larger morphologic units in the body of the animal. The subsequent oligomerization is regularly accompanied by differentiation (V. Dogiel, 1954). We must imagine it as a doubling and as a further multiplication of units which takes place in the complex of genes and which is later, during the development of an individual, materialized in the corresponding morphologic "parts". By way of this process of polymerization we can explain the development of monoflagellate and mononuclear Flagellata into Poly- and Hypermastigida as well as into the polynuclear species, a development which has finally led also to the formation of Ciliata. Various ciliary organelles of a complex nature have evolved by way of a specialization of cilia from this polymerization; the polymerized nuclei have become differentiated into macro and micronuclei by way of oligomerization. The ribs of Ctenophora have been developed by way of oligomerization and differentiation. The single pair of tentacles as it occurs in Turbellaria has developed into circlets which frequently consist of multiplied tentacles as in the Cnidaria. A subsequent oligomerization led in some cases observed in Hydrozoa, to a reduction of tentacles to the number of two, or even to their complete disappearance. The polymerization followed by oligomerization and differentiation finally led to the formation of various forms of tentacles in one and the same individual (e.g. in polyps of *Eleutheria* and of medusae see Fig. 11 and 12).

Naturally, we must be careful to differentiate, when we take into consideration this regularity, between a primary simplicity and a secondary simplicity which has developed by way

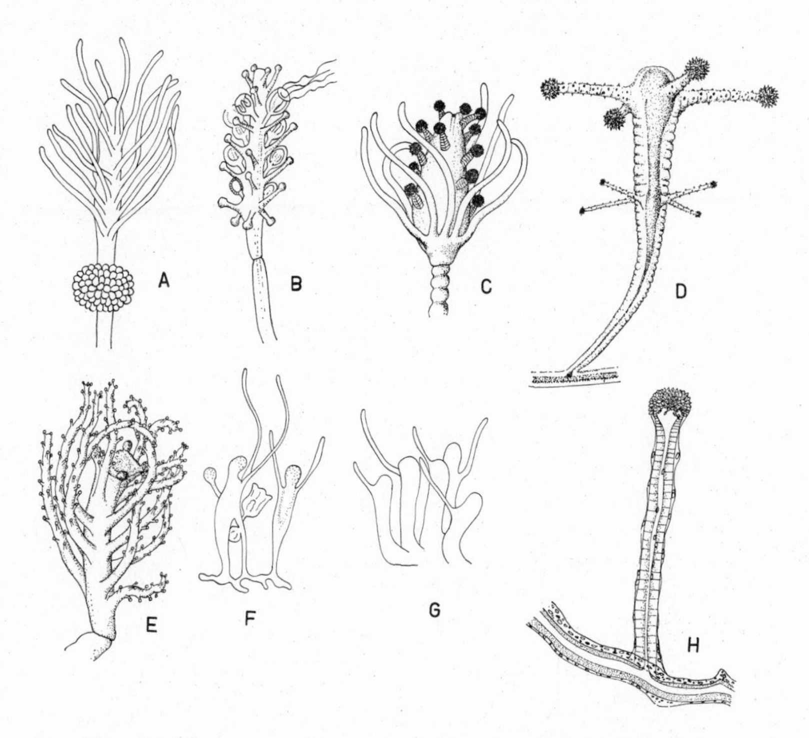

Fig. 11. Some cases of polymerization and oligomerization of tentacles of hydroid polyps; A, *Clava* sp. (after Hyman). B, *Syncoryne* sp. (from Dogiel). C, *Pennaria cavolinii*, (from Broch). D, *Cladonema* sp. (from Hincks). E, *Cladocoryne floccosa* (orig.). F, *Lar sabellarum* (from Dogiel). G, *Monobrachium parasiticum* (from Dogiel). H, *Halocoryne epizoica* (after Hadži).

of oligomerization. As a rule, this will not be difficult when we make detailed comparisons. We meet in our study of the animal world, at every turn, with the phenomena of polymerization and oligomerization. In this connection some regularities have been observed; above all the fact that in case of oligomerization a fixed *number* of multiplied, and thus homologous and homodynamous, parts is found preserved (e.g. in Cnidaria four, six, eight, and their products; eight in Ctenophora; five in Echinodermata; etc.).

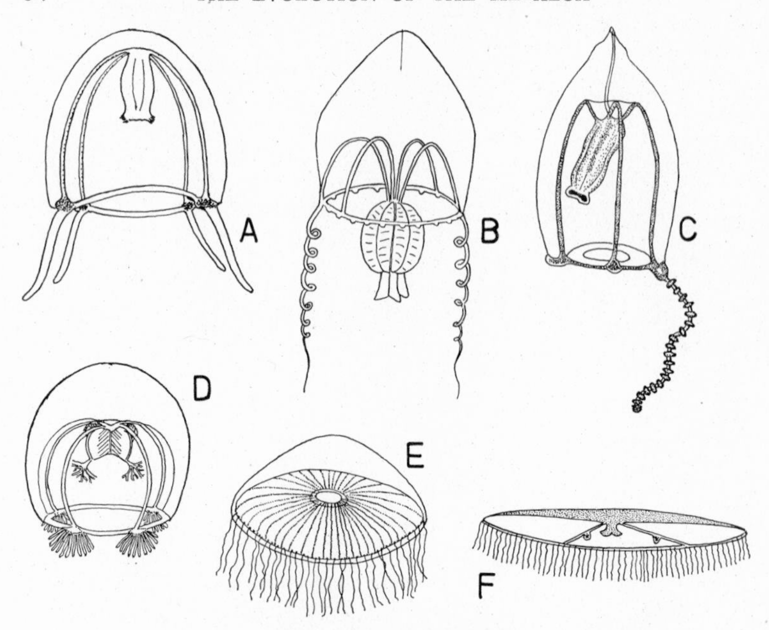

Fig. 12. Oligomerization and polymerization of tentacles in hydromedusae, A, *Podocoryne carnea* (after Grobben). B, *Stomotoca* sp. (from Hyman); C, *Steenstrupia* sp. (after Mayer); D, *Bougainvillea* sp. (after Broch); E, *Aequorea* sp. (after Hyman); F, *Obelia* sp. (after Colosi).

The origin of the metamerization, one of the most important problems of the comparative morphology of the metazoa, is closely connected with that of the polymerization and of the oligomerization. The question naturally arises; can we consider that the all-important metamerization has been developed out of the polymery, by way of a multiplication of whole regions of the animal body; or, conversely, by way of an initial polymerization of individual organs (this is usually called the *pseudomerization)*? This is followed first by a "genuine metamerization," and afterwards either by a wholesale oligomerization with formation of regions, or, by a general oligomerization and a corresponding change of the way of life (the origin of the large type of Oligomeria). We will later return to discuss this problem.

There is one more method which can prove useful in our search to find the relationship connections and herewith the creation of a truly natural animal system. This is my study, the comparison of the so-called parallelisms (they are not identical with analogies!). It has been proved by way of intensive observations that there are certain properties and peculiarities which are easily repeated. We have here, if looked at from the standpoint of genetics, some more or less identical mutations, or complexes of mutations. As an example we can mention the appearance of cnidae. These are complex, not living, but nevertheless organic products of specialized gland cells which are composed of firm (solid) and thickly liquid components. The thickly liquid secretion of cnidocytes is able to liquefy instantly, almost like an explosion with which it can be rightly compared. Here we are particularly interested in the morphological side of this remarkable differentiation in the monocellular glands.

This organelle, which itself is not alive, can be found in varying stages of evolution in various recent animal groups. The highest level in their progressive evolution can certainly be observed in the cnidae of Cnidaria—and this is why the latter have been given their name. If we make a search "downwards" we shall find cnida-like formations in various Protista, even in Protophyta, especially those that stand close to Protozoa *(Polykrikos* and *Pouchetia* among the Dinoflagellata). It seems that these cnidoids—as I called these cnida-like and yet completely special formations (Hadži, 1951)—had been developed repeatedly and independently from each other as early as in Protista; later they have evolved in special directions. The foundation, however, the original mutation which had led to their formation seems to have always been the same. Upwards, i.e. above the level which is taken by Cnidaria in the animal system, no real cnidae can any longer be found. The conditions that prevail in Nemertinea have not been completely cleared up. As for Mollusca (Gastropoda) where cnidae have also been found, it is beyond any doubt that in this case we have really the so-called kleptocnidae, i.e. cnidae which have been taken over from Cnidaria which had been devoured by Mollusca—a certainly very remarkable case. It is very probable that Nemertinea, too, possess kleptocnidae. A special place among all the animal groups that possess cnidoids is occupied by Infusoria–Turbellaria–Cnidaria; to these we must perhaps add Nemertinea. It has been with intent that Ctenophora have been omitted here, even if the presence of genuine cnidae can be frequently found mentioned in the special literature in connection with at least one species of Ctenophora *(Haeckelia* or *Euchlora rubra)*. As has been mentioned earlier, I think that it is very probable (Hadži, 1951) that only kleptocnidae occur in this ctenophore and that they have been taken over from a species of Narcomedusae which serve as the main food of this ctenophore.

There are, besides the typical cnidae, some less specialized forms that occur in the large groups of animals which have been mentioned above. They are essentially glandular; their secretion is partly solid, and partly a fluid that can absorb water and swell. They have been described under various names (trichocysts, rhabdites, sagittocysts).

The form of medusa must be considered as a kind of parallelism; it is neither homologous, nor analogous, nor a result of convergences (see Fig. 13). We shall omit here those Protista which show only a purely external similarity with medusae (among Flagellata e.g. *Medusochloris*, *Craspedotella*, and *Leptodiscus)*; these have been called the "types of the forms of life" by Remane (1944). The genuine medusae must be considered to have evolved beyond any doubt at least twice, independently from each other; both times they have developed from a polyp by way of an adoption of the vagile way of life: the first time from a scyphopolyp, and the second time from a hydropolyp. I will show later that this hydropolyp had been developed later than the scyphopolyp, and in all probability from just this same scyphopolyp. A similar way of life (natural selection!) and a close enough relationship (the same direction

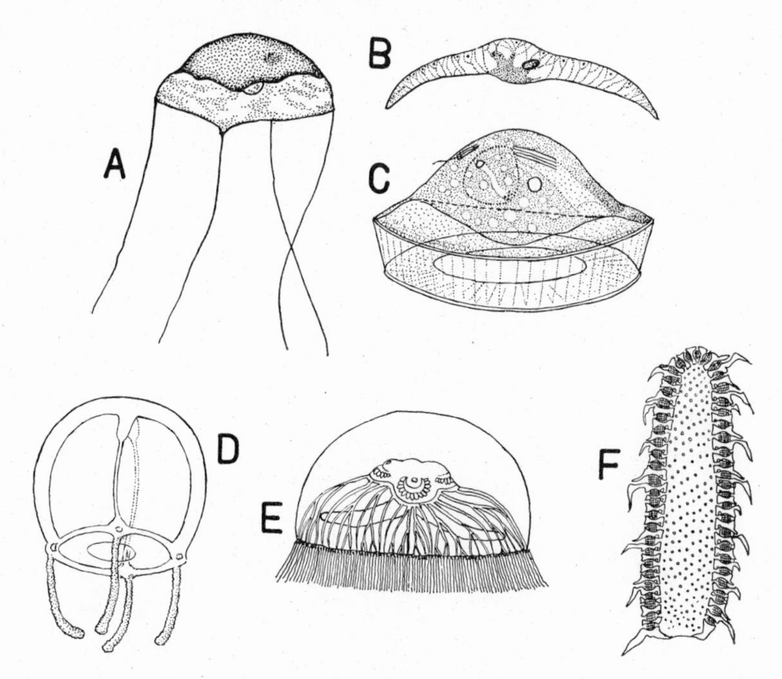

Fig 13. Medusoid forms as cases of parallelism. A, a phytoflagellate, *Medusochloris phiale* (after Pascher). B-C, two heterotrophic dinoflagellates: *Leptodiscus medusoides* (from Hertwig) and *Craspedotella pileolus* (after Kofoid). D, an anthomedusa; E. a scyphomedusa; F, *Pyrosoma* sp. a colony (cormus) of tunicates.

of mutations) have given similar results. Perhaps we could speak of a medusoid form in *Pyrosoma* among Chordata, yet in this case we have actually a cormus and not an individual. Something similar can be observed in Chondrophora among the Siphonophora. The same is actually true for the polypean form too, yet with the difference that the polypean form occurs much more frequently in the animal world since it is connected with a semi-sessile or to a completely sessile way of life. The form of polyps is an oblong rotund form which is set upright on a firm ground. The oral opening occurs, with the exception of Protozoa and Spongiae, at its free end. The tentacle-like excrescences grow regularly all around this oral opening in the form of one or several circlets. It would take us too long to give here a complete survey of all animal groups which have polypean forms. The species of whole large groups can show polypean forms (this is the case with Cnidaria and Entoprocta among the Ameria), or the same thing is true for at least a large part of them (Annelida). Oligomeria are mainly polypoid animals. Even among the Chordonia we can find in the benthonic Ascidia a clear inclination to develop polypean characters. Important from our standpoint, however, is the knowledge that a sessile radially symmetric polypean form had been repeatedly developed from a freely moving bilaterally symmetric form, and that this polypean form itself has been later frequently changed into a freely moving form, either one that creeps over the sea bottom, e.g. Echinodermata, or one that can swim freely in water, e.g. medusae of the Cnidaria.

The Validity of Watson's Rule for the Invertebrates

In our attempt to place the origin of Cnidaria on a new, rational basis we can use the experiences of researchers in Vertebrata who have certainly had to solve much easier problems—even if we do not intend to enter here in to the whole enormous problem of the origin of new animal types, i.e. macro-evolution. The question is whether Watson's rule (de Beer, 1954) of a mosaic-like evolution can be considered valid also in the case of the "lower" invertebrates. A detailed study of the *Archaeopteryx* (a third specimen of this animal has recently been found) has led de Beer to develop the ideas which had been first formulated by D. M. S. Watson and according to which there is a divergent evolution in the subclasses (types) of Vertebrata and a simultaneous mosaic-like mixing of old and new characteristics. In this way a new combined form can be created with a simultaneous change of the way of life, which is stil able to live in the milieu. Thus, there had been no general and parallel change of characteristics, (in this case of the reptilian characteristics) which finally led by way of all transitions to the new type, the birds; but instead there was an accession, or an admixture, of new bird characteristics to the already existing reptilian characteristics, as this can be seen in the remains of *Archaeopteryx*. De Beer believes that in the latter the "reptilian-characters" are still prevalent. In such a case the old characteristics can be preserved, yet they are naturally outweighed by the new, progressive, and specialized characteristics. It has been possible to show that other classes of Vertebrata, too, had probably developed along a similar divergent and mosaic-like way.

It has been possible to find this type of evolution in connection with Vertebrata because their fossil remains which have been found go back to a more or less recent past when this process of transformation had been taking place. The fortunate case of the *Archaeopteryx* has been particularly welcome. Yet unfortunately no such intermediate forms belonging to invertebrate types have been found, nor is there a prospect that they will ever be found; this is particularly true for the lowest, and therefore phylogenetically oldest, invertebrates whose manifold and numerous types had been developed even before the beginning of the era of the formation of the fossil-bearing earth strata. In this naturally disadvantageous situation the researchers in invertebrates have to use methods that are less reliable. Above all, it is *a priori* quite probable that Watson's rule has a general validity as we cannot see the reason why it should be limited to Vertebrata only. Secondly, if Watson's rule can be considered valid at all, then it must consequently be expected that even if the mosaic-like appearance of characteristics be most manifest during the phase of transition—because here the characteristics of ascendants and of their descendants appear most concentrated in individual species, in this case in *Archaeopteryx*—we have nevertheless to expect the same characteristics and properties of the two subsequent types to appear, even if somewhat "thinned down," in the parent as well as in the descendant species. It is natural that in the parents the old characteristics will strongly prevail, and in the descendants the new characteristics which are distinctive for the new type.

We shall find without any difficulty, if we limit ourselves to the group Cnidaria–Turbellaria–Ctenophora, and if we make a comparison of their recent forms, taking simultaneously into

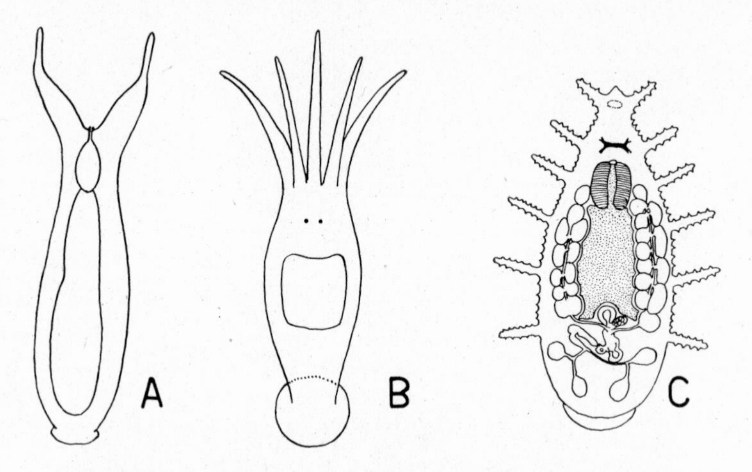

Fig. 14. Three species of Temnocephala; illustrating the polymerization of tentacles like excrescences. A, *Bubalocerus pretneri* (from Matjašič). B, *Temnocephala chilensis* (after Wacke). C, *Actinodactylus blanchardi* (after Haswell).

consideration Watson's rule, that the validity of this rule extends also to the lower invertebrates, and, consequently, over all the animal groups. Here we shall limit ourselves to mention a few characteristic examples only. Thus we can find in various Turbellaria: (1) the body set upright while mobility is at the same time temporarily preserved (this led to a complete sessility and immobility, to the formation of cormi and of colonies, and finally to a polymorphism connected with the formation of medusae); (2) the tentacle-like excrescences at their anterior ends which show an inclination to polymerization (Temnocephala, see Fig. 14), and the growth of the intestinal diverticula into the interior of these tentacles (in polyps this led to the typical circlet of tentacles which serves as the main appliance with which they catch their food); (3) the specialization of the monocellular skin glands with their solid or outflowing secretion (here rhabdites and sagittocysts; cnidae in cnidaria); (4) the tendency of the aproctous intestine to develop diverticula (excrescences) and folds and thus to increase the internal surface (this is so characteristic and manifold in Turbellaria that it has been used as a criterion on which, their classification has been founded: Acoela, Rhabdocoela, Tricladida, Polycladida; in Anthozoa it is best developed in the polyps of Cnidaria in the form of sarcosepta, or of longitudinal folds, yet here we can observe a later gradual regression with exception of the diverticula which grow into the tentacles; an even richer development can be observed in medusae); (5) the inclination to form a cuticle; in Turbellaria this can be observed occasionally only and it is usually strictly localized; it is only in Temnocephala that it covers almost the whole surface of the body; in Anthozoa its occurrence is less extensive; in Hydrozoa which have adopted a completely sessile way of life, it becomes a generally accepted property (here it is known as the periderm formation); (6) the same is true also for the impregnation of the cuticle (periderm) with calcium salts; this can also take place, even if to a lesser degree, in the mesenchymal cells; in Turbellaria this happens to a very limited degree, a fact which can be explained as being due to their free mobility; (7) the inclination to transversal division; in Turbellaria this has been inherited from their supposed infusorial ancestors; even if this is—as well as several other properties that have been mentioned—not a quality that generally appears, it is nevertheless a common property, i.e. it depends on the same gene or on the same complex of genes; in Scyphozoa it has led to the development of a form of medusae, and in Anthozoa to the first step in the same direction *(Fungia)*. Many other facts could be mentioned in this connection, yet the above points should suffice.

Whatever is generally valid for the relationship Turbellaria–Cnidaria, the same can also be proved valid for the evolutionary trends between the three classes of Cnidaria. It can be generally stated that the farther away from Anthozoa we move in the direction of Scyphozoa and Hydrozoa, the fewer properties of Turbellaria we meet; all this is due to a divergent development and to the prevalence of new properties and peculiarities which are typical of Cnidaria. Yet while we can observe that there are also some side branches which have developed out of Turbellaria into several new directions, either in the direction of animal types which have adopted a parasitic way of life (Trematoda, Cestoda), or such that have adopted the free mobility and the free way of life (Nemertinea, etc.; most probably after the transition to an euproctous state, also in the direction of Mollusca), nothing similar can be observed in Cnidaria. On the basis of all this we can conclude—and rightly I think—that these Cnidaria represent a blind side-branch on the tree of Ameria. We can see the climax of a partly progressive development in the strongly individualized cormi of Hydrozoa, in the Siphonophora. It is possible, though it is difficult to prove, that Cnidosporidia, which are attributed to Protozoa, had possibly been developed from the parasitic Narcomedusae. This hypothesis seems to be supported by the so-called polar capsulae, thus cnidae, and by the polycaryontic (polyenergetid) state of their vegetative phase connected with the phenomenon of cellulation.

Parasites have occasionally been used—and this successfully—to explain the phylogenetic conditions of their host animals. This can be considered to be a special method in phylogenetics. If this is valid for parasites then its validity could also be extended to symbionts. It is probably not a mere chance that a frequent symbiosis of monocellular algae that live intracellularly (e.g. *Zoochlorella* and *Zooxanthella)* has been observed on one hand in certain Infusoria, and on the other in the Turbellaria and Cnidaria. In the two last mentioned cases this symbiosis can be so strong that it becomes strictly obligatory and that in connection with this, systems have been developed which secure the "inheritance" of their symbionts.

CHAPTER 2

THE PREVIOUS INTERPRETATIONS OF CNIDARIA

We shall now pass on—after this preparatory introduction which has been necessarily rather extensive—to our main problem: what Cnidaria actually are and what is their origin? We shall be better able to understand our new answer to these questions if we first make a critical survey of the interpretations of the nature of Cnidaria which have been proposed till now. It will be sufficient to divide the history of the study of Cnidaria into two parts only, i.e. the first part which begins with Aristotle, and the second part which commences with Leuckart (ca. 1847) and which covers the Darwinian period.

From the very beginning the larger Cnidaria, i.e. those that can be observed with the naked eye and therefore more easily accessible (medusae, Siphonophora, Actiniae, corals) have given the impression that they were a kind of organism that resembled the flowering plants. Firmly attached to the ground or moving so slowly that this can hardly be noticed, frequently of rich colours, appearing in shrubs, covered with parts that are similar to flowers, and finally stinging like a nettle when touched—all these are properties that are usually attributed only to more highly developed flowering plants. It is therefore not surprising to find acalephs and cnidae mentioned as early as in Aristotle, and that these same organisms were called sea anemones, sea nettles, phytozoa, etc., by the fishing nations that inhabited the shores of the seas. Later there were various other natural scientists who for a long time saw in these organisms, like Aristotle, something that is at least between an animal and a plant. This is why the name

Zoophyta had been created. It was much later that it has finally become clear that these Zoophyta are really animals, and not plants, or something that is between a plant and an animal. It was not till 1723 that it was first suggested, by Peysonell, that these are really the lowest or the most primitive animals. The external forms of these animals, have always been particularly emphasized and many zoologists have become especially impressed by their radial symmetry. This had been important when the first attempts were made to construct a classification of the animal world on the basis of a comparative method. In place of the name Zoophyta, the name Radiata was introduced, with some simultaneous changes of their spheres and of the subgroups they were supposed to include: a possibly worse solution. The name Zoophyta itself (this name was used for a long time) included all kind of animals, or, as this has been said by L. Hyman, "A variety of soft-bodied animals, from sponges to ascidians." Under the banner of Radiata, Cnidaria were again connected with completely different types of animals, especially with the Echinodermata; this was done because of their radial symmetry only (Cuvier). Lamarck himself had tried to separate the medusae from polyps. Many zoologists, especially the French scholars, adhered strictly to this wrong concept of Radiata even a long time after Darwinism had been firmly established and when attempts had been made to create a natural animal system built on the principles of evolution; the same mistakes can be partly encountered even to the present day.

In the mean time great progress has been made in the field of the fine morphology of the lower invertebrates. The progress made in the ontogenetics or in embryology—especially of Vertebrata—has been of considerable importance for the evaluation of Cnidaria; it was in this way that the theory of germ layers was developed. Even the bodies of adult animals have repeatedly been divided into layers: first there was one stratum, then two, and finally three strata or dermas (ecto-, ento-, and finally mesoderm). Even if it was likely that the third stratum, the mesoderm, had been first laid out as a thin leaf which has later lost its leaf-like form, it has nevertheless remained a mesoderm, or something that has been added later, as a final layer. The knowledge which had been first arrived at in connection with Vertabrata was soon extended to invertebrates. And here a great mistake was made: this was in the case of those lower Metazoa where no leaf-like mesoderm could be found in their ontogenies and where for this reason the presence of a third body layer has simply been denied. In this way the notion of Diploblastica was created, i.e. Metazoa with two germ layers, in contrast to the higher developed Triploblastica. Later I will try to show that there is no real justification to believe in the existence of Diploblastica.

There has been a clarification of concepts during the second period which developed under the influence of the theory of evolution, due to the theory of recapitulation. It was very soon (in 1859, when the notion of Coelenterata was created by Leuckart) that the interpretation of these problems became stabilized; and they have been preserved, with few changes only, down to the present day. It is because of this generally accepted situation that it is so difficult to weaken the erroneous basis of this view and to propose something new in its stead. This stabilized interpretation which sees in Cnidaria, and herewith in all Coelenterata, primarily simple animals that consist of two germ layers has been accepted by all the great authorities in the field of zoology, beginning with Ernst Haeckel.

It is certain that it was Ernst Haeckel who developed in detail the basis of the interpretation of Cnidaria and of their gradation. He accepted Leuckart's interpretation of Coelenterata because it seemed suitable to the principle of evolution: whatever shows a simple structure is primary, and it is followed by a progressive evolution. In this way it was not only the sequence: Spongiaria–Cnidaria–Ctenophora which seemed to agree with the "natural evolution," but there was even within the group of Cnidaria the "natural" sequence Hydrozoa–Scyphozoa–Anthozoa which has seemed to indicate a progressive development. Frequently the latter two classes have been united under the name Scyphozoa; for a long time it was believed that both Anthozoa and Scyphozoa have an ectodermal gullet (pharyx). It is worth mentioning that Haeckel himself was partly irresolute whether the border line between Coelenterata and the more highly developed Coelomata should be placed between Ctenophora and the lower Turbellaria, or somewhat higher so that Turbellaria could be included among Coelenterata; it was clear that there was a relationship between Ctenophora (particularly those that lived on the sea bottom) and Turbellaria whose structure seems to be quite close to the structure of the former—and for this reason these lower "worms" could not be genuine Coelomata. On the other hand such an extension of the sphere of Coelenterata could lead to a muddle and to a system which it would be difficult to survey. Carl Börner (1923) later proposed to associate Platyhelminthes and Acanthocephala more closely with Coelenterata.

Still, some changes were proposed in spite of the fact that this part of the natural system of zoology appeared very stable and that it had been generally accepted. T. H. Huxley (1875) already expressed his doubts that there was a close relationship between Spongiae and other Coelenterata, and generally to Metazoa. It was Sollas (1884) who succeeded in transforming this doubt into a fact, into a truth; he made a definite separation of Spongiae, as Parazoa, from Eumetazoa as the genuine Metazoa. This radical step was well supported by numerous and fundamental differences that occur both in the structures and in the ways of life of Spongiae and of other Metazoa. Even greater differences have later been observed in connection with their ontogenies. Delage tried to emphasize this difference when he invented the name Enantiozoa for Spongiae, i.e. Spongiae are Metazoa in whose ontogenies the layers of their bodies become inverted: that layer of cells, which in an embryo or in a larva occurs in their external or anterior parts, develops into the intestine (entoderm) of Eumetazoa, and the internal or posterior layers of cells into their skin (ectoderm).

Such is the situation that appears when we try to make a comparison between two items which are, as a matter of fact, incomparable: we are now certain that Parazoa and Eumetazoa, i.e. all the remaining polycellular animals, cannot have the same origin. It is therefore necessary to separate the Spongiae definitely and for ever from Cnidaria and Ctenophora, and they can not be included among Coelenterata. Even the most recent attempts to try and halt the progress made by Sollas and Delage cannot change this situation. These attempts have been made, as it has already been mentioned, by Tuzet and her collaborators who try to find a justification for this mainly in a supposed discovery of nerve cells in Spongiae, and by Sachwatkin (1956) who tries to overcome the unbridgeable differences that exist in their ontogenies.

Nobody has followed the attempt made by K. C. Schneider (1902) who proposed to connect phylogenetically Spongiae and Ctenophora, with a simultaneous exclusion of Cnidaria from this group, which he had called Diskyneta. This has been, to my knowledge, the only attempt which has endeavoured radically to separate the Cnidaria from Ctenophora and in this way to give up the group of Coelenterata; the attempt, however, remained unsuccessful. Till now the Cnidaria and Ctenophora have been looked upon as closely connected with each other. The main difference which has been mentioned in this connection has been the presence, or the absence, of cnidae (it has been due to this that the names Cnidaria and Acnidaria have been introduced): yet this difference is not by far of the most decisive importance. Even if Ctenophora quite generally possessed their own genuine cnidae, as this has repeatedly been supposed to be the case in the species *Haeckelia (Euchlora) rubra*, it would still be necessary to make a clear distinction between Ctenophora and Cnidaria. Cnidae, however, such as they occur in *Euchlora*, could actually be of an extraneous origin, as this has already been mentioned above.

Jürgen W. Harms (1924) also separated Cnidaria from Ctenophora in his somewhat bizarre system of the animal world; this separation was less radical than the former and it is based on other reasons. The first of his three circles was subdivided into three subcircles; it is defined well enough because it includes all the animal groups which have primarily—as modified Gastraeadae—no anal orifice (aproctous animals; here he should have omitted Spongiae); he uses for his subdivisions the criterion of stability. Harms included in his first subcircle Porifera, Cnidaria, and Turbellaria as labile and regulative forms ("Regulationsformen"). The second subcircle includes the parasitic Platyhelminthes as semi-stabile forms with a partly constant number of cells. The Ctenophora and Acanthocephala, as blindly ending branches of the animal world, with a constant number of cells (this, however, is not even true for Ctenophora) and their stability, have been placed by Harms into the third subcircle; yet, as a matter of fact the Acanthocephala are not primarily aproctous animals: the absence of the whole digestive apparatus, and thus also of the anal orifice, is in these animals a secondary phenomenon since the loss of these organs has been caused by their parasitism.

Among the almost innumerable attempts to construct a natural animal system there are a few who have tried to abandon the notion and the category of Coelenterata (Hyman, Beklemischew, Perrier, Dudich, etc.). Here we are able to mention a few such cases only. Such authors have usually gone back to the old notion and name of Radiata or Radialia, excluding from them Spongiae and Echinodermata. This was made for example, by L. H. Hyman (she uses them as a contrast to Bilateria, adding "Cnidaria [or] Coelenterata"); Beklemischew (1958) divides Metazoa first into Enantiozoa (after Delage, for Porifera) and Enterozoa; the latter are subdivided into Radialia and Bilateria; Radialia, finally, consist of Cnidaria and Acnidaria. Dudich (1957) divides Eumetazoa into Acoelomata (i.e. Cnidaria and Ctenophora) and Coelomata (Proto- and Deuterostomia). Dogiel (1947) takes over the old division into Diploblastica or Radiata—which consist of Spongiae and Coelenterata—and Triploblastica (Bilateria). The influence of the historical moment (or of conservatism?) can be seen in the fact that the old notion of Radiata reappears again and again to be used for systematic–taxonomic purposes, even if in the mean time it has become clear that it is not in Cnidaria only that radial symmetry can be found (in Cnidaria this symmetry is not even completely developed), and that it is arbitrary (even if correct) to exclude Echinodermata from Radiata. It was due to this influence that it has not been perceived that the radially symmetric distribution of various parts (the formation of antimeres) is not connected with any definite type of structure, and that instead it can appear at any level of organization, even if the more or less perfect development of this symmetry can vary: the only condition for it is the adoption of a sessile way of life. Exactly as it has finally become necessary to accept the fact that, phyletically, Cnidaria have nothing in common with Echinodermata even if they are both (secondarily!) more or less radially symmetric, it will be necessary to get used to the fact that Ctenophora must be separated from Cnidaria—like Echinodermata—even if they are not widely different from them: each has developed out of its own "root" and it was the ancestors only of these two groups which were closely related to each other; in both cases the ancestors were turbellarians, yet of different subtypes. The same is naturally true—yet to a considerably greater degree—for the mutual connections between Porifera and Cnidaria.

For historical reasons and because of their external appearance Cnidaria have always been—justly, as it has seemed—connected with Ctenophora. The latter are occasionally called Acnidaria (Bütschli) in order particularly to emphasize in this way their close connection with Cnidaria. The names of these animals have been repeatedly changed in the more distant past as this can be seen in Krumbach (1928); frequently they were called Acalepha, i.e. medusae. Their jelly-like, even watery, consistency, their life in plankton, the strong contractility of their tentacles (even if it is developed in one pair of tentacles only), the inclination to adopt the radial symmetry, and many other minor morphologic phenomena which Haeckel could find in his Hydromedusa *Ctenaria ctenophora* (with a very suggestive name!), all these facts have helped to preserve the idea firmly and faithfully which connects Ctenophora closely with Cnidaria. And what has been the attitude towards those differences that are even more numerous and all-important? These have simply been pushed aside while at the same time attempts have constantly been made to connect these two animal types by way of a common origin; yet these attempts have always remained fruitless. When finally Haeckel's attempt with his Ctenaria had completely failed, new assays were made in the search for the ancestor in the hope to find it in the most remote past. Thus Goette (1912) proposed, to derive the Ctenophora from a common primitive form which was constructed *ad hoc* and which he called a "Scyphula;" this "Scyphula" was freely swimming and "binumeral" *("zweizählig")* (A fine example of a "suitcase theory" ["*Koffertheorie*"]. Those scyphulae which had remained in plankton developed into Ctenophora, and those that had sunk to the sea bottom evolved into the sessile scyphopolyps, first without a medusa stage. This artificial construction could find no acceptance. Not very different from it was the interpretation proposed by Heider (1913) who has tried to derive Ctenophora—surprisingly enough by way of neoteny—from the anthozoan larvae that had lived in the pelagic zone. Heider believed that there was some larval element in Ctenophora.

It has been a sign of emergency when attempts have been made to go even further back into an already completely indifferent past and when the most simply built planula, a modified "gastraea" which had lived in the plankton began to be considered as a starting point for the evolution of all the lowest invertebrates. In this way the question of the origin has been completely watered down. This is how the problem of the origin of Ctenophora, and thus of their relationship connections to Cnidaria, remained unsolved until a new hypothesis was proposed by me, 39 years ago (Hadži, 1923 a), according to which Ctenophora had been evolved from planktonic larvae of the polyclad Turbellaria which had been further developed in plankton by way of neoteny. On the basis of this hypothesis we can best explain the much discussed problem of the genetic relationship between Turbellaria and Ctenophora. It has been generally recognized and accepted that there were such close relationship connections, particularly as regards the Polycladida among Turbellaria. In this way we can make a completely satisfactory explanation both of their general forms, as well as of their symmetric conditions, of their internal structures, and of their ontogenies. Th. Krumbach (1928) who made a detailed study of Ctenophora for his *Handbuch der Zoologie* (edited Kükenthal, and later by Krumbach) has given a critical evaluation of all hypotheses which have tried to explain their origin; he has come closest to the best solution when he wrote, "Die Ctenophora stehen den Turbellarien nahe, stehen keiner Bilateriengruppe so nahe wie den Turbellarien" (p. 978). In the same book E. Bresslau and E. Reisinger (1913) have emphasized how my hypothesis "die eigenartige biradiale Symmetrie der Rippenquallen auf ein Kompromiss zwischen der ererbten bilateralen Symmetrie der Protrochula und der Tendenz zur Radialsymmetrie infolge der planktonischen Lebensweise zurückzuführen sucht."

L. H. Hyman (I: 693–695) refuses to derive Ctenophora from the Cnidaria, especially out of Hydrozoa (Hydroctena!); she prefers to go further back to the very primitive, i.e. completely indifferent ancestors which she supposes to be common to all the "trachyline–hydrozoan, scyphozoan, and anthozoan lines." We have already characterized such an attempt to be simply an auxiliary solution. Hyman does not even mention my hypothesis; it is possible that this hypothesis was not known to her even if it is mentioned—though not in the chapter on Ctenophora—in the extensive *Handbuch der Zoologie*. Hyman, however, finally returns to the problem of Ctenophora in a supplement to the fifth volume of her book *The Invertebrates* where my hypothesis can also be found mentioned under the title "Retrospect" (p. 730). She refuses straightforwardly to accept my hypothesis which she calls "the fantastic theory of Hadži," and adds, "Hadži gives no real grounds for this view, only theoretical vaporizing." This opinion, or rather judgment, is not only unjust, it is also wrong. The way I proceeded to found my hypothesis has been exactly the same as has been done by other zoologists, Hyman included. I referred to well-established facts which I tried to bring into a new focus and to give them new interpretations. In this connection Hyman has omitted to mention that in the meantime, P. Us (1932), one of my students, succeeded in proving the older data about the development of the mesoderm in Ctenophora as it had been published by Metschnikoff to be essentially correct (Fig. 15). One would expect in an objective criticism, to be able to find at least some arguments quoted and an honest statement that there have been zoologists who have considered my hypothesis to be feasable, at least before the author begins a straightforward refusal of my thesis. In this connection Hyman could have remembered what she read in the article "Evolution of Metazoa" by Sir Gavin de Beer (in the book "*Evolution as a Process*," 1954). In it a paragraph from the book by MacBride is quoted which refers to Lang, and which states that the ciliary seams of the eight lobes that occur in Müller's larva are "jointed edgewise so as to form combs." Anyhow, on the basis of the numerous similarities that exist between Ctenophora and Polycladida, MacBride, according to de Beer, comes to the conclusion "that Müller's larva represents a pelagic Ctenophore—like adult ancestor of Polyclada, and that the Platyhelminthes were evolved from the Ctenophora." De Beer accepts my hypothesis because he obviously thinks it to be better founded and more probable than other previous hypotheses. In the introduction to the present study it has been mentioned that in our research in the phylogenetic problems no progress can be made without some imagination, or rather

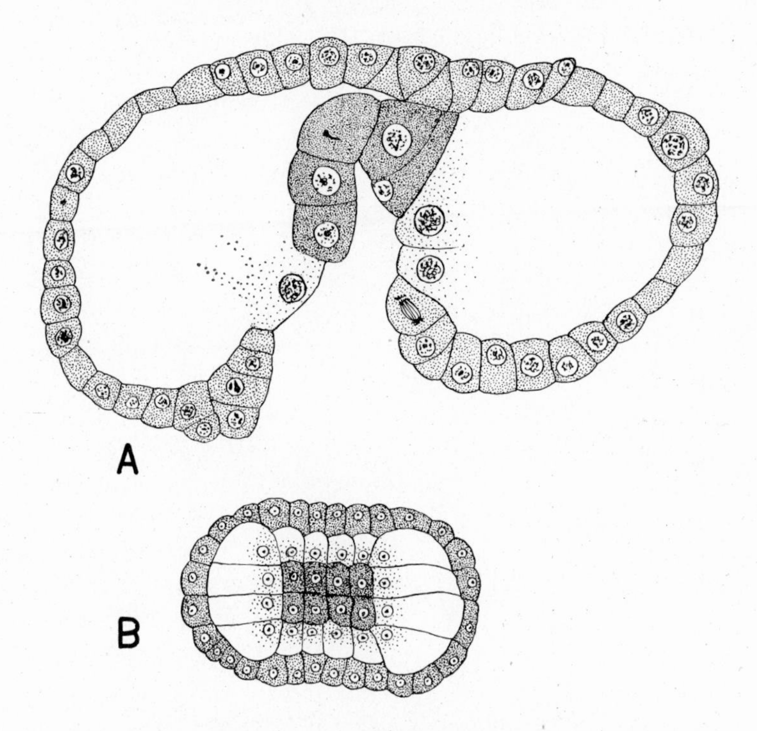

Fig. 15. Young ontogenetic phase of Ctenophora; the dense dotted cells are the primordium of the mesohyl (mesoderm). A, longitudinal section. B, oral view of the embryo (after Us).

without an *esprit*, particularly in those cases where no fossil documents can be found, yet we should realize that this is far from a "fantastic theory" and "theoretical vaporizing."

It should be mentioned in this connection that it is wrong to speak about a "degradation of ctenophores from polyclad larvae;" on the contrary, in my opinion, the evolution of Ctenophora as animals that live in plankton has been progressive; their starting point, the supposed polyclad larva, has also reached a much higher level of evolution than any constructed planuloid form of an "Urcoelenterate" from which Hyman derives both Cnidaria and Ctenophora by way of an equally constructed medusa, a construction which itself is not without some fantasy (cf. the "Hypothetical Diagram" in vol. I., p. 38 of Hyman's work). The reader should also then compare how I explain and understand the origin of bisymmetry in Ctenophora and how this is done by Hyman; she simply writes, "The biradial symmetry of ctenophores is obviously derivative of tetramerous radial symmetry, as seen in Hydrozoan medusae." I should only like to ask why the bisymmetry should be developed from a radial symmetry during the life of the animal in the plankton? We must be aware of the fact that in Ctenophora the paired system can be observed not only in their tentacles.

Here it should be emphasized that no facts are available—as far as I can see them—which disprove the validity of my hypothesis. For some time it seemed that there was an essential difference between Ctenophora and Turbellaria; this difference was thought to be found in the ontogenetic development of the mesoderm (mesohyl). Ctenophora have, according to Metschnikoff, a "genuine mesoderm," such as it also occurs in Turbellaria, particularly in Polycladida among the latter. Hatschek, however, who later investigated the development of Ctenophora maintained that Metschnikoff had made a mistake and that those groups of cells which had been considered by Metschnikoff to be an *Anlage* of a genuine mesoderm belonged in reality to the entoderm. This study by Hatschek which had been completed and illustrated was unfortunately never published. The two authors of the standard work on the ontogeny of invertebrates (Korschelt and Heider, 1936. p. 265) were able to see Hatschek's pictures and they were convinced that his explanations were right. In this they have been followed by Hyman. If no further progress had later been made in this field then the close connection between Ctenophora and Cnidaria would have seemed to be a firmly established fact. I selected this theme for a doctoral thesis to be investigated by one of my students, Peter Us; he made a new investigation of this point in the ontogeny of Ctenophora. This investigation was constantly made under my guidance and supervision. Us (1932) succeeded in showing that Metschnikoff's results correspond fully to the actual facts. In this way the difficulty has been removed, the Ctenophores have a mesoderm and this helps to prove the accuracy of my hypothesis which tries to derive Ctenophora from the planktonic polyclad larvae.

Much later, I found that I was neither the first nor the only person who formulated this idea about the origin of Ctenophora. Garstang developed his idea to explain the origin of Ctenophora from the Müller's larva of Polycladida by way of neoteny; this idea was proposed in an ingenious poetical work whose form, however, did not correspond to that of a serious scholarly interpretation. It was published by Hardy in 1954. I have briefly mentioned this case in the introduction to the present study.

The origin of Turbellaria, and especially of Polycladida, from the Ctenophora has been discussed much more than the origin of Ctenophora. The reason for this can be found in the large number of similarities that exist between Ctenophora and Polycladida; it has been much more obvious to explain these similarities as being due to a development of Polycladida with their complicated genital mechanisms from the simply built Ctenophora, than vice versa. This interpretation has seemed to be supported by the discovery of benthonic, and therefore flattened, species of Ctenophora, e.g. *Coeloplana*, *Platyctena*, etc. Lang (1880) who had proposed this theory, has been followed by numerous zoologists. Nevertheless it soon became clear that these species of benthonic Ctenophora cannot be anything but aberrant species which can lead to no new forms except such as for example the sessile *Tjalfiella*. In this way the Ctenophora must definitely be excluded from the line of evolution of the so-called Coelomata or Bilateria. They only represent a blindly ending side-branch on the tree of the animal world.

Finally, it should be mentioned that there have even been some zoologists who have tried to find a solution of the problem of the origin of Ctenophora in the nebulous idea of Gastraeadae which they consider to be the common origin of Spongiae, Cnidaria, and Ctenophora, while at the same time they wish to give up the old taxon of Coelenterata. This should be done, according to this interpretation, first, because their supposed common origin goes too far back into a vague past, and, secondly, because in the mean time these three types (Spongiae, Cnidaria, Ctenophora) have had such widely diverging evolutions that it is now senseless to try to bring them into one unit. E. Perrier (1921 pp. 284–5), for example wrote in connection with his statement that Ctenophora had a genuine mesoderm, "... font douter qu'on doive rattacher réellement les Cténophores à l'embranchement des Coelentérés." In spite of this E. Perrier (1921) divides Metazoa into Phytozoaires and Artiozoaires, and he mentions as "embranchements" of Phytozoaires: (1) Coelentérés, (2) Spongiaires, and (3) Echinodermes.

We are fully convinced that sooner or later, the taxon Coelenterata will be completely abandoned and that Cnidaria will be the only group which will survive within the frame of Coelenterata; so that finally the names Cnidaria and Coelenterata will become synonymus. In this way Cnidaria will become isolated, yet this isolation will be an apparent isolation only, because at the same time it will become possible to connect them, by way of a supposed derivation from Turbellaria, to a higher category, i.e. to the large group (phylum s. lat.) of Ameria.

Here it should suffice briefly to touch the problem of the connection between Cnidaria and Echinodermata. This problem has repeatedly appeared in the literature since the days of Lamarck and Cuvier and it is connected with the names Radiata or Radialia. The name itself indicates that it is the similarity of symmetric condition only which is here constantly being taken into consideration; yet the conditions are not identical: in Echinodermata a pure radial symmetry is really an exception due to a secondary omission of their anal orifice as is the case in Ophiuroidea; while at the same time the primarily aproctous Cnidaria usually have—with exceptions that can be found above all in the Anthozoa—a pure radial symmetry. We have earlier pointed out that the radial symmetry does not depend on a certain type of the structure and that it is entirely and exclusively influenced by the type of the contact with the environment. The sessile way of life will produce the radial symmetry whatever the type of the structure may be. In a natural system we are therefore not allowed to base a taxonomic unit mainly on such a factor. The names, however, of Radiata or Radialia have been widely compromised and so it is better to avoid them altogether whenever we discuss systematic categories, groups, or taxons. In the zoological literature one can even find cases where Mesozoa, too, can be found attributed to Radiata, either directly (D'Ancona 1955), or as a kind of an appendix to the latter (Bütschli 1921). The Echinodermata, however, do not belong even near the vicinity of Cnidaria; their true position is far away from the latter, among the Oligomeria.

It is interesting to see in this connection how a faithful adherent to the taxon Radiata (E. Perrier) explains the origin of the two groups of Metazoa: the Phytozoaires (i.e. Radiata) and the Artozoaires: According to him the freely swimming Gastraeadae were the first Metazoa. These began to settle on the sea bottom where they grew larger and it was in this way that the radially symmetric Radiata together with Echinodermata developed; or they began to creep over the substratum, and this was the way how the bilaterally symmetric "Artiozoaires" evolved.

The Origin of Cnidaria

Before we begin to discuss the main problem of the present study, i.e. the true nature and the origin of Cnidaria, we have first to touch on the question, "what is the primary or fundamental form of Cnidaria?" It is well known that two forms exist in Cnidaria, and at the first sight they appear to be rather different; above all they differ considerably in their ways of life. These two forms are that of the polyp and that of the medusa. In the literature three possible explanations can be found supported by various scholars: (1) The polyp is the initial form which has been further developed into the medusa as a secondary form; this type of evolution can frequently be observed in recent species. (2) The form of medusa is the primary form; out of this form the polyp has been developed as a larval or post-larval ontogenetic stage; it is possible that this polyp finally takes over the reproductive function. (3) The forms of polyps and of medusae have been evolved in parallell out of an indifferent form; in this way we can imagine "Polyp und Meduse (seien) essentiell ... für den Typus des Nesseltieres," as this has been expressed by E. Reisinger (1957, p. 695).

The last (neutral) of the above mentioned three possibilities seems to be the one least probable. It cannot be proved and it is not supported by any facts. The existence of numerous species of Cnidaria with a complete metagenesis which can be observed particularly among Hydrozoa, somewhat less among Scyphozoa, and not at all among Anthozoa, can be explained by way of any of the above three possibilities. As regards their origin, the conditions in Lucernariidae among Scyphozoa, and in Narcomedusae among Hydrozoa seem to support the third interpretation. Yet these two cases can also be explained on the basis of the first variant, as will be later explained in more detail. Neither Lucernariidae nor Narcomedusae can with certainty be considered to be primitive forms. On the contrary, they are both highly specialized and their position is at the periphery of the groups they belong to. In this way the two opposite possibilities finally remain; polyp or medusa as the primitive form. Let us first take into consideration the second possibility.

There are some zoologists—even if they do not represent a majority of them—who have investigated the Cnidaria and who have firmly accepted the interpretation (or who have been more or less inclined to accept it) which considers the form of the medusa to be the primary form. The adherents to this theory refer above all to its complete radial symmetry and to its life in plankton which are both considered to be a sign of primitiveness. Moreover, there are many species of Cnidaria which occur in the form of medusa only, where this form is therefore directly developed out of a planktonic planula. All the elements which occur in Siphonophora can be traced back to a modified form of medusa (according to the medusa theory). The *Anlagen* of medusoids appear very early in their ontogenies. Yet all these and many other facts which are referred to by those who support the theory of the primacy of the medusa form can be explained even more easily and probably, on the basis of the first interpretation. Even if we disregard the fact that a polyp has never been developed from a medusa (either by way of proliferation or by way of fission) and that the development has always been exactly in the opposite direction so that medusae have been developed out of polyps, we are hardly able to imagine how a highly developed creature with a complicated structure as can be observed in medusae could have evolved out of a planuloid form. One of the most recent advocates of the primacy of the medusa form is L. H. Hyman (I: 634 ff); her arguments can be used here as an illustration of this thesis. Initially, she admits that "nothing definitive can be said" about the origin of Cnidaria. Yet in spite of this she later expresses the following opinion, "It seems unavoidable to assume that they come from a gastrea type..." Then she tries to help herself with Naef's "*Metagastraea*" as the next higher stage; this had been further evolved into an "*Actinea*" which corresponds, according to her, to the present-day actinula larva. What, however, is an actinula? It is clearly a larval stage of a polyp, and it is already highly specialized so that it can be found in Hydroidea only, e.g. only in the highly specialized Tubulariidae. The Actinula descends, so to speak, to the bottom and develops into a sessile hydropolyp. It is in the Trachylinae only whose hypogenetic character is a secondary phenomenon because they have secondarily lost their polyp generation (which had been their first and primitive generation) that a polypoid larva had been developed due to their adaptation to the life in plankton. The evolution of this truly polypoid larva of Trachylinae has been—in connection with its parasitism—progressive and it led finally to a new asexually produced generation.

The rigid adherence to a wrong interpretation of the polyp form in general—and not of Trachylinae only as secondary larval forms—has induced Hyman to the following absurd conclusion, "The hydroid colony thus represents a persistent larval state." In the same way we could be justified to call the medusoid form a persistent larval form of the polyp. Hyman believes that "something like the present actinula larva" was the universal starting point even of Siphonophora, and this was, at a very early point. The Scyphozoa, which could be explained even more easily as exclusively medusoid forms, have been evolved, according to Hyman, from the Trachylinae. The Anthozoa, the third subtype of Cnidaria can then be easily deduced from a scyphistoma which is, naturally enough, again a larvoid form. It is surprising how Hyman acknowledges, and this without any explanation, that in these, "all trace of the medusa is lacking."

The interpretation which considers the medusa form to be the primary form can be defended only if we accept the proposition that the phylogenetic development of Cnidaria began with the Hydrozoa and that it was progressive because no medusa can be found in Anthozoa. This proposition has been generally defended as the correct interpretation. Yet even if we disregard this we can find facts which support the idea of the primacy of the polyp form. We have here, besides others, the fact that medusae develop regularly out of polyps; in those cases where a medusa is developed directly out of its egg—a phenomenon which has been given a special name (hypogenetic development according to Haeckel)—we find that the circumstances (especially the closer relationship) indicate that this direct development is a secondary phenomenon only. Here it should be mentioned that the planktonic way of life must be considered as secondary in comparison to the benthonic way of life. On the basis of this view we can explain that the polyp which became secondarily free, has been developed into the medusoid form as a secondary form

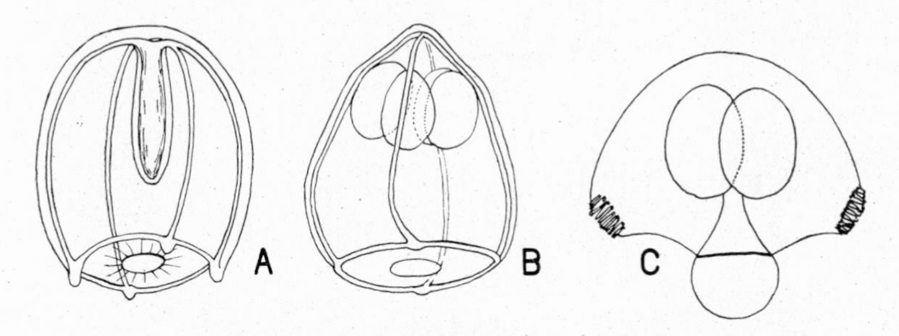

Fig. 16. Three examples of reduced free swimming hydromedusae. A, *Pennaria* sp. (without tentacles, after Hyman). B, *Eugymnanthea inquilina* Palombi (without tentacles and manubrium, after Palombi). C, *Millepora* sp. (after Delage & Hérouard).

whose organization is much higher because it is connected with the free movement. It must be admitted, however, that it is possible to imagine a retrogressive development by way of which the form of medusa evolves into something that resembles a polyp form. Such processes have actually taken place both among Scyphozoa (Lucernariidae) as well as among Hydrozoa (very numerous instances). Yet in all appearance no genuine polyp has ever been developed in this way, but only some polypoidal forms. In the Lucernariidae this has led to a polypo-medusoid form which can be easily recognized as such; in Hydrozoa we can find medusae which are in this way strongly degenerated (resimplified) inasmuch as they have remained freely swimming animals, (see Fig. 16) or they have been degraded into the organs of cormi by becoming attached as buds to the latter (see Fig. 17); and, finally, they have completely disappeared when they have abandoned the state of cormi (the form of a colony). This has been more than probably the case with the freshwater Hydrae.

Again and again the adherents to the idea of the primacy of the medusa form refer to the hypogenetic trachylinae Hydromedusae (Narco- and Trachy-medusae); yet these schol-

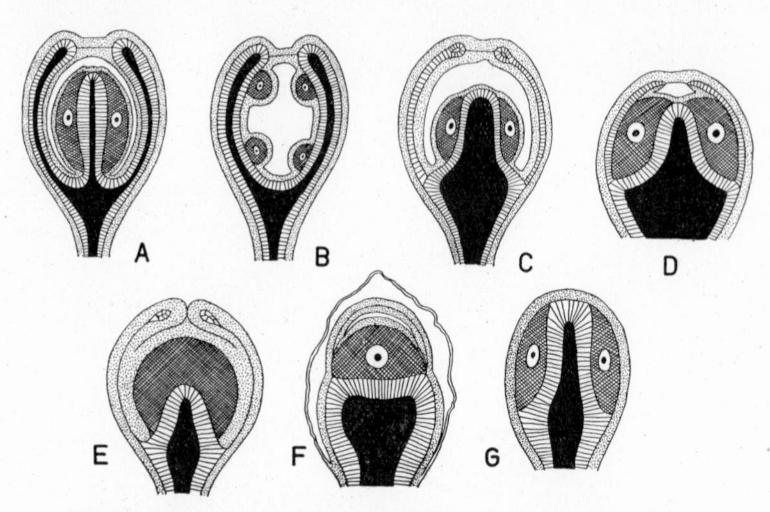

Fig. 17. Progressive reduction of sessile medusae (medusoids). A, B, Eumedusoids of *Tubularia* and *Campanularia*. C, *D*, cryptomedusoid *(Gonothyrea*, *Clava*, etc.). E, heteromedusoid *(Grammaria* sp.). F, G, styloids *(Eudendrium*, etc.). (After Kühn and Broch.)

ars are inconsistent because they do not place Trachylinae in a classification, which is supposed to be natural, at the beginning of Cnidaria, but rather—which is actually quite correct—close to their end, usually as the penultimate group, followed by Siphonophora, i.e. they classify them as one of the most specialized groups (cf. the system proposed by Hyman).

The hypothesis of an actinula as a primitive form and as an ancestor of Narcomedusae as well as of Hydroidea, and thus of all Hydrozoa, and in the last line of all Cnidaria, had been earlier defended by Hjalmar Broch, the author of articles on Hydroidea and Narcomedusae in the extensive German work *Handbuch der Zoologie* (1924), edited by Kükenthal-Krumbach. Broch considered budding to be a common and a very old property which had thus been introduced independently in the planktonic Narcomedusae. This violates the generally accepted rule that budding is due to the sessile way of life and that it can be transferred afterwards to descendants which have later adopted the pelagic way of life (e.g. parasitic larvae of some Narcomedusae). Another difficulty the adherents to the actinula hypothesis meet is the question of the origin of Hydromedusae in the benthonic cormi (colonies). One can refer here to the proposition made by Goette (1912) who tried to derive the metagenetic forms of Hydromedusae from the sessile medusoids.

Here we must briefly touch one of the extreme and least probable hypotheses which try to derive the Cnidaria from the primitive forms that live in the pelagic zone. This is the so-called *medusom theory* which has been proposed by F. Moser (1921–1924). During her study of Siphonophora she came to the idea that the larvae of Siphonophora might correspond exactly to the primitive form of Hydrozoa and, in connection with this—even if she does not state it explicitly—of all Cnidaria. First numerous medusoid organs have developed which have later evolved into full members i.e. *persons (subindivides)* of colonies. In the benthonic colonies of the Hydroidea which are a result of a later development, hydromedusae and polyps have again evolved on their own account. Hyman (1940 I: 636), too, considers this hypothesis to be "not very convincing," and I have submitted it to a severe criticism (Hadži, 1926) in which I have shown its complete untenability. It is certainly absurd to try to find the origin of Hydrozoa in Siphonophora, even in their most primitive forms, since there can be no doubt that they really represent the climax of a progressive and specializing evolution of the colony of Hydrozoa. The very first premise in the concept proposed by Moser—according to which the form of the ancestors of Cnidaria is recapitulated in the siphonula, or in the larva of Siphonophora—is unacceptable and wrong; and the consequences of this supposition are even more so. An individual can never be developed out of an organ, neither can a polyp be evolved out of a medusa. According to this hypothesis proposed by Moser, the Hydromedusae had been developed four times independently from each other, both in plankton as well as in the benthos. It can be truly said that, fortunately enough, Moser has never been followed by anybody else in this interpretation she had proposed. It must be regretted that such an obviously improbable construction could have found admittance into a representative manual on zoology. The construction itself has a purely historical interest now as an entirely erroneous attempt.

Finally we must mention here also the case of *Halammohydra*, an aberrant Narcomedusa (see Hadži, 1959 b), *Halammohydra* is actually not the only Hydromedusa that has readopted a benthonic way of life, yet in their evolution they have developed farthest away from the typical medusa form because they have become adapted to a life in sand on the sea bottom (Fig. 18). One could expect that they would evolve into a polyp form. Yet here the validity of Dollo's rule of irreversibility has again been proved. Though *Halammohydra* has undergone a very considerable change, this change, has not been so intensive (fortunately enough for zoologists!) that their nature as Narcomedusae could not be clearly recognized. The supposed polypoid characteristics which have been thought to have been identified by A. Remane, the discoverer of this aberrant form, and by other scholars, are in reality the excessively changed medusoid properties only, the general polypoid shape is due to a strong reduction of the umbrella and to a considerable lengthening of the manubium. It is interesting to notice that a general ciliation of its skin has secondarily reappeared in this medusa, a case which has been explained by A. Remane as an indication of a neoteny. Thus

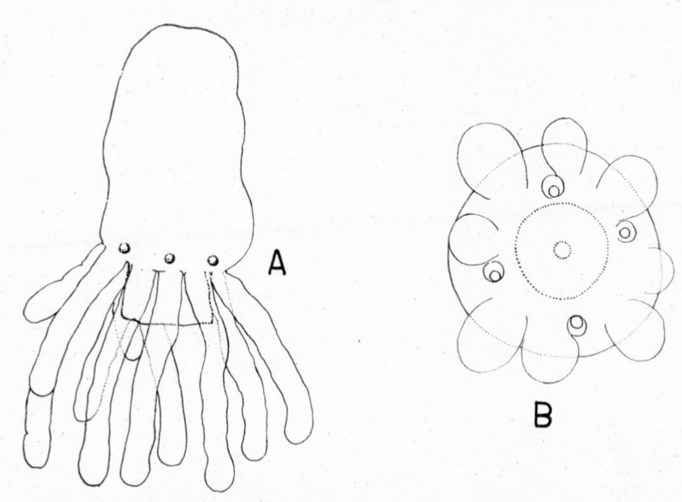

Fig. 18. Aberrant benthonic narcomedusa: *Otohydra vagans* Swedmark & Teissier, with preserved otocysts; A, side-view, B, oral-view. (After Swedmark and Teissier.)

Dollo's rule (which was proposed, according to L. Cuénot, first by Edgar Quinet, [1870]) does not seem to be valid for individual characteristics which are probably due to the mutation of a single gene. We can conclude, as a result of this discussion, that without any doubt the polyp form is the primitive, the initial form in all Cnidaria, and that this form has been secondarily developed into the medusa form. Later we shall try to show how this development took place twice and independently from each other.

The Right Sequence of the Cnidaria Groups

The second major problem we meet in our study of Cnidaria is whether we should arrange the three generally accepted subgroups of Cnidaria which have been given the title of classes, as one after the other, i.e. Hydrozoa—Scyphozoa –Anthozoa, or conversely. It should be remarked in passing that repeated attempts have been made, particularly by

Goette, to prove the close relationship between Scyphozoa and Anthozoa and to unite them into one class. The main reason for these attempts has been the supposed presence of an ectodermal pharynx both in Scyphozoa as well as in Anthozoa. There can be no doubt that an ectodermal gullet does really occur in Anthozoa. On the other hand, I succeeded in showing several years ago (Hadži, 1911), that the Scyphozoa do not possess an ectodermal gullet. It has even been found that the opposite is really true, i.e. the oral area of the scyphopolyp has been raised to an oral cone so that the limit between the ectoderm and the entoderm runs along the oral margin. Even if the taeniolae of scyphopolyps represent the remains of the sarcosepta that can be found in Anthozoa, they have nevertheless been developed in their own direction. In this way the division of the two subgroups of Cnidaria into two independent classes seems to be fully justified.

If we disregard the form of medusa and if we take into consideration the polyp form only, it could seem at first sight to be justified to see in the sequence Hydrozoa—Scyphozoa—Anthozoa a progressive line of development. This would fully correspond to the principle of evolution of a generally progressive development. It is therefore understandable that this sequence has generally and incontestably been regarded as the sequence which agrees with the line that evolution had taken; we can say that it has been accepted as a postulate which nobody has even tried to touch or doubt.

To this should be added the fact that in connection with Hydrozoa, and with the solitarily living *Hydra*,—because of the recapitulation theory—we have an example of a metazoan that embodies an ideal transition from Flagellata among Protozoa to Metazoa and the ideal pattern of a gastraea composed of two body layers. The difference between *Hydra* and gastraea consists in its circlet of tentacles and in its life on the bottom only. It was easy to derive first the scyphopolyp and later the anthopolyp form *Hydra* as the primitive form of all Hydrozoa. Everything seemed to agree well. Nothing amiss was seen in the fact that in Anthozoa there is one polyp form only and no medusa form. Even among Hydrozoa as well as among Scyphozoa there are species that possess no medusa form, and it was possible that the Anthozoa, which have no medusa form either, had completely lost this form and generation.

An important mistake was made in the evaluation of the conditions that prevail in the Cnidaria. The generally valid rule that progressive evolution takes place in connection with the normal way of life, with free movement, and the type of feeding, had been forgotten or at least neglected. There is always a more or less distinct retrogression in the organization —and thus a regressive development—when the free movement is abandoned and the sessile or the sedentary way of life is adopted. This, however, does not exclude the possibility that in spite of a general retrogression of the organization a progressive development could be observed in some details, i.e. in the new developed strictly adaptive characteristics. Thus this rule whose general validity has already been proved in connection with the study of Protozoa (compare Euciliata with Suctoria!) would not be valid in connection with Cnidaria!

The regressive, or, as it has also been less fortunately called, degenerative development of Cnidaria refers to their basic form, i.e. to the form of polyp. Yet the secondary form of medusa supports, if it is interpreted correctly, the idea of a retrogressive evolution in Cnidaria because the emergence of the medusa form (which has actually twice taken place, first in Scyphozoa and later in Hydrozoa) agrees with this rule since the release of a polyp represents the beginning of a new progressive development. The medusa as a freely living form which swims actively in plankton has reached an unquestionably higher level in its organization. The same medusae, however—and this is true both for Scyphomedusae as well as for Hydromedusae—can retrogress so that they cannot even be discerned any longer. They even become "degenerated" (in this case the usage of this word is appropriate), to the level of an organ and, finally, they disappear without any trace when the animal adopts the colonial status.

It would suffice to take into consideration only the unavoidable consequences of the sedentary way of life in order to show the untenability of the concept which has been proposed of a progressive evolution in Cnidaria. Further proofs of the accuracy of our interpretation can be made by a morphological comparison together with a simultaneous consideration of the ecological condition.

First we shall discuss here the symmetrical conditions; they are the most conspicuous element and they have actually been the first reason why scholars have begun to doubt the accuracy of the idea of a progressive line of evolution in Cnidaria. The palaeozoologists were the first who became aware of this fact; in connection with a detailed analysis of the internal skeleton of Madreporaria among Anthopolyps they have discovered that the sclerosepta do not agree with the radial symmetry of these animals as one would expect particularly if we consider the Anthozoa as the most highly developed Cnidaria. It was Otto H. Schindewolf (1930) who has especially discussed this fact in great detail. We can read in his book *Grundlagen der Paläontologie* (1950, Stuttgart, p. 179), "Die erste Anlage des Septalapparates bei den Pterokorallen ist bilateral; die sechs Protosepten werden ausgesprochen zweiseitig-symmetrisch herausgebildet. Erst nach ihrer vollen Ausgestaltung tritt erstmal eine radiale Symmetrieform hervor, und zwar ist diese hexamer, sechszählig." To this he continues, "Die Radialität beschränkt sich jedoch nur auf ein vorübergehendes Stadium." Similar conditions can be observed in numerous recent Anthozoa, particularly those that live as solitary animals.

The palaeozoologist O. Kuhn (1939) has been lead by this important fact to state, in spite of his reserved attitude with regard to the "Wurzel der Coelenteraten," that the ancestral form of Cnidaria must be imagined as a bilaterally built, creeping, or freely swimming organism.

We can observe in Cnidaria, as this has already been the case with Ctenophora, that they also adhere to the rule according to which the arrangement of the internal organs or parts towards symmetrical conditions, is much more definite than that of the peripheral organs. The external form soon becomes changed to a radially symmetrical construction due to the sessile way of life or posture when the animal is firmly attached at one end of its body; this has taken place in such a way that the body which was initially more or less flattened, took on a cylindric form. The earlier ventral and dorsal sides which had previously slightly differed from each other have thus obtained an identical form; the tentacles which in all probability had been earlier arranged in the form of a bow or of a horse-shoe and whose number has been increased by way of polymerization, have now developed into regular circlets. Yet at the same time we find that in the digestive organs of anthopolyps—and this is actually the septal apparatus—the remains of an earlier bilateral symmetry have been preserved. In ontogeny such traces have also been preserved in the process of the formation of tentacles. Some insignificant remains of this old bilateral symmetry can also be found in the young scyphopolyps (the so-called scyphistomae). Any trace of a former bilateral symmetry, however, is completely lost in the adult Scyphozoa and particularly in the Hydrozoa.

There have been some neo-zoologists who did not take easily to the fact of an internal bilateral symmetry observed in Anthozoa. As early as 1879 it has been proposed by Haake (according to Pax 1954, 288), that the primitive form of "Zoophyta" must have been bilaterally symmetric and that it has later become radially symmetrical because of their later transition to a sessile way of life. Professor Dr. Ferdinand Pax, an expert on the Anthozoa, pointed to the fact, in 1914, "dass viele der primitivsten Aktinien, die noch einer Fusscheibe entbehren, durch eine bilaterale Symmetrie ausgezeichnet sind" (Pax, 1954:2889). On the basis of this Pax concluded, "Man könnte daher geneigt sein, die Aktinien von fusslosen, kriechenden oder grabenden Formen mit bilateraler Symmetrie abzuleiten, die später mit dem Übergange zur festsitzenden Lebensweise eine radiale Symmetrie erworben haben...". However this was as far as Pax could go. In the extensively planned *Handbuch der Zoologie* where Pax contributed the section on Hexactiniaria the old classification has been preserved: following the example of Kückenthal we find the Anthozoa as usually placed at the end of the system of Cnidaria.

A similar statement was made by the palaeozoologist O. Kuhn (1939) whom I have already mentioned above, according to which all theories must be rejected which "von den Radialien (Coelenterata) die Bilaterien ableiten und in der Ontogenie von Larven den Übergang von der Radialität zur Bilateralität suchen". This statement has had practically no effect whatever (cf. the books by Hyman, Kaestner, etc.) on subsequent authors.

It is interesting to observe the attitude of neo-zoologists, in their general treatments on Cnidaria, towards the fact of internal bilateral symmetry or bisymmetry in these animals. A. Kaestner (1954) in his recent work on zoology does not even take into consideration this sufficiently important circumstance. At the beginning of his book we can only read (1954:9) that "die Coelenterata (9,000 Arten) sind äusserlich gekennzeichnet durch ihren radiären Bau." In the special part (1954:118) we find the brief explanation, "Ihre Anordnung (sc. of mesenteria) bringt wie der spaltförmige Mund einen Zug bilateraler Symmetrie in die radiäre Anlage der Anthozoa," and, slightly later (1954:121), "die bilaterale Symmetrieachse der Seerose" is briefly mentioned. No explanation is given where this disturbance (as it can be justly called) of an otherwise radial symmetry comes from, and of its significance.

Something else can be found in the manual by Hyman. She does not ignore the actual situation, instead she tries to find some explanation of the internal bilateral symmetry of Anthozoa—a most unpleasant fact for all the adherents to the old interpretation—of a planula-like primitive form of Cnidaria and of the primitiveness of the Hydrozoa. Yet at the same time Hyman does not draw the necessary consequences. First she brings forward some older attempts which had tried to explain this bilateral symmetry. When she first mentions this phenomenon (Hyman I. p. 539) she makes the correct statement that the internal bilateral symmetry of Anthozoa must be a primary property and that it could not have been later developed out of a radial symmetry, a fact which appears especially clearly in their embryology. However, Hyman explains at the end of her discussion that this bilateral symmetry is a secondary phenomenon.

On page 640 Hyman discusses this problem in more detail. She mentions as the first possible interpretation the opinion that the bilateral symmetry could have been developed secondarily as a consequence of the "colonial life." Hyman is right when she rejects this interpretation because the same symmetry occurs also in Actiniaria and Ceriantharia which are primarily solitary animals. To this we could add that in the "colonial" Hydroidea and Siphonophora cases are not rare where the externally developed bilateral symmetry is clearly a secondary phenomenon. The second interpretation mentioned by Hyman and which is, in my opinion, the right one, proposes that the present Anthozoa must go back to ancestors that had crept over the sea bottom, because bilateral symmetry appears in such animals. It can be easily understood that Hyman cannot consider this interpretation to be a good one because it stands in opposition to her concept of the origin of Cnidaria. A third interpretation which has been especially supported by some palaeontologists is based on the idea that the old Anthozoa which had otherwise "stood" erect, had lain down on one side, as must be supposed for some Tetracoralla, and it was in this way that the bilateral symmetry has been developed. Jägersten (1955:331), however, believes that this does not explain the origin of the bilateral symmetry because, "the eccentric attachment was simply a part of the bilateral symmetry."

Hyman finally proposes her own interpretation which she naturally thinks to be the best and the one most acceptable. Bilateral symmetry is a result of a secondary development and it is due to the increased size of anthopolyps and, in connection with this, to an increased need to send water necessary for respiration into the interior of the body by means of a quick water current which is produced by siphonoglyphs. A normal round oral opening was not suitable for this purpose; it was for this reason that the mouth has become elongated. The bilateral symmetry in the arrangement of sarcosepta is a consequence of such a change. Even if we could accept as probable this explanation of the origin of the elongated oral form and of the siphonoglyphs, we must nevertheless reject it in view of the fact that the bisymmetry (or the bilateral symmetry) does not occur only in the arrangement of the sarcosepta but it can also be found in the arrangement of the septal muscles which, are not brought into connection with the water current—a fact which has already been pointed out by Jägersten.

Thus we can conclude that so far nobody has succeeded in explaining the origin of the internal bilateral symmetry observed in the Anthozoa on the basis of the presumption that it is a secondary phenomenon.

Recently G. Jägersten (1955) has come to the conviction that in the Anthozoa the bilateral symmetry must be a primary property inherited from their ancestors. Jägersten, however, has come to this conviction along a different way from the one I have taken and, as he maintains (Jägersten, 1955:333), independently of me. In spite of this Jägersten uses the same arguments I have used, and proposes to reverse the evolutionary sequence which has so far been considered as valid within the system of the group of Cnidaria.

Above all Jägersten was interested in the origin of Metazoa, and especially of Coelomata. He believed that this problem could be solved best if he modernized the old gastraea theory invented by Haeckel. For the purposes of such a modernization he constructed a hypothetical intermediate stage which he called a *Bilaterogastraea* (Fig. 55). He placed it between the blastea which had lived in plankton and those Metazoa that actually exist. He believed that this was an animal which had crept over the sea bottom, and in this it differed from the classical planktonic gastraea. Jägersten's theory of a bilaterogastraea is essentially a variant of the old theory of Enterocoela which had been proposed by Leuckart and Sedgwick. The only difference is that here the *Anlagen* of the three pairs of the future coelom cavities are connected with a somewhat higher stage of development than the old gastraea had been. This is a typical suitcase theory *(Koffertheorie)* which is so general and all-embracing that with only a small modification it will explain anything! I have examined the opinions proposed by Jägersten (Hadži 1955), and I have rejected them because I have found this interpretation improbable and unacceptable. Jägersten's ideas will necessarily have the same fate as the ideas of the blastea and of the gastraea which had been proposed by Haeckel. These ideas have finally had to be abandoned and there is no modernization which could help them. In Jägersten's concept, there are individual points only that are correct, e.g. his opinion that the Cnidaria had been originally bilaterally symmetric animals, that the Anthozoa are the oldest form of Cnidaria, that primarily they had no medusoid form, and, finally, that cnidae had been progressively developed within all the group of Cnidaria. All this was already published by me years ago. Later we will return to Jägersten's proposal to derive Metazoa from the Protista.

Why Is There No Medusoid Form in Anthozoa?

So far scholars have carelessly bypassed the fact that there is no medusoid generation in Anthozoa. This has simply been taken for granted, an attitude that is partly understandable on behalf of the adherents to the thesis that the Hydrozoa are the oldest Cnidaria. It has been quietly accepted that there is no longer any medusoid form in Anthozoa and that such a form had existed only in their ancestors. Yet in spite of this, this "simple" fact should have been thought over. How is it that we see Hydrozoa appear suddenly with both generations so that they immediately develop the two "essential" forms; that the Scyphozoa had been developed out of the Hydrozoa while at the same time it is supposed that they possess only the medusoid form so that they have been called Scyphomedusae, and their scyphistoma considered to be a larval form; and, finally, in the supposed subsequent evolution into the Anthozoa, the highest developed Cnidaria, we suddenly see the polyp form now as the only form in existence! One cannot help feeling that here something must be wrong. How can we explain the complete absence of the medusa form in Anthozoa, or, at least, how can we make it probable?

One would expect, if the Anthozoa had secondarily lost their medusoid generation, that at least some traces of it could still be found. Yet, as a matter of fact, not the slightest trace of a medusoid generation can be identified. There have been numerous enough opportunities for its preservation. The Anthozoa, too, have larvae (actinulae) that live in the plankton and that partly show, like those of Echinodermata, an inclination to bilateral symmetry. They do not show, however, any trace whatever of a recapitulation of the medusoid formation. Planktonic Actiniae are known (Minyidae) which even possess a special apparatus that enables them to float more easily in water and which, in spite of this, do not show any common element with a medusa. Thus the name of "Anthomedusae" has been used for a subtype of Hydromedusae without fear lest it should be understood as a medusoid form of a subtype of Anthozoa. If there were any gene or complex of genes (any "trend") among the inherited properties of Anthozoa to form medusae this would have been apparent in their abundant cormi (colonies) as traces of the polymorphism. In these cormi both budding as well as fission can be observed, yet we always find that pure anthopolyps emerge as a result of such a development.

We come now to the phenomenon of transfission which the Cnidaria, and above all the Anthozoa, have inherited, in our opinion, from their turbellarian ancestors. The conditions in *Gonactinia*, a solitary animal that possess no skeleton, are very simple and resemble to a surprising degree those that can be observed in several rhabdocoelous Turbellaria. One species among the Madreporaria that is most prone to form cormi, has excited a great interest of zoologists. This is *Fungia*. In it the alternation of generations connected with transfission has been introduced, in spite of its well developed and comparatively heavy calcareous skeleton (Fig. 28 p. 155). It closely resembles the alternation of generations that can be observed in Hydrozoa and in Scyphozoa, particularly in Scyphozoa, because of the unequal transfission (which is close to the axial budding). The distal half of the maternal animal becomes considerably broadened and flattened; it liberates itself and, though completely passive, it is caught up by the water current and it settles down with its flattened side on the sea bottom not far from the maternal polyp. This anthopolyp, which is in its form only slightly changed, takes over the sexual function. The maternal polyp by way of an unequal transfission produces another sexual polyp, which is again separated from its maternal body.

Though we are reminded strongly by this situation of conditions that prevail in the metagenetic Hydro- and Scypho-zoa, we find nevertheless that in *Fungia* the sexual generation corresponds to that of an anthopolyp, and there is therefore no trace, or no trend, (with the exception of its flattening) to a medusa form. Here we can raise the question: could *Fungia* perhaps be a very primitive species of Anthozoa so that it could be considered to be the beginning of the formation of medusae which has finally led, in the remotest geological past, to the metagenetic subtype of Scyphozoa with medusa as their sexual generation? This is completely improbable, and on the contrary, *Fungia* appears to be a specialist among Madreporaria.

Its solitary state is probably a secondary phenomenon, developed out of living in cormi, a fact which seems to be supported by its budding which exists to a slight degree only and which no longer leads to the formation of a colony. The main element of the asexual reproduction, or, rather, multiplication, is a transfission with a simultaneous transmission of the sexual function to the freely living (not freely moving!) generation. It is clear that such a situation must be considered as a special "invention" made by *Fungia.* Yet it nevertheless represents an element of the formation of medusae—all this in the sense of Watson's mosaic theory.

It seems much more probable, even if we do not take into consideration the basic problem of the origin of the Anthozoa, that there is no primary medusa form in Anthozoa. If we combine this with the conclusion that in the Anthozoa the internal bilateral symmetry is a primary property, we come to the more probable conclusion that the Anthozoa are the most primitive Cnidaria. In case one would like to stick to the old "belief" in the primitiveness of the Hydrozoa, it would be necessary to take refuge in the comfortable supposition that the Anthozoa had been separated very early from an indifferent ancestor of the Cnidaria. This auxiliary solution, however, is improbable and it does not offer a rational explanation.

The Primarily Solitary Polyps Appear in Anthozoa Only

The next piece of evidence of the primitiveness of the Anthozoa is the fact that it is in the Anthozoa only that the primarily solitary species can with certainty be found. So far, too little significance has been attributed to this fact, or it has not even been taken into consideration. Everywhere, in all the three classes of Cnidaria, solitary species have been found (here the polyp form can only be considered!), and they all have usually been thought of as primarily solitary species.

Hydra was considered as a prototype of all Cnidaria; it usually appears solitary, and it forms only small ephemeral cormi (colonies), a phenomenon which is usually interpreted as a tendency towards the evolution of colonies. In spite of the fact that it can now be shown to be proved that the solitary character of *Hydra* is a secondary phenomenon and that it is far from being a primitive form, there are even now numerous zoologists who find it difficult to accept this fact. An interesting parallel to *Hydra* can be found in the species *Monobryozoon ambulans* Remane (Remane, 1936), which until recently has been thought to be the only solitary ectoproctan (recently, however, another such species has been described); yet in this case the only difference has been that the discoverer of Monobryozoans had immediately been able to establish that in this species the solitary state was a secondary phenomenon. This was not difficult to establish in view of the fact that in this form it shows that it goes back to corm-forming ancestors. The number of solitary species of Hydroidea is comparatively high. A closer comparison with the related species or genera enables us to discover again and again that this solitary life is a secondary phenomenon. Not infrequently we can find all kind of transitions, from species with typical cormi (colonies), and those that, though solitary, still show, clear traces of a former formation of cormi, up to the completely solitary species (e.g. in the hydroid family Tubulariidae). The last remaining trace of a former formation of cormi is the formation of podocysts (Hadži, 1912), i.e. the parts of coenosarcs or of the cellular mass which are covered by the periderm (i.e. cuticule) and which otherwise form the impersonal part of a cormus, above all the hydrorhiza. In our case they take over the role of a resting stage and serve the purposes of asexual reproduction (Fig. 19).

As early as in the Anthozoa, as well as in all the truly sessile animal types up to Chordonia, we can observe an inclination either to an imperfect transfission or to the formation of buds with a simultaneous preservation of an organic contact between the secondary zooids and the maternal polyp. Thus we can see that in the whole large group of Octactiniaria among Anthozoa, not a single primarily (in this case not even secondarily) solitary species does appear. Those species that have occasionally been described as solitary (e.g. *Haimea*, *Monoxenia*, etc.) were primary zooids (or oozooids) only before they began to develop further into colonies. This situation in Oct-

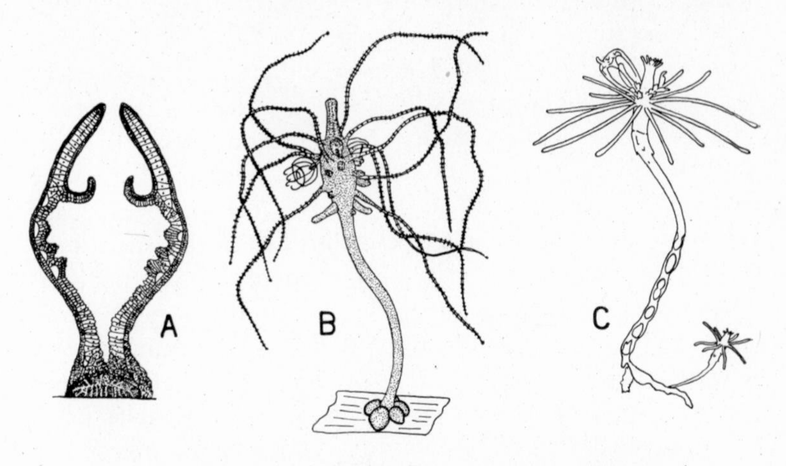

Fig. 19. Podocysts or resting bodies as remains of rhizome. A, scyphopolyp of *Chrysaora hyoscela* (after Hadži). B, hydroidpolyp of *Ostroumovia harii* (after Uchida and Nagao). C, *Hypolytus* sp. (after Miles).

actiniaria, naturally in connection with other properties and characteristics, proves that Octactiniaria do not correspond to the primitive subtype of Anthozoa as this has frequently been believed. The Actiniaria can with all certainty only be considered as primarily solitary animals (with, as it seems, one species only which forms colonies), as can also, in addition to these, the Cerianthraria with their partly rounded off and partly flattened aboral end.

In the Scyphozoa the abolition of the colonies of polyps has gone furthest. In these the species with cormi, which have a completely irregular growth, are a real rarity now (the so-called *Stephanoscyphus*, the polyp generation of *Nausithoë)*; there are, however, numerous species where the polyps have already become solitary individuals, yet with a periderm which they have still preserved as their external skeleton; the periderm must be interpreted as a remnant from the former formation of colonies; in numerous other species the scyphopolyps are completely "naked," i.e. they have no periderm, yet in spite of this they still continue to reproduce by way of budding or by means of the formation of stolons. In not one single case in the Scyphozoa has polymorphism been developed.

Polymorphism Has Reached Its Climax in Hydrozoa

Polymorphism (dimorphism when it is least developed) in the cormi of polyps is another piece of evidence which supports our thesis. It is a sign that a higher stage in evolution has been reached when this polymorphism appears in combination with the individualization of the cormus (colony). In the Anthozoa the dimorphism of polyps has been developed among the Octactiniaria only, a fact which can again be considered as a proof of their higher condition in comparison with Hexactiniaria. Siphonozooids, whose number has been rather reduced, appear either in species that form irregular cormi, e.g. in the red coral *(Corallium rubrum* L.), or in species with regularly, and thus individually, formed cormi e.g. Pennatulacea. No cases of polymorphism have been known in the Scyphozoa and this can be easily understood since they form, with a few exceptions, no cormi.

The highest level in differentiation, and thus of specialization, has been reached in the Hydrozoa, a clear indication that in them the Cnidaria have reached a climax in their evolution. In these polymorphism can even be found in the medusoid form, i.e. in the mixed polypo-medusoid cormi of Siphonophora that live in plankton, with a simultaneous individualization of cormi. Nothing similar can be observed in

Scyphozoa. In Hydroidea the polymorphous cormi usually appear with one medusoid form only and they are mostly irregularly built; the only regular form is that of a plume *(Pennaria)* among Athecata and in the numerous species of Plumulariidae among the Thecata (Fig. 20.).

There are many other properties and characteristics of Cnidaria which can be understood only if we interpret their phy-

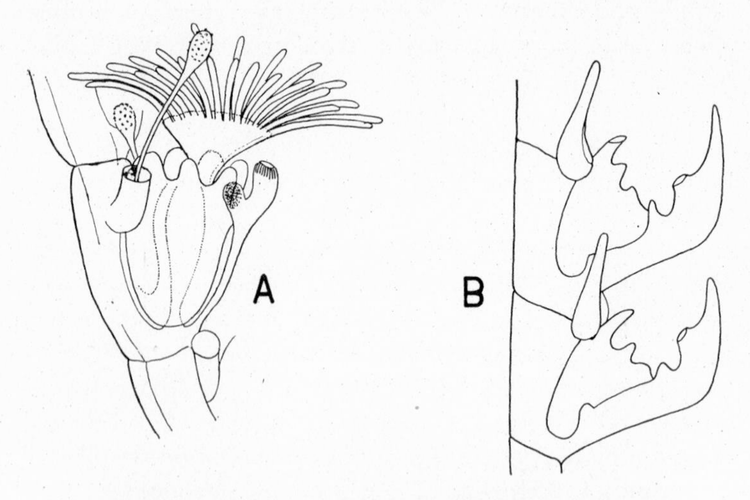

Fig. 20. Polymorphic hydroidpolyps organized as a subcormus or cormidium, composed of a gastropolyp and a few heterozooids (machozooids). A, *Aglaophenia* sp. (after Kühn). B, *Halicornaria cornuta* Allman (after Allman).

logeny as having followed the direction Anthozoa—Scyphozoa—Hydrozoa. In our analysis of these properties we must be constantly aware of the fact that two parallel processes are taking place in connection with the unique specialization which the sessile way of life entails. One process is that of regression, the retrograde development which has also been unsuitably called, as has already been mentioned, degeneration (cf. Laubenfels [1955], and the reply by M. Zalokar [1955]). During such a process all characteristics and peculiarities which serve the purpose of a free movement are gradually lost.

The change in symmetry of the form from a bilateral to a radial symmetry, and simultaneously to the general polyp form of the entire body, is connected with this. On the other hand, we can find progressive morphogenetic processes in individual organs. Here we have first to mention the progressive development of the cnidae together with the tentacles; the strong extensibility connected with an increased contractibility (a special development of the cutaneous muscle tube), connected with the ability to move in all directions (nutations). We must certainly attribute the evolution of secondary freely swimming medusae, and, finally, the liberation of whole cormi (Siphonophora) and the formation of a special impersonal floating apparatus, the pneumatophore (cf. Hadži, 1954), to such progressive properties.

Both regressive as well as progressive developments have reached their climax in the Hydrozoa which can be easily understood if viewed from our standpoint. So far it has been the regressive element in particular which has been taken into consideration, and it has been wrongly interpreted as a sign of a primary simplicity. This has been especially done because of the epithelization of the three body layers which is a characteristic of all the sedentary groups of Metazoa; the intermediate body layer can be strongly reduced by way of such an epithelization so that locally it can almost completely disappear. It was in this way that T. H. Huxley concluded (1875) with regard to medusae, and Allman with regard to Hydroidea, that these animals consisted of two body layers only, an ectoderm and an entoderm. This circumstance, together with events that take place during their ontogenies, was used by Haeckel when he formulated his gastraea theory. As a matter of fact, however, there is not a single species in Cnidaria which would really consist of two "skins" or epithelia only. If we disregard sex cells which cannot be properly attributed to any body layer even in those cases where they adhere closely either to the ectoderm or to the entoderm, there have always been found other cells between these two epithelia which have been given various names and which have been variously interpreted (indifferent, interstitial, mesenchymal, mesogloeal cells). These are frequently hidden between the somewhat dehiscent basal ends either of the one or of the other, or, finally, of the two epithelium layers. Neither during their ontogenies, nor in their fully developed state do these cells represent a compact layer or an epithelial organisation, and so the name *mesoderm* which is frequently used in this connection is wrong. I have therefore proposed a new name instead of the former: *mesohyl.*

The Regressive Development of the Intermediate Layer in Cnidaria

I must emphasize, when we first make a brief study of the mesohyl, that it is most developed in the Anthozoa where it often contains even muscle cells. This layer can be found well developed in the tentacles of anthopolyps. In the Scyphozoa and in the Hydrozoa it has almost completely disappeared and it is only occasionally revived by the actively moving cnidocytes (Hadži 1907, 1911 b, c). In the Cnidaria among others a jelly-like hyaline substance which plays an important role is secreted into this middle layer (Fig. 21). This so-called mesogloeal layer has usually been wrongly interpreted as a limit between the entodermal and ectodermal epithelia. Whatever occurs on one side of this layer has been attributed to the entoderm, and whatever appears on the other side has been attributed to the ectoderm, and in this no exception has been made even in connection with gonocytes. Attempts have even been made (Hertwig) to use this as a basis for a systematic division of Cnidaria into Ectocarpa and Endocarpa. We really get the impression that Nature herself had tried to make it easier for zoologists to differentiate between the two body layers which alone have been supposed to exist (Diblastica, according to Ray Lankester).

The layer of the jelly-like substance partly takes over the role of an extensible internal skeleton as early as in Anthozoa, and even more so in the Scyphozoa and in the Hydrozoa, concordantly with its new position: the appendices of the muscular tissue of the two epithelia, which find support in this skeleton,

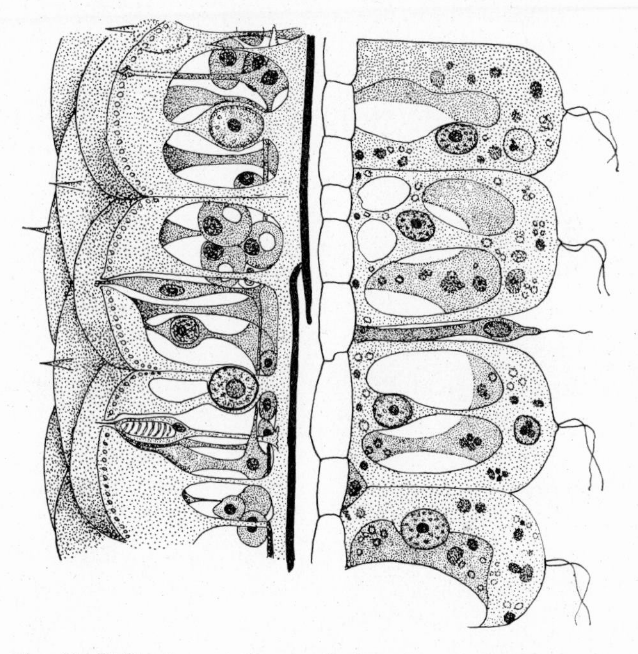

Fig. 21. Half schematic longitudinal section of the body wall of *Hydra*; *left*, the skin, *right*, the gut; *centre*, the mesohyl (after Hadži).

passively share the stretching and the shrinking which takes place during the thickening and the flattening of the body. This is true for the actively moving parts of polyps. In medusae this layer of a jelly-like substance can occasionally be of considerable size; here it represents a firm elastic substance which takes over the role of an antagonist to the rhythmically contracting subumbrellar muscles. In the Anthozoa and in the Scyphozoa this layer of a jelly-like substance contains individual, usually amoeboid, mesohyl cells, while in the Hydromedusae no such cells can any longer be found. Thus we see that this intermediate layer represents a property which has been developed in Cnidaria partly progressively and partly regressively.

In this connection it is interesting to observe that these mesohyl cells—whether they are cnidocytes, or genital cells, or *I*-cells—do not heed the imaginary limit between the two epithelia. We can observe how these cells freely pass this "limit" in their amoeboid movements (Hadži, 1907, 1911). I have been able to show this both during the formation of buds in Hydra (Hadži, 1909 a, b) and in other Hydrozoa (the medusa buds at the manubrium of Hydromedusae, Hadži, 1912 d), as well as during the widely practiced migrations of cnidocytes (Hadži, 1907 a), and of the primitive sex cells, as had been formerly shown by Weisman (1883).

The Morphological Proof of the New Interpretation of the Phylogeny of Cnidaria

Muscular Tissue

Let us study now the muscles of Cnidaria. We must attribute these to the middle layer even in those cases where the contractile fibres do not form an independent middle layer, so that it appears only as an appendix either of the ectodermal or of the entodermal epithelia. Such a situation is generally considered as a very primitive one. We wish to show here that the same is true for the muscles as has been said for the whole middle layes, i.e. their development has been progressive or regressive, concordant with the changes of the type of movement. The consequence of the sessile way of life has been a simplification of the cutaneous muscle tube, and, parallel to this, a specialization of the body muscles in the movements on a given spot. A new specialization has taken place during the secondary transition to the free movement, which applies especially to the medusoid form, yet this specialization again follows Dollo's rule and it does not represent a return to those conditions that had been observed in the movements of their creeping ancestors.

We will maintain, even if this may appear surprising, that it is right to attribute the muscular tissue of Cnidaria to the middle layer even in those cases where it appears as a basal appendix of the epithelium cells of the ecto- or entoderm and where it does not possess its own nuclei, i.e. where it does not consist of independent cells. In numerous anthopolyps we can observe how this muscular tissue subsequently develops locally into independent cells with their own nuclei. Chester (1912:755) observed in the species *Pseudoplexaura crassa* how the epithelial cells (they were classified as entodermal cells) that occur in mesenteries and that had each previously produced a single differentiated muscle fibre, leave the epithelial group and sink into the subepithelium, i.e. into the intermediate layer, and in this way develop into the pure muscular cells.

We can obtain a good understanding of the muscular conditions in Cnidaria only if we derive them from conditions that can be observed in Turbellaria, and if we pass from the situation that can be observed in Anthozoa to those that occur in the Scyphozoa and in the Hydrozoa. A very misleading idea of the primitive nature of the so-called neuro-muscular-epithelial cells has been proposed by Nikolaus Kleinenberg. According to this interpretation such a cell has differentiated in three directions, into the pure epithelium cells on the surface, and into the muscle and nerve cells in the interior of the body. With regard to the nerve cells it soon became necessary to relinquish this concept after the nerve cells had been discovered in *Hydra*. Yet in spite of this, the idea of the primitive character of the muscle epithelium cells has been preserved down to the present day. H. Wolf (1903) developed this hypothesis for the nerve cells and supported it with beautiful, even if completely imaginary, pictures to show that they originate, like the muscle cells, in the immersed epithelium cells. It has seemed that this interpretation was supported by the fact that during the ontogeny, the *Anlage* of the nerve system emerges in close connection with the *Anlage* of the ectoderm, a fact which can especially be observed in the higher developed animals.

The destiny of the muscular system of Cnidaria has been completely determined by the transition to the sessile way of life and that in two directions. Due to the formation of colonies (cormogony) which they had early begun to develop, the polyps as dependent "persons" or subindividuals have grown smaller and smaller (a progressive diminution). It is because of this fact that the smallest subindividuals can be found, as this can be expected, in the Hydrozoa. It is evident that the regressive development of the whole muscular system has been conditioned by this fact. On the other hand, and because of the emerging restriction and the change of the role of the muscular system, a cutaneous muscle tube has been formed which is typical of Cnidaria; a layer of longitudinal muscular fibres under the skin, and another layer of circularly placed muscular fibres under the intestinal epithelium. We have here actually two types of movement only: retraction which is followed by extension, and nutation (curving), due to the contraction of individual sectors of the layer of longitudinal fibres. In species whose solitary life is a secondary phenomenon, e.g. in *Hydra*, this has led to a new type of movement, such as can be observed in the loop-worm or in Hirudinea.

The anthopolyps have inherited a richly developed muscular system from their turbellarian ancestors. Besides a strongly developed cutaneous muscle tube which consists of three body layers there are also "internal" ("gastrodermal") muscular fibres that show a particularly strong development in the sarcosepta and as the sphincter of the oral area, and finally the dorsoventral and the obliquely placed lateral muscle fibres. In the primitive, solitary anthopolyps which stand erect and glide slowly over the sea bottom, it was the middle layer with its diagonally placed muscular fibres which was first lost because it had become superfluous. Thus two external layers only have been preserved here; these have lost their independent character, yet they have become specifically differentiated, and they have been wholly preserved in the active parts of polyps. These layers, have disappeared in the impersonal colonial parts (solenia, caulus, rhiza). It is only among the pelagic individualized cormi of the Siphonophora with their well developed hydrocauli (hydrosomes) that the layer with muscles can be found well developed even in the impersonal parts, a fact which can be easily understood.

Several remains of an internal muscle system have been preserved in the anthopolyps of the solitary Actiniaria. These are the basally situated transversal muscles which are active when the animal creeps forward; a whole system of the so-called septal muscles that occur in sarcosepta and whose fibres are placed longitudinally because they function as retractors; and, finally, the circular muscles that can be found close to the oral disc and which function as an oral sphincter. Here, it becomes clear how little it corresponds to the facts, if we speak about entodermal or ectodermal muscles for the sole reason that sometimes these muscular fibres appear to be more closely connected with the skin epithelium, another time with the intestinal epithelium, and as the third possibility they become independent because they had been separated from these epithelia. Scholars of the old school have frequently run into difficulties when they have tried to decide to which of the two body layers (either ectoderm or entoderm) they should have attributed a certain group of muscular fibres. Yet, as a matter of fact, all these muscular fibres belong to the middle layer only, regardless whether we call this third middle layer a mesogloea, mesoderm, mesoblast, mesenchyme, or, as I have called it, a mesohyl; it is always one and the same part of the body.

In the Scyphozoa, the polyps have inherited as their inner muscles from their anthozoan ancestors the poorly preserved taeniolan bundles of muscles. There are, with few exceptions (*Nausithoë–Stephanoscyphus*), four such retractors which used to be called ectodermal, even when the taeniolae of Scyphopolyps (the retrograded sarcosepta) were found to be built of an entodermal epithelium, together with some "mesenchyme". Ontogenetically, however, these retractors are formed from the basis of cutaneous infundibula which lie in the oral disc and which are therefore of the "ectodermal origin". These septal retractors have lost their function during the formation of medusae and they have therefore disappeared. On the other hand, we frequently find in Scyphomedusae the layer of longitudinally placed muscular fibres to be progressively developed and specialized, in agreement with their swimming type of movement. As this was the case in anthopolyps we also find here the function of the layer of muscular fibres considerably increased, which has led to fold formation in this layer. It is not rare for "mountains" of folds to become separated, obviously secondarily, from the skin epithelium and it is in this way that they develop into the mesogloeal muscles. The outer layer of muscular fibres shows a particularly strong development under the oral disc of Scyphopolyps. Here it has been given a special function: it helps to open the oral orifice in order to make it possible for the predator to swallow its prey, and for this reason the arrangement of these fibres is radially symmetric. I pointed out, some time ago (Hadži, 1907) that these muscular fibres can be found cross-striated as early as in Scyphopolyps, a fact which has been little noticed, but which I have found, however, to be of considerable importance in view of the fact that the subumbrellar muscles, which are so important for the swimming ability of these animals, had been evolved in both medusoid forms (Scypho- and Hydro-medusae) out of this layer of muscular fibres. In those Scyphomedusae which have reached a larger size these muscles have become progressively widely differentiated (radial, coronal, delta muscles).

In Hydropolyps that have become very small (there are a few species only that have become secondarily solitary and whose size is therefore slightly larger) the subcutaneous layer of longitudinal fibres has been sufficient for the quick and complete retraction of the hydranths; and this was the reason why, besides the taeniolae, the inner retractors of Scyphopolyps have also been lost. The same situation has also been preserved in their medusae even in those cases when these have grown larger (e.g. *Aequorea*). Contrary to this situation in Scyphomedusae, we can find that the exumbrella of Hydromedusae does not show any layer of muscular fibres while at the same time these are strongly developed in the subumbrella where they even begin to form folds (e.g. in *Gonionemus*); in this they are helped by the velum, a speciality of Hydromedusae, as well as by the firm stratum of a jelly-like substance that can be found in the umbrella.

According to our interpretation, a thin longitudinal stratum is the only thing that has been preserved in Cnidaria, that have adopted the sessile way of life, of the cutaneous muscle tube which had consisted of three layers in their turbellarian ancestors. The inner transversal layer of fibres which is attached to the entodermal epithelium obviously goes back to the muscularis of the intestinal tract of Turbellaria, regardless whether in Turbellaria this stratum of muscular fibres (Bresslau, 1933, K.C. Schneider, 1902) have a transverse or a longitudinal and transverse position, or whether these be independent muscle cells, or only appendices of the entodermal epithelium cells. We have here, moreover, a change of the function inasmuch as in Turbellaria the muscularis exclusively serves the intestinal peristalsis, and in Cnidaria where it works as a part of the general system of the body muscles, in coordination with the external longitudinally placed layer of fibres. In contractions of the animal body—which are very important for animals that have adopted a sessile way of life because they are enabled by such contractions to liberate themselves quickly from contact with a foe or from an unfavourable effect of an environment—the main function lies in the longitudinally placed muscle fibres. During the stretching or extension which follows a contraction when the animal searches for food,

9*

the main function is taken by the transversally placed layer of muscular fibres which adjoins the entodermal epithelium.

The muscular conditions that can be observed in Cnidaria —not less than those that can be observed in Turbellaria—show clearly that so far it has been much exaggerated when attempts have been made to establish a sharp division between the skin and the intestine on one hand which both show a strong inclination to the epithelization, and the mesohyl on the other as the layer which is situated between them. We are justified in maintaining, on the basis of known facts, that in Cnidaria and in Turbellaria the cytoplasma has the ability to develop special strongly contractile fibres (the muscle fibres), regardless of whether it has become differentiated as skin cells (ectoderm), intestinal cells (entoderm), or mesenchyme cells (mesoderm or mesohyl), as well as the ability to grow undulipodia (cilia or flagella) on its free surfaces (either external, or internal, or intermediate). This process is reversible, i.e. the ability can be lost again, and under special conditions it can again become active.

The mesenchymal muscle system which plays a major role in Turbellaria has been lost in Cnidaria, and the "mesenchyme" itself has become strongly reduced. These muscles, however, have been preserved in Ctenophora, while in Cnidaria which have adopted the sessile way of life they have become more closely connected with the two body epithelia and it has been only secondarily that they have occasionally again liberated themselves from the epithelium cells and sunk under the epithelium.

It should be mentioned here that in some primitive Turbellaria (e.g. in the aloeocoelous species *Prorhynchus haswelli* according to Steinböck and Reisinger; Bresslau, 1933) the contractile muscle fibres have been developed in the skin stratum itself, i.e. in the cytoplasm of the skin epithelium, and thus intraepithelially. This development has been so rich that here they form even four strata, i.e. in the distal zone (in the "cover stratum") one longitudinally and one transversally placed stratum, and similarly in the basal zone.

The hydrosome of some Siphonophora *(Apolemia uvaria,* according to K.C. Schneider, and *Halistemma tergestinum*, according to Claus) can be mentioned as an example of newly formed muscle fibres. This so-called hydrosome of Siphonophora is nothing else but the hydrocaulus of the Hydroidea which has developed no muscle fibres because the slight general contractility of the cytoplasm has been clearly sufficient, and because of the periderm which as an external skeleton covers the "coenosarc." Yet a strong contractility of the "stem," as the bearer of the whole colony, has been useful for the planktonic Siphonophora and we can therefore observe here not only muscle fibres that have been developed as appendices to the skin layer, but also that the epithelium muscle cells which had been developed in this way have sunk into the "mesogloea." It is natural that K.C. Schneider speaks here of "...in die Tiefe gesunkenen Deckmuskelzellen" which must be interpreted "also als eine Vorstufe echter Muskelzellen" (K.C. Schneider, 1902:607). According to our interpretation we have here, not muscle cells in the process of development, but rather parts of the so-called *Deckmuskelzellen* which have been secondarily developed into the former.

The subepithelial cells are frequently mentioned in the histology of Cnidaria. They lie close-wedged between the basal epithelium cells and they are usually attributed to the skin layer or to the ectoderm. This, however, is wrong. Everything that lies under the skin epithelium, whether migrated to this place from the epithelium through immersion, or that originated here, belongs to the middle layer ("mesoderm"), and it must be attributed to it even if there is no sharply delineated and clear limit in between. Cnidocytes can serve here as an example; they are recruited from indifferent "mesenchymal cells," and, after their further development, they are ranged into the skin epithelium either "on the spot" or after a shorter or longer wandering; they must therefore be attributed to the skin layer in their fully developed state only. Recently the theory of an active wandering of cnidocytes has been doubted by some authors (Brien and Reniers-Decoin, 1950). To this it can be answered that it is easy to observe this wandering, which is frequently very complicated, in a living object (cf. the most recent work by Lenhoff, 1959).

In conclusion, we can state that conditions that can be observed in the muscular system of Cnidaria show (in comparison with conditions that can be observed in the freely living Turbellaria) a generally retrograde development in polyps as the primary form of Cnidaria, a fact due to their sessile way of life. Yet at the same time they have been reorganized and specialized, concordantly with their mode of life. These changes which are partly progressive and partly regressive can be clearly identified as early as in Anthozoa. Here the development followed the direction, solitary Hexactiniaria–colonial Hexactiniaria–colonial Octactiniaria. It is therefore wrong to put the Octactiniaria (as has been done for example by Hyman) as a supposedly more primitive form into the first place of the system of Anthozoa. The Octactiniaria with their sarcosepta (whose number is constantly eight) follow the rule; first polymerization with an unfixed number of multiplied "parts," followed by an oligomerization with a reduced and fixed number of "parts." In the extremely specialized Antipatharia, among Hexactiniaria, whose anthopolyps have a strongly decreased size and which are, moreover, very short, the septal muscles have been mainly lost, while at the same time other strata of the muscular tissue also show a very poor development; the skin, however, has again become covered with cilia. Thus the changes in the muscle system have gone much further in the colonial Hexacorallia than in the typical Octactiniaria.

The muscular conditions that can be observed in medusa of Scyphoza and Hydrozoa which are even more specialized can be deduced from those of polyps, and not conversely as this has been done by numerous zoologists, Hyman among them. Neither the septal muscles nor sphincters can be found in the two main forms of medusae (Scypho- and Hydromedusae), and so there is no trace left of the primary internal muscles. On the other hand, we can observe a strengthening of the longitudinal muscular tissue which lies under the skin epithelium. This strengthening is appropriate to the function these muscles have in certain areas, especially close to the marginal tentacles, so that these muscles frequently show a higher level of specialization and they become transversally striped (e.g. according to Krasińska, in the subumbrella of the trachyline hydromedusa *Carmarina hastata*), or they can even appear as independent myoblasts (e.g. according to Krasińska, in the subumbrella of the hydromedusa *Neoturris*).

The opponents to the view that considers the polyp form as primary in comparison to the medusoid form and which sees in Anthopolyps the oldest form Cnidaria, should compare the muscular conditions that can be found in Cnidaria with those that can be found in other sessile animal types; thus to compare those in Turbellaria with those in Endoprocta (Camptozoa), those in Annelida with those in Phoronidea and further with those in Ectoprocta, and finally those in *Branchiostoma* with those in Tunicata. It is wrong to require or to expect a progressive development in the general muscle system of an animal body which adheres to the sessile way of life, a supposition which one has to accept if one tries to derive the Scypho- and Anthozoa from the Hydrozoa.

The unique case of Stauromedusae, or better, say, Lucernariidae is very interesting in this connection. These are not simply medusae as they have frequently been depicted, but real polypomedusae instead (Fig. 22). These Scyphozoa are secondary solitary animals and they usually have readopted the ability to move slowly over the sea bottom. At the same time they have also abandoned the alternation of generations; their medusoid generation which was formed by way of transverse division or strobilation is not severed any longer but instead it remains with the polyp with which it forms a double animal, a genuine polypomedusa, or a combination of a basal

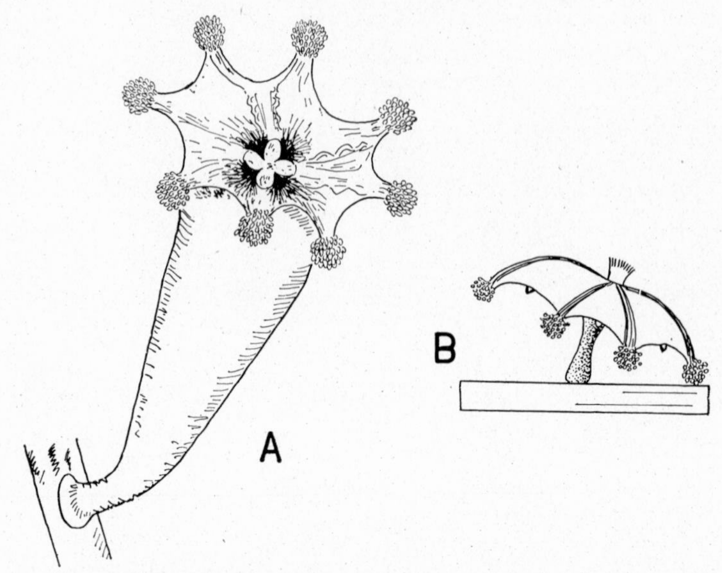

Fig. 22. Scyphozoa, Lucernariidae. A, *Lucernaria* sp. (from Hyman). B, *Haliclystus auricula* (after H. J. Clark).

scyphopolyp and of a distal scyphomedusa. The same combination can also be found in its muscle system; in one and the same individual we can find the peculiarities of a polyp as well as those of a medusa, i.e. on one hand, the taeniolan or septal muscles, and the coronal muscles in the form of bands, as well as the radially oriented muscular tissue of the oral disc (manubrium).

The Nervous System

Cnidaria have played a special role in the history of the development of neurology. Nobody has succeeded so far in finding either individual nerve cells or, even less so, a real nerve system in Spongiae; this is the true situation in spite of the contrary assertions made by Tuzet and by her collaborators. On the other hand it has been possible to identify in Cnidaria, and especially in *Hydra* which has been intensively studied, not only individual nerve cells but also whole coherent nerve systems and sensory cells. These results have been arrived at first by means of usual methods (serial sections, and the staining of sections with the iron haematoxylin) which have been used by O. and R. Hertwig (1878), K. C. Schneider (1890), M. Miyashima (1898) and finally by means of the specific *intra vitam* colouring with the methylene blue (Hadži, 1908). This has disproved Kleinenberg's theory of nerve–muscle–epithelium cells which has been mentioned above, in spite of the attempts made by Eimer to support it. They, and numerous other scholars after them (among these I mention especially P. Grošelj [1909] who has suceeded in *intra vitam* staining the elements and mutual relationships of the nerve systems of anthopolyps) have established the generally valid fact that there can be no doubt that Cnidaria possess a nervous system, though in the form of a nerve net which can be locally denser and which can even lead, though in medusae only, to the formation of nerve chains and to the local accumulation of ganglion cells into small ganglia. Yet, on the other hand no typical nervous system with one centre, the brain ganglion, and with regular nerve trunks can be found anywhere in Cnidaria.

It has been easy to conclude—and such a conclusion has really been made and it is still generally accepted—that in Cnidaria we can find the primary primitive conditions of the nervous system which has been further developed by way of a progressive evolution into the typical nervous system on a higher level of evolution. G. Wolf (1903), as has already been mentioned, has even tried to construct the origin of the nervous system in the following way: nerve cells have been developed, according to this interpretation, from the epithelially placed sensory cells by way of the latter sinking into the subepithelium; in this way it has been believed that the theory of synapses, or of a secondary conjugation of primarily individual nerve cells, has been confirmed.

It cannot be doubted that the nervous system found in the polyps of Cnidaria (we will first discuss the primary form and the basic generation of Cnidaria, i.e. the polypoids as a morphological and a physiological whole) really represent the simplest organization that can be found in the entire animal world. The only problem is whether this simplicity be primary, or a result of a retrogressive development from an earlier higher level of organization. In an analysis like ours we must take into consideration the function of the nervous system as that of an intermediary between the sensory cells or sensory organs as receptors, and the muscles as effectors. I have already shown with regard to the muscle system, that it had gone through a generally retrogressive development, with the exception of that specialization which is appropriate to the sessile way of life. To my knowledge not a single complex sensory organ has been found so far anywhere among the polyps of Cnidaria, nor has there been published a description of such an organ. There have always been only individual sensory cells observed in all the exposed parts of the skin stratum or even in the gut epithelium. It is therefore not surprising if the absence of a distinct nerve centre had been formerly attributed by the brothers Hertwig (1878:185) to the absence of sensory organs. They were right, with the exception that they should have added that this absence of sensory organs has been a result of the sessile way of life, similarly as has been the case with the simplification of the muscular system.

In my opinion there are two facts which have not been satisfactorily taken into consideration in the interpretation of the nervous system that can be observed in the polyps of Cnidaria. That idea occurred to me when I succeeded in selectively *intra vitam* staining the nervous system together with the sensory cells that occur in green *Hydra*. This system appears to be cytologically–histologically strongly differentiated, in spite of its actually quite simple general structure. On the basis of this fact alone one could conclude that the general simplicity of this nervous system cannot be a primary phenomenon.

The second fact that should be mentioned in this connection is that the "nerve net" of the polyps of Cnidaria is not developed in one layer, or in the ectoderm, only, as we are now used to saying (thus subepithelially or under the skin), but it also occurs deeper, in the intermediate layer (C.A. Pantin, 1952). Furthermore, the nerve processes do not respect in this connection the limit between the two layers (the supporting lamellae or interstitial lamellae). This fact, taken separately, does not seem to be very surprising, yet it becomes clear if we make a comparison of the nervous system of Cnidaria with the one that can be found in Turbellaria.

Yet before we begin to deal with this problem, let us first make a cursory survey of the nervous systems that exist in other animal types that have also adopted the sedentary way of life. It can be observed in such sedentary animal types that have evolved from freely living ancestors that already possessed a well developed central nervous system, that the main centre, the brain ganglion, has been preserved with obstinate tenacity, long after their transition to the sessile way of life, and it can still be found when other parts, especially the ventral nerve cord, had disappeared, and when the peripheral nervous system only has been kept. A centre has been preserved even in those cases where sensory organs have not been developed in great abundance. As a rule we find the supraoesophageal ganglion preserved. This centre has disappeared, as it seems, in Endoprocta only and this was probably due to the part of the body which was used by these animals when they began to attach themselves to the bottom. On the other hand, we find the suboesophageal ganglion preserved and it functions as a brain ganglion. In addition to these, the brain ganglion with its ventral extension (the nerve cord) has been lost in Echinodermata when they definitely adopted the sedentary way of life; in these a peripheral nerve net only has been preserved. We can observe, as a fine analogy to the medusae of Cnidaria, that no younger types of Echinodermata have developed a nerve centre similar to a brain ganglion, not even in those cases where they have evolved secondary ambulatory abilities. We can find in the freely moving Echinodermata, as well as in medusae, a secondary thickening or condensation of nerve elements (nerve cells and fibres, neurites) into a nerve ring which cannot therefore be homologous to the nerve ring together with the upper gullet and lower gullet ganglia of Polymera, because they do not possess real ganglia. The ambulacral nerve trunks spread radially out of the nerve ring.

When zoologists abandon the accepted idea of a supposedly primary nerve net in *Hydra* they will have to search for the solution of the problem of the origin of the nervous system somewhere else. In my opinion we must consider the Turbellaria. This suggestion stands in opposition to what has been taught by many comparative morphologists (cf. Hanström, 1928). The simplest conditions of the nervous system can be found in Acoela and in the small Turbellaria that are related to the former. There is no real foundation for the supposition which has been frequently proposed that the Turbellaria are secondarily simplified animals, an interpretation which seems to be supported by the fact that their size has decreased. The Turbellaria are freely moving, and they search actively both for food as well as (even though hermaphroditic animals) for their partners. Their primitive nervous system is situated close under the skin and it forms a primitive nerve net without any real nerve centres, without ganglia or nerve trunks. Without being afraid that the future will prove me wrong (so far no factual data about this have been available) we can expect that this nerve net does not develop during the ontogeny by way of an invagination of the skin epithelium cells (ectocytium), but rather "on the spot," out of the "mesenchyme" cells. We will return to this when we discuss the problem of the origin of Eumetazoa.

During the second stage of the development of Turbellaria a condensation of nerve cells and of nerve fibres into longitudinal bundles that are mutually connected by way of transverse commissures (the orthogon, according to Reisinger) can be observed. At the same time a second plexus is being developed more deeply in the interior of the animal body. During the third stage a brain is formed in the anterior part of the body, at the place where the longitudinal bundles develop a mutual contact; this development is aided by sensory organs that had evolved in the front part of the animal. Here we are not interested in the subsequent development of the nervous system during which the polymerization (the increase of the number of the longitudinal nerve trunks) is followed by an oligomerization (two pairs of longitudinal trunks, a ventral pair, the merging of this pair with the nerve cord).

Fortunately enough there exist even now species of Turbellaria that have preserved the primitive conditions of their nervous system. O. Steinböck has given a description of the species *Nematoderma bathycola*, which has been found in the deep regions of the polar sea, close to Greenland; Steinböck says about this species, "Ein Gehirn in gewöhnlichem Sinne, wie wir es bei Turbellarien gewohnt sind anzutreffen, besitzt unser Tier nicht" (Steinböck, 1931). On the other hand there is in *Nematoderma* a denser and, as it seems, less regularly formed nerve plexus which is situated close under the skin and which shows indications of some thickenings or of condensation in the longitudinal direction. Hanström is inclined to attribute the main role in the formation of the brain to the emergence of sensory organs. We are convinced, however, that the influence of the function of the muscle system during the active forward movement, with the anterior end orientated forwards, has been at least as important. It is even possible that the static organ, the light receptors, and even more probably the special chemoreceptors have been developed only after the *Anlage* of the brain had been founded.

If we stick obstinately to the thesis of the evolution of Cnidaria in the direction Hydrozoa–Scyphozoa–Anthozoa and to the belief that Cnidaria have nothing in common with Turbellaria, we are forced to suppose that the nervous system of Eumetazoa has developed at least twice, thus diphyletically, and so to speak, out of nothing. The opinion cannot be taken seriously (though it is still occasionally met) which considers the Turbellaria together with all Acoelomata and "Pseudocoelomata" (we call them Ameria) to be a result of a retrogressive development ("degeneration"), and according to which the simple nervous system of small species of Turbellaria must be a secondary element. The specialists in Turbellaria all disagree with such an interpretation. This interpretation has been accepted only by those zoologists who would like to derive, on the basis of the enterocoele theory, the perigastrocoele from the intestinal cavities of anthopolyps, a plan which cannot be condemned sharply enough.

In view of the fact that in the Anthozoa the polyps certainly have a more highly developed nervous system than the one that can be found, in *Hydra*, we would be obliged, if we adhered to the old interpretation of the development of Cnidaria, to accept the proposition that they had progressively developed their nervous system in spite of their unchanged sedentary way of life. This contradicts all that is known about "the influence of the sessile way of life." In a certain sense there has really been a progressive development, as in the case of the muscle system, yet only inasmuch it has led to a specialization which stands in a causal relationship to the sedentary way of life. With regard to the whole structure, however, we can observe in the nervous system of Cnidaria indications of a progressive retrogression. It is only in the case of the primarily solitary and, even if slightly, moving Actiniae that a clear condensation of nerve elements can be identified at their aboral ends (the foot plate) (P. Grošelj, and recently Pantin and his school). A reduction of the nervous system can be observed as early as in Anthozoa that have become colonial animals. This reduction goes parallel to the reduction of the muscle system and we can see, as the final result, the nerve net limited to the oral region only.

In Scyphopolyps and in Hydropolyps the condensation of the nervous system disappears completely. In connection with the secondarily solitary *Hydra* which has again become an actively moving animal I have been able to show that the nervous system has again become locally dense, especially in the aboral foot plate, with a clear direction (radial or circular) of nerve fibres (Hadži, 1908).

A distinctly progressive tendency can be observed in the stem (siphonosome) of Siphonophora, among Hydrozoa. They have developed, as polypersonal cormi, the ability to move freely. This development of nervous system is parallel to the development of muscles in this strongly contractile stem of cormus (according to K. C. Schneider, 1896–1898).

Now let us pass over to the medusoid form. Since we derive the Cnidaria from the Turbellaria we must consequently consider the medusoid form as secondary and as evolved from the polypoid form. The same, however, has also been considered as the correct interpretation by numerous experts in Cnidaria who have believed at the same time that the Hydrozoa were the most primitive Cnidaria because there were such numerous and convincing proofs which seem to support such an interpretation. The development of the medusoid form, which has twice taken place (Scypho- and Hydro-medusae), is above all a secondary liberation, or a readoption of mobility with a simultaneous transition of the sexual function from one form to the other. This is the quintessence of the metagenesis, of the alternation of generations. It is senseless to deny the existence of an alternation of generations in Cnidaria, as has been recently attempted by Hyman: this is a consequence of an incorrect interpretation of the polyp form and of the polyp generation as if these were a larval stage which had not been developed into an adult form earlier than in Anthozoa. And what are *Hydra* and other Hydrozoa that have become secondarily solitary animals under a simultaneous loss of their medusa generation, in spite of the fact that they become sexually ripe? Is this a case of neoteny? This cannot possibly be so, in view of the fact that in the Hydroidea we can find all possible degrees of reduction of the medusoid generation; we must therefore have here a secondary omission of the medusoid generation.

If we disregard a clearly secondary retrogression of the medusoid form that can be observed in Hydrozoa, and if we disregard the case of Lucernariidae among Scyphozoa, we can see all the remaining developments to have been clearly progressive, a fact which can be easily understood because it is connected with a secondary adaptation of free life, in this case in the free water zone and with a simultaneous preservation of the essential characteristics of the older polyp form. On the basis of this standpoint we are also enabled to understand the conditions that can be found in the nervous system of medusae. The progressive development of the whole nervous system went parallel to the progressive development of the muscular system and of the marginal sensory organs. In this connection two regularities can be observed. This progressive development did not lead back to the old conditions that had existed in their freely moving ancestors (Turbellaria). The radially symmetrical form has now been preserved by medusae which developed the ability to swim freely and to creep over the sea bottom. When they swim, they orientate their aboral end forwards. In this way the development did not lead to a cephalization; the new anterior end remained empty, i.e. it did not develop sensory organs. A new centre of sensory and nervous functions has been developed around the margin of the swimming bell, and in this way the nerve rings have been evolved. The fact that there are two such nerve rings can be understood if we take into consideration that there are two nerve nets which are situated one above the other in the original polyp form. The formation of nerve rings is simply due to an intensive local thickening or condensation of the two nerve nets.

The second regularity (in the past people preferred to call them laws), is the fact that the evolution of the polyp into medusa has led to essentially identical results though it had taken place twice. Thus both times a double ring of nervous tissue has been developed along the margin of the umbrella, and both times this evolution has led to similar marginal sensory organs. In spite of this, however, there are differences between the two medusoid forms, even if we disregard such differences as, for example, the presence of a velum (only in Hydromedusae), or its absence (primary in all Scyphomedusae, secondary, and rare, in Hydromedusae, e.g. in *Obelia* species), and the completely different way the two medusoid forms develop; Scyphomedusae are formed by way of transverse division or strobilation, and Hydromedusae by way of budding. As for the velum, I have succeeded in showing that this auxiliary swimming organ developed genetically from the bud, i.e., out of the embryonic protective stratum, with a simultaneous change of its function (Hadži, 1909 b).

Various sense organs, that in the two medusoid forms appear as new formations, can be found developed as early as in Turbellaria (statocysts, light receptors [eyes], and chemoreceptors); as in the Turbellaria we can find in the medusae variants that show considerable differences. The main changes that can be observed, above all in the mechanoreceptors, are due to the transition to the new, specialized type of movement, i.e. to the rhythmic contractions of the umbrella muscles; this, however, is not true for the movement of the manubrium which had previously been found in the oral cone of polyps.

In their progressive evolution the Scyphomedusae have made greater advances than the Hydromedusae; this can be partly attributed to their greater size. This, however, must not be interpreted as if the Scyphomedusae had been developed out of the Hydromedusae; in reality their developments have been parallel and they had proceeded from two completely separate initial stages. The Scyphomedusae are, in my opinion, phylogenetically older, because the Scyphozoa themselves are older and must be interpreted as animals that had evolved from the Anthozoa. In the Scyphomedusae a localized agglomeration of various sensory organs (rhopalia) can be observed to have taken place in certain parts of the umbrella margin that are separated from each other at regular distances. As a consequence of this we can see an accumulation or condensation of nerve cells in the same spots of the nerve ring which has led to the formation of (imperfect though they are) ganglia (rhopalium ganglia). Something similar took place, it seems to me, in the Mollusca in the case of an assymetrically distorted bilateral symmetry. Data is available (Horridge, 1956) which shows a nerve net to have been developed in the exumbrellar subepithelium of the Scyphomedusae (nothing similar is known to me in the Hydromedusae). It has already been pointed out that no sensory organs, and, in connection with this, no nerve cell aggregates have been evolved in the pole of the exumbrella, in spite of expectations that these should be developed in the anterior part of the body which comes into most contact with the surrounding milieu when the animal swims. It is therefore impossible that the so-called "*Hydroctena salenskii*" (Dawydoff) could be a Hydromedusa (Hadži, 1959). In the Hydromedusae, a combination of two different sensory organs can sometimes be observed at the margin of their umbrellas (e.g. *Tiaropsis)*, a fact which has been used for an attempted division of Hydromedusae into Ocellatae and Vesiculatae. It should be also noted that in the subumbrella of Hydromedusae an agglomeration of the nerve tissue can also take place along their radial canals. It agrees with our interpretation of the origin of the velum that no nerve net has been developed in it; yet in spite of this the velum is able to perform rhythmic contractions.

The sense organs of medusae, if compared with those of polyps, are, as this has already been stated, new formations. Yet if we try to pursue the development further back we see that those sense organs that occur in medusae had also been essentially developed in their free living ancestors, in the Turbellaria (tango-, stato- [or tono-], chemo-, and light-receptors). The main difference is that in the Turbellaria that creep actively over firm surfaces, these sense organs show a bilaterally symmetric distribution (distribution in pairs) in the anterior end of their body which represents a primitive head, while in medusae they are distributed in groups and, in agreement with their radial symmetry and bell shape, at regular intervals along the margin of their umbrellas.

If we consider polyps as the primary form of Cnidaria, and if we do not find in them any complex sense organs, we must come to the conclusion that these sense organs had been lost due to their sessile way of life. This indicates that in medusae, which in Scyphozoa and Hydrozoa had been secondarily evolved out of polyps, these sense organs have been newly developed—probably only after they have long been adapted to the free life in water. We must here point to the fact—without any intention to enter into greater details—that there is nothing unusual in the reappearance of complex sense organs in the two subtypes of medusae. These sense organs represent, according to Grošelj, "extremely variable values," and they reappear again and again whenever they are required by the circumstances in which an animal lives; they frequently appear in the most unusual parts of the body, e.g. in the tentacle-like processes of the cloak margin of *Pecten*, or in the minute feathers of the tentacle crown of some Polychaeta. The consequences of considerable changes in the way of life are first, a reduction of those sense organs that had become useless and finally a complete loss of these; this can also be observed in those species that live in underground caves, regardless of the fact that they can belong to different systematic groups. With the same facility such sense organs can again and again be reintroduced. The explantation of this may be that the mutations that are necessary for the development of these sense organs return, even in those cases when such organs do not appear to be very useful. If again they are ("something to be desired"), useful because of the change of environment, the corresponding mutations win the protection and guidance of Natural Selection and they can again be further progressively developed.

It is therefore not a contradiction of facts when we maintain, on one hand, that Cnidaria have inherited their ability to develop complex sense organs from their turbellarian ancestors, and, on the other hand, when we declare these organs of Cnidaria to be new formations. In details the structures of these sense organs can show considerable differences from each other, which does not surprise us because of the complex nature of these organs and because they have been developed under different circumstances.

It is just in connection with the sense organs of medusae that we can observe numerous and interesting examples of the variability of these organs. Thus, the statocysts, as organs of equilibration and stimulation, show considerable differences in their structures not only if we compare the way they occur in Hydromedusae on one hand, and in Scyphomedusae on the other; there are also considerable differences in statocysts even within Hydromedusae themselves. Sometimes, such organs are developed with participation of the entoderm (as, for example, in tentacles); at other times, however, they are of a purely ectodermal origin; they can lie exposed, or they can be surrounded by other tissue, they can be free or immersed, etc. In Scyphomedusae, these marginal organs (rhopalia) are very complex, i.e. they are composed of several different partial organs. The same is true for the light receptors that can appear in very different stages of development and which have clearly been evolved several times and independently from each other.

It should be mentioned, with regard to the retrogressive development of the nervous system of polyps, that in hydropolyps this process has gone so far that we are hardly justified to speak any longer of a nervous system because it appears as a very sparse net only, and frequently we find even this last remnant of a former nervous system completely absent in many parts of the animal body. It should be added here that parallel to this sparsity of the nerve net, the "nervous tissue" is moved from the intermediate layer into the skin layer, i.e. to the base of the skin epithelium cells.

A reversion of this process can be observed in the medusoid forms—inasmuch as these themselves do not tend to retrogress (Hydromedusae that have adopted the sessile way of life).

Parallel to the development of their muscle system and of their sense organs, which is connected with an increased density of the nervous tissue, we can observe a sinking of the latter into the skin epithelium, thus into the jelly-like basic substance of the intermediate layer. This development can be observed along the margin of their umbrella and also in their tentacles, as has been proved in *Pelagia* by Krasińska (1914).

In principle, it would be wrong to suppose the presence of such an advanced nervous system in the sessile polyps.

The Emunctory–Excretory Organ

As is well known, no visible special excretory organ of a type which would resemble a protonephridium, for instance, can be found in the Cnidaria. On the other hand, we can often find a well developed protonephridial excretory system in the Turbellaria. Those who adhere to the old interpretation, find an easy explanation of this difference: they suppose that in Cnidaria the absence of protonephridia is a primary characteristic, because the Cnidaria are, so they believe, as far as their primary organization is concerned, at a lower level of evolution. Yet, we too can find an explanation of this difference between Cnidaria and Turbellaria, which at the first glance seems to be so important, on the basis of the following arguments:

(1) There is a considerable uncertainty about the origin of protonephridia that have developed later into other nephridial organs, above all into the metanephridia of molluscs among the Ameria and Polymeria. While there are no protonephridia in "Coelenterata," they appear, as it seems, suddenly in the lowest "Coelomata," in the Platyhelminthes. They have, without any previous intermediate stage, a well-developed tube system with specialized terminal cells equipped with beating undulipodia; internally they end blindly, while externally they end in pores. It cannot be supposed that they have developed as such out of nothing. Krumbach (in his *Handbuch der Zoo-*

logie) has tried to avoid this situation by attempting to derive the protonephridia from the invaginated and immersed "ribs" of Ctenophora. Fortunately, this interpretation did not find any favourable reception among other zoologists because such an evolution is completely devoid of probability. No other attempt to interpret the origin of these protonephridia has been known to me. We will approach this problem from another standpoint.

Our starting point is the fact that as early as in the Protista an apparatus can be found for the excretion of the superfluous water which constantly enters from the watery environment into the cytoplasm, where it absorbs the dissolved products of the metabolism. This is the contractile vacuole which may have developed from the small intermediate cavities that occur in the cytoplasm. A high level in the evolution of these vacuoles has been reached in the swimming Euciliata so that in this case we are entitled to speak of a special excretory–emunctory organelle (Fig. 23). This organelle is particularly well developed in species that live in fresh water; it shows a considerable lability because it can easily disappear. This frequently takes place in species that live in the sea and in those whose size has been greatly diminished.

From this point of view we can come to the conclusion that the ancestors of the Turbellaria had inherited from their Euciliata ancestors (apart from numerous other things) an emunctory system also as well as the middle layer which also contains the body muscles. It should be remembered in this connection that as early as in Euciliata this emunctory system had been developed into a canal which later becomes its regular form in the Eumetazoa. From the orifice of these excretory canals, i.e. from the porus excretorius, the skin layer (actually quite similarly to the margin of the cytostome where it has led to the formation of the cytopharynx), together with its cilia, has moved by way of invagination into the interior of the body, and in this way the ciliated and pulsating terminal and canal wall cells have been developed. In this connection we can observe in the ontogenies of numerous Eumetazoa that their nephridia are developed at least partly by way of the invagination of the skin layer. Later these protonephridia have been influenced first by the polymerization, and subsequently, ac-

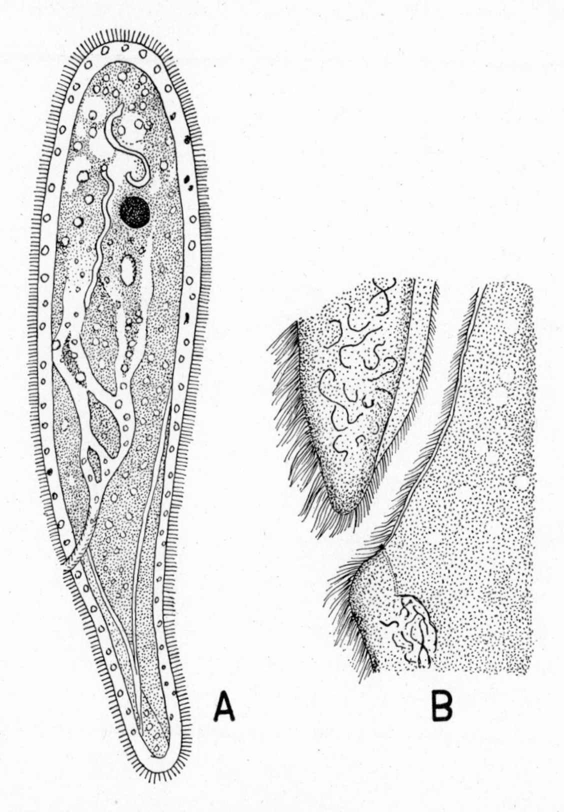

Fig. 23. Excretorial-emunctorial organelle of a ciliate *(Pycnothrix monocystoides)*. A, habit. B, the ciliated end of the canal. (From Dogiel.)

cording to circumstances, by the oligomerization which has frequently led to a complete disappearance of the nephridial organs. Here we are interested in the fact that, as far as we can judge on the basis of our present knowledge, the small acoelous Turbellaria do not possess—and this without an exception—any protonephridia. On the other hand we cannot find, according to Lang, any protonephridia in the rather large Polycladida that live exclusively in the sea, a fact which must be explained as being due to their secondary disappearance. Many other species of Turbellaria, especially those that have adopted the parasitic way of life, have lost their protonephridia, while at the same time these are preserved in the small Temnocephala that live epizoically in the fresh water. In my opinion we must attribute a greater importance to the older data provided by v. Graff (1904–1908, in Bronn's *Classen und Ord. des Tierreiches)*, and by Löhners (1911), as well as to those that have been published more recently by Westblad (1948), according to which there can be found an accumulation of excretory products in the form of cellular and plasmatic inclusions in the external body layer, in the so-called ectocyte, which, however, is not equivalent to the ectoepithelium and thus to the epidermis (e.g. in *Paraphanostoma crassum*, *P. trianguliferum*, the *Convoluta* species, etc.). This is the same body layer which in Infusoria regularly contains the contractile vacuoles. If the functioning of these contractile vacuoles ceases because of the retrogression of the emunctory function, the excrement is deposited as firm bodies (eventually as crystalloids) in the cytoplasm either of the mesenchymal or of the digestive cells.

(2) It is therefore not surprising, in view of the fact that the protonephridia had been so labile both during their development as well as in their occurrence, that they have been lost during the evolution from the turbellarian ancestors to the Cnidaria, at first semi-sessile and slowly creeping, and afterwards to the completely sessile and immobile animals. In addition to this, first Cnidaria were in all probability small animals. In these circumstances, the protonephridia became superfluous and they did not stand any longer under the protection of Natural Selection. It is quite possible that in the period of the separation of Cnidaria from their turbellarian ancestors the formation of protonephridia had been very labile.

The following factors had supposedly contributed to the complete disappearance of special emunctory–excretory organs: (a) life in the sea; (b) the abandonment of active movement; (c) the progressive diminution of the size of polyps in connection with the formation of cormi; (d) the relative enlargement of free surfaces (external as well as internal); and, (e) the epithelization of the tissue.

It is characteristic that during the subsequent evolution of the Cnidaria, protonephridia have never reappeared, either in the secondarily solitary polyps whose size has also been simultaneously increased, or in the secondarily free medusae that have also reached a considerable size. In all probability this can be attributed to Dollo's rule of irreversibility. The functions of the abandoned organs have been taken over by the parts of the body that have been preserved, occasionally with a partially progressive development of the latter (the pores in numerous medusae, the so-called liver in Chondrophores among Siphonophora).

(3) We can see, if we look around at a somewhat broader circle, especially among the numerous subtypes of Ameria, how frequently under special conditions protonephridia have been reduced or even abandoned. Protonephridia are extremely reduced in the Endoprocta (Kamptozoa, according to Cori) that live mostly in the sea and that have become sessile animals. Two very short canals, each with one ciliated cell at its internal end and with one pore, is all that has been preserved of all the variously twisted canals with their numerous terminal organs. The protonephridia have completely disappeared in the species of two orders, out of the three, of endoparasitic Acanthocephala. In a majority of Nemertinea that live in the sea, the nephridial apparatus, which is otherwise considerably specialized, is strongly reduced, and it is completely abandoned in numerous bathypelagic species.

Most interesting in this connection are the Ctenophora, Zoologists are usually of the opinion that the Ctenophora as Coelenterata, do not primarily possess any protonephridia.

I have shown it to be very probable that in the Ctenophora the last remains of protonephridia have still been preserved, even if their condition as well as their function have been considerably changed. These remains have developed the form of the so-called "ciliate rosettes" and they correspond, in my opinion, to the terminal organs of the typical protonephridia which have been grown over by the intestinal wall (Hadži, 1957, see Fig. 24). In this way they have re-established their contact with the external world by way of an intestinal lumen instead of the lost contact by way of pores.

A very interesting case is that of Nematoidea. They are characterized by the fact that they can no longer produce undulipodia, not even in connection with androgametes. Correspondingly there are no terminal organs in Nematoidea so that here the excretory function has been taken over by a device which consists of two cells. An eventual homology of this device with protonephridia is more than questionable; it is in all probability a new substitute form.

It should be briefly mentioned that in the Annelida among Polymeria, where the general polymerization has also influenced the excretory organs that developed into metanephridia, the nephridia have been reduced either to a sole pair or to an unpaired nephridium. This has been partly due to their transition to a semi-sessile or sedentary way of life, and partly to their extensive diminution. This is true even to a greater extent for Oligomeria that have adopted the sessile way of life; in these we can find developed either individual nephridia or none whatever. Even among the sessile Chordata, the Tunicata, no real nephridia have been preserved.

If we presuppose, though cannot, strictly speaking prove it, that protonephridia have been secondarily lost in Cnidaria because of their sessile way of life, we will find such an interpretation strongly supported by analogies to numerous other cases, where it is immediately clear that protonephridia had been reduced or abandoned under similar circumstances. In all these cases we find the emunctory part of the nephridial function considerably reduced as is particularly true for types whose bodies are covered with a cuticle. The real excretory function is always taken over by other organs or tissues because this function remains unavoidably necessary due to the metabolism of the animals, regardless of the way in which these animals feed. On one hand we can see nephrocytes (mesohyl

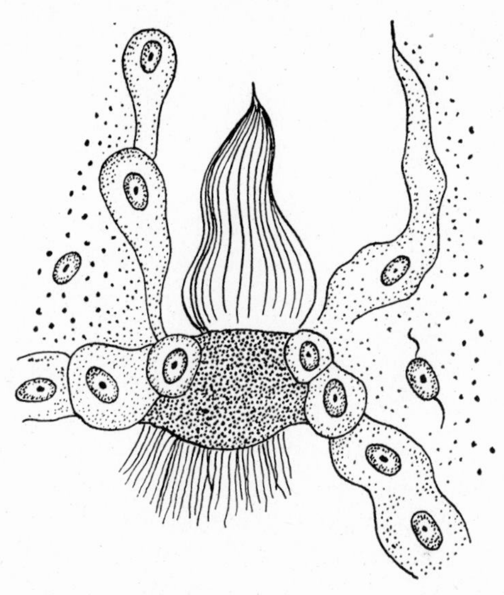

Fig. 24. "Ciliate rosette" of the ctenophore species *Coeloplana* sp. (after Komai).

cells), i.e. cells of the same origin as protonephridial cells, and on the other hand the intestinal cells, take over the function of the lost protonephridia. This is also true for Cnidaria: the second type of substitution is especially characteristic of the rapidly moving medusae which have developed, as has already been mentioned, excretory pores at ring canals as special auxiliary organs.

Finally we must not forget that it was aeons ago that Cnidaria (as the first Eumetazoa to have adopted the sessile way of life) were separated from Turbellaria. There has therefore been plenty of time available for the reduction and for the final elimination of the canal system which had become superfluous. Thus the protonephridia were replaced by an auxiliary apparatus a development which has later also taken place in other groups of Eumetazoa.

A question could perhaps appear justified: is it more probable that the protonephridia of Turbellaria had been developed from the nephrocytes as probably the most primitive excretive organ of Cnidaria? Has anything at all been known which could point to such a direction?

The Spongiae appear, as in so many other instances, in connection with the nephridial system, as standing apart from all other genuine Metazoa, the Eumetazoa. In the Spongiae we find that not only are nephridia absent (this absence is in all probability a primary characteristic), but we cannot even find a substitute for them. The monocellular protozoic ancestors of Spongiae possessed, as this is also the case with other Flagellata, contractile vacuoles that served as special emunctory–excretory organelles. No special excretory organs, no nephridia, developed during the transition from the colonies of Flagellata into the polycellular Spongiae. It seems to us that in the Spongiae the formation of special excretory organs was not necessary, because the Spongiae have been able to live easily without them, first, due to the fact that even after the integration their individual cells have preserved a considerable degree of independence; secondly, because their bodies have considerable external as well as internal surfaces; and, thirdly, because the Spongiae have preserved a very slow life rhythm, and because they have generally remained, with a few exceptions only, marine animals.

On the basis of all this we come to the conclusion that the Cnidaria secondarily do not possess any protonephridia because they have adopted the sessile way of life and as such they can dispense with them or they can replace them with other simpler forms. Furthermore, it seems that Dollo's rule is valid for protonephridia as complex excretory organs; those organs which had completely disappeared cannot be later re-developed.

The Genital System

Of all the differences that exist between the Turbellaria and Cnidaria the differences that can be found between their genital systems seem to be the greatest. As a matter of fact these differences at the first glance seem to be so great that any attempt to derive the Cnidaria from the Turbellaria appears as a completely hopeless venture. Yet if we study the conditions that can be found in these two groups, and if we compare them with those that can be found in other more closely related groups of Ameria, we find the situation changed so that it does not seem that such a deduction is hopeless. It is certain that the Turbellaria, whose organisation shows in all other respects a lower stage of development, possess at the same time a genital system which has a complex structure and such a variety of forms, that cannot be surpassed by any other animal group, and we do not exclude even the most highly developed Vertebrata. As is well known, the Turbellaria are, with a few exceptions hermaphrodites. I will return later to discuss the probable origin of this hermaphroditism. Without any intention to go into details that are well known to zoologists (frequently the Turbellaria are systematically grouped and identified on the basis of their complicated genital systems), I wish only to mention here that these complexities affect both the gonads themselves (e.g. the division of female gonads into an germarium and a vitellarium), as well as their gonoducts, various auxiliary glands, and, finally, the organs of copulation. Due to their mobility these animals not only search for their food but also seek out their sexual partners. The advantage of the hermaphroditic state consists in the fact that any meeting with a member of the same species makes possible copulation and thus also reproduction.

It has been too little considered that though a hermaphroditic genital apparatus with a complicated structure can be found in a large majority of Turbellaria, there are among the primitive Turbellaria species, a quite simple genital apparatus (Fig. 25) which is similar to the condition found in the Cnidaria. Yet even if there were in recent times no such primitive species of Turbellaria, if they had all died out, we would still be justified in defending the thesis (in view of other

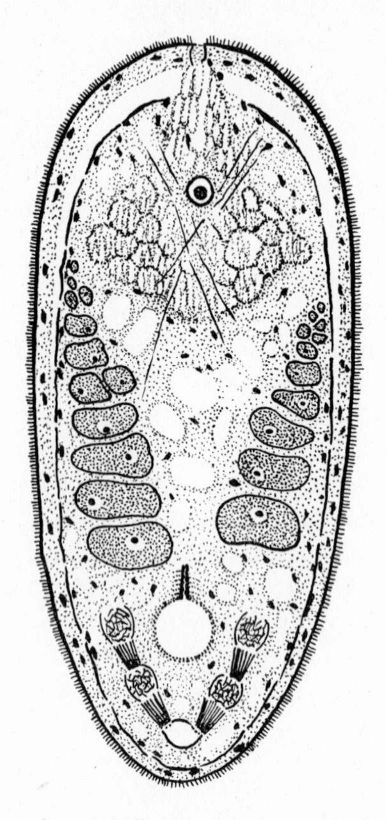

Fig. 25. An acoeleus turbellarian with its simple genital apparatus *(Tetraposthis colymbetes)*. (From An der Lahn.)

circumstances) that the genital organization of Cnidaria had been developed out of that which had existed in Turbellaria.

It is illuminating to observe in this connection the destiny of the complicated genital system of Turbellaria as they evolved. The whole system has been taken over from their tubellarian ancestors by two types which have both developed into parasites; by the Trematoda and by the Cestoda. In all other cases we can observe a very radical reduction of this complex, frequently with a transition to gonochorism. In the Nemertinea which are now quite generally considered as being direct descendants from the Turbellaria and thus their closest relatives, we find all the richly developed "decoration" lost, and of all the oppulence of their auxiliary organs there is hardly the formation of a conduit = canal left. Though hermaphrodites can still be found among the Nemertinea, the latter have nevertheless abandoned the pairing associated with internal fertilization. It is in the pelagic species *Phallonemertes* only that simple copulatory organs can be found in the male animals (yet even this case is problematic because we do not know whether these organs are a remnants of a primary apparatus, or whether they are secondarily developed organs, due to the secondary pelagic way of life). In *Carcinonemertes* even the direct contact of gonads with the external world has been relinquished, and the gametes are secreted into the digestive organ. The Rotifera, however, have preserved more numerous elements of the complex structure of the turbellarian genital system the female animals have the division of the ovary into a germarium and a vitellarium, and the male animals have developed a special copulation organ. The generally hermaphroditic Gastrostricha do not differ widely in their genital apparatus from that found in Rotatoria. The turbellarian genital apparatus has been somewhat more preserved in the parasitic Acanthocephala. On the other hand, the auxiliary organs show a complete retrogression in Endoprocta which have adopted a sessile way of life; in these the situation resembles that which can be observed in Cnidaria with the difference that in the former the canals of gonads are always developed while in the polyps of Cnidaria the remains of these canals can be found only in Anthopolyps, just as in Ctenophora which have developed secondarily into pelagic animals. Finally we must mention here the Mollusca. In the primitive Mollusca an advanced retrogression can be observed. In these, only the canals can be observed but it is not clear if we are concerned with genuine gonoducts or with coelomoducts, or with metanephridia; it is natural that under such conditions no pairing can take place. Subsequently, however, a secondary complication of the genital system appears in Mollusca, especially in the dioecious species of gastropods.

With regard to their genital system, there is in Cnidaria on one hand a progressive simplification, and, on the other, an increased complexity. The simplification does not only affect the auxiliary organs but also the gonads themselves; the complications can be observed to take place in the bearers of gonads and in their surroundings in the cormus, which is clearly a consequence of the sedentary way of life.

With regard to the distribution of the two sexes there is a clear trend towards the dioecious state. The hermaphroditic state had been inherited at least partly by Anthozoa from their turbellarian ancestors. It is not rare for this state to become hidden and develop into a protandry; the protandrous individuals are therefore usually considered as monoecious. It should be mentioned here that an inclination to protandry appears as early in Turbellaria. On the other hand, we can observe, according to Bresslau (1933:115), that in such Turbellaria, with a lower status of general organization as in the Acoela, *Hofstenia* among the Alloeocoela and Polyclads also, as the genital apparatus shows a lower stage of organization. This trend in their evolution was inherited by the Cnidaria from their turbellarian ancestors.

The hermaphroditic Anthozoa occur above all among the primarily solitary, and therefore, according to our interpretation, primitive species (Ceriantharia, Actiniaria) with polymerized gonads. In the Anthozoa, just as in Ctenophora, we can find the gonads of both sexes in one and the same sarcoseptum (this name is better than that of mesentery); each gonad is bisexual in the species *Boloceroides hermaphroditicus*, as in the garden-snail; their centre is the testis, and the periphery is the ovary. "*Stephanoscyphus racemosus*" (Komai) is a scyphozoan which we consider as a primitive one and which is, according to Komai (1935) still hermaphroditic in its polyp generation. In its medusa generation *(Nausithoë)*, however, we can observe a division of sexes. The same is true for the whole group Ephyropsidia where during strobilation the sex cells of only one of the two types of sex cells enter the *Anlage* of ephyrae by migrating from the basis of taeniolae (sarcosepta). During the retrogression or even the complete loss of the polyp generation, gonochorism becomes prevalent and as a consequence of this the Lucernariidae which have secondarily developed into purely sessile animals become monoecious.

On the other hand, we can again find some hermaphroditic species among the generally gonochoristic Hydrozoa, e.g. among the extremely retrogressed and secondarily solitary *Hydra*. The hermaphroditic state is quite rare among Hydrozoa (e.g. in the medusoid generation of *Eleutheria* which, however, has become "degenerated" so that it has been changed into an animal that lives on the sea bottom (Fig. 26).

As for the structure of gonads (the word "gland" instead of "gonad" is not suitable for the gonads of the lowest Eumetazoa; gonads can contain gland cells yet they do not always have them; as a rule they are built of sex cells which after all are not gland cells) we can observe, in agreement with our thesis, that it is in the Anthozoa, which have evolved as the first (the word "lowermost" would not be suitable here) group of Cnidaria from the Turbellaria, that the gonads are compact and that they possess at least a few auxiliary devices; to be more precise this is true for the primarily solitary Actiniaria only. There occasionally appear follicular forms with traces of spermoducts which are produced by their testes; their oöcytes show a type of feeding device which was correctly interpreted by F. Pax (1924:787) as a remnant of a former oviduct whose function had been changed. It is therefore probable that we have here the remains of an earlier stage in which evolutionary progress had reached a much higher level.

No regular sack gonad, i.e. a gonad with a central cavity or with a gonocoele and with a gonoduct, can be found among the Cnidaria. It is in accordance with the progressive

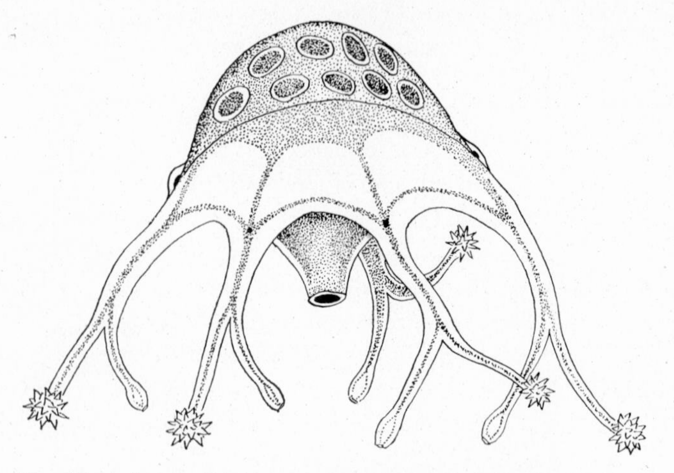

Fig. 26. A benthonic hydromedusa (*Eleutheria dichotoma*), from Hincks.

retrogression of the middle layer (mesohyl) that the gonad first loses its sharply circumscribed massive character. It develops more and more into a simple agglomeration of gametocytes. Those gonads which in the Turbellaria had been situated in the depth of the parenchyma are transplaced in the Anthozoa into the sarcosepta which is more usefull for the feeding of gametocytes. In this way the gonads have completely lost their contact with the skin layer and they have entered into a closer union with the intestinal epithelium. This, however, should not be understood as a transition to an endocarpic state, as was formerly interpreted by experts in Cnidaria. The gonads have remained in the cnidaria in the intermediate layer and then had developed as such into a corpus separatum.

We can observe, as a consequence of the progressive retrogression of sarcosepta (which had been developed from the longitudinal folds of the intestine), as early as in Scyphomedusae and quite generally in Hydrozoa, the transition of gonads into the body wall itself, thus into the very narrow area between the skin and the intestine. In the *Anlage* the gonad comes into the subepithelium either of the skin or of the intestine. In the ripe state the gonad causes a corresponding swelling either of the skin surface (e.g. in *Hydra)* during which gametes, that had become free, move into freedom through a dehiscence, or the gonad presses in the direction of the intestinal epithelium and passes over into the gastral space, and the gametes finally leave by way of the oral opening (this is the case, for example, in the supposedly primitive *Protohydra*, *Boreohydra*, etc.). The older data, which show the primitive sex cells to have developed out of the functioning skin (or intestinal epithelium cells), need revision during which it will be necessary to pay special attention to the subepithelial elements, this data is valid for a few species only of the Hydroids.

In the metagenetic Hydrozoa the gonads were transferred to the medusoid generation after they had been allotted certain areas of the animal body either along the radial canals, or on the manubrium. As a rule, the primitive sex cells become active as early as in the corm-building polyp generation and frequently far from the place where the medusa buds had been formed, so that the primitive sex cells have to move actively over considerable distances, as was formerly shown especially by A. Weismann. The same seems to be true, even if to a considerably smaller extent, for those Scyphozoa which have still preserved a corm-forming polyp generation (e.g. *Nausithoë)*. This wandering of the primitive sex cells reminds one of the wandering of cnidocytes.

In the Hydrozoa the location of gonads can again be changed with a secondary retrogression of their medusoid generation. In this connection we must mention the unique case of *Eleutheria* medusae where the gonads have been transferred into the exumbrella with a simultaneous development of a brooding cavity during their transition to the benthonic way of life (Fig. 27). We have, furthermore, to mention here the Aeginidae, a group of Narcomedusae, which no longer possess

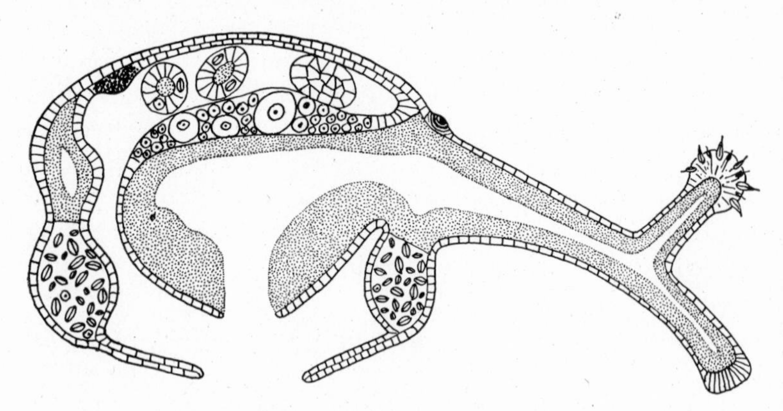

Fig. 27. Half schematic longitudinal section of a benthonic hydromedusa *(Eleutheria radiata)* with brood pouch in its umbrella (after Lengerich).

any distinct gonads and whose sex cells are scattered all over the subumbrella. In *Hydra* it is a trace of former conditions—when sex cells still had to move and when they were therefore amoeboid—that the young egg-cells still move like amoebae, simultaneously eating food cells. There are some authorities who deny that an active migration of gametocytes really takes place. All these singularities can be found in Hydrozoa; they represent, in our interpretation, the final level that retrogression of the sexual apparatus has reached in Cnidaria, and not a primarily primitive condition.

Parallel to this retrogressive development of the sexual apparatus that can be observed in Cnidaria and in clear causal connection with the sessile way of life, another process takes place which, however, follows a progressive line of evolution. This process does not affect the gonads themselves but rather their bearers and the immediate surroundings in the cormus. Events have been created by these gonads which have led to far-reaching morphogenetic processes typical of Cnidaria but which, however, can also be found in a similar form in many other animal types. Due to polymorphism, special individuals had evolved which have later developed into specific bearers of gonads. This has finally led evolution to the complex gonosomes besides the medusoid generation (Fig. 31).

The Alternation of Generations in Cnidaria

It is in agreement with our thesis of the origin of Cnidaria that we find in the Anthozoa the most primitive conditions that can be observed in connection with the alternation of generations. The primarily solitary species of Anthozoa develop into sexually ripe individuals directly from larvae. In some species as, in *Gonactinia prolifera*, we can observe that an asexual reproduction by way of transverse division takes place before the animal becomes sexually mature; this is also the case in numerous Turbellaria. The transverse division is followed by sexual maturation and the only difference that exists between the two generations is that one had been reproduced sexually and the other asexually. In this case we can already speak of an alternation of generations if we attach greater importance to the type of reproduction than to the morphological or eventually ecological differences. It is my firm conviction that it is senseless to declare a form to be a larva when it is produced sexually and when itself reproduces asexually. Only a form which had been produced sexually can further develop through a pelagic larva. Finally in the solitary species all individuals become, in all probability, sexually ripe regardless of the way that they had been produced. Thus we get a simple growth cycle by way of an alternation of generations and without a sharp difference between the two generations.

Subsequent to this we find in a majority of Anthozoa the formation of cormi where the incomplete transverse division developed into longitudinal division and even more so into reproduction by way of buds. The conditions were initially the same as those that can be found in the solitary species that reproduce asexually. There is always a larger number of asexually produced generations. We find occasionally in the formation of cormi that not all asexually produced individuals (they are now subindividuals or persons) become sexually active. In many species of the genus *Corallium* there are, surprisingly enough, only the changed siphonozooids that become sexually active; the two generations live together as sessile animals in one cormus.

An interesting and, as it seems, unique case among Anthozoa is represented by *Fungia* which has been already mentioned above (Fig. 28). This is an apparently secondarily and not completely solitary madreporarian. Its sexually produced anthopolyp reproduces in two parallel ways; one by way of lateral budding which can lead to the formation of a cormus (colony). In this *Fungia* resembles other species of Madreporaria. The maternal polyp, however, can reproduce asexually, by way of transverse division; yet this division is unequal. The destiny of the two halves as well as their forms are different. The distal part which is slightly broadened and which takes over the circlet of tentacles and corresponds to the so-called anthocodium of anthopolyps descends, after its separation from the basal part, the former polypid, to the sea bottom. It grows into a large "coral" which continues to lie on its flat side and develops into sexual maturity. Special names have been given to the two generations which have thus been developed by way of transverse division. The basal part has been called an "anthocaulus," and the distal sexually ripe individual an "anthocyathus." There can be no doubt that in *Fungia* we have a typical case of the alternation of generations (metagenesis) where the two generations are first a typically polypoid generation, and then the sexual generation which does not at all reproduce asexually. We do not find acceptable Hyman's description of the sexual generation as an "adult disc" (I.:611). Due to the transition of gonads

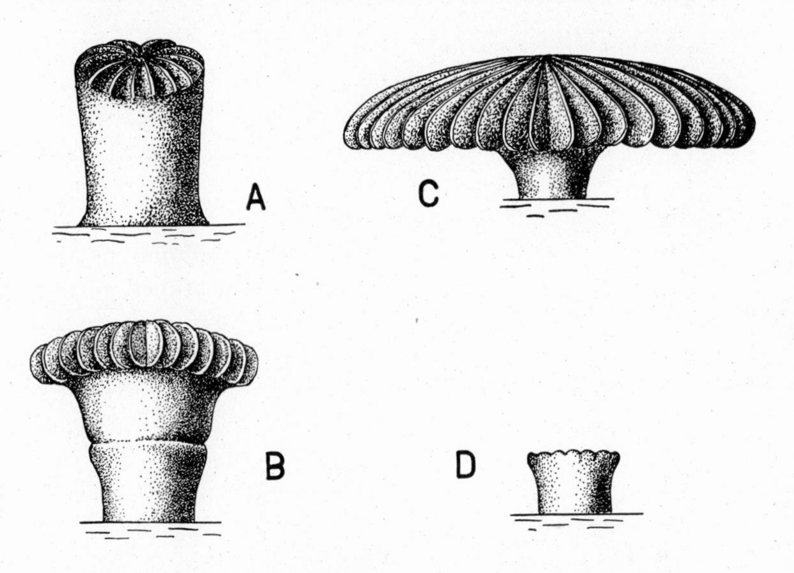

Fig. 28. The life cycle of *Fungia* sp. A, a young coral polyp. B, the beginning of transverse scission. C, anthocyathus is fully developed. D, after separation of the anthocyathus, the anthocaulus remains (after Delage and Hérouard).

into the second generation which has been developed by way of asexual reproduction, this generation has been considerably changed, morphologically, ecologically and biologically under the influence of these gonads.

In *Fungia*, and quite generally in the Anthozoa, we cannot speak of a medusoid generation. It is improbable that the case *Fungia* represents has in any way contributed to the formation of the medusoid generation, in spite of the fact that in it we can see something parallel, a certain common "trend."

Even the word "medusoid" does not seem to be suitable here, it should continue to be used in connection with the anthocyathus, if it is necessary at all to have a special name in this case. The luxuriously developed inner calcareous skeleton had probably been a very important factor of the case of *Fungia*. With regard to the life cycle, there exists a deep chasm between the recent Anthozoa and Scyphozoa. A closer union of these two classes into one of Anthozoa, a suggestion which goes back to Goette, is a mistake which has fortunately now been completely rejected. In the Scyphozoa a special freely swimming generation has been developed by way of the transverse division which they had inherited from their anthozoan ancestors and because of the absence of a heavy inner calcareous skeleton. This generation, i.e. the Scyphomedusae, have taken over the sexual function and later it has assumed the leading role. In this way metagenesis becomes even more clearly perceptible. To the primary polyp form (it is now called a scyphopolyp in opposition to the anthopolyp) which reproduces only asexually has been given a special name, i.e. a scyphistoma or a scyphostoma, and this again has been a reason for unnecessary misunderstandings. Scholars have frequently tried to represent the polyp generation of Scyphozoa as a purely juvenile form, and thus to degrade it to a larva. They have referred in this connection to a completely special and abnormal case which occurs under special circumstances, i.e. when a scyphopolyp transmutes *in toto* into a scyphomedusa, or an ephyra (i.e. a medusan larva), instead of developing a "medusan larva" by way of transverse division (strobilation).

Fortunately enough, there have survived many species of Scyphozoa that have preserved conditions that were formerly typical of them. *Nausithoë punctata* is one such species which has already been mentioned. Its polyp generation produces irregularly formed cormi (colonies) with a rich development of the "periderm." Though gonocytes still continue to be produced in the basal part of the polyps, they migrate now into their distal part (corresponding to the anthocyathus of *Fungia;* one could therefore speak here of a "scyphocyathus" which, however, would be completely superfluous) which produces the larvae (ephyrae) of Scyphomedusae by way of a repeated transverse division (i.e. strobilation). It is in these ephyrae that the gonads arrive at their sexual maturity. I maintain that originally individual ephyrae only were developed (the primarily monodiscal strobilation); it was only later that the transverse division began to be repeated at certain regular intervals. The genuine strobilation, however,

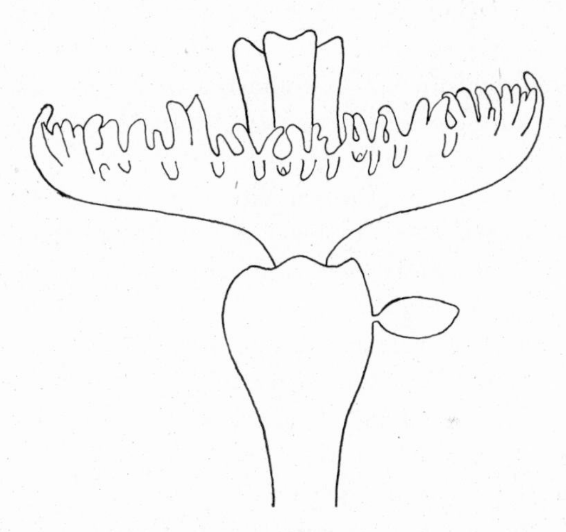

Fig. 29. Monodisc strobilation of *Cassiopea* sp., with a bud, (after Bigelow).

has been developed only secondarily, i.e. when the transverse division became a multiple one (the appearance of several simultaneous transverse divisions, or the polydiscal strobilation). This again has further led to a secondary single and unequal transverse division (the secondary monodiscal strobilation which is actually no longer a strobilation because it does not lead to the formation of a strobila-like form [Fig. 29]). This has finally led to a complete abandonment of the transverse division.

Parallel to this we find in the Scyphozoa a characteristic retrogression of the polyp generation. As a consequence of this retrogression the whole class has been given the name of Scyphomedusae, because in this class the medusoid generation has become the prevalent one. No primarily solitary polyps have been known so far. The solitarization of the polyp generation took place by way of a secondary reduction of cormi. The periderm which was originally preserved by scyphopolyps was the same as had been inherited by the corm-forming species from their anthozoan ancestors of the type of the recent Stolonifera, among Octocorallia (e.g. *Cornularia cornucopiae*, [Fig. 42]). The cuticular external skeleton had been reduced during the solitarization and the elimination of the polyp generation so that finally there are only resting states, as for example podocysts (Hadži, 1912) that have remained covered with this cuticle. The sexual function, the formation of gonads, has been entirely transfered to the freely living medusoid generation. The completely weakened primary generation has finally been completely relinquished, so that it is the very progressively developed medusoid generation only which has been preserved. It has already been mentioned that a side branch has also been evolved in the Scyphozoa which has become completely benthonic so that cilia do not even occur in its planula (Fig. 35). These are the Lucernariidae whose medusoid generation remains hanging on the maternal polyp and is united with it into a new whole which represents a special case of hypogenesis (polypomedusae).

As among Scyphozoa, there are no primarily solitary species of polyps among Hydrozoa which should naturally also be sexually mature, and we dare maintain that in the Hydrozoa such species of polyps have really never existed. In all probability they were corm-forming from the very beginning. The sexual function has been taken over by the medusoid generation which has become secondarily free. We have already mentioned that in the more primitive species the primitive sex cells develop first in the cormus, after which they migrate actively into the *Anlagen* of special sex individuals; these finally develop into independent freely swimming individuals, into the second generation.

In this the Hydrozoa resemble the Scyphozoa, with the only difference that in the Hydrozoa the medusoid generation does not develop by way of a transverse division but rather by way of lateral budding so that they are therefore further developed from an independent root. We can observe, moreover, in Hydrozoa a secondary disappearance of the primary polyp generation and the prevalence of the secondary medusa form, hypogenesis (Trachylina), without a development of special auxiliary sex organs.

It is clearly in connection with this that in Hydrozoa the second sexual medusoid generation develops from "heads" of polyps (hydranths) which had been developed by way of budding, on the bearer of these polyps. This has frequently led to further complications. The colonial or cormus state which made it possible that those zooids in which the budding of medusae takes place, abandon their normal feeding function and develop into pure bearers (which are without tentacles and without a mouth) of medusae or of reduced medusae—of gonophores. They have been given a special name, that of a blastostyle. This again has led to a polymorphism (e.g. *Podocoryne carnea)*. It is frequently difficult to determine whether we have in a certain case a strongly retrogressed polyp type bearer of gonophores or whether we have perhaps a special form, e.g. a stem of a bud (Fig. 30).

Frequently the development does not stop here, and an even greater influence can be exerted in a cormus by the *Anlage* of a gonad upon its whole environment. Thus in the case of Aglaopheniidae, among the Thecata, where medusae had become strongly retrogressed and where they remain attached to the cormus, we can observe the transformation of a whole branch of the cormus together with its minute twigs so that they form a protective receptacle around the "gonangia;" this is called a corbula because of its similarity with a basket. Simultaneously the polypoid individuals have been strongly modified and they have become in this way polymorphous. It was originally thought that this was a case of other species living epizoically on the cormi of Hydroidea, and for this reason these groups of accumulated gonophores and of transformed other zooids have been given special

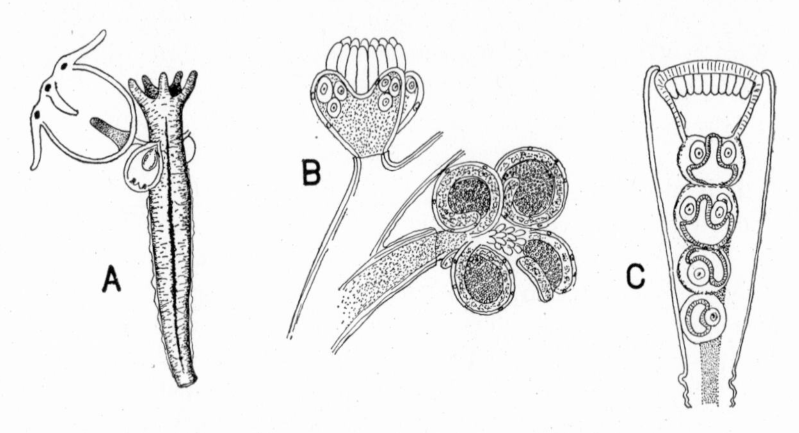

Fig. 30. Reduction of hydropolyps as bearers of gonophores. A, *Podocoryne carnea* (after Brooks). B, *Eudendrium* sp., (from Hyman); C, gonangium of *Gonothyrea* sp., with gonotheca, blastostyl and medusoid-buds (after Hyman).

names, e.g. Coppinia in *Lafoëa pygmaea* Alder (Hebellidae), or Scapus in *Lictorella pinnata* (Fig. 31).

In the Hydrozoa the Siphonophora form an interesting case. Contrary to the recent attempts made by A. K. Totton (1954) to separate part of the Siphonophora–Disconanthes or Chondrophora from the remaining Siphonophora and to establish them as a special taxon, I am of the opinion that the Siphonophora had evolved monophyletically and that they must therefore be considered as an indivisible unit, i.e. as an order of the Hydrozoa. The old discussion on how to interpret the organisation of the Siphonophora and their origin has not come to an end yet, still I think that the most probable interpretation is the suggestion which I have already proposed in one of my studies (Hadži, 1954), i.e. that the Siphonophora had evolved from the sessile cormi of the athecate Hydroidea by way of a transition to a life in plankton; they therefore represent an order of very polymorphous individuals partly of a polypoid and partly of a medusoid character. In all cases the basis of the cormus is an impersonal stock (siphonosome) which corresponds to the hydrocaulus of the Hydroidea. The orientation of the cormus had been turned similarly

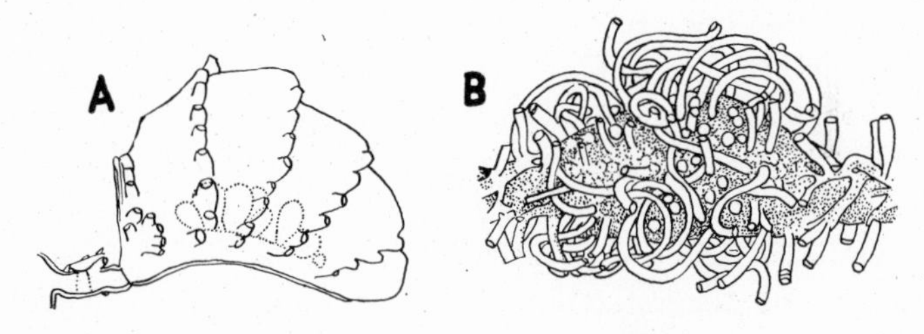

Fig. 31. Two examples of gonosomas of the hydroids. A, corbula of *Aglaophenia pluma* and B, coppinia of *Lictorella pinnata*; (after Broch).

as in the case of medusae. In part of the Siphonophora (Pneumatophorae Chun 1897 or Siphonanthes) we can find at the root of the stock which can secondarily be flattened and which can resemble externally a medusoid form, that a pneumatophore had been developed as an organ of the cormus and it therefore does not correspond to a medusoid individual. The Calycophorae (Leuckart 1854) and Pneumatophorae (Chun 1987), the two suborders of the Siphonophora, had separated phylogenetically quite early so that the species belonging to the first subgroup had not developed their own pneumatophore (or is it possible that they had originally possessed it and had lost it only subsequently?) and they use as their hydrostatic and swimming apparatus, the more or less modified swimming medusoids only. The Disconanthes are the most specialized subgroup of the Pneumatophorae.

We cannot accept Garstang's thesis (W. Garstang, 1946) that the Siphonophora are "bud communities." This thesis is quite untenable because buds are in fact the asexual primordia of these subindividuals. Thus the "bud communities" are in fact true cormi (usually called colonies) which is also true for the chondrophore Siphonophora; Garstang, however, considers them as polypoid individuals.

With regard to the origin of the Siphonophora I again maintain that it is wrong to point in this connection to the planktonic larvae (planula and actinula) and to try to deduce the Siphonophora from them as has recently been done by E. Leloup (1929) and Hyman (1940). We can easily understand that as a consequence of a long progressive evolution within the frame of the subtype of the Siphonophora the ontogenetic process had also been modified and that the siphonula had evolved as a special larval form from the planula (and the ratarula as an even more specialized form which had been developed by the Chondrophora) so that it had developed into an *Anlage* of the cormus (Fig. 46 a). It can easily be understood why a primary polyp (i.e. a primary gastrozooid) develops as a kind of an *Anlage* of an oozooid on the larva of the Siphonophora and why it later grows as a monopodium into the *Anlage* of the cormus, i.e. into the basis of the cormus, into the impersonal stock on which the first members of the family bud as subindividuals either as the first swimming bell which is true for the subgroup Cylycophorae, or as an *Anlage* of the pneumatophores which is true for the Pneumatophorae.

The Siphonophora must be considered as the climax in the evolution not only of the Hydrozoa but also of the Cnidaria as a whole.

Because of our imperfect knowledge of the whole development cycle of a large number of the Hydroidea we must for the time being still accept the existence of a double system, i.e. that of the hydropolyps and that of the hydromedusae. This certainly is an anomaly which will soon have to disappear. The polypoid form (generation) must serve as basis for the construction of the definitive system of the Hydroidea. We cannot begin to discuss here the details of such a system and we must limit ourselves to a few general observations only.

We have here a progressive trend in evolution which has reached its climax in Hydroidea. All these phenomena can be completely understood only if we accept the standpoint which considers Anthozoa to be "the most primitive," and Hydrozoa as the most specialized, i.e. phylogenetically the youngest Cnidaria.

The Digestive System

While the external form of all three classes of Cnidaria remains essentially identical with their basic form, i.e. with the form of polyps (a cylindrical or a cup-shaped form) we find such differences in the form of the digestive system (of the internal layer or of the entoderm) that by means of these differences we are able to make clear-cut distinctions between the three classes. It was under the influence of the thesis of a generally progressive evolution of all living beings that the polyps of Cnidaria with a simple and smooth intestinal tube generally considered as the most primitive ones, those which show the formation of longitudinal septa in their "initial" stages as the next more highly developed ones, and finally those with strongly developed sarcosepta as the most highly developed polyps, an interpretation which agrees with the generally supposed line of evolution Hydrozoa → Scyphozoa → Anthozoa.

In addition to this there is one more complication in their digestive systems. On one hand we can observe in cormi that the digestive organs of zooids develop mutual communications; on the other hand, in medusae the tubes grew out of the central part of their digestive system, thus out of the "stomach," and this has finally led to the formation of a complete gastrovascular system. Since at the first glance similar complications were also known to occur in Spongiae and Ctenophora, the three animal types were united into the group of Coelenterata (Leuckart). In addition to this there developed the idea that the two principal body cavities (the intestine and the coelom) which appear in the "more highly" developed animal types, are in these animals mutually combined. This, however, has been proved to be wrong. It is almost unbelievable how obstinately the idea has been preserved according to which there should be a genetic relationship between the intestinal cavity and the coelomic cavities (i.e. the part of the coelomic cavities which surrounds the intestine and which we have called a perigastrocoel); this has led to the formulation of the so-called enterocoele theory which is doubtlessly wrong and which has been the cause of numerous controversies.

We have to make here a sharp distinction between three facts; first, between the digestive system of a single individual and that of cormi. It is only in the cormi of Cnidaria that the digestive organs of zooids that form a cormus are directly connected into a uniform canal system. The connecting canals (solenia, as they are frequently called) are impersonal, i.e. they are purely the organs of the cormi. The conditions that exist in the Spongiae are basically different from those that occur in Cnidaria (the Ctenophora, on the other hand, do not form cormi), and it is therefore clear that the Spongiae are completely disassociated from Coelenterata and also from Eumetazoa.

Secondly, in the Cnidaria we must make a sharp distinction between the digestive system of polyps—whether these be primarily or secondarily solitary animals, or whether the digestive system belongs to a zooid—and the "gastrovascular" system of medusae. The peripheral part of the digestive system of medusae with exception of the tentacular canals is a new formation and it has no homologue in the polyp. The principal part of the gastrovascular system is not a continuation of the peripheral part of the digestive canal of the anthopolyps.

Thirdly, the digestive system of Ctenophora seems at the first glance to resemble that of medusae; in reality, however, it is quite different from the latter: and is, in our opinion, not a new formation but rather a transformation of conditions that had existed in their turbellarian ancestors, in Polycladida. It has been repeatedly emphasized that Ctenophora are not Coelenterata. The similarities that exist in their digestive systems are due to the fact that both Cnidaria as well as Ctenophora come from Turbellaria whose intestine shows a characteristic inclination to form diverticula or excrescences. The roots of the two groups, however, are separate. It was quite wrong when Haeckel tried to deduce the "gastrovascular conditions" of Ctenophora from those that occur in the hydromedusa (anthomedusa) *Ctenaria ctenophora.* On the basis of this wrong hypothesis we should assume that Turbellaria, as descendants from Ctenophora, had inherited from the latter the tendency of their intestine to form diverticula. In reality the development went in just the opposite direction.

When we pass to the discussion of the digestive organs of individual polyps of the Cnidaria (Fig. 32) we meet the generally accepted opinion that they followed a progressive line of development. If this were true, then it would be necessary to consider both the ectodermal gullet (pharynx) as well as sarcosepta as newly acquired complications. We must here raise the question whether we are allowed to suppose that the intestinal apparatus has been progressively developed in individuals in spite of their consistently sedentary way of life and the constant diminution of the size of the corm-forming zooids? If we take into consideration our experiences with other sessile animal groups we must straight away deny the probability of such a supposition; we must do this especially because this supposition is contradicted by our analyses of other systems of organs.

The situation becomes much more clear if we reverse the interpretation and if we derive the conditions that can be observed in the digestive organ of Anthozoa from those of

Turbellaria. The two typical properties of this organ system in Anthozoa, the ectodermal gullet and sarcosepta, had been inherited at least as primordia from their turbellarian ancestors. This standpoint explains many facts which could not be understood till now. Both the pharynx as well as the tendency to form

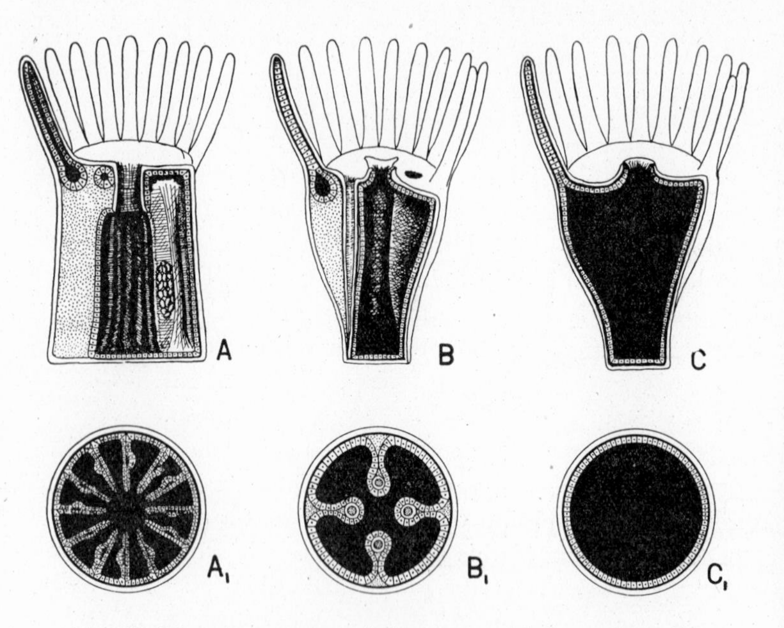

Fig. 32. Digestive systems of the three cnidarian polyps (A, anthopolyp, B, scyphopolyp, C, hydropolyp); above longitudinal sections, below, crossections (after Remane, somewhat altered).

variously shaped diverticula are properties that occur generally in Turbellaria. The formation of a gullet is phylogenetically even older than the tendency of the intestine to form diverticula, because the former had been inherited by Turbellaria from their protozoan ancestors, as we will try to prove later.

Among the Cnidaria we find a pharynx as an invagination of the external body layer and of the muscles that surround the oral opening only in the Anthozoa. Previously it was quite generally believed that an ectodermal gullet was also found in Scyphozoa, and this lead Goette to unite the two classes into one taxon of Scyphozoa. There were some zoologists who were opposed to such a classification. I finally succeeded in showing (Hadži, 1907) that there is no ectodermal gullet in scyphopolyps, neither is there one in Scyphomedusae (Heric, 1907), and this has now been generally accepted. It seems that in the Anthozoa both a functional as well as genetic correlation had been developed between the formation of sarcosepta and the formation of the gullet so that they are simultaneously subject to a progressive reduction when the retrogression starts. We must atribute to the formation of retractors in the taeniolae the fact that we can neverthless find remainder of earlier richly developed septal apparatus in the scyphopolyps. The formation of a gullet is extremely characteristic of Turbellaria. Organs with a very complicated structure have been developed in several directions from a simple invagination of the skin around the oral opening (pharynx simplex). Special names have been given to these organs. The pharynx became protractile due to the formation of circular folds so that finally it developed into an important organ by means of which animals that adopted the vagile and predatory way of life were able to catch their prey. This gullet has been called an *Ergreifungsorgan* (organ of gripping) by Ludwig Graff de Pancsova, who came from the region of present day Yugoslavia, formerly the leading expert in Turbellaria (v. Graff, 1878: 199). This organ has been developed progressively, in the same way as the hermaphroditic copulation organ. It may not be superfluous to mention here that the formation of a pharynx had been adopted by all the numerous descendants from Turbellaria, either in its complex form as a genuine muscular pharynx (e.g. in many classes of Ameria), or in its reduced form as a stomodaeum. We can find the stomodaeum everywhere up to the Chordata. This stomodaeum has been preserved even in those animal types which have entirely adopted the sessile way of life, as in Endoprocta, among Ameria, and in nearly all Oligomeria (it is in the Pogonophora and in the entoparasitic Acanthocephala that the stomodaeum together with the whole digestive system has been lost). Not infrequently the gullet has preserved its ability to protract, or if it had lost this ability, it has been secondarily regained.

It is therefore not surprising to see that the Anthozoa, too, had inherited their ectodermal gullet from their turbellarian ancestors, and this in the form of a pharynx simplex. Here I should like to call attention to some older observations which previously did not appear so important, but whose importance has been increased due to my interpretation. This is the use of the gullet of anthopolyps as a gripping organ similarly as observed in the Turbellaria. The first of such observations were made, as it seems, by C. Claus (1864) in a pelagic larva belonging to Actiniae (Claus believed that it resembled a ctenophore). Hertwig considered it to be a larva of *Edwardsia* which had a "protrusile stomach tube" ("ein vorstülpbares Magenrohr"). Young *Halcampia* that are ectoparasites and live as such on medusae behave like Turbellaria and they are even able to adopt their form. Carlgren (1904) reports about the species *Halcampogeton papillosus* that it can evaginate its "actinopharynx." The pharynx has an active role also in other Anthozoa, especially in the adult individuals. According to the brothers Hertwig (1879) gullet "fungiert als Magen, da in seinem Inneren die von den Tentakeln ergriffenen und nach dem Munde beförderten Thiere, kleine Mollusken und Crustacean, längere Zeit verweilen und dem Verdauungsprocess unterworfen werden."

Cases have been known where the pharynx has been reduced or even lost in Turbellaria in spite of the fact that in these it has been progressively developed. Such a reduction or loss has naturally taken place under the corresponding ecological and biological circumstances. The parasitic Vorticidae show, according to v. Graff (1882:181) a distinct inclination to reduce their gullet; it has been known that during its adult state the parasitic *Fecampia* does not possess a gullet.

Quite generally we can reconstruct the history of the pharyngeal tube as follows. The primitive Turbellaria (there are such species even among the recent Turbellaria) do not yet possess a constantly developed pharynx. *Palmenia* has, according to Bresslau (1909), an oral opening in its surface through which the animal can stretch its digestive plasmodium (a real intestine has not yet been developed) in order to pick up particles of food. There is no reason to doubt that these are really the primitive conditions which had been inherited by the acoelous Turbellaria from their supposed infusorial ancestors. During the next higher stage in the evolution of Turbellaria, the invagination of the skin at the oral opening took place —with simultaneous active locomotion and macrophagia— this development took place also as early as in Infusoria; it led afterwards to the development of a special protrusile pharynx. The ability to form a gullet tube had been inherited by Cnidaria, that is specifically the Anthozoa, from their turbellarian ancestors. We are unable to determine the relationship between the structure of the present-day Anthozoan pharynx, the primitive Anthozoan pharynx, and the primitive Turbellarian pharynx. The pharynx had anyhow been developed in the Anthozoa in a progressive and independent direction, and that in connection with the evolution of the septal apparatus. Even if there are at present whole families among the recent primitive rhabdocoelous Turbellaria which have a pharynx simplex (e.g. Catenulidae, Microstomidae), this does not necessarily mean that the turbellarian ancestors of Anthozoa had only a pharynx simplex. The possibility must also be taken into consideration that at best the present state could be a result of a retrogressive development, especially in view of the fact that the sessile way of life leads to a reduction of the general organization.

In the Anthozoa a diversity can be observed in the subsequent destiny of their gullet tube (pharynx); whether it occurs in solitary species which are capable, however slightly, of locomotion, or in species which form cormi and which are attached to the bottom. In the first case, the evolution has followed a somewhat progressive line even if in a different direction to the one that can be observed in Turbellaria. In the second case, there was a strong retrogression which finally led to a complete loss of the gullet. The form of the gullet tube changed in accordance with the change of the form of the mouth (it is only rarely that the round opening has been preserved) into an oblong or oval opening which can be laterally or transversally closed. It is not easy to determine which corner of the mouth is dorsal and which is ventral. The two corners frequently continue in a long tip which extends deep into the interior of the body. A well-known groove, the siphonoglyph or the sulcus, which is densely covered with cilia, develops along one corner of the mouth (called the "ventral" corner), and frequently also along the two corners of the oral opening. Furthermore, a rich longitudinal folding can appear in this oral tube, a sphincter at its lower end, and special, even if poorly developed, muscles which usually extend in the longitudinal direction, a so-called concha, etc. Polymerization can be observed, surprisingly enough, in siphonoglyphs, this reminds us at least partly of the polymerization of whole pharynxes of some planarian species. A further complication appears due to the linkage of the gullet tube with the proximal parts of sarcosepta. Because of this, the gullet tube can reach deeply into the interior of the animal's body. Parallel to the morphological changes, which have led to a further specialization, physiological changes also took place (e.g. respiration by means of a circulation of water).

A reduction of the gullet tube appears as early as in Anthozoa; it is frequently a consequence of the formation of cormi and, in connection with this, of a considerable diminution of subindividuals, combined with microphagy. The gullet tube becomes shorter and shorter, the siphonoglyphs and muscles disappear, and finally there develops an oral cone which surmounts the oral surface, as can be observed in some Madreporaria of the solitary species *Balanophylia*. In this way conditions had been prepared as early as in the Anthozoa which have become generally characteristic of Scyphozoa and Hydrozoa. It is in agreement with the way of life and with the type of feeding that the peristome evaginates into an oral cone, a development which begins to prevail over the opposite trend, i.e. over the invagination of the oral area.

The oral cone, as a process of the oral area, possesses a well-developed muscle system (externally these muscles are placed longitudinally, internally they are placed transversally); by means of these muscles the oral cone is enabled to move in all directions, as well as to contract and to extend, always with the oral opening at its top. The oral cone, or the manubrium of medusae, develops again into a gripping organ; frequently it can even take over the function of tentacles which makes macrophagy possible and this can finally lead to a total loss of tentacles. Not a single trace of an ectodermal gullet can be found either in Scyphozoa or in the Hydrozoa. The entoderm of the anterior intestine—which passes over into an ectoderm exactly at the oral margin—is richly equipped with gland cells which help swallowing and digestion.

It has already been mentioned that among the Cnidaria an ectodermal gullet as well as true sarcosepta can be found in Anthozoa only as special elements of their digestive system. Neither the one nor the other of these two elements can be found in the most primitive Turbellaria, even if both of them can be found to a certain degree in a large number of Turbellaria. Certainly, we do not find here sarcosepta but rather a general and distinct trend of their intestine to form diverticula. The oldest fossilized Anthozoa possessed well developed sarcosepta, even if these cannot be seen; the fact, however, that they possessed sclerosepta which alone could be fossilized is a certain indication that they also possessed sarcosepta which could not be preserved by fossilization. The supposed presence of sarcosepta allows us to consider that these primitive anthopolyps had already had a pharynx. The supposed transition from Turbellaria—with intestinal diverticula—to anthopolyps with primitive forms that do not yet deserve the name of sarcosepta but which resemble rather some longitudinal folds, apparently took place in the period when no mineralized skeletons had yet been developed; we can therefore not expect that we will ever be able to find such transitional fossils. This makes it necessary for us to resort to a reconstruction.

We can see considerable differences between the two forms when we compare sarcosepta such as they occur now in Anthozoa with the intestinal diverticula of Turbellaria. These differences seem to support the old interpretation of the evolution of Cnidaria, and they have actually been used by those who adhere to the old interpretation in their critiques of my new thesis. This new thesis, however, becomes clearer if we make a detailed comparison, taking simultaneously into consideration the radical change in the way of life, i.e. the transition from creeping movements to the sessile way of life, and the erection of the body. By means of this new interpretation many things can now be explained which could not be explained on the basis of the old theory.

The tendency of the intestine to form folds that finally leads to the formation of excrescences—the diverticula—which is so generally prevalent among Turbellaria (with the exception of the primitive groups of Acoela and the majority of Rhabdocoela) must be considered as the starting point for the development of sarcosepta which are characteristic of Anthozoa. Here we will first study that part of this tendency which is connected with the formation of excrescences of the body skin at the anterior end of a somewhat cephalized body. This tendency is not so marked in Turbellaria as it is in Cnidaria. We meet here the case of the Ctenophora which we derive from the pelagic larvae of Polycladida, obviously from such where no intestinal diverticula had yet grown into the pair of tentacles. This has led to one of the most conspicuous differences that exist between Cnidaria and Ctenophora. We must suppose that the ancestors of Cnidaria had already developed the tentacular diverticula, and this is the reason why this property has become a general and unexceptional characteristic of Cnidaria. The polymerization did not remain limited to the tentacles only, it was also extended to the intestinal diverticula. The only change which took place in these intestinal diverticula of tentacles was a secondary obliteration of the lumen of these diverticula; as a consequence of this change the axis of tentacles became solid and the function of the diverticulum changed. It has now been developed into a supporting organ whose function has become more mechanical. This development has not occured, as it seems, even in single cases in the Anthozoa: their tentacles are always hollow, i.e. the lumen of the diverticula of these tentacles has been preserved as a part of the so-called gastrovascular system. It is only in Scyphozoa, and even more so in Hydrozoa, that the cavities of the intestinal diverticula of tentacles have become obliterated.

In this connection, I cannot silently pass the fact that this morpho-physiological specialization of the intestinal excrescences, which were originally hollow in order to make possible the distribution of the fluid food, into solid organs with a purely mechanical function can be repeatedly observed in the phylogeny of Metazoa (Fig. 33). Here I must limit myself to a few remarks only. Even among the Cnidaria we can find, besides the solid entodermal axes of tentacles, a case in Tubularidae, among Hydrozoa, where a cushion in the form of a circlet and consisting of vacuolized entodermal cells had been developed around the stomach. Other cases have been described in connection with the Turbellaria. I wish particularly to mention here the so-called *Hemichordata (Enteropneusta* and *Pterobranchia)* with their "bucal diverticulm," and finally the *chorda dorsalis* which has given its name to the whole highest phylum, to Chordata. These are certainly not homologous forms in the strict sense of the classical comparative anatomy; they are, nevertheless, parallel organs. We have here a morphogenetic inclination of the intestinal tube locally to take over functions which are not connected with the digestion; this has finally led to the formation of new organs.

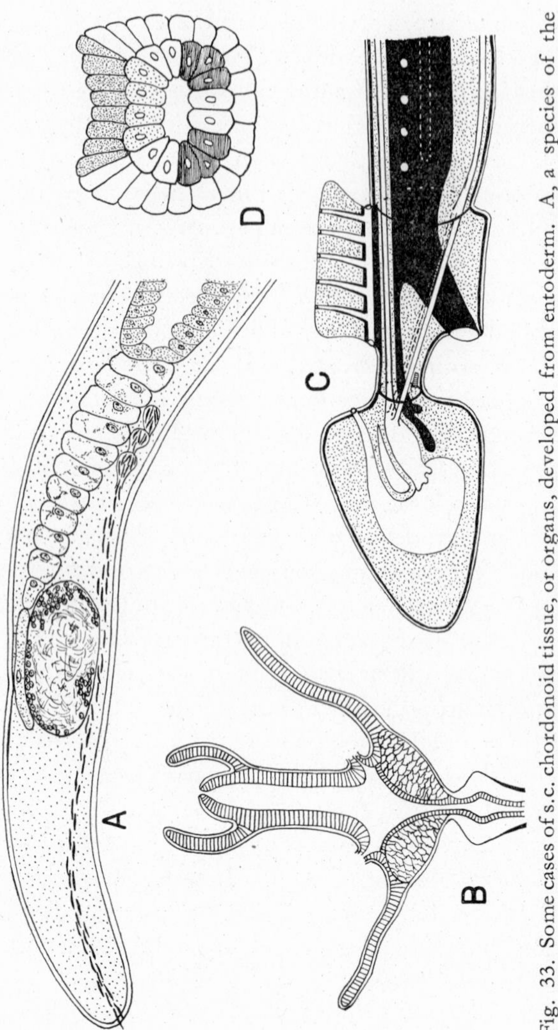

Fig. 33. Some cases of s.c. chordonoid tissue, or organs, developed from entoderm. A, a species of the turbellarian (*Polystylophora filum* Ax), (from Ax). B, an athecate hydroid (*Tubularia* sp.). C, enteropneust (*Balanoglossus* sp., after Colosi). D, cross-section of neurula of an ascidian species, with the primordia of chorda dorsalis and mesoderm in connection with entoderm (from Berrill).

When we now pass to the discussion which has taken place within the field of the comparative morphology about the intestinal tube itself, we have first to state that according to the old, and now prevalent, interpretation there can be no homology between the intestinal diverticula of Turbellaria and the sarcosepta of Anthozoa and Scyphozoa. The intestinal tube of hydropolyps has a smooth cylindrical form. A new complication, i.e. four simple sarcosepta or longitudinal folds of the intestine, does not develop earlier than in scyphopolyps (these are usually considered as larvae or young forms of Scyphomedusae). According to Goette, these four sarcosepta have been developed in such a way that there first appeared two intestinal pouches situated one against the other which were followed by another transverse pair; four taeniolae which disappear downwards were developed between these pouches. In the higher level, i.e. Anthozoa, sarcosepta with a complex structure are formed by way of polymerization with a simultaneous formation of a gullet tube. These sarcosepta are usually depicted, quite statically, under the influence of what we see when we make a transverse section through the body of an anthopolyp, as septa which extend longitudinally into the gastral space. W. Kükenthal, an expert in anthopolyps, does not mention, surprisingly enough, "mesenteries" in his general characterization of Anthozoa which was published in the extensive *Handbuch der Zoologie* (1924:688) in the additional characterization, however, he reports as follows, "Der Gastralraum des Korallenpolypen wird durch Längscheidewände, die vom Maueblatt nach innen vorspringen, in eine Anzahl peripherer Kammern und einen gemeinsamen zentralen Teil zerlegt." In the same work the following definition of sarcosepta has been made by F. Pax (1924:783), "Die Mesenterien (Sarcosepten) sind bindegewebliche, an ihrer Aussenseite hauptsächlich mit Entoderm bekleidete Stützlamellen, die von der Körperwand gegen den Gastralraum radiär vorspringen." The supporting lamellae are, according to this definition, the most important part of sarcosepta. The characterization of sarcosepta that occur in scypho- and anthopolyps as longitudinal folds of the "*Darmblatt*" (intestinal layer) is not so frequent; it was made, by Grobben and Kühn in the well known *Lehrbuch der Zoologie* (1932:461), "Die Septen . . . sind senkrechte von der Seitenwand, der Fuss- und Mundscheibe entspringenden Falten des Darmes . . ." A. Kästner, in the recent "*Lehrbuch der speziellen Zoologie*," avoids defining the sarcosepta of Anthozoa; he mentions, however, in connection with scyphopolyps, four folds of the entodermal wall which are directed centralwards (1954:109). Hyman, in her *Manual of the Zoology of Invertebrata* (1954:367), tries to combine the two standpoints and writes as follows, "Primitively consisting of a simple tube, the digestive system displays through the phylum a tendency to complication by putting out branches and pockets and in the Scyphozoa and Anthozoa is divided into compartments by gastrodermal-mesogloeal projections."

The septa of scyphopolyps (earlier they were frequently called taeniolae) were previously considered by zoologists as homologous to the sarcosepta of Anthozoa; these were previously called mesenteries, in spite of the fact that the conditions that can be found in scyphopolyps give the impression of longitudinal folds which are developed due to the formation of peripheral sacks. On the other hand, there was nobody who thought of a possible homology of these septa, together with the intestinal pockets that occur between them, with the intestinal diverticula of Turbellaria. It was considered that the two forms had been developed quite independently from each other. There is not yet a distinct intestinal tube in Acoela, in Rhabdocoela this tube is smooth, approximately as it is in hydropolyps, and it is only in the "higher" Turbellaria (Polycladida, Tricladida, etc., according to the old system) that a gastrovascular system has been developed which becomes increasingly complex, whose ramifications can finally develop into a whole net, similar to that observed in some Ctenophora. It was therefore quite impossible to believe that Cnidaria could be deduced from Turbellaria, or vice versa.

When finally the idea has been given up, quite correctly, by modern experts in Turbellaria to derive the Turbellaria from the Cnidaria by way of Ctenophora, they have endeavoured, together with von Graff, to go back to some common planuloid ancestors and wait cautiously until the last word of the origin of Cnidaria was said by the experts in Cnidaria.

Here the question appears of what the anthozoan sarcosepta actually are if we take into consideration their origin? What is their function? How do they appear if compared with the intestinal diverticula of Turbellaria, as well as of Ctenophora? We can get a clear idea if we study the morphogeny of sarcosepta during ontogeny. Sarcosepta have developed due to a longitudinal folding of the intestinal tube. We can say that the first active step (similarly as in the formation of the *Anlagen* of radial canals in the buds of Hydromedusae) is made by the wall of the intestine by way of a stripe-like allometry. During the next step the mesenchyme (mesogloea) grows into the longitudinal folds in the interstices between these folds; thus from the periphery and towards the centre, while at the same time the growth of the longitudinal folds goes in the opposite direction. We can therefore say that sarcosepta as fully developed forms have been evolved due to a longitudinal folding of the intestinal tube. This longitudinal folding is, from the physiological standpoint, in reality the same thing as the formation of diverticula by the intestine of Turbellaria; both represent an increase of the internal digestive surface of the entodermal epithelium and they both make possible the transportation of the fluid food to the periphery of a body whose size has been increased. A connective tissue (mesohyl) grows between these diverticula and the longitudinal folds; gonads and muscular fibres are later transplaced into it.

At the first glance it does not seem to be important whether in connection with the formation of sarcosepta we speak about longitudinal folds, or about an ingrowth of septa. This difference, however, is fundamental. It is the effect only, the final static state, which are similar.

We must again emphasize that old as well as the modern embryologists who have studied the ontogeny of Anthozoa and of scyphopolyps agree that sarcosepta (frequently these have been less fortunately called mesenteries) develop by way of a longitudinal folding of the intestinal wall. Kowalevsky (1873) already had established this and he made fine illustrations of it. Korschelt and Heider (1936:198) described this process in their large *Lehrbuch der Embryologie der Avertebrata*, "Die Mesenterialsepten entstehen an der Wand als Längsfalten des Entoderms." In Actiniaria, as a rule, the first pair of sarcosepta which shows a strictly bilaterally symmetric distribution develops in this way. L. Faurot (1913:283) is right when he speaks of "deux plissements entodermiques." In scyphopolyps this process has been described as a formation of the peripheral pockets of the intestine; and this has actually the same meaning. This formation of folds starts regularly closer to the oral pole and develops in the direction of the lower end of the body until it finally more or less disappears.

Even if it is admitted by those who criticize the interpretation which derives Anthozoa from Turbellaria that the sarcosepta are a result of a longitudinal folding of the intestinal wall (e.g., Luther in lit.), there still remains a great difference from the conditions that can be found in Turbellaria. In the Turbellaria we do not have, they state, septa or a longitudinal folding but rather the formation of intestinal diverticula. These are placed transversally to the longitudinal axis of these animals and they follow each other bilaterally. This objection is certainly true. It is true that in the more or less flattened and bilaterally symmetrical Turbellaria the intestinal diverticula appear, as a rule, as excrescences that are placed transversally to the longitudinal axis of the animal, they are therefore on the right and on the left sides of the intestinal tube, and not around the intestine as this is the case with the cylindric Actiniae which stand erect. If we tried to derive by all means (which would be certainly wrong) one extreme case, an *Actinia* with its numerous partly perfect and partly imperfect sarcosepta which appear in a bisymmetric distribution, out of another extreme case, e.g. out of a polyclad turbellarian, whose body is maximally flattened and extended with a possibly large number of diverticula or which can even form a net of digestive canals we would have to accept, first, that diverticula had grown additionally in other transversal directions and not only on the right and left sides, and, secondly, that diverticula grew together which appeared successively in lines parallel to the intestine, and that this has finally led to the formation of longitudinal sarco-septa. The first possibility is not only probable; it actually takes place even if to slight degree and only in such species which are not flattened but show instead in their transverse sections the form of a square, and which possess four or even more (instead of two) longitudinal series of intestinal diverticula (e.g. the polyclad species *Thysanoplana indica* Plehn and *Pseudocerops periphaeus* Bock). The second possibility is theoretically probable, but it has not been supported by observations and we will therefore prefer not to take this possibility into consideration.

We will rather consider it more probable that in Anthozoa, the formation of sarcosepta had been newly developed by them; yet this formation goes back to a general tendency of the intestine to form excrescences, diverticula, and folds. This tendency had been inherited by the Cnidaria from their turbellarian ancestors and it has finally led to the formation of the gastrovascular system. The formation of longitudinal folds agrees better than the formation of diverticula (which has been preserved in the development of the circlet of tentacles!) with the transition to the polyp form which stands erect and whose size has been constantly increased. It should be mentioned here that the progressive development of subtypes of Actiniaria led to the formation of species which have remained solitary and whose size can be considered as comparatively very large (up to 1 m in diameter). Sarcosepta have evolved both quantitatively (under the influence of polymerization) as well as qualitatively (differentiation) in those groups of Anthozoa which have remained solitary animals. The subsequent evolution took a retrogressive direction after they had passed over to cormogony, a simultaneous decrease of the size of individual zooids and, in connection with this, of the internal surfaces.

I think it useless to discuss whether the intestinal diverticula of Turbellaria be homologous or homotypic to the intestinal pockets of Anthozoa that can be found between their sarcosepta. It is certain, however, that both these forms are due to a tendency of these animals to increase the digestive or resorptive surface of their intestinal tubes; these forms diverged in their evolution which in these animals also pursued different directions: on one hand we have (in Turbellaria) a flattened form of an animal which creeps over the ground, and on the other hand (solitary anthopolyps) a cylindric form which stands erect and which can move actively only slightly, or not at all.

On the other hand, we can find that even in Turbellaria an inclination to develop longitudinal folds in their intestinal tubes is not completely unknown to them. What other than a longitudinal folding can finally be the forked form of that part of the intestine of Tricladida which can be observed in the posterior half of their body? One could expect, if more extensive investigations had been made in this respect, that the formation of such longitudinal folds could be found even more frequently in small species of Turbellaria whose transverse sections show a rounded-off form. It would be permissible, I think, to classify the longitudinal folds and herewith the septal apparatus under the notion of the intestinal diverticule and also the terminal diverticula (prochorda) as well as the *chorda dorsalis*. The fact is not without a significance that during the transition from anthopolyp to scyphopolyp the sarcosepta which had been reduced into taeniolae had clearly obtained the form of longitudinal folds. It should be added that the wrong interpretation of the true nature of sarcosepta is partly due to the fact that sclerosepta, which are externally similar to sarcosepta, really grow from the outside inwards. Yet these two forms are two completely different things if viewed from the standpoint of the comparative morphology, as well as that of physiology. In both cases, in Turbellaria as well as in Cnidaria, a vascularization of the periphery takes place by means of which fluid food can be brought to any part of body. The experts in Turbellaria are inclined to accept such an interpretation. The middle layer contains powerful strings of muscular tissue; some experts in Turbellaria, particularly O. Steinböck (1924:495–502), think that these strings of muscles that usually extend dorsoventrally have a major role in the formation of intestinal lobes and of intestinal diverticula, much as the sex apparatus dominates the middle part of the posterior half of the body. Yet the tendancy of the intestine to form diverticula is not mentioned in this connection. I believe it probable that here the intestinal wall has an active role, pressing forward the diverticula into the tentacles as can be observed in some species, or into some other excrescences, as can be observed in the species belonging to the genus *Thysanozoon*. It is possible that the strings of muscles that extend in the dorsoventral direction were developed later or almost simultaneously with the formation of diverticula. Obviously, we have to distinguish between the formation of limbs and intestinal diverticula.

A progressive trend can be observed in the evolution of sarcosepta in the primarily solitary anthopolyps. A strong, locally developed system of longitudinal muscles has been developed in their interior; these muscles can be observed in transverse sections as the well-known flags of muscles. Besides these muscles other, weaker, muscular systems have also been developed which extend in other directions. Gonads are transferred into the mesenchyme of sarcosepta (frequently into certain pairs of septa only) which has influenced scholars so that they have begun to speak about entodermal gonads (Endocarpa), similarly as in the Ctenophora: gonads, however, should not be attributed to any body layer. A special histologic–cytological differentiation took place in the free margins of sarcosepta which protrude into the gastrovascular space. These free margins have become thickened (in a transverse section they appear completely round), and in the epithelium we find not only gland cells but also cnidae. The curled margins can grow locally into long filaments which can be pressed into the free water through special openings that develop in the body wall (cynclidae) to be used there as weapons (acontia).

The transition to cormogony (the formation of colonies), connected with the decrease of the size of the polyp individual has led to a reduction of sarcosepta. This reduction was both quantitative (the reduction and simultaneously the fixation of the number of sarcosepta to six or eight), as well as qualitative (small acontia, fewer filaments, etc.). In the skeleton forming Madreporaria, the digestive surface has been secondarily increased by means of sclerosepta which grow from below into the gastral space. This reduction is coordinated with the reduction of the gullet pharynx tube. Sarcosepta are not present at all in the solenia of corm-forming species and here we therefore have the opportunity to observe all possible transitions in one and the same object, from a typically anthozoan intestinal tube, to the kind that can be found in Scyphozoa, and finally to a perfectly smooth intestinal tube, a state that has been reached in Hydrozoa.

The reduction of the septal apparatus has gone even further in scyphopolyps, parallel to the decrease of their size and to their sessile way of life. In this way this reduction can now be understood. The number of strongly diminished and cytologically simplified sarcosepta (they are also called taeniolae) has been reduced to the possible minimum, i.e. to four, in an increasingly developed radial symmetry. If we take the old view of a progressive evolution along the line Hydrozoa → Scyphozoa → Anthozoa, we find it impossible to explain how the sessile polyp of Cnidaria could suddenly begin to form sarcosepta. This situation becomes even more difficult to understand if we deny to the scyphopolyp the character of a special generation, as was done by Hyman.

It will be easier to understand the actual conditions if we begin our comparison of anthopolyps and scyphopolyps with such forms as Antipatharia among Anthozoa, and with *Nausithoë* whose polyp generation has been described under the name *Stephanoscyphus* or *Spongicola*. The polyp generation of *Nausithoë* (probably also of several other genera) forms genuine cormi (colonies) and an organic exoskeleton (periderm). There are four sarcosepta only which are richly equipped with filaments, and a large quantity of longitudinal strings of muscular tissue (they were called taeniolae by Komai) which occur under the skin in the wall layer. Gonads appear in the sarcosepta of the scyphopolyp of *Nausithoë*, a phenomenon which cannot be observed in a typical scyphystoma (a completely unnecessary name); this has been partly the cause of the erroneous interpretation that we have here a medusa larva, even if gonads do not come to their sexual maturity in it, but only later in the medusoid generation which in Scyphozoa takes over the sexual function.

Nobody can, in view of all these facts, doubt the homology between the sarcosepta of Anthozoa and the so-called taeniolae of scyphopolyps. We must only give up the supposition that sarcosepta had been developed from taeniolae. In the ontogeny of scyphopolyps we can observe even more clearly than in the ontogeny of anthopolyps, the development of sarcosepta as longitudinal folds or excrescences of the "stomach pockets." This is actually the same as the formation of intestinal diverticula. In the literature (Goette) we can even find data which show that there is first one pair of such intestinal diverticula, so that for a short time bisymmetry prevails, just as in the ontogenies of Actiniae.

One of the greatest differences between the sarcosepta of anthopolyps and of scyphopolyps can be found in their muscle systems. It is an important and unexplainable difference for those who adhere to the outdated and erroneous gastraea theory and to the theory of two body layers that are separated from each other by a Chinese Wall, when in Anthozoa the flag shaped strings of muscles that can be observed in the sarcosepta have developed from entoderm, while the muscles of the taeniolae of scyphopolyps have developed from the ectoderm. A similar situation can also be found in connection with gonads (endocarpous–ectocarpous). As a matter of fact, however, this is not a fundamental difference. Neither the muscle fibres nor the sex cells should be considered as entodermal or ectodermal, even if they appear one time as appendages of the skin epithelium, and at another time as those of the intestinal epithelium. It should be added that in the large and certainly primarily solitary Cerianthidae no concentration of longitudinal muscle fibres into flags can be observed (cf. brothers Hertwig, 1879:117). Longitudinal muscles appear under the skin in the body wall; muscle fibres that extend somewhat transversally can be found in the proximal parts of their numerous sarcosepta, and it is only in the thickened free ends of sarcosepta where stronger strings of longitudinal muscles appear. With regard to the latter it could be stated that they are in all probability "ectodermal" in their origin because it is supposed that the ectodermal tissue sinks downwards from the intestinal tube along the free ends of sarcosepta. We find, conspicuously enough, in *Cerianthus* and in the polyp of *Nausithoë* a tendency of the free ends of their septa to fork when they grow into filaments.

The strings of longitudinal muscles of antho- and scyphopolyps were in all probability even better developed in the now extinct Tetracorallia (e.g. in *Calceola)*; they helped the animal to retract.

Here may be the right place to try to get a clear understanding of the fact that a strong tendency to tetramerous radial symmetry can be observed quite generally in the interior (and partly also in the exterior) of Cnidaria, and particularly in Scyphozoa and in Hydrozoa. First I wish to emphasize that this is not a general characteristic of sessile animals as such. There is, to give an example, a pentamerous radial symmetry in Echinodermata which had certainly evolved from some sessile ancestors; this pentamerous symmetry, however, is not a property which occurs 100 per cent in all Echinodermata; neither is the tetramerous radial symmetry such a property in Cnidaria.

Among the recent Cnidaria the tetramerous radial symmetry can be found especially strongly developed in Scyphozoa and in Hydrozoa, both in their polyp as well as in their medusa forms. It is least developed in Anthozoa. This could lead us to a conclusion, if we accept the view that the evolution took the course Anthozoa → Scyphozoa → Hydrozoa, that this inclination to the tetramerous radial symmetry had not been developed earlier than during the phylogeny of Cnidaria. On the other hand, if we consider the opposite interpretation to be true we are obliged to accept that in Hydrozoa the tetraradial symmetry had been developed for an unknown reason, and that it had been inherited from them by Scyphozoa. We will not find this problem so simple if we accept the interpretation which sees in Anthozoa the most primitive Cnidaria, yet the problem is still such that it can be rationally solved.

No recent subgroup of Anthozoa with a tetramerous radial symmetry has been known. Neither can such a group be found among the fossil species, even if one large subgroup which is now extinct bears the name Tetracorallia or Rugosa (palaeozoologists prefer now to call this subgroup Pterocorallia). The number four does not refer here to the individual scelerosepta, but rather to their groups (see Fig. 10). All this is due to the fact that those forms only have been preserved as fossils whose bodies had already reached a considerable degree of specialization and a well-developed set of sclerosepta. This state (which was reached during the Ordovician) was preceded by a long evolution, when anthopolyps did not yet possess a calcareous skeleton and when in all probability they still continued to live as mainly solitary animals. Stages can be observed in the ontogenies of both extinct as well as of the still living Anthozoa which are equipped with the first four septa. This can rightly be considered as a recapitulation of a state reached in their ancestors.

The supposition that the primary tetraradial symmetry represents the first stage reached in the transition from a creeping way of life with an explicit bilateral symmetry, is justified in view of the fact that during such a transition it is first the difference between the ventral and dorsal sides which disappears, and, in connection with this, the difference between the two lateral sides and the median sides. In this way a natural basis, or precondition, has been developed, we may say, for the formation of the tetraradial (as the first possible) symmetry. Soon the polymerization of the so-called antimeres took place in anthopolyps which have grown larger and larger, and which have become more and more sessile and solitary animals. This led to a polymerous radial symmetry with clear traces of a primary bilateral symmetry. This was followed by the formation of cormi and, in connection with this, by a secondary diminution of the polypoid individuals; oligomerization finally occured as a consequence of this development, so that ultimately the hexa- and octo-merous states have been developed in Anthozoa. Simultaneous with the disappearance of the tendency to the old bilateral symmetry and with the decrease of the size of polyps went the reduction until the number of antimeres was reduced to four and a complete radial symmetry has been developed. It can be easily understood that this reduction of the polymerous parts was least effective in the tentacles; it is even possible that the number of tentacles has been considerably increased as can be seen in the case of the *Nausithoë* polyp among Scyphozoa, and in numerous other instances among hydropolyps that had inherited their tendency to tetraradial symmetry from their scyphozoic ancestors.

When we pass over to hydropolyps we must first state that in these the last trace of a formation of sarcosepta has disappeared while simultaneously their size has been further decreased. Not infrequently we can find in the oral part of the hydranth a contour of the surface of the intestinal epithelium which resembles that of folds; this is not, however, due to a genuine formation of folds but rather to the fact that epithelium cells grow in unequal lengths which leads to the formation of longitudinal stripes. The last traces of the former longitudinal folds can be found in buds and occasionally in the fully developed hydranths (see Fig. 34 with the transverse sections of the hydranth of *Clava squamata* and of the manubrium

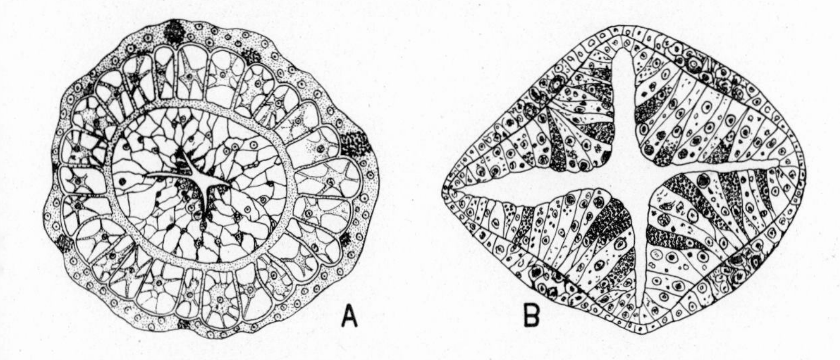

Fig. 34. Transverse sections of the oral region of two hydrozoans to demonstrate the false gutfolds. A, *Hebella parasitica*. B, medusa of *Obelia* sp. (after Hadži).

of an *Obelia* sp.). We think it unimportant whether there is a participation of the mesenchyme in these last traces of longitudinal folds or not. On the other hand, the intestinal diverticula which had grown into tentacles have been preserved till the very end, regardless of whether these tentacles have remained hollow or whether they have become secondarily solid as can be observed in scyphopolyps and very frequently in hydroids.

It is interesting to observe the behaviour of the gastral cavity during the period when Scyphozoa began to form medusae, and the later similar development which took place in Hydrozoa independently from the former. We can immediately state that this development has led to conditions that resemble closely those that can be observed in Turbellaria and in Ctenophora that have become more and more flat and large, i.e. to the formation of a richly branched system of peripheral pockets and canals which correspond to the general (here medusoid) form of a spheric calotte. A basis for this can be found in the conditions that occur in the corresponding polyp forms. The conditions in the primitive scyphomedusae whose height is greater than their width (e.g. in Cubomedusae) are still very primitive; they are similar to those that exist in scyphopolyps. In these no canals can yet be found, and in particular there is no circular canal along the periphery of their umbrellas. Their central part (stomach) is connected with the gastral pockets by way of four ostia; these are separated from each other by four broad septa and they do not yet contain a funnel-shaped cavity. The gonads grow out of the bases of septa into the cavities of the gastral pockets. The peripheral gastral cavities have been developed later, after a further flattening and extension of the umbrella; they are due either to a further growth of the intestine, or to the fact that the two gastral walls have grown together locally. There are frequently whole bunches of septal filaments growing into the gastral cavity in those places where septa (taeniolae) had been reduced. It is unnecessary to discuss further details here.

Additional complications appear in the oral lobes of the most highly developed scyphomedusae (Rhizostomae); in these the original oral openings have grown together while at the same time "suctorial mouths" have been formed at the very numerous fringes of the oral lobes. The intestinal diverticula of tentacles that have become solid in scyphopolyps (as has already been mentioned) can again become hollow in scyphomedusae, or they can completely disappear together with the tentacles while at the same time their function is taken over by the excrescences of the oral lobes. All this development took place while microphagy was strongly advanced. Because of the complications of their gastrovascular system, scyphomedusae have been enabled to grow to considerable dimensions and overshadow the polyp generation as a whole so that the latter frequently gives the impression that it were a larval form only.

It is easy, after everything we have learned about the intestinal system of scyphomedusae, to understand correctly this system as it occurs in hydromedusae. Since there are no sarcosepta in Hydrozoa, there is also no division of their intestine into a central part, the stomach, and into the four gastral pockets. Attempts were made earlier to find something similar in the formation of the medusa buds. This has been an important contribution made by Goette (1907) whose suggestion has been supported by Hadži (1909) and by Kühn (1914). He disproved the older interpretation of the development of the medusae buds in Hydrozoa. The intestinal diverticula of tentacles represent the starting point for the formation of the peripheric gastrovascular system of hydromedusae, a situation which is quite different from the one we have found in scyphomedusae. These diverticula have become elongated when the cup-shaped part has been extended, thus when the umbrella has been developed. This has led to the development of the radial canals. Also here, as in Scyphozoa, the basic number of these diverticula has been four. An additional circular canal has been developed due to the tendency of their intestine to form diverticulae. This has finally, even if not generally, led to a secondary polymerization of these canals which especially took place in larger species either by way of a centrifugal growth of these canals from the stomach, or to a centripetal growth of these canals from the circular canal (in some Trachylinae, etc.).

As a conclusion, we can state that the changes of the digestive system of Cnidaria can be perfectly well understood if viewed from our standpoint: in polyps which have become sessile animals, a simplification of this system can be observed so that only a smooth intestinal wall has been preserved, while at the same time only the intestinal diverticula of tentacles have persisted. In the medusa form which has become secondarily free, the intestine has been progressively developed into a rich system of pockets and canals which corresponds to the change of the whole form and to the increased size of their bodies. We have here generally a further development of the intestinal system such as had been evolved in their turbellarian ancestors.

The Skin and Cnidae

The skin of Cnidaria together with their characteristic cnidae, which have given their name to Cnidaria, offer facts which convincingly support our thesis of the origin of Cnidaria from the Turbellaria and, as a consequence of this, of the evolution in the direction Anthozoa → Scyphozoa → Hydrozoa. It really is suprising how it has been possible for these facts to have been overlooked for so long. This attitude, which one is hardly able to understand, can be partly attributed to an almost hypnotic influence of Haeckel's gastraea theory and to the authority of Haeckel. Quite similar is the situation about the lore of the germ layers and with everything that is connected with it.

Cnidae have in their evolution reached their climax in Cnidaria. No species of Cnidaria has been known which does not possess cnidae distinctive of this same species. Their size, form, organization, and the way they are distributed, as well as the different places where they are developed and used, are frequently characteristic of various taxons of Cnidaria. Attempts have been made to solve taxonomic problems connected with Cnidaria on the basis of conditions that can be found in their cnidae. It is well known, however, that Cnidaria are not the only animal group which produce cnidae.

When we speak about cnidae, we must first know what a cnida actually is. The most highly developed cnidae are wonderful products of very specialized individual cells of skin gland cells. Their secretion becomes partly solid (the capsule, and the long thin tube which represents a continuation of the elastic capsule), and partly remains a viscous fluid (within the capsule); it can gush powerfully out of the cnida and it produces physiological effects. The cell itself can mostly be found in the ectoderm and does not actually belong to it but rather to the middle layer (mesohyl or mesenchyme); it is amoeboid and it can function once only. The cell itself (the cnidoblast or nematoblast) as the producer of the cnida is destroyed when this cnida is used in the explosion.

If we disregard the few and therefore very interesting cases of the so-called kleptocnidae, where a predatory species takes over and uses those weapons of its prey which had not yet been used, we find that there are several animal types which are able to produce either genuine cnidae or some closely similar forms (gland cells with a partly formed secretion). Is it a pure coincidence that it is only in Turbellaria that such forms are produced quite generally and in large quantities, in spite of the fact that they have remained on a lower level in their organization and in their phylesis? This again can be easily understood in view of the fact that Turbellaria have remained freely moving animals while Cnidaria have adopted the sessile way of life. It has not yet been clarified whether Nemertinea possess their own cnidae. The fact, however, seems to be much more important that even among Protozoa species or even larger taxons can be found which produce either genuine cnidae or forms which resemble closely a cnida (cnidoid). Cnidaria can therefore not be considered as animals which have "invented" cnidae or which alone can be found in the possession of cnidae.

Before we begin to study in detail the problem of cnidae, let us first make a critical and comparative study of the skin. Similarly, as the Cnidaria owe their name to cnidae, the Turbellaria have been so named because of the tiny water current produced by the ciliate cover of their skin. The surface of their skin remains bare due to this ciliate cover, by means of which the animal is able to move actively, in the same way as in Ciliata

(Euciliata) among Protozoa; this property had obviously been inherited by Turbellaria from the latter. This same property has afterwards been inherited from Turbellaria by their numerous descendants among Ameria that live a normal, i.e. a free (and not a parasitic) life. It has even passed on (with few exceptions that can be easily explained) to the Polymeria and Oligomeria and up to Chordata, even if here it has been preserved locally only and in the interior of their bodies, particularly during the transition from a wet to a dry environment.

It may not be out of place to mention that the active organelles of cells that could practically be called undulipodia appear phylogenetically first as single (per individual) flagella which are later developed by way of polymerization into numerous cilia; subsequently they can readopt, by way of oligomerization, the form of flagella. The possibility must also be taken into consideration that such an ability to form undulipodia which had been phylogenetically lost (by way of a minus mutation) can again be restored (by way of a plus mutation), perhaps with the limitation that not too long a period had passed from the time of the minus mutation.

Such minus mutations have also taken place in Turbellaria; they have been supported by the natural selection when the mechanism used for the movements develops in their muscular system due to a change in their way of life. In this case, the epidermal cells cease to form cilia and begin to develop a protective organic cover, the cuticle. Among Turbellaria this has been above all the case in Temnocephala. These are Turbellaria that live as epizoic or even as ectoparasitic animals; they are able to move easily (Matjašič, 1959) and they closely resemble Trematoda so that some scholars have even included them among Trematoda. The ciliation of the body surface has been completely lost in Trematoda and in Cestoda that have certainly developed from Turbellaria.

The ciliation of the body surface has been preserved in all small animals that move freely in water. All the young (larval) freely moving stages of Cnidaria are covered with cilia. There are few specialized cases only that appear here as exceptions. Thus planulae of Lucernariidae immediately begin to creep over the substratum after they had abandoned their eggs (Fig. 35). No cilia can again be found in young Hydrae which become free during a very advanced state, etc. The primary larvae which live in water (in opposition to the secon-

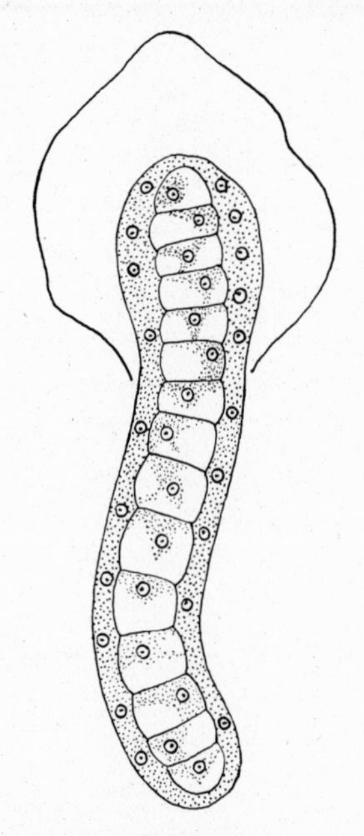

Fig. 35. Hatching planula of *Lucernaria* sp. (without ciliature). (After Wietrzykowski.)

dary larvae which become free during a much older ontogenetic state) move by means of cilia, regardless of the phylum the adult form belongs to (the branchiostoma larvae). Even in the ciliation we can observe the working of the general rule that polymerization is followed by an oligomerization with a differentiation, here in the form of localizations, formations of bunches of cilia, circlets of cilia, etc.

In Cnidaria we can expect *a priori* a reduction of the general ciliation due to their transition to a sessile way of life, and such a reduction has actually taken place. It is in agreement with our interpretation of the evolution of Cnidaria that this ciliation is best preserved in those Anthozoa which have remained solitary animals, i.e. in Actiniaria and in Ceriantharia. In those species that have become purely sessile and colonial animals, as well as in other sedentary animal types, the external ciliation has been limited more or less to the surface of the tentacle apparatus and to its surroundings, especially to the entrance into the intestinal cavity. Those freely moving (swimming) species have ceased to form cilia whose size has been increased and whose active movement is effected by means of contractions of muscles (medusae, Siphonophora); these cilia can, however, return if the size of the species has been subsequently diminished (*Halammohydra*, sporosacs of the hydroids, *Dicoryne conferta*, see Fig. 8).

There is a great need of protection in the sedentary animal types. The protective measures regularly take place on the free surfaces of the animals; these measures are such that they do not prevent the animal from making partial movements (usually contractions). This protection is usually achieved in such a way that part of the free surface of the animal body becomes covered with a firm cuticle, and a smaller intermediate part with an extensile cuticle (Endoprocta, Ectoprocta, Phoronidea, etc.). This is also the situation in Cnidaria. To this protection have additionally come secretions from the cells of the skin glands as a new means of protection. In Cnidaria this has largely been done by cnidae.

As early as in Octocorallia we can see the formation of the so-called periderm to be connected with the formation of colonies (Stolonifera). It is a secretion of an organic substance in the form of a cuticle which must not remain in its entire extent connected with the skin epithelium and which is in spite of this able to increase constantly its thickness. The contractile and extensible part of anthopolyps is covered with a thin extensible cuticle so that in case of need the polyp is able to retract entirely into the broadened part (the theca) of its periderm. The same can also be found in Scyphozoa, even if here to a lesser degree because scyphopolyps are less inclined to form cormi. The formation of a periderm is widely developed among the Hydrozoa (Hydroidea), especially in the most primitive Thecata. These have even developed devices in the form of a lid by means of which the animal is enabled to close the opening of its theca so that finally the entire body of the hydranth is protected by its periderm. The Athecata have ceased to form the hydrothecae and they have replaced the personal protection with the so-called renovation of damaged or destroyed hydranthes.

The formation of a periderm is not an invention of Cnidaria; similarly as in the case of cnidae, Cnidaria had inherited this inclination and ability from their turbellarian ancestors. It is natural that in Turbellaria as freely moving animals a general and strongly formed periderm has never been developed. In Turbellaria a thick and firm cuticle can appear locally only and under special circumstances. Thus cuticular thorns (they are probably built of scleroprotein) can be found on the dorsal side of the genus *Enantia*, among Polycladida. Much more frequently we find firm cuticular formations developed in connection with their genital organs (the male organs of copulation). It should be mentioned in passing that this ability to form a firm cuticle had also been inherited by numerous types of Ameria. The best parallel to Cnidaria can be found in Endoprocta as sessile descendants from Turbellaria which usually form cormi. In these, similarly as in Cnidaria, we can find in one and the same individual all possible transitions from a ciliate and bare epidermis, to such that one has cilia and that is covered by a thin and extensible cuticle, and finally to one that is covered by a thick periderm which can be occasionally equipped with spines. This periderm can serve, as it does in Cnidaria, as a true exoskeleton.

In Anthozoa and in Hydrozoa, especially in the former, the formation of cormi is attended with a secondary impregnation of the organic skeleton matter with mineral salts; this has led to the formation of a firm skeleton that can be polished and rubbed. Even in this Cnidaria do not show an originality. The first steps in this direction had again been made by Turbellaria, even if in these this development has preserved a local and moderate character due to the fact that Turbellaria are freely moving animals. As a matter of fact, not even Turbellaria have been the first to have discovered this possibility—similar things can be found as early as in Protozoa. Calcium salts have been used as a skeleton material in two different ways, either as a substance which impregnates the periderm, or as biocrystals (spicula). Both these elements can also be found elsewhere in the animal world; Mollusca and Brachiopoda can serve as examples of the former development; Cestoda, Nematoda (male animals), Brachiopoda with their spicula, Tunicata, and others, as examples of the latter. These spicula or calcoblasts have been occasionally cemented together into a firm skeleton (e.g. in Octocorallia, etc.)

In two species of Turbellaria (*Turbella klostermanni* and *Sidonia elegans)* L. v. Graff (1882) was able to observe skin inclusions that produced an effervescent effect when treated with the acetic acid; they had therefore been impregnated with a lime-containing carbonic acid. Similar morphological elements have been described by O. Steinböck (1931) as "small calcareous bodies" in connection with the primitive Acoela *Nematoderma bathycola*; he did not determine, however, the true chemical nature of this substance.

This ability to deposit mineral salts in their own cells or in the products of their cells (traces of which can be found in the freely moving Turbellaria) has undergone further progressive development during the transition to a sessile way of life and to the formation of cormi. The madreporic corals and so-called Hydrocorallia (Milleporidae and Stylasteridae) are some of the most important absorbers of the sea chalk. Frequently it has been maintained (e.g. by Kükenthal, Kästner, etc.) that the calcareous skeleton is formed by the ectoderm only. This is not true for Octocorallia, and probably it is not true for other Anthozoa either. Why should we deny the mesenchymal (mesodermal) character to such cells that ontogenetically and phylogenetically arise in the skin layer and which later migrate into the middle layer, when in other animal types the same cells are considered forthwith as mesenchymal cells?

As for the cellular structure of the skin layer it can be stated that from our standpoint we can expect in Anthozoa the conditions to be more primitive than in Hydrozoa (we speak here of the polyp generation only). Similarly as in Turbellaria, where a slightly cellularized epidermal epithelium (ectocyte) can regularly be found in the primitive Acoela and where we therefore speak of a syncytial structure, we find cases with a plasmodial (syncytial) ectoderm (epidermis) first in Anthozoa among Cnidaria. The cellularization, i.e. the morphological–physiological division of the elementary units of Eumetazoa (of the true cells) in the primarily polycaryontic plasmodium becomes more and more complete in the direction Anthozoa → Scyphozoa → Hydrozoa. This, however, is not true for the skin layer only. In sessile animals we find this cellularization to be connected with an epithelization, and it is especially developed in those animal types that form cormi. In this sense the middle layer (and the nervous system) lags behind. In Cnidaria the middle layer retrogresses more and more until finally the climax of this development is reached in hydromedusae and in the hydranths of the corm-forming Hydroidea. I have already stated that this development has never led to a complete loss of the middle layer (it can occur locally only).

Finally we also find the actual conditions of the skin gland cells to agree better with our interpretation of the origin of Cnidaria than with the earlier theory. A mucous membrane can be found in the primarily solitary Anthozoa only. Some Actiniae (e.g. the common red *Actinia equina*) are able to live in the tidal zone because at ebb-tide they cover their bare and contracted bodies with a thick layer of mucus. This lowest form of the activity of skin glands, the secretion of the mucus, has later been developed into various other more specialized secretions. As early as in solitary Anthozoa we can find on one hand a more local (at the flattened sole of the foot) secretion of a glutinous and therefore thicker slime, and on the other hand (especially in Ceriantharia) a glutinous and tubular secretion whose duty is to protect the animal body. The formation of the periderm also belongs here, with the difference that here slime has become solid matter. If we disregard the formation of slime, which is connected with the feeding mechanism of the animal, we find in scypho- and hydro-polyps the glutinous slime to have an active role in their aboral poles only; this is especially true for those polyps that have become secondarily solitary animals, as is the case with *Hydra*. The gas gland in the pneumatophore of numerous Siphonophora represents a special case. It is proved by such isolated and specialized cases that mutations in the skin gland cells can reappear again and again.

In Cnidaria we see how the skin progressively loses the character of a mucous membrane, a fact which can be explained as being due to the formation of cormi and, in connection with this, to the sessility and to the formation of a periderm. In Turbellaria, on the other hand, the character of the mucous membrane has been better preserved; it has especially been developed at the anterior ends (the deeply sunk-in front glands) and on the ventral surface; here it has been specialized and the slime has been given an important role which enables the animal to creep over the substratum. This property has later been inherited and further developed, by others (e.g. Gastrotricha), and also by Mollusca. This slime secreted by the skin glands can become so firm that it can be extended into glutinous threads that can be used by the animal for the formation of nets by means of which the animal can catch its prey, and for the formation of thin cords which the animal uses to descend. What else can the colloblasts of Ctenophora be than specialized cells of skin glands which behave like cnidae and which can be used by the animal when it catches its living prey? Colloblasts had ultimately been developed from the same source as cnidocytes, i.e. from the cells of the skin glands of the old Turbellaria; in both these cases, however, the development took place independently, and therefore parallel, and this is the reason why it is senseless to combine Ctenophora, as Acnidaria, with Cnidaria into one higher taxonomic unit of Coelenterata. The main difference that can be noticed between colloblasts and cnidae is that colloblasts do not represent a firm and formed unit (glutinous kernels cannot be attributed to it!) and that they function as a glutinous substance without the aid of an explosion. In spite of the fact that they form two types of elastic, or contractile, filaments (a straight and a spiral filament), they have reached a lower level of differentiation than the one that has been reached by cnidae.

Thus we return now to the cnidoblast as the skin gland cell which shows the best developed differentiation and specialization in the entire animal world. Once separated from its "maternal cell" (cnidocyte, stinging cell, nettle cell), or after the death of the maternal cell, the capsule or the nematocyst, though itself not alive, even if it possesses a complex structure, can continue to function in a foreign environment as is proved by the so-called kleptocnidae. The fact has frequently been forgotten or quietly passed over (e.g. in the book by Hyman) that cnidocytes are originally monocellular gland cells and that they did not appear as such, i.e. as fully developed, suddenly in the Cnidaria; they had a long phylogenetic development behind them which leads by way of Turbellaria down to the Protozoa. It has already been mentioned that similar forms had probably been developed polyphyletically as early as in Protozoa. Even a cursory comparison of the "nettle capsule" of the dinoflagellate *Polykrikos schwartzi*, with the trichocyst from the paramecium and from the so-called polar capsule of the *Myxobolus* (Cnidosporidia), with cnidae of Cnidaria, and finally with various partly solid secretions of the turbellarian gland cells (rhabdites, rhamnites, sagittocysts) shows clearly that the development has gone here into considerable width.

Here we can bypass the problem whether genuine and autonomous cnidae can be found as early as in Infusoria; the so-called cnidotrichocysts of the *Prorodon* are, according to Krüger (1934, 1936), certainly very close to a genuine cnida. Since we consider that the Turbellaria as the lowermost Eumetazoa, had been developed from the ciliate Protozoa, we accept it as certain that Turbellaria had inherited their tendency to gland cells with a strongly gushing and partly firm secretion from their protozoan ancestors; in Cnidaria this same ability has developed into a real virtuosity (Fig. 36).

It seems, especially on the basis of studies made by Meixner and by Kepner and his school on *Microstoma*, that no genuine cnidae have been developed anywhere among the Turbellaria. In Turbellaria the highest level reached in the development in this direction seems to be in sagittocysts, a fact which, as has already been mentioned, can easily be understood if we take into consideration the way of life on one hand of Cnidaria and on the other of Turbellaria.

The Nemertinea, too, had inherited from their turbellarian ancestors, even if to a lesser degree, the ability to produce forms similar to cnidae. It may not be a mere chance that, especially in Nemertinea, such secretion products can be found on their unarmed proboscides. Frequently one can find in the epidermis cells of the anterior part of their proboscis rod-like structures which are very similar to rhabdites of Turbellaria. It is improbable that these rod-like structures could be of a foreign origin. Genuine cnidae have been found in the wall of the proboscis of several species belonging to the genera *Micrura*, *Cerebratulus*, and *Lineus;* these cnidae show a regular distribution (in two longitudinal lines); their origin has unfortunately not yet been determined, so that we do not know whether they are autonomous. The cnidoid forms, however, cannot be expected in Nemertinea with an

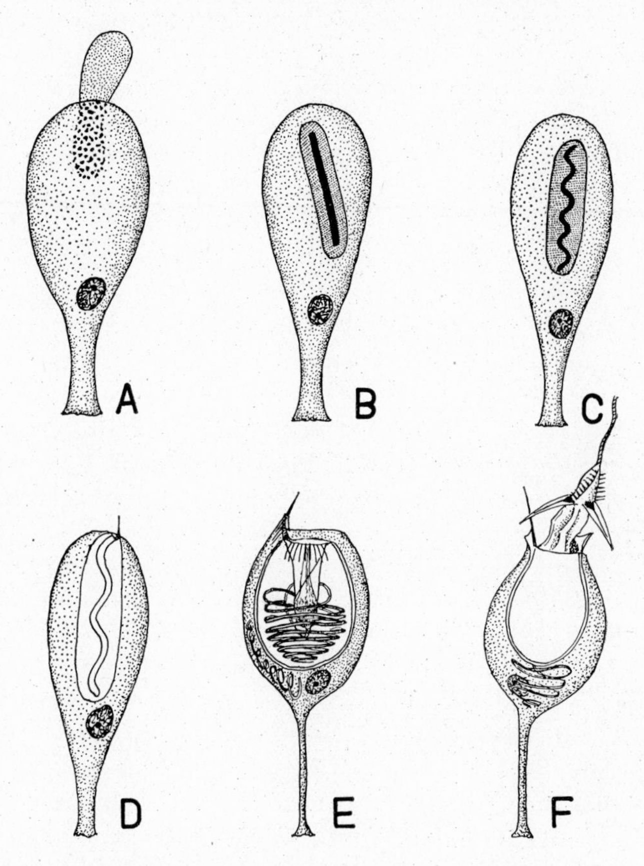

Fig. 36. Hypothetical evolution of cnidae from secretory cell without solid secretion, (A) to fully developed cnidae (B-F).

armed proboscis, where poisonous glands are used, together with stilettos, as an effective weapon.

In the Cnidaria genuine cnidae only appear, as has already been mentioned, quite generally and without a single exception. This should not be considered as surprising, since all levels of evolution in the direction towards a genuine cnida can already be observed in Turbellaria. This fact which must be expected if we accept our standpoint, i.e. a progressive evolution of cnidae within the group of Cnidaria, can point to the direction Anthozoa → Scyphozoa → Hydrozoa. This progressive evolution can be observed in several elements. First, in the general form of the capsule, we find in Anthozoa an oblong or rod-like form to be prevalent. It is only in Scyphozoa, and especially in Hydrozoa, that it becomes differentiated into several other external forms, particularly into a spheric or into a pear-shaped form. Another development can be observed in the wall of the capsule. It is in Anthozoa only that we find cnidae with a thin-walled capsule and with a predilection for acid colouring substances; they have been given a special name, i.e. that of spirocysts. Earlier it was believed to be a sign of the primitive character of these spirocysts that they do not show a continuity between the wall of their capsules and the "thread." Will (1909), Weill (1930), and recently C. E. Cutries (1955), however, have been able to show that we nevertheless have here genuine cnidae, even if the connection between the capsule and the thread still seems to be a tenuous one.

A further progressive evolution can be observed in the equipment and in the form of the thread. It has been used as a basis for the systematization of cnidae by Weill (1930) and by Carlgren (1945). A further subtle morphological and physiological difference can be observed on and around the capsule of the cnidae if we compare the anthozoan and hydrozoan cnidae (cnidocil, lasso, various fibrous forms in the cytoplasmic body of the cnidoblast, the formation of the stem, etc.). A conspicuous phenomenon is a progressive variety of the cnidarian apparatus that can be observed in one and the same species of Cnidaria, a fact which has led to the notion of a "cnidom." Such a differentiation can be further developed in another direction, i.e. to a more regular and therefore to a more effective grouping of cnidae into variously formed batteries. Again this development has reached its climax in Hydrozoa, especially in Siphonophora. In this connection we also find a more and more distinct differentiation of the strictly localized place of origin of cnidocytes, combined with an increasingly complicated migration of half-formed cnidocytes to those parts of the animal body where they can be used (this has first been described by Hadži (1907), later confirmed by numerous other authors). From a physiological and ecological standpoint we can notice a further specialization into penetrating, volvent, and glutinating cnidae, a development which again has reached its climax in Hydrozoa.

Finally we can observe that when the climax has been reached in the progressive evolution the subsequent development can turn in a retrogressive direction. This can be seen, first, in the fact that a polycnidom can secondarily be changed into a monocnidom, thus to a simplification in the selection of cnidae, as this is the case with Trachylinae. Another retrogression can be observed in those cases where cnidae degenerate, as can be seen in the so-called rhopalonemes and desmonemes in Siphonophora *(Diphyes)*. Cnidae have lost their primary function in numerous hydromedusae, especially in Trachylinae. Here they remain, half developed, in the middle layer; amassed in the margin of the umbrella and behaving passively, they serve as an elastic and strengthening inner skeleton.

As a conclusion it can be stated that cnidoid forms belong to the category of non-living, even if organic, secretions of the cytoplasm. They first appear, in an acellular state, as early as in Protozoa; they have been continuously progressively developed in several directions and they have reached their climax in Dinoflagellata (Kofoid and Swezy, 1921; Weil, 1925; Chatton, 1914); they have reached another climax in Infusoria (Krüger, 1934). The Turbellaria, as the first Eumetazoa, had inherited their inclination to form cnidoids and passed it on to several of their descendants. An absolute climax has been reached in this development in the sessile Cnidaria. The progressive line of evolution points clearly in the direction Anthozoa → Scyphozoa → Hydrozoa, reaching its final and general culmination in Hydrozoa. In the latter, a partly retrogressive development can also be observed. It is probably a unique case in the whole animal world that animals that use Cnidaria (this is true, as it seems, for Hydrozoa only) as their food, e.g. Turbellaria, Ctenophora, Gastropoda, are able to use cnidae which have been taken from their prey, as the so-called kleptocnidae (Martin, 1914). It seems that the cnidae of only the Hydrozoa can be used as kleptoknidae because they are of the highest quality.

Ontogeny

Initially, I gave a general explanation of my interpretation of the relationship between ontogeny and phylogeny. I agree with Garstang, de Beer, Steinböck, Sacarao, and numerous other zoologists who have resolutely rejected as wrong and misleading the so called "fundamental biogenetic law" as it was formulated by Ernst Haeckel. According to this law, ontogeny is supposed to be a shortened and somewhat changed ("falsified!") phylogeny; the phylogeny did not represent some old ontogenies (ontogenetic stages), but rather a chain of adult stages or forms. Even if basically wrong, this interpretation as proposed by Haeckel was originally useful for propagating the idea of Evolution. This quasi-law has now been banished for all times from the demesne of biology; this, however, should not mean that ontogenies cannot serve as a useful material when we are attempting to come to some phylogenetic conclusions by means of a comparative method. It is only necessary that we proceed cautiously in order to avoid the pitfalls of the so called caenogenesis.

We are aware of the fact that we will have to overcome considerable difficulties in the struggle for a new interpretation of the phylogeny of Cnidaria; this is due especially to a widely believed, yet false, combination of two concepts that were proposed by Haeckel; this is, on the one hand, the concept of a general repetition of the phylogeny in individual ontogenies; and, on the other, the concept of a gastraea as the primitive form of all Metazoa. The moruloid and blastoid forms have simply been presupposed and taken over from the plant world when they could not be found among the animals. It should be mentioned in passing that in my opinion there have never existed any Gastraeadae. I even maintain that the ontogenetic stage called gastrula does not represent any recapitulation of a "gastraeadic" ancestor.

It is quite surprising that various zoologists could not see that the well-known facts in the field of the ontogeny of the cnidaria do in no way agree with their concept of the origin of Cnidaria from some gastraea-like ancestors, with Hydrozoa as the earliest form. It was within this important sphere that it was necessary to take into consideration the factor of "caenogeneses" from some unknown origins. One could expect, on the basis of this preconceived scheme, that the ontogeny of Hydrozoa as that of the supposedly most primitive Cnidaria should have the most typical course, i.e. that the impregnated and fertilized egg cell should pass, by way of a total and equal segmentation, through the stages of a morula and of a blastula (or coeloblastula) to grow finally by way of an invagination of its vegetative half into a double-layered gastrula. The facts, however, tell a different tale. Such a "typical" recapitulation can be found nowhere in the ontogenies of all Hydrozoa that have been investigated up to this point. Occasionally an invagination-gastrula can be found in Scyphozoa and in Anthozoa; there is also everywhere an *Anlage* of the intermediate layer, as yet not that of a third "germ layer," as a mesoderm. Here the types of development show an extraordinary variety and they depend strongly and obviously on the quantity of the food substance which has here a purely passive role. It can be therefore easily understood that a sharp opposition to the gastraea theory soon appeared after this theory had been formulated by Haeckel; Ilya Metschnikoff, an expert in the ontogenies of Cnidaria, proposed his own theory of a parenchymella, and in this he was followed by several other scholars; Lankester (1877), on the other hand, developed simultaneously with Metchnikoff the planula theory.

It is characteristic that so far there has been nobody who prepared to interpret the ontogeny of Hydra as typical in spite of the fact that until recently Hydra has been considered as the most primitive cnidarian (even now we can find in the recent book by Hyman the family Hydridae given the first place in the system of Hydrozoa, a classification which must presuppose these to be the most primitive Hydroidea and therefore also the most primitive forms of Cnidaria). A. A. Sachwatkin (1956), also tried to derive Metazoa (together with sponges) from the colonies of Flagellata. He considers the flagellate blastula to be the primitive form, and correspondingly had to bring forward the "metagenetic Leptolida" in order to demonstrate his ideas in one example of the supposedly primitive Metazoa. The examples selected by Sachwatkin, i.e. the calcareous sponges, the metagenetic Leptolida, the "lower Scyphozoa," and sea urchins represent a poorly selected group because they all belong, without exception, to very specialized types, and because they cannot actually even be compared with each other.

In our analysis and comparison of ontogenetic morphogenies we will consequently begin with the study of conditions as they occur in Anthozoa, above all in those that live a primarily solitary life. These are the Actiniaria and Ceriantharia. We find a "typical" ontogeny with a total cleavage, with a flagellate blastula, and with an invagination gastrula in Actiniaria, among Anthozoa: this in spite of a presence of various vitelline substances. Haeckel himself selected a species of anthopolyp as a typical example (Fig. 37). As early as in Octocorallia we find this situation changed. The segmentation, though total and subequal, is followed by a stereoblastula; gastrulation takes place by way of a secondary delamination. Few species only belonging to Scyphozoa have been studied so far from this point of view (mainly *Nausithoë* and *Chrysaora)*. Cleavage seems to be more unequal here, and its result is a coeloblastula which develops later into an invagination gastrula. It has already been mentioned that no invagination gastrulae can be found in Hydrozoa; their early ontogeny is in reality very plastic and it can be easily changed. This can

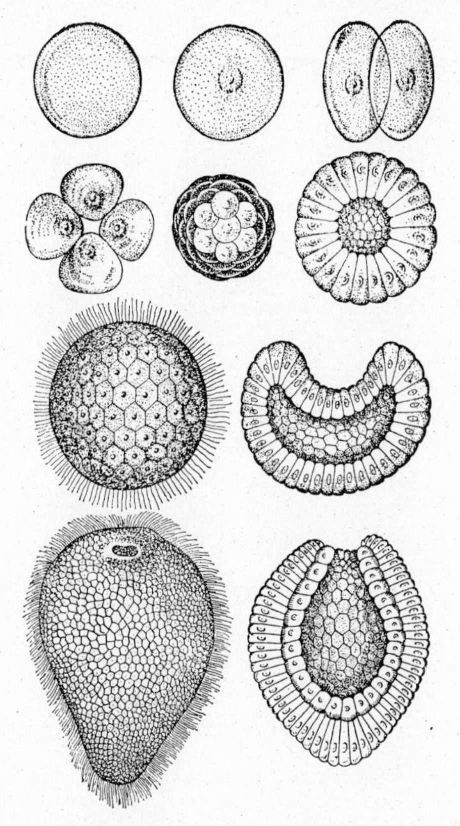

Fig. 37. The early ontogeny of an anthopolyp after E. Haeckel.

be explained as being due to the partial influence of two factors. One of these is the progressive trend to develop a freely living larva, a planula; the second factor is the prevalent role which is given to the formation of cormi. As a consequence of this, the planula does not develop first into a primary individual but instead it immediately begins to form cormi, a phenomenon which can be observed above all in Siphonophora.

The conditions that can be observed in the ontogenies of Cnidaria as a whole, show that the phylogenetic development must have followed the direction Anthozoa → Scyphozoa → Hydrozoa, and not the opposite direction, as has been believed till now. The modes of evolution show considerable variety and they are therefore not uniform. The younger pelagic larva, the planula, seems to be most characteristic in the ontogeny of Cnidaria; it had been evolved parallel to the sessility of the adult form of polyp. It would be misleading if we tried to see in this planula a recapitulation of a common adult ancestral form. This planula does not feed independently, and it can therefore not live long when swimming freely. A slight prolongation of the planula stage can be achieved by means of a reserve food given to the egg before it starts on its way; yet in this way the mode of evolution is changed.

In Cnidaria a significant prolongation of the pelagic stage—without the usage of a medusoid generation (primary or secondary)—has been reached, as it seems polyphyletically, so that the subsequent development (yet not a real metamorphosis) takes place in the pelagic zone; the larva as such becomes able in this way to feed independently. Such a larva has been called an "actinula;" attempts have been made to suggest that the actinula represents the primitive form of Cnidaria, an equally misleading interpretation. The more progressively developed planktonic larvae have no longer a freely moving medusoid generation.

Actinulae of a very specified form can be found as early as among the primarily solitary Anthozoa, i.e. in Ceriantharia (Fig. 46). They are known as Semper's larvae, while at the same time their relationship to certain adult forms could not be determined. They develop some properties of the adult form preserving simultaneously, as it seems, certain archaic characteristics, e.g. a phase with four tentacles only, with six sarcosepta, and with a well-developed bilateral symmetry. Such a larva is known as a cerinula. The inclination to prolong the pelagic stage can even lead so far, that it is already during the plankton phase that sexual maturity is reached *(Dyctylactis benedeni)*. In these larvae we find a combination of transient larval characteristics and of the definite properties of the grown-up individuals. A higher level of development can be observed above all in their ciliation. "Zoanthellae" with their oblong form, possess a long cilia-line along the ventral side; "zoanthinae" whose form resembles that of a vat, have a circlet of cilia and they swim in a special way by means of pulsations, somewhat similar to the type of swimming that can be observed in medusae. As early as in the Anthozoa we can find cases (Zoantharia) where the planktonic phase of the planula has been given up. This planula itself has a life of short duration only and it soon develops into an oözoöid.

No actinulae can be found among Scyphozoa where medusae are the prevalent generation. In the metagenetic species we find the planula stage to be completed early; in Lucernariidae, as has already been mentioned, planulae do not rise into the pelagic zone, they have no cilia, and they creep for a short while only over the sea bottom (Fig. 35).

Among Hydrozoa, freely swimming larvae which resemble an actinula can again be found in the very specialized Athecata (Myriothelidae, Tubulariidae). They become free only as such and they are certainly of an independent origin. They have been developed parallel to the retrogression of the free medusoid generation. Larvae of Narcomedusae, which have also been called actinulae, have nothing in common either with the larvae of Ceriantharia or with those of the athecate Hydroidea, except if we allow the homology (homotypy) to be completely watered down—something that has often been done in recent researches. The Scyphozoa which have no actinulae appear between Anthozoa which have actinulae and Hydrozoa. The supposed actinulae of Narcomedusae and of Trachomedusae are larvae which are medusae and not polyps: in these the polyp generation has been abandoned as completely as in the hypogenetic Scyphozoa. The larval stage has been prolonged (it is only externally polypoid) by means of a transition to a temporarily parasitic way of life, it has been more strongly developed, and it has even become able to reproduce asexually.

It should be mentioned in passing that it has not been proved that the planula either of Scyphozoa or of Hydrozoa has evolved into the adult form of a medusa by way of a prolonged life in plankton. We always have a case of a secondary direct change due to the abolition of the benthonic polyp generation wherever a planula has actually been changed directly into a medusa, a fact which can always be proved if we make comparisons with the closely related species. All hypotheses which suggest that the medusa form, or that the planktonic planula or actinula represent the primary form in the phylogeny of Cnidaria must therefore be rejected.

We can state, when we now compare the ontogenetic development of Cnidaria with those of Turbellaria, that little actual material is available especially about the Acoela. Furthermore, we can see (as was also the case with the genital apparatus) that the ontogenetic morphogeneses show a strong inclination to a specialization which has reached its climax in groups whose eggs represent extreme cases of exolecithality. On the other hand, a trend of evolution can be observed towards a strictly determined and differentiated type of development that can be found as early as among the Acoela (e.g. in the species of the genus *Convoluta*). This trend, combined with the formation of a duet (in Acoela) and of a quartet (in higher Turbellaria), as well as the formation of an *Anlage* of a middle body layer which is closely connected with the *Anlage* of the intestine from a strictly fixed blastomere (4 *d*), had been inherited by Ctenophora by way of Polycladida. Here already the mesohyl is formed during the ontogeny out of two sources, evidently a contrivance of the evolutional technique.

The conditions that can be observed in the ontogenies of Cnidaria had certainly not been developed from such trends, but rather from others that were more primitive, more plastic, more changeable, and less determined. It appears, in opposition to the previously widely accepted interpretation, that it is the youngest stages in the ontogeny i.e. cleavage that are changed first, and it is therefore necessary to be very careful when attempts are made on this basis to derive conclusions regarding phylogeny.

We must mention here in passing the extremely interesting example of a turbellarian *(Prorhynchus stagnalis* M. Sch.) where two rather different ontogenetic processes could be observed in one and the same species (O. Steinböck and Sister Bernardina Ausserhofer, 1950). Hyman (1957, II:171) is right when she emphasizes, "Practically nothing is known of the development of these Rhabdocoela and Alloeocoela that have endolecithal eggs." To this it should be added that much depends even in endolecithal eggs, on the quantity and on the type of the distribution of the egg yolk.

As a matter of fact, no larva clearly of a planula type can be found among the Turbellaria. It can, however, be said that it had been prepared in the Turbellaria as a transient stereogastrula which was later developed in the benthonic and sessile Cnidaria into a typical pelagic larva. Turbellaria as a whole show little inclination to develop genuine larvae, and this is particularly true for those species that have begun to live in the fresh water or even on the land. It is only in the Polycladida that planktonic larvae (Goette–Müller's larva) have been developed as a parallel (and nothing more!) to an actinula.

If we disregard the special characteristic of Acoela (that they have lost the second meridian cleavage which has led in micromeres to the formation of a duet instead of a quartet) we see that conditions that can be found in Cnidaria, and especially in Anthozoa, show in reality close resemblance to those that occur in Acoela. In these a stereogastrula which is very similar to a planula is usually formed by way of epiboly.

The oral opening is developed later by means of an invagination. The contents of such a stereogastrula is naturally not an entoderm but rather an entomesoderm which was called an archihiston by Steinböck—inasmuch as it still shows the primitive character of a plasmodium (syncytium). It becomes clear that the supposedly primitive formation of the entoderm, which has been considered as typical and which takes place by way of an invagination of the vegetative half of the coeloblastula, had been evolved so to speak in the "technique of embryogenesis" from a combination of an immersion ("passing into the interior") of certain macromeres, e.g., 4*A* and 4*B*, and of an epiboly (surrounding growth by means of micromeres; cf. conditions in the early ontogeny of the *Polychoerus caudatus*, according to Gardiner, 1895, and of *Convoluta roscoffensis*, according to Georgévich, 1899).

It can be given as a direct proof of the origin of Cnidaria from Turbellaria that it is in the Anthozoa only that we find instances of an inclination to spiral cleavage which is typical of Turbellaria and which was passed over from Turbellaria to Mollusca as well as to Annelida. The simplification of the in-determined character of the early development of Cnidaria has been mainly due to the retrogression of the middle body layer which was caused by their sessile way of life. In this connection the role of the blastomere 4 *d* as that of a supplier of the entomesoderm (coeloblast, according to Dawydoff) has been diminished so that what has remained has been the irregular formation of the so-called entomesoderm, the mesenchyme.

It is characteristic, if viewed from the standpoint of a general study of ontogeny (embryology), that no typical formation of the so-called germ layers can be observed either in Turbellaria or in their descendants Cnidaria. Kühn (1914) was obliged to state in connection with Hydrozoa that "...die Keimblätterbildung (takes place) durch Differenzierung aus einem soliden, indifferenten Blastodermhaufen oder einem Syncytium." Is it better not to speak here of any germ layers at all? An illuminating example in this connection is the athecate hydroid *Turritopsis nutricola* whose ontogeny begins with a regular cleavage that soon becomes irregular in order finally to lead to a syncytial state; naturally enough this develops later into a cellular state. Even in other cases in the Cnidaria, a return to a syncytial state is not at all rare.

As a conclusion we can say that the facts that have been known so far about the ontogeny of Cnidaria and Ctenophora do not stand in opposition to our concept. On the contrary, we find these facts if viewed from our standpoint are more understandable than they have been till now. Two trends can be found in ontogeny (as in the morphology) of the adult forms: a retrogressive development, and a progressive trend. The retrogressive evolution which takes place parallel to the simplification of structure leads to a reduction of the middle layer and to the in-determined character of the early development, and the progressive trend leads to the formation of a planula larva typical of Cnidaria. Both these developments depend on the sessile way of life, combined with the formation of cormi.

Asexual Reproduction and Regeneration

No phylogenetic significance has usually been attributed to asexual reproduction. It is usually considered that where the sessile way of life has been adopted by Eumetazoa it appeared spontaneously. This is generally true even if there are numerous exceptions. It should suffice to mention here, on one hand, Rotatoria, Gastropoda, and Lamellibranchiata which incline to partial sessility, and the completely sessile Brachiopoda: among all these animals not a single case of asexual reproduction has been known so far; and, on the other hand, Annelida which move freely and which show, in spite of this, instances of an asexual reproduction not only by means of division but also by way of budding. In all those cases where freely moving animals reproduce asexually we have usually (though by no means always) animal groups which developed directly from some related animals that lead a sessile way of life and which as such reproduce asexually. As examples we can mention, among Cnidaria, some species of hydromedusae (above all those that belong to the Hydroidea); hydropolyps that have become secondarily solitary animals; the Thaliacea among Tunicata; two secondarily solitary species of Ectoprocta (*Monobryozoon ambulans* and *M. limicola*), and perhaps the *Loxosoma* species among Endoprocta (it is possible that these are primarily solitary animals!).

In agreement with the rule that a tendency to asexual reproduction can be observed in sessile animals the Cnidaria (in clear contrast to Ctenophora!) show asexual reproduction in widely adopted and manifold ways. This has led in all three subclasses to the formation of cormi—these are least developed in Scyphozoa—and in this way to polymorphism (polyp-medusa, polypean polymorphism, medusan polymorphism). It is usually supposed, even if it is not always explicitly stated, that in Cnidaria this type of reproduction appeared, so to speak, spontaneously as a consequence of a general plasticity. This has been linked with the regenerative ability. This, however, is an explanation born of a dilemma. Reproduction by means of transverse division can be found in Turbellaria, even if it is not of quite a general distribution and it occurs in spite of the fact that they live as freely-moving animals. Here, too, attempts have been made to bring this property into a causal connection with the well-developed ability to regenerate.

These conditions become clear and understandable if viewed from the point of view of my concept (Cnidaria as descendants from Turbellaria). First it should be mentioned that there are—besides specialized forms of asexual reproduction, laceration, formation of podocysts, cladogony, etc.—mainly two types of asexual reproduction: division and budding. Of these two types, division seems to be the more primitive form, because it appears early in the freely living Protozoa, especially in Flagellata and in Ciliata; in Flagellata as a longitudinal division, and in Euciliata as a transverse division. It is not difficult to imagine that budding had evolved out of division during the sessile way of life; this can be observed as early as in Ciliata (Euciliata on one hand, Suctoria on the other).

We can rightly reverse the situation and can maintain that the facts observed in connection with asexual reproduction give support to our interpretation of the origin of Cnidaria from Turbellaria. In the freely-moving Turbellaria transverse division only appears; they inherited it from their euciliate ancestors both in its primitive form as an architomy as well as in its more progressive form as a paratomy. It is true that this transverse division does not appear equally well developed in all animals that belong to the class Turbellaria because it is coordinated with the way of life and the degree of plasticity; we can find it mainly in their "lower" subgroups: in Acoela (cf. the recent studies by P. Ax and Schulze and O. Steinböck) and Rhadocoela, in Tricladida, and in the terrestrial Planaria. These are animals which reproduce regularly only by means of division. In the terrestrial Planaria, fragmentation can frequently be observed which slightly resembles laceration such as occurs in Actiniae. It can be easily understood that in Turbellaria no budding has been developed because of their active movements. Yet in spite of this we find in some Rhabdocoela that paratomy has reached a state which is so similar to budding that experts in Turbellaria have believed that it really was budding.

Transverse division appears, as can be expected from our standpoint, in the primarily solitary Anthozoa, even if it is not frequent. The best known case is that of *Gonactinia prolifera;* Carlgren was able to show that here transverse division occurs serially in the form of a paratomy. The case of *Fungia* which has also been closely studied shows that transverse division can be found among Madreporaria, even if in a somewhat different connection (unequal division and the alternation of generations). This type of division was taken over by the Scyphozoa from their anthozoan ancestors; here it is called strobilation even if this word suits those cases only where we have a probably primary multiple transverse division (e.g. the polydisc strobila). The products of this special form of transverse division develop into medusae simultaneously taking over the sexual function. Since scyphomedusae are developed primarily by way of transverse division, it can be understood that they never reproduce asexually (e.g., by way of budding), as can occcasionally be observed in hydromedusae.

It is interesting to notice that in Hydrozoa, which do not include any species that live as primarily solitary animals, transverse division has reappeared in those species that have secondarily adopted a solitary life. This is known for *Protohydra* (besides a longitudinal division), and apparently abnormally even in *Hydra*. The transverse division of the coenosarc in the hydrorhiza which can lead to the formation of podocysts can perhaps also be attributed to it as well as the decomposition of the Polypodium chain. Here we can also include the isolated case of hydromedusa *(Gastroblata raffaeli)* which reproduce asexually by means of longitudinal fission (Fig. 38).

A direct transverse division cannot lead to the formation of cormi. We cannot know how the formation of cormi began during the geological past. Yet if we refer to conditions that exist in Ciliata and above all if we take into consideration those that exist in the primarily solitary Anthozoa we can come to the conclusion that the formation of cormi had begun in all probablity as an imperfect division when budding had developed from division due to the great inequality of its products: in this way the larger "half" of the divided polyp grew into the maternal animal, and the smaller "half" into the bud. The longitudinal division, too, had possibly been secondarily developed from the primary transverse division, such as it occurs in Ciliata and in Turbellaria by way of an oblique division. In the higher sessile animals we find budding preserved as the only form of the asexual reproduction.

As early as in Actiniaria which possess no skeleton and which we consider to be the most primitive Cnidaria, laceration appears as well as transverse division, as a form of the asexual reproduction: it takes place close to the margin of the foot disc, thus close to the aboral end of the anthopolyp; it represents an intermediate form between an oblique division

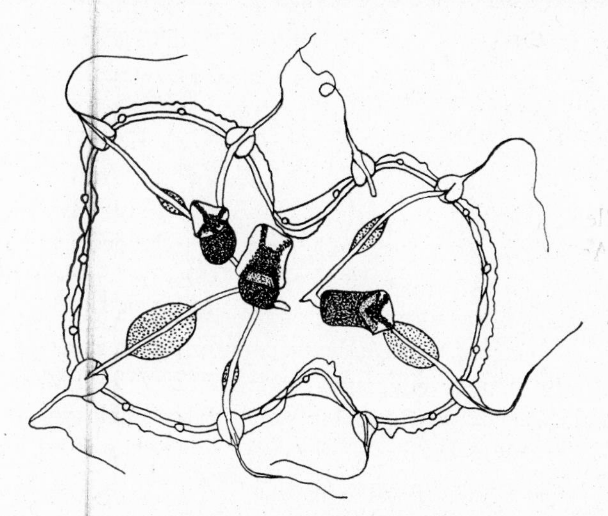

Fig. 38. The leptomeduse *Gastroblasta raffaeli* with longitudinal scission; (after Babić).

and budding. To this we must add the appearance of the formation of cormi in Actiniaria (family Corrallimorphidae). So far this has been too little taken into consideration; in its form it is connected with conditions that exist in those solitary species that have the ability to lacerate. Processes resembling stolons are formed with the production of blastozooids; they are the forerunners of the coenenchyme. This was also the way that Anthozoa first began to be attached to the substratum, how they became sessile animals.

Only the Ceriantharia are, as it seems, all primarily solitary animals and as such they have remained without asexual reproduction. In all other Hexacorallia, however, the formation of colonies had been introduced by means of an imperfect budding or division; frequently it is not easy to distinguish budding from division. Even budding itself does not always take place in such a way that one could distinguish between extratentacular and intratentacular budding. As early as in Anthozoa, i.e. in Octactiniae, development has led to the formation of regularly excrescing and individualized cormi as well as (even if in a moderate degree) to the polymorphism (dimorphism) of the polypoid individuals (subindividuals).

All the three body layers participate, as much as this has been known till now, in the budding of Anthozoa (the so-called typical budding); this may also be true for Scyphozoa. As will be seen later, it is first in the Hydrozoa that so-called atypical budding appears. In this the main role is always played by those cells of the middle layer which are usually considered as un-differentiated cells; an interpretation which was sharply contested by Steinböck (1954). We must mention that in the higher types with a sessile way of life of corms the budding always takes place in the so-called atypical way, without participation of the endoderm. It has already been mentioned that scyphomedusae which have a prevalent role among Scyphozoa do not reproduce asexually. Transverse division appears regularly (even if not generally!) in scyphopolyps, yet here it has become so specialized that normally polyps are not developed by way of transverse division, only medusae. This transverse division which has become multiple can be so profuse and impetuous that it gives the impression of a terminal budding (the formation of the so-called polydiscal strobilae). Lateral budding and the simultaneous formation of colonies becomes rare. The buds of polyps which grow directly on the maternal polyp or on the stolons, become free and finally asexual reproduction is completely abandoned (Lucernariidae, the hypogenetic species). The formation of podocysts develops in the secondarily solitarized scyphopolyps which live in a shallow sea (Hadži, 1912); they represent a specialized remnant of the formation of stolons and in this connection also of cormi.

As in the case of budding, regeneration which is well developed in Anthozoa (just as in Turbellaria) regularly takes place from out of the body wall. Tentacles which have been cut off are unable to develop into a whole new animal apparently because of the absence of mesohyl. The species *Boloceroides* however, represents according to Okada and Komori (1932), an exception. This is a case of specialization.

Even in the evolution of asexual reproduction the climax has been reached in Hydrozoa, both as regards the frequency and variety combined with specialization (the formation of polymorphic and individualized cormi), as well as in the sense of the so-called atypical formation of buds without the participation of the intestinal epithelium. The transverse division recedes completely into the background, and the individuals (hydranths) more and more lose their ability to form buds and to regenerate. The colony prefers to abandon a damaged polyp and to renew it out of the un-differentiated "coenosarc" (Hadži, 1915) than to replace it by means of renovation (Fig. 39).

In Hydrozoa, just as in the case of Scyphozoa, medusae are developed (and they certainly had been developed during the geological past) as special sexual individuals primarily by way of asexual reproduction only, combined with alternation of generations. It is certain that medusae had been evolved by the two groups in two completely different ways, once by means of a transverse division of the maternal polyp, and the second time by way of budding either of the polyp or of the medusa. On the other hand we find that in the two groups, species which had evolved in the same way where the medusa is developed directly from an egg and where the benthonic polyp generation has completely disappeared (the hypogenetic species).

It is in the Hydrozoa only that divisions of whole parts of cormi can serve the purposes of reproduction and of spreading.

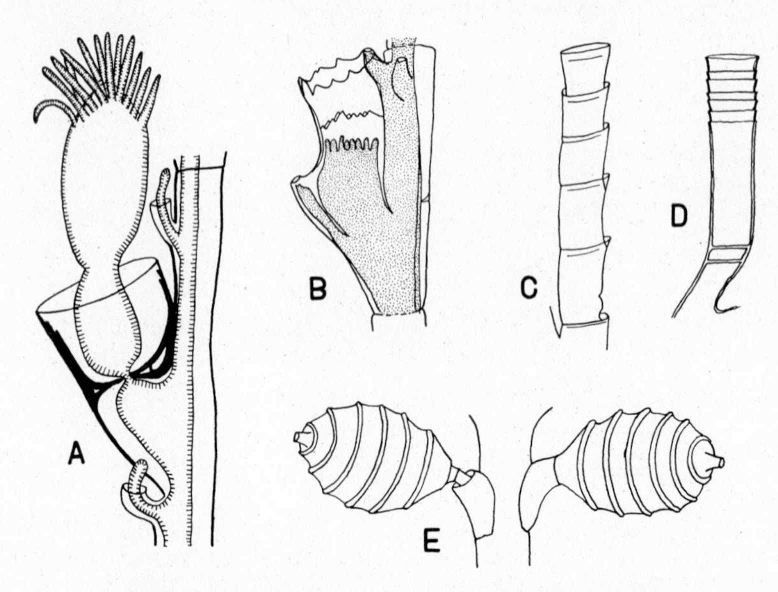

Fig. 39. A few cases of renovation in the thecate hydroids. A, *Plumularia* sp. with embedded hydrothecae as result of reiterated renovations. B, *Aglaophenia* sp. with reduplicated hydrotheca; C, *Halecium* sp. D, *Lictorella* sp., E, *Synthecium* sp. with gonangia as renovants. (A-B, after Hadži, C-E, after Broch.)

Such is the case with cladogony which I described (Hadži, 1919 Fig. 40), i.e. the separation of twigs of the colonies of Thecata which are transported by the sea current or which become attached to a substratum in the vicinity of the maternal colony. Something similar can be found in some Siphonophora which belong to the group Calycophora where whole specially organized cormidia are separated from the maternal colony and continue to live independently, producing sexual individuals. Finally, we find only in Hydrozoa an asexual reproduction of cormi as such.

The fact may not be completely irrelevant that, contrary to what has been found in Scyphozoa whose medusae can never reproduce asexually, this kind of reproduction does not appear quite so rarely in hydromedusae where it is more frequent in

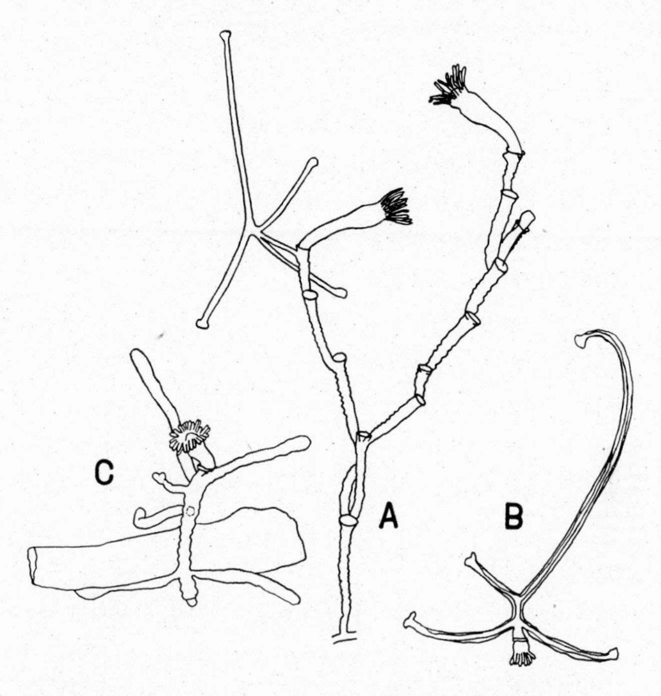

Fig. 40. Cladogony as a special form of asexual reproduction of thecate hydroids (Fam. Haleciidae). A, *Halecium pusillum*, a cormus in cladogony. B, cladogonium freely floating. C, young cormus of *Halecium* sp. developed from a cladogonium on *Cystosira* (after Hadži).

the form of budding than in that of a division *(Gastroblasta raffaeli*, Fig. 38). The buds can appear in various places, even at the manubrium which corresponds to the oral cone of hydropolyps. In the young parasitic and hypogenetic Narcomedusae, budding can occur even at their aboral ends (e.g. in *Pegantha*, according to Bigelow Fig. 46 D). It must be emphasized in this connection that, by way of budding, hydromedusae only can be developed from hydromedusae (the one supposed exception is still a matter of dispute).

Endosymbiotic Monocellular Algae

The fact that the so-called zooxanthellae and zoochlorellae which live intracellularly can be frequently found in Cnidaria as well as in Turbellaria cannot yet alone be considered as a direct proof of a close relationship between these two animal groups; in particular it does not help us to distinguish which of the two groups is the parent and which the descendant. Nor is it proved that this appearance can be considered as a pure coincidence only. This situation, however, is altered when we notice that in the Turbellaria the mutual relationship between the animal and the alga stands on a more primitive level than the level which has been reached in this connection in Cnidaria. So far the physiological circumstances of this symbiosis have not been clarified (the extent of the mutual dependence as regards breathing and feeding); we will take into considerations those conditions only that can be observed during the transmission of symbionts from one generation to the other.

We can disregard the circumstance that there are at least two types of symbiotic algae, the green coloured zoochlorellae (this is, as a matter of fact, not a taxonomic idea), and the zooxanthellae whose colour is yellow to brown (they are actually Dinoflagellata, according to Chatton). The situation is usually such that zooxanthellae prevail in those animal partners that live in the sea, while zoochlorellae are more numerous in those partners that live in fresh water. It should also be mentioned here that such endosymbioses occur as early as in Protozoa (especially in Radiolaria and in Euciliata). As for the Turbellaria, we can read in the manual written by Hyman (II:143), "Most acoela and some rhabdocoela and alleocoela harbour symbiotic chlorellae and xanthellae;" these live mainly in the mesenchymal cells under the skin muscle tube. It is important in this connection that these algae do not pass over into the egg cells so that the young animals which have just developed from an egg do not possess symbionts and they must be later "infected" by food which contains these algae, e.g. by the egg shell whose surface is covered with these algae.

It is characteristic that no case of a symbiosis with these algae is known in Polycladida and that correspondingly zooxanthellae do not occur in the completely transparent pelagic Ctenophora which derive from Goette–Müller's larvae that have adopted neoteny—even if such a symbiosis could be expected.

In Turbellaria the majority of cases of endosymbiosis can be found in Acoela and in other primitive groups. It is not impossible that in Acoela the absence of nephridia could be attributed at least partly as being due to this endosymbiosis since the algae which live in the cytoplasm use up the products of excretion of their partners. The physiological relationship with these algae can be very complex in numerous species of Acoela (e.g. in species belonging to the genus *Convoluta)*. Yet in spite of this we find that the continuity of this symbiosis has not been secured in the most reliable way, i.e. by means of a transition of algae into the egg cells. It could perhaps be said that as early as in Acoela the eggs are better isolated against their surroundings in the body of the partner. The possibility, however, cannot be excluded that in those Turbellaria which regularly possess symbiotic algae, cases will be found where symbionts are directly transferred by means of egg cells. This could be the case in Acoela with a primitive sexual apparatus. Von Graff (1908, 1943) admits the possibility that in the species *Polychoerus caudatus* Mark. the algae are present even in the cleaving egg.

It is well known that in Cnidaria a symbiosis with monocellular algae can be frequently found. We can observe such cases in all the three subdivisions, and most frequently in Anthozoa, among others in Actiniae and in Madreporaria. This symbiosis occurs so regularly in the cliff-building corals, whose most profuse growth takes place in the well-lit upper zone of water, that earlier it was quite generally believed that these corals lived and grew mainly or even exclusively at the expense of their endosymbionts. This endosymbiosis, however, does not go so far, as has been shown by recent researches, their animal food is usually consumed during the night and therefore during the day-time we do not find any food of animal origin in the gastrovascular system of polyps belonging to corals. It seems that the sessile way of life favoured the stabilization and further development of this mutual relation-

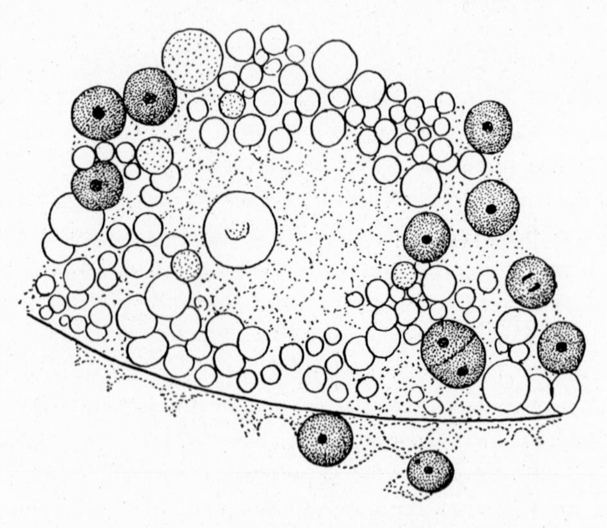

Fig. 41. A section of the egg-cell of *Halecium* sp. with symbiotic zooxanthellae pervading in the egg (from Hadži).

ship, so that finally these algae could be regularly passed over to the eggs, a development which was facilitated by the position of ovaries and by their approachability. It was more than 40 years ago that I was able to show how zooxanthellae actively penetrate into the young egg cells of a species belonging to the hydroid genus *Halecium* (Hadži, 1912 Fig. 41). At about the same time (1906) I succeeded at the then established "Biologische Versuchsanstalt in Wien," which was headed by the well-known experimental zoologist Hans Przibram, in making green *Hydra* colourless, after I had reared the sexually ripe animals in complete darkness (the same experiment was repeated later by others with the same result). Not only as a species but also as a genus, the green *Hydra (Chlorohydra vivridissima)* is so closely connected with its green symbiont that it is only with difficulty able to live without it.

The fact may not be completely without significance that in the lower Turbellaria the symbiotic algae appear everywhere in their interior ("entomesoderm," or better archihiston, according to Steinböck), clearly a sign of a lower level of development. In Cnidaria we find, with a few exceptions, these algae in the intestinal cells only.

Thus the facts that can be observed in the symbiosis between animals and the monocellular algae support my thesis that this symbiosis had been developed as early as in Protozoa, that it had been inherited from these by the lowermost Eumetazoa, then by Turbellaria, and that from these it was transferred to Cnidaria where it has been further evolved.

With this we can conclude the second part of our present study. In it I have endeavoured to make it at least more probable that, contrary to the widely accepted opinion, the phylogenetic development of Cnidaria followed the direction Anthozoa—Scyphozoa—Hydrozoa, a direction which also agrees with the generally accepted principle that the sessile way of life leads both to the radial symmetry and to the retrogression of the organization (especially inasmuch this is connected with the free movement) with a simultaneous progressive development of new or of already present properties that are connected with the sessile way of life, and that in this way a new animal type is being developed. No well-warranted facts are known to me which would be incompatible with this new interpretation. On the contrary, I find that many facts which could not be understood or which were obscure, become understandable and clear if viewed from this standpoint.

CHAPTER 3

THE CONSEQUENCES OF THE NEW INTERPRETATION OF CNIDARIA

In numerous other cases where a similar change of a sequence of subgroups within the frame of larger group had to be made, the consequences of such a change have not been important. It was simply necessary to change the sequence, and this was all. The larger group could still preserve the position it had previously occupied in the natural animal system. In our case, too, we find as the first consequence of the new interpretation of Cnidaria that a similar change inside this group becomes necessary. We must expect in advance and reckon with the fact that the sessile way of life must necessarily lead to a retrogression of the general structure, especially since we have here, taken geologically, a very old animal group. A profounder comparison has shown us that this generally valid rule must also be true for Cnidaria. Thus the evolution of Cnidaria began in all probability with the primarily solitary and only slightly moving anthopolyps, and it continued within this same subgroup so that finally cormic and completely immobile species have developed which have nevertheless preserved, till the present day, clear remains of an earlier bilateral symmetry. In addition to this, the development led to the purely radial symmetric scyphopolyps which have a simpler structure and which were changed partly into the freely swimming medusae; the latter have reached as such a higher level of organization and they have begun as a whole to prevail over the primitive polyp form. The hydropolyp, with its even simpler structure, had not evolved from scyphomedusae but rather from the more primitive scyphopolyps; it had again developed—as a repetition of the development which had already taken place in Scyphozoa—a freely swimming medusa form. Several subgroups of Cnidaria which have in the meantime disappeared had occasionally branched off along the very long road that evolution of Cnidaria had taken. This is how the most probable reconstruction of the phylogeny of Cnidaria should appear in brief outline.

Because of the interpretation which believed in a primary simplicity of Hydrozoa, with *Hydra*, *Protohydra*, *Boreohydra*, etc., at the beginning (an interpretation which we are now obliged to abandon), the Cnidaria have been placed, usually in connection with sponges and with Ctenophora, at the very beginning, at the root of all polycellular animals; they have been branded as animals with two body layers. This group of animals has also been given a special name, that of Coelenterata, in contrast to the more highly developed polycellular animals, the Coelomata, they have, besides the digestive cavity, a second body cavity, the coelom.

This grouping which has been artificially formed has now become senseless. Sponges were the first animals which had to be excluded from this group. They are in reality not Coelenterata at all and the recent attempts which try to make out the sponges as true Coelenterata are therefore useless. Sponges were followed by Ctenophora which were formerly, and even sometimes now, simply called Acnidaria, i.e. animals related to Cnidaria which do not possess cnidae. They are Coelenterata inasmuch as they do not possess a coelom (actually they are Acoelomata, a notion which is considerably broader and more suitable which, however, I do not wish to introduce and even less to propose as a name of a new taxon; yet they are certainly not Coelenterata, as I have shown above, since Coelenterata as such do not exist at all and what is more, they have never existed). The Ctenophora evolved from some somewhat more highly developed Turbellaria (from the planktonic larvae of Polycladida).

In this way only Cnidaria remain, as the last of the Mohicans, in the large group of Coelenterata. As a matter of fact, we can even now find books on zoology (cf. D'Ancona, *Lezioni di Biologia e Zoologia Generale*, 1939) where Cnidaria only appear under the heading of Coelenterata. Nevertheless, they have left an impoverished Coelenterata in the old place of the natural system.

Important problems arise as soon as we place Hydrozoa with their secondarily solitary and simplified species at the end of the system of Cnidaria and when we put the primarily solitary Actiniaria in their stead; such a problem is, for example, the question of how to connect Actiniaria "downwards," or where to derive them from? Can we still continue to use the gastraea theory which is irrevocably connected with the hypothesis that Coelenterata consist of two body layers? Or should we rather take into consideration the next "lower" Eumetazoa, the Turbellaria, which scholars have tried again and again somehow to connect with Coelenterata, usually in the same way as they have tried to derive Turbellaria from Coelenterata. If, however, we accept the opposite thesis, which seems *a priori* to be the more probable one, that Cnidaria had developed from Turbellaria, then suddenly a new difficulty arises; though repeatedly mentioned in passing, nobody (with one exception, O. Steinböck) has ever earnestly attempted to solve the problem of the origin of Turbellaria. This again opens the important question of the origin of the eumetazoan Turbellaria from their protozoan ancestors. Were these Protozoa which stood closest to the present day Euciliata, or colonies of Flagellata?

The zoologist who proposes a new interpretation of the evolution of Cnidaria which he wishes to be generally accepted, is also obliged to give rational answers to all the questions raised above; these answers must be at least more probable than the answers that have been given and defended till now.

In a series of sactions I will endeavour to discuss the most important consequences of the new interpretation of Cnidaria, firstly the detailed problems (e.g. the new system of Cnidaria and the position of Cnidaria in the natural animal system, the probable origin of Cnidaria or the turbellarian theory of Cnidaria) and secondly the more general problems as, for example the origin of Metazoa, the origin of Turbellaria, the relationship between Protozoa and Metazoa, the criticism of Haeckel's theory of a blastea and of a gastraea, as well as the idea of germ layers, the problem of mesoderm and of metamerization, the origin of the ontogeny and its further development together with secondary cellularization, the general division of the animal world connected with a reconstruction of the animal classification—all this connected with an objective discussion of the opposite interpretations.

The New System of Cnidaria

It will be our first task to construct a system of Cnidaria which will be a truly natural system and which will agree with the new interpretation of the origin and of the phyletic development of Cnidaria. Since this is not the right place to discuss in detail various taxonomic problems, we will limit ourselves to an outline of the system as it appears in larger groups or taxons. The division of Cnidaria (the corresponding system category will be later defined) into three main groups remains unchanged since it agrees well with facts; we only have to change the sequence of these three groups into the direction Anthozoa → Scyphozoa → Hydrozoa. With regard to the relationship connections of these three groups with each other we have to take into consideration two possibilities. It is possible either that both Scyphozoa and Hydrozoa had developed independently from each other, from the Anthozoa; or that Scyphozoa had developed from Anthozoa and that later these Scyphozoa themselves had evolved into Hydrozoa, the youngest representatives of Cnidaria. The second possibility seems to be more probable since Scyphozoa appear, so to speak, in the middle between Anthozoa and Hydrozoa. Theoretically, a third type of evolution is also possible, i.e. that all the three subtypes of the Cnidaria had developed in parallel, from a hypothetical indifferent state. Such a concept, however, seems to me as completely improbable. As for the classification however, it is irrelevant which of the possibilities be true. It appears as very probable, in view of the great difference which can be found in the way that the medusa form is primarily developed from the primitive polyp form in the two groups of Cnidaria, that the separation of both Scyphozoa as well as of Hydrozoa took place at a time when neither the former nor the latter had yet developed their medusa forms.

The main characteristics of Anthozoa can be enumerated as follows: (1) they have a muscular gullet (pharynx with siphonoglyphs (2) they have primarily solitary individuals (3) they have a polyp form and no medusa form; (4) they have well-developed longitudinal folds in their intestine, the genuine sarcosepta which are orally connected with the gullet; (5) they form intracellular sclerites which are permeated with the calcium carbonate; (6) they still have a well-developed middle layer.

The following elements are characteristic of Scyphozoa: (1) their "septal apparatus" is strongly reduced in the form of usually four short taeniolae with taeniolan muscles and teaniolan funnels; (2) they have developed scyphomedusae as a special sexual generation which has become the predominant form of Scyphozoa or even a form which alone has been preserved (the hypogenetic species); (3) they do not possess an ectodermal gullet; (4) scyphomedusae are developed, with the exception of the hypogenetic species, where they develop directly from the egg and the lanal cells, from polyps by way of a transverse division.

The following characteristics should be mentioned in connection with Hydrozoa: (1) no traces of sarcosepta or pharynx can any longer be found in their polyps; (2) their middle layer is strongly reduced so they give the impression that they consist of two body layers only; (3) they have developed their own medusa form, the hydromedusa, which is formed primarily by way of budding (and secondarily directly from the egg cell); secondarily the medusa generation is frequently more or less reduced; (4) only they have developed pelagic, polymorphous (also with regard to the medusa form), and strongly individualized cormi (Siphonophora).

Changes that have occurred within the frame of individual groups (subclasses, earlier classes) must also be studied in agreement with this new interpretation of the phylogeny of Cnidaria; they cannot, however, be discussed here in greater detail. As for Anthozoa, we can preserve their present subdivision into two groups of Hexactiniaria (Hexacorallia) and Octactiniaria (Octocorallia), yet with the difference that, in contrast to the present sequence, we give Hexactiniaria the first place, and Octocorallia the second. This is not difficult to justify. The polymerous state with large and not fixed numbers is, according to a very generally valid rule, the primitive state, and the oligomerized state with a fixed and diminished number is secondarily developed from the former. We must therefore reverse the presently valid sequence and put Hexactiniaria into the first place and Octactiniaria into the second place. Other properties of these two groups also agree with this new sequence. Thus we find, for example, the primarily solitary anthopolyps (among these a type with a rounded off aboral end) among the Hexactiniaria only. A dimorphism of polyps and the individualized cormi can be found in Octactiniaria only. Octactiniaria each have (with one exception where we find a different number of septa) eight branched tentacles. Hexacorallia have been given the first place also by some other zoologists (e.g. A Kästner, in his *Lehrbuch der speziellen Zoologie*, yet he does not give his reasons for such a sequence).

It is clear that the first order within the group Hexacorallia is that of Actiniaria. This has usually been the case in earlier classifications, too. As for the remaining orders, we find the equally primarily solitary Ceriantharia regularly placed at the end of Hexacorallia, because of their aberrant septal apparatus; more rarely, however (for example, Beklemischew, 1958), they are considered as a category equal to that of Hexacorallia. It is certain that the Ceriantharia had evolved as a side branch from a root which has remained unknown so far (we cannot expect that we will ever be able to find the corresponding fossil material since we have here animals that possess no skeletons whose development goes far back into geological past). It may be better, however, to place them immediately after the Actiniaria because they have remained, like Actiniaria, primarily solitary animals. They should be followed by the remaining orders: Madreporaria (it is possible that among these there still exist primarily solitary and now already completely immobile species), Antipatharia, and finally Zoantharia. The last two orders are highly specialized, each in its own direction.

Fortunately enough, the subdivision of Octocorallia (Octactiniaria) has already been well made. The most important difference between various systems that have been proposed can be found in the number of subgroups. Some zoologists are satisfied with three orders (Alcyonaria, Gorgonaria, and Pennatularia) while it is believed by others that five orders must be distinguished (Stolonifera, Telestacea, Alcyonacea, Coenothecalia, Gorgonacea, and Pennatulacea). This difference, however, is not important in connection with the present study.

At present, we are hardly able to determine with certainty where and when Scyphozoa had branched off from the Anthozoa. Those Anthozoa which stand closest to the present day Stolonifera among Octocorallia, represent in all probability the starting point for the evolution of Scyphozoa (Fig. 42). This development had probably taken place at a time when their ancestors did not yet of necessity possess branched tentacles and when their polyps, which were protected by a periderm that extended high over the body of the animal, formed the "creeping" (stolonate) cormi. Medusae began to be developed from some intermediate forms which have now become extinct. Viewed from our standpoint we must put into the first place of the classification of Scyphozoa those species where the two generations are found equally well developed, where both the periderm as well as the formation of cormi can be observed in the polyp generation, and where the medusa form stands closest to the polyp form. A definite classification of the more primitive Scyphozoa will only be possible when we know the whole life-cycle of a majority of species belonging to them. Now

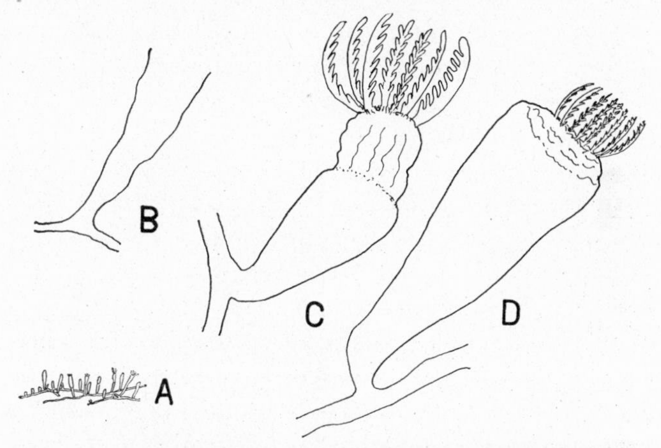

Fig. 42. A stoloniferous octocoral *(Cornularia cornucopiae)* with peridermal theca. A, a colony (cormus) nat. size (after Delage and Hérouard). B, empty periderm. C-D two polyps (orig.).

we are able to propose a provisional system only. It can be said in connection with the numerous attempts to develop a system of Scyphozoa which have been proposed till now (this group has been usually and improperly called Scyphomedusae) that all these attempts completely disregard the actually primary polyp generation (this is usually mentioned as a polypoid larva, as a "scyphistoma"). Scyphopolyps are not even mentioned among the enumerated characteristic properties of individual subgroups.

Two peculiarities of these systems can be mentioned as common to almost all the attempts which we have not the space to enumerate here. The first is that the order Lucernariidea is placed at the beginning and that of Rhizostomae at the end of the system; the second generally prevalent characteristic of this system is that Lucernariidea are followed by Carybdeidea (also called Cubomedusae), and Rhizostomae by Semaeostomata. The fifth order Coronata is placed in the middle (this is the sequence in Krumbach's *Handbuch der Zoologie*). Frequently, we find three orders only mentioned (e.g. by Claus), and the two orders Semaeostomata and Rhizostomae united in one order (as Discomedusae or Discophora), and the first two orders grouped together as Calycozoa, etc.

It is clear already now that Lucernariidea cannot be placed at the basis of the system of Scyphozoa, even if they give the impression of being more primitive forms. It is completely impossible that scyphomedusae had developed from scyphopolyps during their sessile way of life, as was formerly believed by Goette in connection with hydromedusae. Taking into consideration the well-founded supposition that the polyp is the primary form, we must consider it as possible that the broadened oral half had been separated by means of a transverse division from the aboral half of the polyp which continued to live as a sessile animal. This oral half had simultaneously taken over the gonads and was transformed into a medusa. We must therefore explain the mixture of characteristic properties of the polypoid and medusoid forms that can be observed in Lucernariidea, and that has been correctly emphasized by numerous specialists (especially by Krumbach and by Tochru Uchida, 1929) as being due to the fact that the separation of the medusoid half had been secondarily discontinued (we will meet something similar in Hydrozoa), and that since then the medusoid form has become well enough adjusted to the life in the benthos so that finally something new has been developed as a result of this amalgamation. The transverse division (not the budding) which takes place but once, seems also to be a primary event; it can be repeated after the passage of an interval of time; this can lead finally to a quick series of multiple transverse divisions, a development which has been called a strobilation and which can thus be considered as a secondary phenomenon. In the blindly ending trend of the Lucernariidea, the monodiscal strobilation without a separation has appeared as a consequence of a regressive evolution.

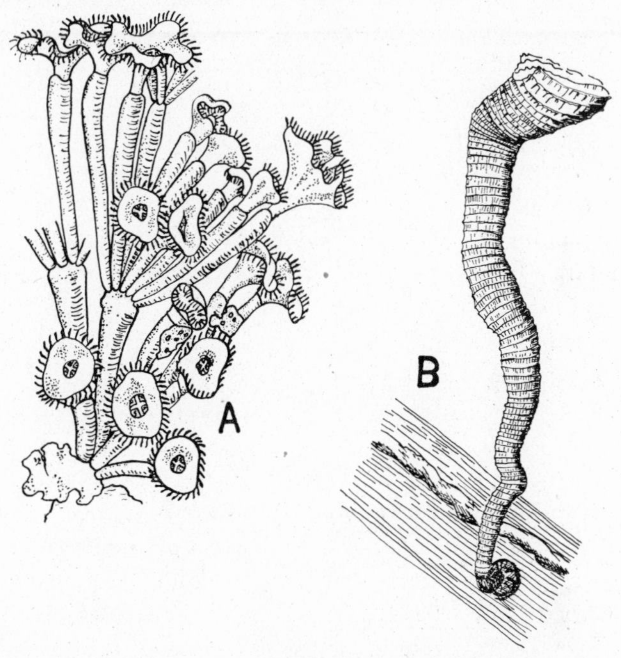

Fig. 43. Two species of scyphopolyps with peridermal thecae. A, *Nausithoë* sp. (from Komai). B, "*Tubularia striata*" Vanhöffen a solitary scyphopolyp of unknown systematic position; (after Vanhöffen).

In this way Cubomedusae, or rather Carybdeidea, come into the first place; they should be followed by Lucernariidea (they have also been called, less fortunately, Stauromedusae). The further sequence can remain the same as it now usually appears in these classifications, i.e., Coronata, Semaeostomata, and Rhizostomae. The polyp generation of the Coronata show a few signs of primitivism as has already been mentioned

(Fig. 43). The ending "-medusae" should rather be avoided since in Scyphozoa there is—as far as we know on the basis of our present research—not a single large systematic group (e.g. an order) which includes the hypogenetic species (i.e., the medusa forms) only. I have discussed this problem at a greater length in another study (Hadži, 1955 a).

No radical changes are necessary because of the new interpretation of Cnidaria in connection with orders that belong to Hydrozoa. The order Hydroidea has been, and still remains, the basis order of Hydrozoa and there can be no doubt that other orders had evolved from it. No primarily solitary hydropolyps exist any longer. All those species that live now as solitary animals, as well as those that do not have any tentacles, are a result of a secondary development. For the present two additional orders, besides that of Hydroidea, are sufficient, i.e., Trachylina, as a group of all the hypogenetic species which have been wrongly interpreted to be highly primitive animals yet which are, in fact, highly specialized forms (just as in the case of the benthonic *Hydra* which occurs in the polypoid form only); and Siphonophora. As for Trachylina, it seems very probable that they evolved diphyletically, once as Narcomedusae, and the second time as Trachomedusae. It can therefore be expected that sooner or later it will become necessary to make a sharper distinction between these two groups of Hydrozoa if we continue to make taxonomic distinctions between two "sister groups" that had evolved separately even if they look similar, because their evolutions pursued two parallel ways and because their roots were closely related to each other.

With regard to Siphonophora it can now be considered as certain that they had evolved from the benthonic cormi of the polypo-medusoid athecate Hydroidea (Hadži, 1918, 1954). They therefore represent the climax in the progressive evolution within the order Hydrozoa and thus also of Cnidaria as a whole. In these the polymorphism is finally extended to the medusoid form also. The individualization of cormi, the way to which had been prepared as early as in Anthozoa, finds its climax in the Siphonophora.

It was in agreement with the old interpretation which believed in a progressive evolution of Cnidaria, that within the Hydroidea, the Athecata were considered quite generally and

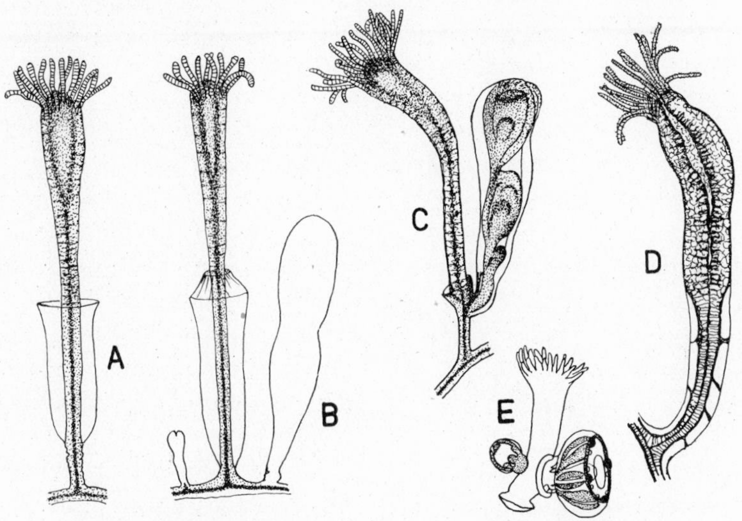

Fig. 44. The progressive and regressive evolution of the hydrothecae. A, *Hebella* sp. B, *Lafoëina vilae-velebiti* Hadži, with operculate hydrotheca; C, *Haleciella microtheca* Hadži. D, *Halanthus adriaticus* Hadži, the theca has fully disappeared, and remains only as the tonofibrilles. E, *Eugymnantha inquilina* Palombi, a "thecate hydroid" without the rest of periderm (A-D after Hadži, E, after Palombi).

without exception in comparison with the Thecata, as the more primitive initial group. It was considered that since Athecata have simpler forms that they must also be the more primitive animals; at the same time solitary species, and above all Hydra, have been known as Athecata. There are no really solitary Thecata, close to this state is only the species *Eugymnantha inquilina* Palombi (Fig. 44). Furthermore, it is known that the cormi of Thecata show a higher degree of individualization than those of Athecata. Because of the new interpretation of the origin and the evolution of Cnidaria, and also of Hydrozoa, we are forced to change the sequence, i.e. we consider Thecata as the more primitive group ot Hydroidea. A whole series of facts make it probable that the rich evolution of Hydroidea had begun with the Thecata. First we must imagine the most probable way in which the Hydrozoa eventually developed from Scyphozoa. It may prove useful to trace even further back in phylogeny, back to the origin of Scyphozoa. The reader will remember that I derive the Scyphozoa, especially their polyps, from the so-called "creeping" and therefore stolonate cormi of Anthozoa (probably from some forms that stood closest to the ancestors of Stolonifera, among the recent Octactiniaria) that had developed a cuticular periderm, (which can be easily distinguished from the skin high over their anthocodium, the head of the polyp; Fig. 43). It was from the Scyphozoa, which had the polyp form only and which did not yet produce a medusa generation, that the equally stolonate and creeping cormi of Hydroidea was in all probability developed, first in the form of hydropolyps. The personal part of the hydropolyp had been further divided into the basal and undifferentiated stem and into the differentiated head (hydranth). The hydrotheca with its special form had evolved in several directions from the undifferentiated peridermal part, reaching its climax in those species which have an automatically closing cover lid (Fig. 44). During this phase of the progressive evolution, the Hydrozoa already began to produce their medusae, a development which was independent from the otherwise similar morphogenetic process of the formation of medusae that can be found in Scyphozoa—as has already been repeatedly emphasized in the present study; in Scyphozoa the medusae formed by means of a transverse division, and in the thecate Hydroidea from the separated buds of hydranths. This also agrees with the fact that quite generally budding as a consequence of a prolonged sessile way of life prevails over transverse division.

The species (genera and families) with a more or less cylindrical or with a down-turned conic hydrotheca, with the formation of medusae as individual buds, and without the theca lid, should be placed at the beginning of the system of Hydroidea (e.g. Hebellidae). The subsequent evolution of Thecata diverged into several directions with a great variety in the forms of thecae, with polymorphism, retrogression of the medusa form, and with various forms of cormi which can also include individualized forms (a secondary monopodial growth). A special direction in evolution can be observed in those species whose hydrotheca has been progressively reduced (fam. Haleciidae) so that finally these animals have completely ceased to form a theca (fam. Campanopsidae). The last remains of a former theca can be found in the so-called tonofibrils which in the Thecata had provided an elastic connection between the basis of the theca and the hydranth (the so-called luminous dots over the diaphragm which separate the hydranth from its stem). This is how we can understand the evolution of the Athecata from the Thecata. The possibility cannot be completely excluded that the evolution from a thecate to an athecate state did not occur once only, yet such a polyphyletic development must be first specifically proved.

This is not the right place to discuss all the details. It should suffice that we give here in a broad outline, a new and more suitable system of Hydrozoa, as it appears if we view Hydrozoa as animals that have evolved from Scyphozoa. The old systems which are mainly based on the actinula hypothesis and which try to avoid comparisons between hydromedusae and scyphomedusae must now be abandoned. The classification of Cnidaria must be necessarily based on the morphology of the main primitive form which is common to all Cnidaria, i.e. that of the polyp. The hypogenetic species that can be found both among Hydrozoa as well as among Scyphozoa, are a result of a secondary development. This development, however, had followed two different lines which can be understood only if we take into consideration the way that medusae had evolved in both these cases from their respective polyps. In Scyphozoa again this development had pursued two completely different paths; in the first type of development the medusoid distal half of the polyp had remained attached and this was followed by a reduction and by a change of the medusa form. In the second type the planula continued to exist in the plankton, the polypoid generation has been omitted and it is in this way that the scyphomedusa can develop directly from a planula. This second variant has been repeated in Hydrozoa—we speak here of the hypogenetic species or even groups, using the expression as it was proposed by Haeckel (Trachylina). The Hydromedusae remain attached to their cormi because here medusae are developed from the whole hydranth (and not out of half only), and that by way of budding; these medusae are afterwards changed into a more and more reduced medusoid form which can finally completely disappear, the polyp generation which was earlier sterile is now changed into a sexual and the only existing generation.

The classification of Hydrozoa, and especially that of Hydroidea, which tries to express the evolutionary path these animals had taken, must be based on conditions that can be observed in their polyp generation; yet at the same time it must also take into consideration the younger medusa generation as regards the details of morphology. It is important that we adhere, in our endeavours to work out the details of this system, to the fact that Hydroidea do not include any primarily solitary species, and that in these animals solitarization has been evolved several times, along several lines of evolution (Fig. 45). This is not a theoretical supposition but it can be also easily observed in the recent material (in the so-called Limnomedusae).

It seems that three orders are sufficient for the division of Hydrozoa, i.e. Hydroidea, Trachylinea, Siphonophora. Since we do not know which, taken geologically, of Siphonophora and Trachylinea is the older (it is even possible that both of them had evolved diphyletically), so it is the same if the first place is given to the first or to the second group. It was a retrograde step in the classification of Hydrozoa when the accepted rank of order was given to two families by Hyman in spite of the fact that this classification has now been found to be erroneous; to Stylasteridae (they are valued by Stechow only as

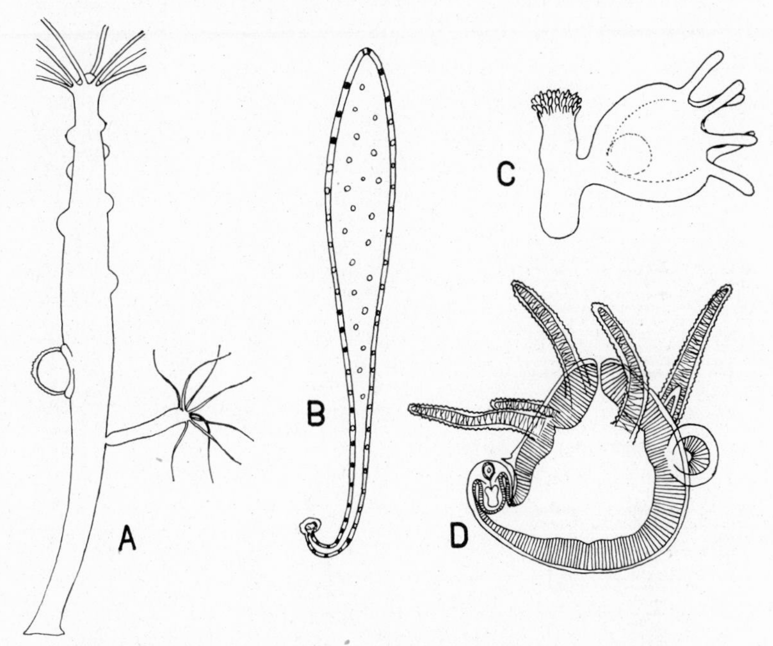

Fig. 45. A few secondarily solitary hydropolyps. A, *Hydra* sp. B, *Protohydra* sp. C, "*Microhydra*"-polyp of *Craspedacusta* sp.: D. "*Haleremita*"-polyp of *Gonionemus* sp. (after various authors.).

a subfamily), and to Milleporidae (which have also been degraded by Stechow to the rank of a subfamily).

In spite of the fact that from our viewpoint there can be no doubt that the Hydrozoa had inherited their tendency to alternation of generations from their scyphozoan ancestors, it seems nevertheless more probable that the ancestors of the present Hydrozoa had separated from the ancient Scyphozoa before the latter had developed their own medusa generation.

Thus the typical alternation of generations, medusa: polyp, had evolved twice, and each time from its own root. In spite of the great similarities that can be observed in the forms and basic organisations of scyphomedusae and hydromedusae—a fact which can be explained as due to the similarities that exist in scyphopolyps and hydropolyps—there exist considerable differences between the two medusa forms especially as regards the way how they are developed. With the exception of the secondarily acquired hypogenesis, we find that all the scyphomedusae develop without any exception from scyphopolyps by way of an unequal transverse division, while all the hydromedusae develop equally, without any exception, by way of budding. The division must be considered as the more primitive form of the asexual reproduction, and budding as its more advanced form. I wish to mention in passing that as early as in the Anthozoa we can find in the higher subtype of the Octactiniaria budding only as the form of their vegetative reproduction while division prevails in the Hexactiniaria. In the scyphozoan polyps budding prevails, yet transverse division has been preserved in the formation of the medusa generation.

It should be mentioned in passing that it is already time that the hydroidologists as well as other zoologists adhere strictly to the names Thecata (after Fleming, 1828), and Athecata (after Hincks, 1868) when they speak of the two groups of Hydroidea; they should avoid the awkward names Calyptoblastea (or even Calyptoblastiques), Thecaphora, or the too narrowly interpreted Campanulariidea (Stechow, 1922), Gymnoblastea (Gymnoblastiques with the addition Hydroida), Tubulariidea (Stechow, 1922). The double names: Thecaphorae–Leptomedusae and Athecatae–Anthomedusae (after Broch, 1924) can also be dispensed with.

Capitata (Kühn, 1914; Coryninea, according to Stechow, 1922) have been placed, within the group Athecata, in front of Filifera or Bougainvillinea; this has been so because it has been believed that the actinula with tentacles that had thickened ends represents the starting point not only in the evolution of Hydroidea or Hydrozoa but also of Cnidaria as a whole. It is quite possible that we have here two parallel lines of evolution both of which end in very specialized solitary forms; once with Hydrae, the other time with Branchioceriantinae.

The Rank and the Position of Cnidaria in the Animal Classification

According to our interpretation, Cnidaria represents a blindly ending side branch on the main stem of Turbellaria. The Cnidaria assume the position or the category (taxon) of a class within the stem (phylum) of Ameria. Thus the three subgroups, Anthozoa, Scyphozoa, and Hydrozoa, are in reality three subclasses. A graphic representation of this position and of their division will be found in the final chapter of the present study.

The Cnidaria with this, as we believe, well-founded, connection with Turbellaria to which we will later return, lose the isolated position they have enjoyed till now. It seems to us therefore an exaggeration when they are given the rank of a phylum, as has recently been done by Hyman, by Kästner, and by numerous other scholars. I consider that the category (taxon) of a phylum should be used less liberally and that the number of phyla must be limited to the absolute minimum. I will later show that a very small number of recent phyla is in reality fully sufficient (thus the Eumetazoa can be divided well enough into four phyla). Usually we will find the taxon of a "class" to be satisfactory.

As a welcome side effect of the new classification which tries to avoid the high categories of Radiata and Coelenterata (after the system by A. S. Pearson, the editor of the *Zoological Names*, etc., prepared for the Section of American Association for the Advancement of Science, Durham, N. C., 1949), we find that the whole animal system becomes considerably simplified. This has not only a scientific value but also a value in teaching (Hadži, 1952 a). We must discourage the use of the group phylum Coelenterata (Leuckart 1848 after A. S. Pearson) instead of Cnidaria, regardless of priority which is anyhow not internationally binding in connection with the names of the highest categories. I have already emphasized that the notion, and thus also the category, of Coelenterata—and correspondingly the opposite notion of Coelomata—have now become completely superfluous because they do not find support in the natural facts. They must now take their place in the archives. If we have to dismiss the group Coelenterata then we must also necessarily abandon the group which represents the opposite to Cnidaria and which has been given the name of Acnidaria. These are in reality Ctenophora that constitute a class of Ameria, which has the same rank as Cnidaria because they had evolved from Turbellaria parallel to, and independently from, Cnidaria.

The Cnidaria, together with Turbellaria, Ctenophora, Trematoda and Cestoda seem to be somewhat more closely connected because of one important common property, and that is that they all are aproctous animals, i.e. their digestive tract does not possess a primary anal orifice. In spite of this it is unnecessary to establish a special category which would include all of them and to give it a special name. In practice the usual pair Aprocta–Euprocta can be well enough used in comparative morphology.

It is unfortunate that, even recently, attempts have been made to use for systematic purposes such an antiquated notion as that of Radialia (or some similar ones) even if it appears with a somewhat changed scope (e.g. without Echinodermata). This attempt has been made, by Beklemischev (1958) who classifies Ctenophora as Acnidaria among Radialia. In both cases the radial symmetry, which is usually partial only, had evolved, as has been already shown, secondarily from the bilateral symmetry. Moreover, the structure of Ctenophora is in reality bisymmetric and not radially symmetric. Parallel to the necessary abolition of the notion Radialia (or Radiata) we must also abandon the opposite notion of Bilateria. The structure of all Eumetazoa was originally bilaterally symmetric and it was secondarily only, usually as a consequence of a prolonged sessile way of life, that they have developed a more or less explicit inclination to the radial symmetry.

Each change of the animal system, especially when it involves the higher systematic categories, is unwelcome and scholars will therefore try to avoid it. Yet if we endeavour to develop a natural system we are obliged to change this system until it agrees with facts and with the interpretations that are based on them. It is all the better if a simplification of this classifacition appears as a result of our endeavours.

Discussion of the New Interpretation of the Evolution of Cnidaria

The division of the taxon Cnidaria—regardless of the system category which should be attributed to it—into the next lower units, has been so firmly accepted by expert zoologists and by others, in the sequence Hydrozoa → Scyphozoa → Anthozoa that no attempt will be easily accepted which tries to change this sequence. This is, in my opinion, not only a consequence of an otherwise healthy conservatism which suggests caution; it is also due to the fact that the suggested change of a widely accepted sequence has not been supported by a discovery of, for example, a "living fossil," or at least by some special new facts. The majority of zoologists have been influenced even more by the consequences which this new interpretation implies, than by the first two motives.

In spite of the fact that the first publication of my thesis appeared as early as in 1944, the new sequence of the groups of Cnidaria has not found acceptance, as far as I know, in any manual or text book on neozoology. It should be remembered here that some palaeozoologists (Schindewolf, 1950;

Kühn, 1939) have emphasized even before the publication of my study, that the Anthozoa with a primary bilaterally symmetric organization should be regarded as the most primitive Cnidaria, even if these scholars did not use quite the same words. To the best of my knowledge there were only a few neo-zoologists who, prior to the publication of my studies, expressed the idea of a primitive character for bilateral symmetry in Anthozoa; thus Haacke (1879 and 1893) who suggested, that the primitive group "zoophyta" were bilaterally symmetrical, and that radial symmetry had developed due to the transition to the sessile way of life. F. Pax (1910), an expert in Anthozoa, must also be mentioned; he wrote very cautiously, and limiting himself to Anthozoa, as follows, "Man könnte daher geneigt sein, die Aktinien von fusslosen, kriechenden oder grabenden Formen mit bilateraler Symmetrie abzuleiten, die später mit dem Übergange zur festsitzenden Lebensweise eine radiale Symmetrie erworben haben." Pax believed that the subsequent evolution depended on the type of development of the aboral end of the animal body (whether a foot disc was present or not). In the study on Hexacorallia which was written by Pax and which appeared in the large German work *Handbuch der Zoologie* (edited by Kükenthal–Krumbach), Pax did not express this his opinion, clearly because he had to comply with the systematic division that had already been determined by the editors. In 1954 Pax agreed entirely with my suggestion.

Jägersten (1955 and 1959) has accepted my views regarding the priority of Anthozoa. It is true that Jägersten did not do this as a cnidariologist, nor for the reasons which have induced me to consider Anthozoa as the first group of Cnidaria, but rather because he has found my interpretation suits his theory of a bilaterogastraea, a theory which I will return to later. Marcus (1958:26) adopts the interpretation we find in Jägersten's work.

Kästner, even if he is under the influence of the fascinating ideas that had been formulated by Haeckel, has nevertheless written in his most recent "Lehrbuch der speziellen Zoologie" (1:92) the gratifying note that it is "keineswegs entschieden, ob die traditionelle Reihenfolge Hydrozoa, Scyphozoa, Anthozoa der Stammesgeschichte entspricht, und ob die Coelenterata stammesgeschichtlich die Wurzel der Bilateria bilden oder einen frühen, blind endigenden Seitenast der Eumetazoa."

It was in the form of rhetoric questions only that Ulrich (1951:260) expressed his support of the idea of the primitive character of Anthozoa within the frame of Cnidaria. These questions refer to actual difficulties one meets if one tries to consider the Hydrozoa as the most primitive Cnidaria. Ulrich concludes his discussion of the problem with the observation, "lassen sich alle Schwierigkeiten recht gut beheben, wenn man die Evolution des heutigen Cnidariënmaterials nicht als progressiv, sondern als regressiv beurteilt." Simultaneously Ulrich promises a special work which will discuss this theme; to the best of my knowledge, however, nothing has so far been published.

Remane, too, is undecided when he writes on Cnidaria in the extensive *Handbuch der Biologie* which is still being published under the editorship of L. von Bertalanffy. In the text Remane preserves the traditional sequence of the three classes of Cnidaria. In the final paragraph ("Phylogenie, Systematik"), however, Remane states as follows, "Den phylogenetischen Zusammenhang der drei Klassen Hydrozoa, Scyphozoa und Anthozoa kennen wir noch nicht... Wer der einfacheren Organisation hohe stammesgeschichtliche Bedeutung zumisst, wird die Hydrozoen als primitivste Gruppe betrachten, doch lassen sich mit gleicher Berechtigung auch andere Auffassungen vertreten." We can see the reverse sequence—whose correctness I have tried to prove—to be more justified in the fact that later Remane himself has made a more positive statement in favour of the new interpretation (Remane, 1960). On the basis of a statement made by Steinböck (1958) and according to which Coelenterata as well as the oldest Metazoa as a whole had been bilaterally symmetric animals we can think Steinböck, too, considers the Anthozoa as the most primitive Cnidaria. I think that I am justified to include Sir Gavin de Beer among those prominent zoologists to have repeatedly evaluated positively my suggestions regarding the evolution of the Cnidaria (1948, 1951, 1958).

The Probable Origin of Cnidaria

We come now to the question of what the origin of Cnidaria could be if we declare the Anthozoa as the most primitive Cnidaria? Is it impossible to change the now prevalent opinion according to which the Cnidaria evolved as the lowest Eumetazoa from some colonies (cormi) of Flagellata by way of the three stages moraea–blastea–gastraea? This second question also remains if we take into consideration other initial forms, e.g. a placula, a parenchymella, a parenchymula, a planea, a planula, a phagocytella, etc., instead of a gastraea; all these forms are in reality variants only, which do not differ in principle from the classical form even if they are held in high esteem by a number of scholars.

At first, one feels inclined to say that a reversion of the line of evolution of the three subgroups of Cnidaria is incompatible with the traditional derivation of Cnidaria from an ancestral form similar to a gastraea. The difference between such a form and an anthopolyp seems to be too great and a more extensive change of the old interpretation seems to be a necessity. So far there have been, to my knowledge, two attempts only to overcome these difficulties. The first such attempt was made by Remane (1920), and the second by Jägersten (1955). The motives for such attempts lay in both these cases outside the sphere of the comparative morphology of Cnidaria; both were closely connected with the problem of the formation of the coelom. Remane adheres in his interpretation closer to the old concept. He finds the primitive form in an "Urcoelenterate" with four gastral pockets and thus with a radial symmetry; yet at the same time he admits the possibility that this "Ausgangsform der Cnidaria vor ihrer Festsetzung einige bilaterale Züge des Baues schon besass." Jägersten, on the other hand, constructs a completely new initial form which he calls a "bilatero-gastraea" (Fig. 55). This, at first sight, original and ingenious construction, however, has all the characteristics of a so-called "suitcase theory" *(Koffertheorie)*. Jägersten places into this constructions all those elements which he afterwards needs in his subsequent derivations. This is clearly a combination of the gastraea theory as it had been proposed by Haeckel (Jägersten [1955:333] himself admits that it is a "modification of Haeckel's theory"), and of the enterocoele theory as it had been proposed by Sedgwick, with the addition of an otherwise sound idea which had already been supported by several other scholars that the structure of the primitive form had after all been bilaterally symmetrical, and that this form as such had crept over the bottom of the sea. The construction as it has been proposed by Jägersten shows therefore numerous advantages over the interpretation as given by Remane. Yet if we look at Jägersten's bilaterogastraea from a somewhat different angle we find in it a similarity to the primitive Turbellaria, a similarity which Jägersten himself failed to notice. Jägersten had to overcome both great and small difficulties when he derived all other larger types of Eumetazoa, including sponges, from this bilaterogastraea. These difficulties force him to take refuge in a very large number of speculations (it is quite true, however, that we cannot avoid speculating to a certain extent). We miss among these large types (Cnidaria, Ctenophora, Coelomata) a direct derivation of the actually coelomless Coelomata which do not possess an anal orifice (by a coelom we understand in reality a perigastrocoele and not a gonocoele). Jägersten, however, mixes up these two notions; he believes the enterocoele theory to be changed now into a gonocoele theory, as he states this himself

(1955:353). The final result of all this is that the intestinal pockets become at one time an enterocoele (= perigastrocoele), and another time a gonocoele (in a large number and without any actual order in Nemertinea). This, however, is not the right place to make an analysis of the other statements that have been made by Jägersten.

A criticism of Haeckel's concept of the origin of Cnidaria must naturally be extended to the modifications of the same concept as found in the works by Remane and by Jägersten (together with Naef); they have both preserved Haeckel's basic ideas. The situation becomes even worse, because we find here, in addition to the old mistakes, a new blunder also, i.e. the idea of a colonial origin of Eumetazoa (Coelenterata); moreover, the old idea of enterocoely is here found transferred to an earlier phyletic stage in order to preserve the validity of Haeckel's so-called "fundamental biogenetic law" and of the gastraea theory, while at the same time not a single real argument is given by the author which could support his suggestions. The only progress which can be found in Jägersten's interpretation, if it is compared with similar older combinations, lies in the fact that he believes in an early transition of the "blastea" to a life on the sea bottom and, in connection with this, in a transformation of the form of its body in the sense of a bilateral symmetry (this constructed primitive form has therefore been called by the author a bilaterogastraea*).

The main difference which exists between Jägersten's standpoint and the interpretation proposed in the present study is that we both come to the conclusion that it is necessary to reverse the phylogenetic sequence of the subgroups of Cnidaria while at the same time we have both begun

* Prof. O. Steinböck has kindly called my attention to the fact that as early as in 1874 Haeckel had suggested that some gastraea which had sunk to the sea botton began to creep over the substratum and in this way had developed bilateral symmetry; it was called by Haeckel a gastraea bilateralis (repens).

our research from two completely different starting points and motivated by two different aims. Jägersten wishes to improve and therefore to save the old concept, and in this he finds an obstacle in the old interpretation of the evolution of Cnidaria; this induces him to reverse the direction of the evolution of Cnidaria. I, on the other hand, have started my research with a study of Cnidaria; facts which had already been known have induced me to submit to a revision of the connections that exist first among the Cnidaria themselves, which was followed by a study of the relationship connections among Coelenterata, and finally among Metazoa. Ultimately, this has led me to a new interpretation of the evolution of the animal world. As a result I have found that it has become necessary to make much more radical changes in the present interpretations (starting with a reform of the system of Cnidaria) than those changes that have been proposed by Jägersten and by other well-known zoologists.

Jägersten, and Remane before him, have only made the situation increasingly worse. This has happened in such a way that on one hand the contrast between a primary mesenchyme and a secondary coelothelium (mesoderm s.str.) which was previously quite unpleasant, has now become all the more acute; and, on the other hand, the uncertainty regarding the groups of Ameria which do not possess an actual coelom s. str. (perigastrocoele) and even less a metameric perigastrocoele has become all the more evident. Jägersten could not, as it seems, accept unreservedly a solution, dictated by this situation, of a large scale retrogressive evolution while at the same time Remane finds himself obliged to admit such a possibility. Jägersten remains silent about all this while at the same time he promises a special study; yet to the best of my knowledge no such study has not appeared so far. It would have been better if Jägersten in order to remain consistent, had gone further and connected his bilaterogastraea with the Enterocoela, since it is clear that Annelida are Ecterocoela. It is improbable, because it is unfounded, that a retrogressive evolution of freely moving animals could possibly have reached the extent that Remane, and even more so Jägersten, are obliged to construct. The problem of the "mesoderm" becomes complicated beyond any solution (see p. 100 in Jägersten's study, 1959). Jägersten will finally be obliged to admit the existence of a coelenterate type, and this in an even wider scope than was previously done by Haeckel, who even classified Platyhelminthes among Coelenterata. This is more consistent since Platyhelminthes are in reality not Coelomata in the usual sense of the word; see in this connection Jägersten's discussion of Xenoturbella (1959:101). The uncertainty Jägersten finally feels can be seen in the fact that in his diagram (1955: Fig. 8, p. 352) he does not use the notion and the category of Coelenterata in opposition to Coelomata—he only mentions Cnidaria and Ctenophora. In a more recent publication (1959:101) he quite misleadingly classifies Xenoturbella among Coelenterata, yet in the same paragraph he also speaks of the "so-called coelenterates."

It is not important that I have been the first neo-zoologist who has (earlier and independently from Jägersten) come to the conclusion, on the basis of a study of comparative morphology, that the Anthozoa had evolved as the earliest form of Cnidaria. The important thing is that I have come to this conclusion by means of a study of comparative morphology while taking into consideration the ecological conditions. Because of this new situation it has become necessary to try to find the probable origin of Cnidaria: it was in this way that new problems arose and that a whole new sphere of research has been opened.

It was clear from the very beginning that the old concept can be used no longer in this new situation, even if it has been used so long without any reservations in spite of the fact that there have been numerous well-known zoologists who have expressed doubts about the foundations of the same concept, such as is the so-called "fundamental biogenetic law" as it was formulated by Haeckel, and the hypothesis that the polycellular animals had evolved from some colonies of monocellular animals. In this situation it was most obvious to think first of the Turbellaria. The Turbellaria have been interpreted by almost all zoologists and above all by experts in Turbellaria, as "Coelomata" with a primarily primitive structure. The zoologists who represent an exception here are those who adhere to the enterocoele theory, i.e., those who, like Sedgwick, try to deduce the metamery of Eucoelomata from the cyclomery of anthopolyps. The typical Turbellaria, however, i.e. the higher Turbellaria which stand above the Acoela and which are usually taken into consideration by zoologists when Turbellaria are mentioned, seem to be more highly developed than Cnidaria because of their organization and above all because of their extremely complex hermaphroditic genital apparatus. For all these reasons it appeared as an almost hopeless task to try to derive the Cnidaria from the Turbellaria.

This situation, however, changes quickly when we take into consideration the frequently noticed fact that here we have a case of a transition from the freely mobile to a sessile way of life. Take for example Endoprocta (Kamptozoa), Ectoprocta (Bryozoa), etc. Even among the Turbellaria themselves the sexual apparatus shows a high degree of variability and there are some recent species of Turbellaria with a very simple genital apparatus. We are therefore fully justified in concluding that the possibilities of negative mutations had existed at the time when the ancestors of Cnidaria first evolved from the old forms of Turbellaria. It should be mentioned in passing that a reduction of the genital apparatus did not take place in individual cases of parasitism (e.g. in *Fecampia)* that can be observed among the more highly developed Turbellaria, but also in several cases of Ameria whose development from Turbellaria can be considered as more than probable (e.g. Nemertini, Gastrotricha, etc.). Such a reduction took place even while free mobility was preserved. It has already been shown that the last traces of the hermaphroditic state can still be found in Anthozoa. It is probable that Cnidaria branched off from their turbellarian ancestors even before the same was done by Nemertinea and by Gastrotricha.

It has already been shown that all the differences that exist between the anthopolyps of the Cnidaria and the Turbellaria can be divided into two groups: the first group includes those changes which had been brought about by the transition to the sessile way of life usually characterized by some kind of reduction, and the second group which, though connected with the sessility, must be interpreted as a result of a progressive evolution (cnidae, tentacles, strong contractility, etc.). All these properties can be found developed earlier than in Cnidaria, even if then only to a lesser degree.

In view of the fact that there is now hardly a single zoologist who could doubt that the Turbellaria represent the starting point in the evolution of many other animal types, it may be possible to accept at least as a possibility that Cnidaria, too, had evolved from some turbellarian ancestors, provided that the anthopolyps are the most primitive among the free and solitary polyps of Cnidaria. There are now few experts in Turbellaria who still support the interpretation which sees in the acoelous Turbellaria as well as in the Turbellaria as a whole, a result of a retrogressive evolution. The most prominent among these scholars is Marcus, a well-known expert in Turbellaria, who goes his own way in his interpretations of the phylogeny of the animal world (E. Marcus, 1958:52, Fig. 1). It would take us too long to investigate his opinions in detail here. He and I speak two different languages, and his line of thought remains unintelligible to me (e.g. when Marcus considers the larvae of Anthozoa to represent a special animal group; or, when he refers, on one hand, to a similarity between the form of cleavage in Ctenophora, and on the other in the ctenostome and cheilostome Ectoprocta, which he prefers to call Bryozoa). Marcus too, it seems, considers my interpretation as undiscussable, for he maintains a complete silence about it; it is improbable that my interpretation could have remained unknown to him since he must have read at least my article which appeared in *Systematic Zoology*.

When we have suceeded in suggesting that it was at least probable that the Cnidaria, with Anthozoa as their first group, had evolved from Turbellaria, we soon meet a new problem, i.e. which subgroup of Turbellaria can be considered as the closest relation of the Cnidaria? In our attempts to solve problems where the theoretical or logical conclusions cannot be avoided (they can also be called speculations) we must be constantly aware of the fact that the animals concerned had long ago ceased to exist, that the information at our disposal covers the recent animals only, that no transitional forms are available, and that nothing is known of a possible existence of some other "side branches" which have now disappeared without leaving any trace. We must be content with the determination of the degrees of probability.

Initially we were helped, by the fact that among the recent animal groups we do not find progressive and specialized species only, but also some more primitive forms. The possibility of arriving at a correct solution of such a problem is therefore not quite so small.

Scholars, in their earlier endeavours to make phylogenetic deductions, have tried to go far back and to identify indifferent initial forms or ancestors. The planula hypothesis can be mentioned here as a typical example which is at the same time closely connected with our problem itself. It was concluded, under the influence of the so-called "fundamental biogenetic law" that a polycellular organism had originally existed, similar to a planula of Cnidaria; and that it had evolved from an equally hypothetic gastraea which itself was considered as a possible starting point for the evolution of three groups of Coelenterata: Spongiaria–Cnidaria–Ctenophora. It was the third group only which had formed the basis for further progressive evolution in the direction of Coelomata. There are many zoologists who still adhere more or less to this interpretation. In our case we should attempt to derive the Cnidaria from the lowest Turbellaria, thus from Acoela. Yet even a slightly closer comparison shows that this cannot be made. Anthopolyps—taking into consideration the solitary forms only—have a much more highly developed organization than the Acoela, even if there are some recent species of Acoela which already possess a complex genital apparatus.

Among the Turbellaria we must search for forms that had later evolved into Anthozoa among those groups that are already more highly developed than the Acoela. A completely unjustified accusation has been made by Remane (1960) who states that I wish to derive the Cnidaria from the Temnocephala. I have never either mentioned or maintained anything of this kind (cf. Hadži, 1958 a). On the other hand, I see in the Temnocephala with their one-sided specialization, an instructive example, in effect an experiment made by Nature, which shows what can and what must evolve from an animal type when a species that reached a certain level in its organization, abandons the creeping way of life and begins to live as a semi-sessile animal. The Temnocephala are Turbellaria that are closely related to Rhabdocoela; in all probability they had evolved from the latter. Matjašič even considers that they are still similar enough to the latter so that they can still be classified among Rhabdocoela. The Temnocephala had become specialized as epizoic animals and have therefore ceased to creep by means of their ventral surface covered with cilia; they have assumed an erect position and at the same time they have developed a special disc at their aboral end, by means of which they attach themselves to the substratum; their oral orifice has been transplaced to the anterior end of the animal (now to its upper end). An initially solitary pair of tentacle-like excrescences has been polymerized. The ciliation has been reduced due to the fact that they move actively by means of body muscles, and their skin has become protected with a cuticle which serves as a means of defence and support.

In all probability the Temnocephala have preserved their free mobility because of their epizoic way of life, and in this they differ greatly from Cnidaria. The recent researches that have been made by Matjašič (1959) have shown that this free mobility can even be very active. It is due to their free mobility that Temnocephala have also preserved their ability to pair; this is the reason why we can still find in Temnocephala the typical complex turbellarian hermaphroditic genital apparatus, while the same has been lost in Cnidaria which have evolved into purely sessile animals.

I believe that I am not wrong when I conclude, on the basis of well-known facts, that phylogenetically (and also geologically) the Temnocephala must be younger than the Cnidaria. The Temnocephala can still be considered as Turbellaria; they had branched off from their rhabdocoelan ancestors and have finally developed into a new subtype, into a new order. They are therefore not related to Cnidaria in a direct line; they rather represent a parallel development to the evolution of the latter, a development which can nevertheless prove helpful in our attempts to understand the way the Cnidaria had evolved from their turbellarian ancestors.

The case of Temnocephala can thus serve us as a kind of pattern. In spite of objections made by several zoologists, and above all by Beklemischev and by Reisinger, we will suggest that like a temnocephalian the primitive anthopolyp had raised, first for a briefer period, and later permanently, its posterior end which is now its aboral end. The oral orifice which was originally placed on the ventral side, even if in the anterior part of the body, has been transferred to a purely terminal position when the animal began to be attached to the ground. The Temnocephala had thus repeated the first stage in the older evolution of Cnidaria; yet here they have stopped, or rather they have evolved further in their own direction as epizoic, or let us better say, as ectoparasitic animals. They have remained strictly individualized, i.e. they have not adopted asexual reproduction.

There were probably times when the Acoela were the only Turbellaria in existence; at a somewhat later date the Acoela appeared together with the younger (let us call it) eucoelous subtype which had already been equipped with a distinct intestine. There can be no doubt that those recent Turbellaria which stand closest to this younger form are now classified as Rhabdocoela. We will therefore call these hypothetical ancient Turbellaria as "rhabdocoeloid Turbellaria," in order to avoid in this way the accusation that we wish to derive one recent form from other recent forms. We will therefore avoid the problem whether these rhabdocoeloid Turbellaria would already be called Rhabdocoela by an expert in Turbellaria, or whether he would give some other name to them as, for example, Prorhabdocoela; such a problem is not important.

Regardless of whether the Turbellaria have been considered as primarily primitive animals—which is certainly a more probable interpretation—or whether they have been viewed as animals with a secondarily simplified organization which is a result of an eventual retrogression, it has nevertheless been usually thought that various other "lower worms" and not only Platyhelminthes had evolved from the older turbellarian forms. A majority of zoologists (let us hope that in the near future they will be followed by the others) consider the Turbellaria to be primarily primitive animals; they can thus easily imagine how ages ago these Turbellaria, together with some Protozoa, were the prevalent animal forms which represent the starting point of the whole subsequent evolution of the eumetazoan animal world. It is therefore quite natural that we also try to derive the Cnidaria from these rhabdocoeloid Turbellaria which have shown such an exceptional ability to evolve. At the same time it has been necessary to dethrone the Cnidaria, with *Hydra* in the front row, from the position they had in the animal system. The Cnidaria have to abandon the first place in the animal system, and thus the starting point of the subsequent progressive evolution; they must yield this place to such unrepresentative worms as the Turbellaria which creep by means of their bellies. The concept which sees in *Hydra* as well as in all Hydrozoa the most primitive forms of Eumetazoa among all the recent species has been the main obstacle to the reception of our interpretation.

It is quite unimportant what name we give to the supposed turbellarian ancestors of the present Cnidaria; this is even more true since there are still considerable shortcomings in the classification of the recent Turbellaria so that it is constantly necessary to change the classification. It can only be stated with full certainty that the direct ascendants of Cnidaria had already possessed an intestine with an ectodermal gullet and that they had no intestinal diverticula; that instead their intestine had developed a tendency to form longitudinal folds.

The Larvae of Cnidaria

This may be now the best place to discuss in more detail the formation of larvae in Cnidaria as well as their possible phyletic significance.

According to a generally valid rule, the larval stage is usually developed in the ontogenies of benthonic animals, and above all in animal types that live in the sea, as sessile animals. This larval stage lives regularly in plankton. It is therefore a case of a typical and probably also of the oldest and of the most widely accepted deviation that can be observed in the ontogenetic process. The ecologic significance of this stage is clear and it does not need any further discussion, while at the same time there is even now no unanimity among the zoologists regarding the phyletic significance of larvae. During the flowering of comparative embryology (which should be rather called ontogenetics), and under the fresh influence of the Theory of Evolution when everyone was eager to find further proofs of the descendence theory, scholars became convinced that these larvae must represent something more than a transitional stage only in the individual ontogenies. Following the example of Darwin, Müller, and Haeckel, scholars became used to the concept of recapitulations. Yet here they have made a mistake which appears rather insignificant at first sight and which has been afterwards pointed out by several critics, above all by Garstang. On one hand they have confounded the repeated (yet changeable) ontogenetic stages with the adult forms of ancestors, and on the other hand they believed in a recapitulation not only of individual characteristic properties of the ancestral embryos and of larvae but also of whole ontogenies or at least of whole stages as such. These methodological blunders have proved fatal. A large amount of honest and intensive work was made completely useless. Numerous theories and hypotheses were proposed and courageously defended which were built on the basis of the so-called "fundamental biogenetic law." As an example, I wish to mention here the famous trochophore theory as it was formulated by Berthold Hatschek, an ingenious zoologist and my greatly admired teacher. Yet in spite of all this, these theories can still contain some useful elements, they still have some element of truth in them. There can be no doubt that recapitulations take place and that the comparative morphology of larvae can prove as useful and informative for our phylogenetic speculations as is the comparative morphology of embryos; provided that it is taken from the right angle and that the probability of true recapitulations is kept within limits. Mistakes of the old type continue to be made down to the present day as can be seen in the case of Endoprocta (Kamptozoa) that have been united with Ectoprocta into a new group Bryozoa because of certain similarities that can be observed in their larvae.

There have been three main reasons which induced scholars to see in larvae a recapitulation of an ancestral form.

First, we see that larvae which belong to large, and not infrequently even to very large, animal groups, can have a very similar form and structure. Secondly, the organization of these larvae is almost always simpler (exceptions, however, can be found almost everywhere in the field of biology); larvae are therefore believed to be closer to their supposed ancestors. Thirdly, not a few cases have been known where there can be no doubt that certain characteristic properties can be found in larvae, or in embryos, that are also known to occur in their supposed ancestors; while at the same time these properties can be found no longer, or at least no longer function, in the corresponding recent grown-up forms.

We do not intend to make here a detailed analysis of the problem as to what can be understood as a larval stage. It is certain that the distinction must be made of very different orders of larvae (primary, secondary, possibly even younger), i.e. larvae can be developed from various stages in the development of embryo. This takes place in such a way that any such stage begins to evolve in its own direction, and it adopts its own system of feeding which is usually not parasitic. There are, however, also some parasitic larvae; the problem remains open whether there exist any sessile larvae: and it seems that such larvae can be found among the Echinodermata, the Pentacrinus stage of the Comatula. A necessary transformation by means of which the animal endeavours to reach the organization and the way of life of the adult form is the consequence of such a development. A radical metamorphosis frequently becomes necessary in these cases.

We are finally able, after prolonged and repeated discussions, to make a more uniform evaluation of the morphologic significance of larvae and to use it correctly for phyletic purposes. At all events, it can be stated that similar larvae had been evolved quite independently along several lines of evolution by sessile sea animals. Convergence has played an important role; it was brought about by the adaptation to a planktonic way of life. It can be maintained that one of the worst mistakes that have been committed in the history of the comparative morphology and of the phylogenetics (and which is, unfortunately enough, still made) has been the attempt to use these changes in the ontogenies as a basis for phylogenetic speculations and simply to transfer these ontogenetic and morphogenetic processes into the phylogeny of the adult forms. This has been done in spite of the numerous cases where it is obviously impossible that an organ or an orifice (e.g. the anal and oral orifices) had originally evolved in the same way as it is now developed in the ontogenies.

I mention here as an example the pilidium of Nemertinea. Who could think even for a moment that the "formation of a worm" as it can be observed in connection with the pilidium could be at the same time a recapitulation of an ancestral form? How can it be certain, or at least probable, that we have a recapitulation when one and the same organ or characteristic property can be found in such widely different forms in the ontogenies of closely related species, or even (as has already been mentioned, see p. 211) in the ontogeny of one and the same species; especially when it occurs in a way which cannot possibly be reconciled with the way of life of the adult ancestral form (e.g. the coalescence of the so-called primitive mouth, and the new formation of an anal or oral orifice in the same place)?

What is then the situation in connection with the larvae of Cnidaria? We can state that no genuine and generally occurring planktonic larva has actually been developed by the Cnidaria (Fig. 46). The Planula which is the most frequent form has usually been interpreted, as well as actinula as the (ontogenetically and phylogenetically) "younger" larva. Besides these there are also some other larval forms, the cerinula, the ratarula, and the siphonula which can be met with within the limits of some smaller groups. In no case can we find among Cnidaria a more highly developed larval type whose subsequent development would be subject to a metamorphosis as this is the case, even if to a small degree only, with the larvae of some Polycladida, among the Turbellaria (Goette–Müller's larva).

It is hardly correct to use the word "larva" when we speak about the planula. A planula is in reality only a slightly more accentuated stage of development which is unable to feed

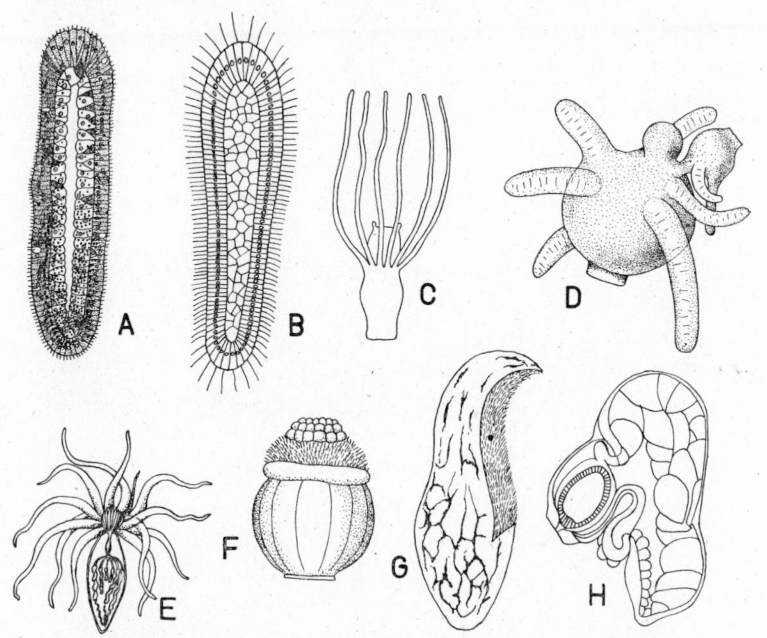

Fig. 46. Some examples of planktonic larvae of the Cnidaria. A, longitudinal section of a planula with gastral cavity *(Gonothyrea* sp., after Wulfert). B, a solid planula. C, actinula of *Tubularia* sp. (after Hyman). D, later actinula of a narcomedusa *(Pegantha* sp., after Bigelow.) E, cerinula of a ceriantthide larva (*Arachnactis albida* after Vanhöffen). F-G larvae of unknown zoantharians *Zoanthina* sp. and *Zoanthella* sp. (after Senna). G, siphonula, a calycoforean larva *(Galeolaria* sp.) (after Metschnikoff).

independently and which is therefore not fit to live long in the real plankton. Its function, with a few exceptions, is clearly to settle down not far from the place inhabited by its "parents" and to develop into a new primary polyp. The absence of an oral orifice and of an intestine which can be observed in the planula is a primary phenomenon, in comparison with numerous Ectoprocta where the same phenomenon is clearly a result of a secondary development. No metamorphosis is necessary for the further development of the planula. It is well known that in a few aberrant cases the planula does not develop directly into a polyp, but rather into an actinula or into an *Anlage* of a cormus.

The question finally arises whether this planula could represent a recapitulation of an ancestral state? Our answer must already be negative for reasons of principle alone. Moreover, such a creature is clearly unable to live as an independent organism because it has neither a mouth nor an intestine. We would be obliged, if we tried by all means to see in a typical planula a recapitulated ancestral form, to make further suppositions, and explain above all the absence of a mouth and of an intestine as secondary phenomena. This would finally lead us to the question what had been the reason that such a development had taken place. It should be mentioned in passing that this planula in no way corresponds to a gastrula (nor does it correspond to a gastraea); its contents is not a "pure" entoderm such as is known in a gastrula, but rather a mixture of entoderm and of the mesohyl (mesoderm), and thus an entomesohyl. The planula is therefore not a coelenterate larva.

In the Anthozoa, which we consider to be the most primitive Cnidaria, a trend can be observed which tries to prolong the free life in the plankton of the younger stage of their development. Two main lines of evolution can be identified in this connection, if we disregard a possible third line of evolution where the free stage no longer leaves the benthos, a case that can be observed in some Zoantharia (Rakovec, 1960). In Ceriantharia a real beginning can be observed of the subsequent progressive evolution of the plankton stage which has even induced scholars to give special names to this stage (cerinula, cerianthula, etc.). Unfortunately, little is known of the subsequent development of these already specialized larvae.

Frequently an "actinula" is developed also by other species of Anthozoa; it represents a more progressive stage in the development towards an anthopolyp whose most important requisites can already be found here during the life in free water (the mouth together with gullet [pharynx], septa, tentacles). Hardly any development can be observed in special larval organs (e.g. in the tuft of sensory cilia that occur at the aboral end of larvae). We have here a prolongation of the plankton phase only, or an early development in the direction of the adult state. Neither can we speak here of a metamorphosis (the primary tentacles are not, as it seems, abandoned).

The occurence of a true actinula is limited to Anthozoa. The form which has been developed by Hydrozoa and which has also been called an actinula is not identical to a genuine actinula and it should be given a different name (perhaps a hydrula). The latter form has neither a gullet nor septa; it has only an oral opening, and intestinal cavity, and few tentacles whose ends are thickened. It seems that larvae similar to an actinula had repeatedly been evolved by Cnidaria, a development which had perhaps even been repeated by Hydrozoa several times (e.g. the actinula of Tubularidae, and the actinula of Narcomedusae).

If we adhere to our interpretation of an evolution of Cnidaria in the direction Anthozoa → Hydrozoa we could rightly expect that a progressive evolution of larvae could be observed in Scyphozoa and in Hydrozoa. This, however, is not the case. How can this fact be explained? I believe I have found an acceptable interpretation of this situation in the fact that during the subsequent evolution a completely new generation of individuals that live in plankton had been invented both by Scyphozoa and by Hydrozoa, i.e. medusae in their two "editions." The medusa generation had taken over not only the sexual function but also the "task" of distributing its own species, a development which is especially characteristic in those cases where as a result of a secondary development the species is represented by the medusa generation alone. In this way a further general evolution of the larval stage has become completely unnecessary. Ephyrae can occasionally be found mentioned as if they were larvae of scyphozoan medusae; they are in reality their juvenile stages only.

No actinulae have been found among the Scyphozoa; we find instead planulae which, however, have never been observed to reach the real plankton and to live there. Just as we can speak here of a planula larva, we could also speak of an ephyra larva of the metagenetic medusae; the only difference is that the ephyra as a larva of medusae does not develop out of an egg but rather by way of asexual reproduction. In Narcomedusae, on the other hand, we find that a so-called polypoid larva had been developed after the primary polyp generation had been lost; this larva even shows an inclination to a parasitic way of life. It is only superficially similar to an actinula and it must be therefore treated as a formation *sui generis*.

Among the Siphonophora we find conditions that are somewhat more unusual; they stand in connection with the individualization of the planktonic cormi and resemble slightly those that can be found among the phylactolaematous Ectoprocta. The planula of Siphonophora (e.g. the ratarula of Chondrophora) soon begins to form secondary individuals as well as the impersonal parts of a polymorphous cormus (siphonula). Here there are even provisional individuals (nectocalyces, etc.) which are later abandoned, thus a development which is similar to a metamorphosis. We must not forget that Siphonophora represent the peak in the evolution of Cnidaria!

A Comparison of Cnidaria Larvae with Other Larvae

A comparison of larval conditions such as they occur in Cnidaria with those that exist in the equally sessile Endoprocta (Kamptozoa), among the Ameria is very illustrative in this connection. The Endoprocta are not only an animal group which lives on the sea bottom; they also show a strong inclination to form cormi; they have not, however, developed, a stage which would correspond to a medusa generation and which would be able to live in plankton. Taken geologically, Endoprocta may be younger than Cnidaria because they are euproctous animals. Thus their phylogenetic root had reached a higher level of evolution than the level that has been reached by the aproctous Turbellaria. The Endoprocta, on the other hand, have developed a planktonic larva whose organization is even more highly developed than is the organization of the adult animal form. Moreover, this differentation had pursued its own direction which made it necessary that a radical metamorphosis be introduced. This is a typical example of a special evolution of a larva which leads its own way of life. It would be completely wrong to see a recapitulation in this kind of development, i.e. to conclude on the basis of present conditions that the ancestors of Endoprocta had lived in plankton and that they had the form and the structure of a trochophore. It is even misleading to call the larva of Endoprocta, a trochophore and to compare it in any way with the larva of Ectoprocta in order to justify in this way a systematic union of these two groups, as this was done by Marcus (Hadži, 1956). These are in reality pure convergences only which were caused by very similar ways of life, a fact which can also be observed, for example, in all the sessile animal types.

Since Endoprocta, as euproctous Ameria, are in all probability (as has already been emphasized) phylogenetically younger than Cnidaria, it seems incomprehensible why the older Cnidaria, which are equally sessile animals that form cormi, had not developed a planktonic larva with a higher level of organization. We have already tried to give an answer to this problem, taking into consideration the formation of the medusa generation which had taken over the role of planktonic larvae. A medusa, however, cannot be considered to be essentially a larva; it rather represents a special generation, it is an adult individual which belongs to the same species and which can secondarily completely replace the primary polypean individual.

We will add here some observations regarding the conditions that exist among the Turbellaria in order to complete in this way our study of the Cnidaria larvae. It can be stated quite generally that the mobile Turbellaria which live in benthos do not show an inclination to develop larvae. There are only a few and usually bigger species of Polycladida which had evolved their own larvae (the so-called Müller's larva); yet these larvae have not reached a very high level of evolution either in their organization or in the special larval devices. This larva assumes another position, i.e. it hangs in free water with its head turned upwards, and it forms a girdle of body process (usually eight) whose margins are covered with stronger cilia. I cannot agree with Kaestner who tries to connect this margin covered with cilia with the praeoral circlet of cilia that can be found in the trochophore of Annelida, and with the tuft of cilia that occurs on the vortex of larvae. It is much more simple to suppose that larva of Polycladida has phyletically nothing in common with the trochophore (actually we have here quite different larvae which resemble a trochophore!) of Annelida. The circlets of cilia and the terminal tufts of the same are requisites that can be frequently found among the primary planktonic larvae.

Müller's larva represents (this is not true for all the Müller's larvae) in all probability the starting point for a side line of evolution which had finally led to the formation of Ctenophora by way of an early sexual maturity and of a continued life in plankton. Here we can observe a very interesting case of the invention of a larva. The typical Ctenophora, themselves planktonic animals, had no need of a special larva for the distribution of their own species. Let us say that a typical transitional stage only had developed in the ontogenies of Ctenophora; its form and organization resemble closely those of an actually existing species (the so-called Cydippe-stage). Some Ctenophora, however, have become specialized and they have descended to a life in the benthos. It is in connection with these species and subgroups that the earlier Cydippe stage has taken over the role of a true larva which must even go through a metamorphosis during its subsequent development. In this case, we can rightly speak of a recapitulation; yet this is a recapitulation of a transitional ontogenetic stage which is very similar to—even if not exactly the same as, a species in its grown-up state.

It should be mentioned, for comparison, that no larval form had been developed by the Chaetognatha that had also evolved by way of neoteny from the planktonic larvae of Brachiopoda (Hadži, 1959 a, 1959 d). No typical common transitional stage of Chaetognatha has become known either. The possibility cannot be excluded, however, that in future a common ontogenetic transitional stage of Chaetognatha will be found after a detailed study of their ontogenies.

The Origin of Turbellaria

We will return now to our main problem. We have refused to accept the attempt made by Jägersten who has tried to support the enterocoele theory by means of a supposed initial form which he constructed *ad hoc* and which he called a bilaterogastraea. He equipped this form with all those elements which could prove useful in his subsequent derivation of the Metazoa from it. Our new task will be to show or, rather, to find the most probable place where the origin of Turbellaria, and thus also of all Eumetazoa, has to be sought. I must state at the very beginning that no well-founded reason is known to me which could justify considering Turbellaria as a product of a retrogressive evolution. I share this opinion with the leading experts in Turbellaria and I refer here among others to Otto Steinböck (1958). The same standpoint regarding the Turbellaria has also been accepted by a majority of other zoologists who are not experts in this field. It will be therefore sufficient if we mention that Turbellaria are freely moving animals, and that they feed independently, mostly as predatory animals. There is no reason why we should try to derive them from some sessile or parasitic ancestors. It is therefore very surprising to see how Marcus, an expert in Turbellaria, places the Turbellaria in his sketch of the genealogical tree of the animal world (Marcus, 1958:52, Fig. 1) high above the Tentaculata which he locates between the Turbellaria and Cnidaria (Coelenterata = Radiata). Even Chaetognatha appear in this sketch closer to the Coelenterata than to the Platyhelminthes. At the same time Marcus derives both the Platyhelminthes and Nemertinea from the Sipunculoidea. One would expect that Marcus considers Turbellaria to be a progressive type because they are placed (together with other "-helminthes") by him so high on the genealogical tree. I find it completely incomprehensible when Marcus tries to derive all these lower "worms" from the coelomatic Bilateria (Marcus 1958:33) endeavouring to find in them traces of the coelom cavities while at the same time he makes no difference between an actual coelom (our perigastrocoele) and other coelom cavities, above all the gonocoele. Marcus thus believes the Turbellaria to be secondarily simplified animals which have played a subordinate role only in the phyletic development; he even considers Nemertinea to be more primitive than Turbellaria.

Remane (1957), too, does not stand far from the view proposed in Marcus' work. In Remane's sketch of the genealogical tree of the animal world, the Tentaculata can be found placed under the Platyhelminthes whose position is somewhat hesitatingly indicated. Remane defends himself against Steinböck's accusation that he tries to derive Turbellaria from Annelida; at the same time he states that both these groups had a common ancestral form which as an already segmented animal had necessarily been anneloid. It is not important whether complete parapodia and the so-called secondary or somatic segments had already been developed. In any case Remane, too, sees in Turbellaria a product of a retrogressive evolution (admitting at the same time that some properties of Turbellarians also be a result of a progressive development above all their complex genital apparatus). Remane consequently does not attribute any great phyletic significance to Turbellaria. The Turbellaria must be content to represent a small side twig on the mighty branch of Protostomia.

Let us now pass over to the next problem. What is the situation regarding the line of evolution within the group of Turbellaria itself? Do the Acoela represent the starting point of the evolution of Turbellaria, are they not only the simplest but also the most primitive Turbellaria, or perhaps the most highly developed Eucoela? We consider it as certain (the same opinion is shared also by Steinböck, Hanson, Beklemischev, and the majority of other zoologists, beginning with v. Graff) that the Acoela do not only have the simplest structure or organization of all the Turbellaria that we know; they are also primarily the most primitive Turbellaria. If we disregard here all the problems regarding the origin of Turbellaria, and if we observe Turbellaria as a whole as an independent animal group, we cannot find a reason why we should not place the Acoela at the beginning of a natural system of Turbellaria. The interpretation which sees in a simple phenomenon a primitive element also, is certainly justified here, even if it is not justified in a number of other cases: a fact which I am well aware of and which is repeated unnecessarily by competent zoologists in their criticisms of my thesis. In spite of the fact that the Acoela lead the same way of life as the remaining typical Turbellaria nevertheless their organisation is far behind the others. At the same time a clear trend towards a progressive evolution can be observed in the Acoela. Beklemischev has already shown this trend as particularly evident in their hermaphroditic genital apparatus. We will presuppose all this as a well-known fact and limit ourselves to the statement that in reality there is no justification to consider the Acoela as secondarily simplified Turbellaria. The only objection to this that could be mentioned in this connection is the small size of the Acoela. There is a generally valid rule that a general decrease of an animal body, when it passes certain limits, not infrequently leads to an extensive reduction of the animal organization which appears as its simplification. It can lead not only to an abolition of the system of blood vessels and of the respiratory organs (numerous instances in the very small species of the Acarina) but also of the whole feeding and digestive systems (the dwarfed males of numerous Rotatoria). The conditions are clear in these and in many other cases because here the causal relationship between the diminution of the size of the animal and the simplification of the organization can easily be identified. In all these cases organs and systems of organs can be found in certain forms while the same cannot be found in the related forms whose size has been secondarily diminished. In the case of the dwarfed male Rotatoria we find even the female animals that belong to the same form equipped with such organs; these female forms have at the same time also a considerably larger size.

Somewhat less easy to survey are those cases where a larger animal group consists exclusively of very small species, which at the same time also have a simpler structure, this can be observed, for example, in the Rotatoria and in the Tardigrada. A detailed study of these groups, however, shows that there are some facts which prove with great certainty that the size of the species, which belong to these groups, had been secondarily diminished and that a simplification of their organization had taken place as a consequence of such a diminution. One of the elements that can be helpful in this connection is the trend towards a decreased number of cells and their constancy; another element is the loss of ability to regenerate (in Rotatoria the lost parts of cells only are able to regenerate). Thirdly, we can take into consideration a highly developed ecologic specialization, e.g. the adaptation to small recesses in which an animal lives.

A primary small size of an animal type must be strictly distinguished from a secondary diminution (Hadži, 1956 b). No element which has been mentioned above and which could serve as an indication of a secondary diminution can be found in the Acoela; they must therefore be considered as primarily small animals, and the simplicity of their structure which is everywhere clearly evident as a primitive characteristic. We will repeat here, in order to emphasize this statement the better, that the Acoela are genuine, perfect, freely living animals which are able to make rapid active movements (certainly in the most primitive way, by means of a pulsation of cilia) and which feed as predatory species; they did not develop all these properties *de novo* but rather had inherited the same—as we will soon try to prove—from some equally small ancestors.

The Acoela, as well as all the Turbellaria, are typical bilaterally symmetric animals. They show no traces of a radial symmetry, unless we agree with Beklemischev who believes he sees an indication of the radial symmetry in the presence of several pairs of longitudinal nerve trunks. This fact, however, is quite unimportant because it did not lead to the development of a general radial symmetry and because the central nervous system of the whole group of Turbellaria had become consolidated in the direction of the bilateral symmetry.

The Origin of the Acoelous Turbellaria

We have shown that Cnidaria had evolved first as anthopolyps and in all probability from the rhabdocoeloid Turbellaria, and also that the Acoela are the most primitive subgroup of Turbellaria. Our next problem will be the origin of the Acoela, and the question, "how can the origin of the Acoela be explained?" We are well aware of the fact that in an attempt to answer such a question we are on very uncertain ground, that the only solid facts that can be found are in the recent animal types, and that we cannot avoid making conjectures. We must be content with the degrees of probability, and we have no right to declare any attempt to represent or reconstruct another path of evolution as impossible.

We could make our task very easy if we accepted the interpretation that was proposed by v. Graff, and, in a somewhat modernized form, by Beklemischev. According to this interpretation a planuloid being which resembled a gastrula (Grobben) has been the starting point for the evolution of Turbellaria (and at the same time of Coelenterata and of Eumetazoa generally). Beklemischev (1958 : 109) modified this widely accepted interpretation stating that the Turbellaria had developed "von einem Zweig der Urcoelenteraten, die durch Neotenie im Planulastadium geschlechtsreif wurden." I consider such a deduction as completely improbable and, moreover, as a purely auxiliary solution. Those who accept this interpretation like to refer to larvae as recapitulations of their adult ancestors. The planula appears in reality among the Cnidaria as a larval form without being at the same time a recapitulation of some ancestral form, as it has been already stated. The latter, however, could not at all be found among the Turbellaria, and especially not among the Acoela where one would expect above all such a recapitulating planula. Yet even if it had been found, this could not be considered as a proof for a planuloid origin of the Acoela, and thus of Turbellaria. Matters being such as they are, we have no real basis of deriving the Acoela from some planuloid ancestors.

G. S. Carter (1954), who agrees with several points of my interpretation, considers that I underrate the facts of ontogeny and that in this I make a mistake. It is true that in my opinion we must place more emphasis in our phylogenetic conclusions and constructions on the conditions of comparative morphology of the adult forms, than on the data that can be obtained by means of a comparative ontogenetics (embryology). I especially insist that we must be more than careful in our evaluations of the freely living larval forms. I support my view not only with the well-founded abrogation of the so-called "fundamental biogenetic law" as it was proposed by Haeckel (even if recently an apology was written by Remane (1960) in favour of the same law), but also with facts that can be observed in the ontogenies; these facts show how easily and radically the morphogenetic conditions of the ontogenetic as well as of the embryonic and of postembryonic stages can be changed. Such changes can even take place within one and the same line of evolution (animal group). It should be pointed out that during the development which takes place under the protection of a husk or of the maternal body, thus free of the direct influences of the environment, as well as towards the close of an eventual larval life in another biotope when a metamorphosis has become necessary, morphogenetic processes can frequently be observed which would be impossible during an adult stage which leads an independent life (e.g. the changes of the intestinal openings). Because of these changes, zoologists are now divided into two opposite groups. Unfortunately enough it must be repeated again and again: in our phylogenetic conclusions we must take into consideration the comparative morphology of the adult form (this should above all be considered!) as well as the stages of the ontogenetic development; yet in the latter study we must proceed even more carefully and critically, taking constantly into consideration the peculiarities of the ontogenetic processes.

In our case, i.e. in the study of the origin of Turbellaria we consider that it agrees better with the given facts (we must not forget that this is an opinion only, based on a probable conclusion) when we do not take the easiest road by simply supposing (this, too, is a supposition only, and nothing else) that the most primitive Turbellaria had evolved from some planuloid ancestors. Regardless of the fact that no planuloid forms can be found now among the living animals (this is not decisive because it is possible that such forms had formerly existed and that they have now become extinct)—we cannot consider the so-called Mesozoa to be such animals because they are endoparasites—it is my opinion that no planuloid animal type can actually be able to live. I cannot see any likelihood that the supposition that either a planuloid (a "planaea," corresponding to a planula of Cnidaria) or a gastruloid animal (a gastraea, corresponding to a gastrula of numerous animal types) had ever existed, is correct. I therefore do not take into consideration such ancestral forms.

As long as we believe that the Eumetazoa had evolved exclusively as a formation of cormi on the pattern of the early stages of the animal ontogeny, which usually takes place by means of a complete cleavage of the fertilized egg cell, we will hardly be able to find any other solution than to accept the existence of a planuloid form or of a modification of the same. Yet if we succeed in freeing ourselves of this truly fascinating idea we find new possibilities, new probabilities emerging before us. Some older zoologists have already thought along the same lines (Dobell, 1911, and before him Saville Kent, Sedgwick, etc.).

Some zoologists have already called our attention to the extraordinary similarity that exists between the structure of a holotrichous infusorian and of a turbellarian (Fig. 47), at the same time they had no intention of making phylogenetic conclusions on this basis, even if such conclusions have seemed to be tangibly close. We will mention here the detailed comparison only between the Infusoria and the Turbellaria which was made by the well-known Hungarian zoologist V. Gelei, an expert in Infusoria, in *Hydra*, and in Turbellaria. In this comparison a whole list of striking similarities has come to light which can naturally also be considered as pure parallelisms or as accidental similarities. V. Gelei did not think here of possible homologies because there are also differences between these two animal types that can above all be observed in the extremely specialized nuclear apparatus and in the sexual phase of the Infusoria.

Let us mention here briefly these similarities: (1) the range of the body size; (2) the general form of the body (habitus); (3) the general ciliation of the body surface and the type of

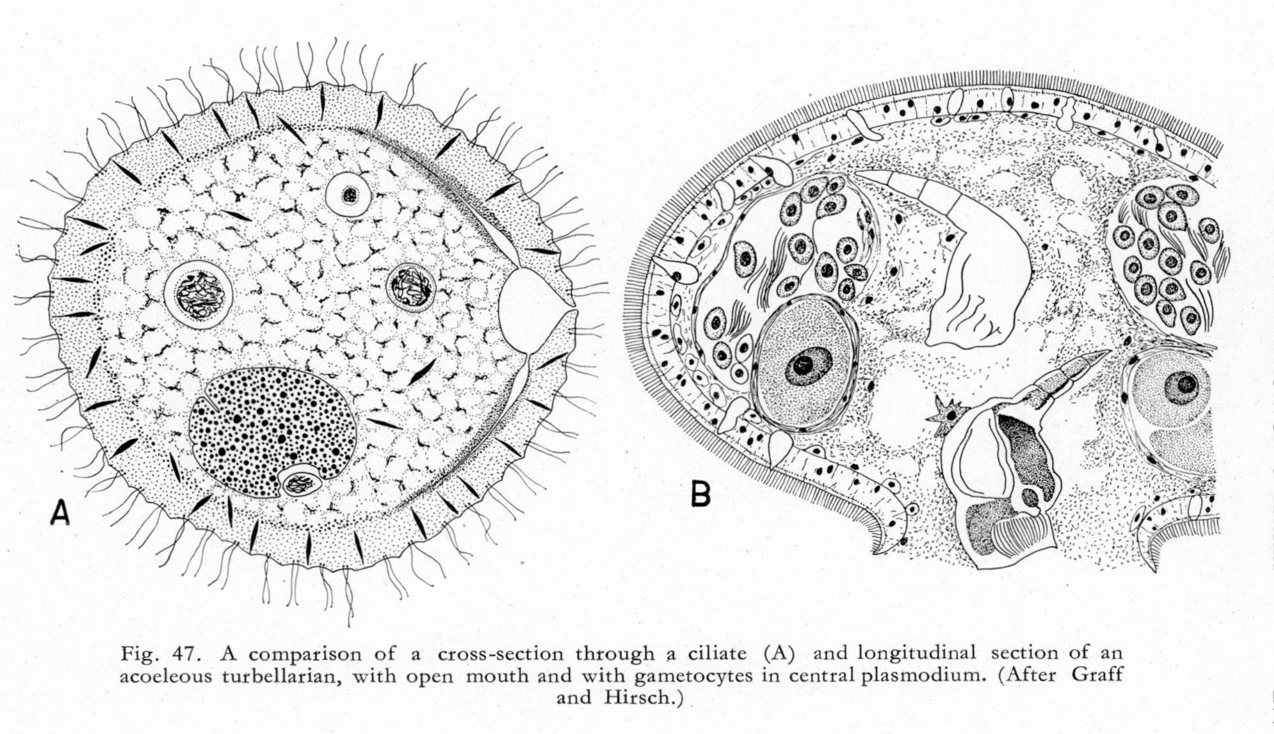

Fig. 47. A comparison of a cross-section through a ciliate (A) and longitudinal section of an acoeleous turbellarian, with open mouth and with gametocytes in central plasmodium. (After Graff and Hirsch.)

movement which is connected with it; (4) the fact that the interior of their bodies consists of three body layers, with (a) a more or less solidified external layer, with fine variations especially as regards its fibrillar and sculptural nature, (b) a somewhat softer middle layer (without streamings) which contains nuclei, the contractile myonemes, and the contractile emunctories (vacuoles), (c) the streaming digestive internal layer (cyclosis), with the digestive vacuoles; (5) a cytostome; (6) a cytopharynx, and not unfrequently (7) a cytopyge; (8) the trichocysts; (9) a hermaphroditic regime combined with pairing and with an internal fertilization; (10) the asexual reproduction by means of transverse division.

All these, and other similarities which are not mentioned here, should thus be accidental analogies or parallelisms! Can this be probable? The improbability of such a group of analogies becomes even less acceptable if we succeed in clarifying or in rationally solving the most important differences that now seem to exist between these two animal groups.

There is one more important reason why we should consider these similarities as true homologies and why we should accept the derivation of the Acoela, as the lowest Eumetazoa, from some infusorial ancestors as more probable than the derivation of Coelenterata from some colonies of Flagellata. This reason can be found in the continuity of development of the whole polycellular unit which I will return to discuss on a later page. It is quite natural that the similarities that exist between a holotrichous infusorian, as it is now known and a recent acoelan, are explained by those who adhere to the widely accepted colonial theory, as if they were analogies or parallelisms only; they are logically obliged to come to this conclusion. It is easy to understand why these scholars try to bring forward possibly good arguments against the "plasmodium theory" ("Plasmodiumtheorie") as it was called by Steinböck. Thus Remane wished that those scholars who accepted the plasmodium theory could bring forward evidence in the form of "transitional forms," "proved patterns," "certain intermediate forms," "certain special homologies." Steinböck (1958 : 204) is right when he emphasizes that Remane is much less strict when he tries to prove his own thesis and that in connection with his thesis he is satisfied mainly with one rather remote analogy of green algae (the frequently misused *Volvox)* as well as with an (according to our interpretation wrong) application of the misused "fundamental biogenetic law" as it was proposed by Haeckel (cleavage = a recapitulation of the formation of the colony of Flagellata, etc.).

Several scholars have objected in principle against any possibility of deriving the Eumetazoa from some ancestors that resembled the present day Infusoria, stating that the Infusoria are a much too specialized animal group, a blind alley, and that therefore no new animal type could possibly have evolved from them. The fact that they harbour of two nuclei only with a clear dimorphism of the two nuclei, the absence of free gametes, conjugation as an isolated form of the sexual reproduction are all unique properties which can only be a result of a long evolution in their own direction. I must admit the great importance of these differences and that at the first sight these differences really seem to disprove a possible deduction of Eumetazoa from Infusoria. I myself (Hadži, 1944 : 160) was initially under the influence of these facts: I endeavoured to avoid them and tried to find an origin of the Acoela farther back among the Protozoa, i.e. among the polykaryonic Flagellata. This, however, is in principle not so important.

After a thorough analysis of the sexual conditions that can be found both in the Infusoria and in the Acoela and after an intensive comparison of the two (Hadži, 1950) I have finally come to the conclusion that it is possible to overcome these seemingly unbridgeable difficulties, that these differences do not represent a matter of principle, that instead they have only been gradually increased. This has finally led to the widely different forms that can be observed in the extreme cases in the two animal types. In this connection I can also mention the study by Hansen (1958).

It cannot be emphasized strongly enough that quite naturally the recent Infusoria with their frequently extreme specializations cannot be taken into consideration as ancestors of the equally recent Acoela. The time when the line of Turbellaria had supposedly branched off from its infusorian stem lies far back in geologic time. It is even questionable whether a name like infusorian, or the acoelous turbellarian, could still be given to this common original form, by a modern zoologist. It is quite irrational and beyond understanding to expect or to require that some recent transitional forms should be shown to those who oppose our thesis, as proofs of this development which has been so important for the evolution of the animal world. The phylogeneticists have repeatedly emphasized that such fatal steps in evolution have frequently taken place much faster than did the development of some less important "novelties" and the evolution of large types.

The Relationship Between the Conjugation and the Copulation

First a problem of terminology. The word "copulation" has unfortunately been used for two entirely different phenomena. On one hand, it is a union of the gametes of the two sexes, or the fertilization itself. On the other hand, it means an act by which the individuals become united which belong to the two sexes, i.e. a pairing, and this is the reason why we speak quite generally of organs of copulation: they play the main role in such a union. The etymology of the word itself shows that it was originally coined for the second interpretation. It would therefore be better if we use the equally well-known word syngamy when we speak of the union of the two gametes.

It has already been mentioned that conjugation is considered as an opposite to syngamy as if it were something entirely different from the latter. This has been the main reason why the Ciliata—as the only Protozoa that have adopted conjugation—all the remaining Protozoa reproduce by means of syngamy—have been considered as basically different from other animals and that a derivation of Eumetazoa, where syngamy regularly occurs, from Ciliata was looked upon as an unacceptable principle. In various manuals and text books conjugation is usually defined in the same way as it appears in the book by Hyman (I:75). "... conjugation or temporary contact of two protozoans with nuclear change." Almost the same words are used by Kudo (1946 : 154) in his *Protozoology*, and by numerous other authors when they characterize this phenomenon. The emphasis in this sentence is on the "nuclear change." A little later Hyman (I : 173) gives quite a rational interpretation of this "nuclear change" when she writes, "The micronuclei, which play the important role in conjugation all divide twice, and these divisions probably correspond to the maturation divisions of metazoan germ cells, involving a reduction of chromosomes." Even better is the statement made by Hall (1953 : 80) who writes, "Typical conjungation involves the change of haploid pronuclei (gametic nuclei) between two paired organisms, the formation of a syncaryon in each, and then nuclear reorganization."

I will now endeavour to show (Hadži, 1950) of this conjugation, a true peculiarity of Ciliata, that its individual elements had been inherited by Eumetazoa via Turbellaria, Acoela. Conjugation does not represent an obstacle to such a derivation, provided that we place the point of separation of Ciliata and Turbellaria, and thus of Eumetazoa, farther back to a time before the Ciliata have become specialized and before they have evolved the conjugation which is now typical of them. Numerous peculiarities of sexual conditions that can be observed in the lowest Eumetazoa, in the Acoela, can be better understood if viewed from our standpoint.

There certainly was a time when, sexuality had not yet been developed by the living organism—only the Protista existed. This sexuality, however, had already appeared when the Protista still wielded an unlimited authority. Why and how this has taken place cannot be discussed in the present study. This bisexuality has proved to be of great advantage to organisms in their further development and so it was quite generally accepted. Later it was even combined with propagation and thus with the preservation of the continuity, a function which it did not originally possess. The sexual phase of the life-cycle had been developed by Protozoa along different lines and in very different ways. Very primitive conditions can be found preserved even now in various species of Protista. In these the sexual phase is represented by a special sexual generation which however does not differ morphologically from the usual, the so-called vegetative generation (Dogiel prefers to call it a "neutral" generation). This most primitive type of syngamy has been called, as is well known, a hologamous isogamy. The sexualized generation differs from the vegetative generation in its chemical properties only—sexuality itself was originally a biochemical phenomenon. We are hardly justified to speak of gametes during this primitive stage of the sexuality. The two units are naturally attracted because of the biochemical differentiation into two opposite directions which cover each other in the 0-point (there is, according to the well-founded theory by Hartmann, no absolutely + and no absolutely — developed sexuality). This finally leads to a union of the two. This was the basis from which special conditions had evolved parallel to the various lines of evolution of Protozoa (we will omit here the Protophyta). The development went mainly into two directions. On one hand it led to a strong differentation of the two partners in the sexual generation. Two gametes had evolved that differ from each other, in agreement with the function they have: the slender, actively swimming androgametes have also been called microgametes (usually in the form of spermatozoa, resembling flagellates; secondarily, however, they can become atypical and they can lose their free mobility), and the passive gynogametes (macrogametes) which are usually equipped with a reserve food substance. The gametes no longer feed independently; they have ceased to be a special generation, and thus complete individuals. They preserve the monokaryonic state, because it is during this state that syngamy, with the act of fertilization can be accomplished most easily. This state has been preserved throughout a mainly progressive evolution, right up to man. This is the reason why this primitive state (the monokaryonic state, i.e. the monocellularity) can be found recapitulated even now at the beginning of the ontogenies. The second line of evolution led (as early as in Protozoa!) to a transference of the biochemical sexualization to the "vegetative" generation which we call the generation of gamonts and which had preceded the earlier generation of gametes; this transference took place in a somewhat different way. This is the generation (later when asexual reproduction is abandoned, it is the only existing generation) which produces gametes. Approximately half of its individuals have developed into gynogamonts (the later females), and another half into the androgamonts (the subsequent males). Similarly as in the case of the primitive gametes, no externally visible morphological differences had been initially developed by the primitive gamonts of the two sexes. Yet they attract and repel each other depending on the fact whether the two gamonts that meet have the same or the opposite values.

As early as in Protozoa the formation of gametes (combined with meiosis) and their differentiation, reaches its climax in oögamy; this was accepted by Metazoa as the only form known to them and it has been preserved throughout phyletic evolution, i.e. up to the formation of man. Sexualization can go even further; as early as in Protozoa it was transferred to the earlier vegetative generation (as the so-called agametes). This has led to the sexualization of the whole life-cycle (e.g. in *Cyclospora caryolitica*, according to Schaudinn).

It may be useful to point in this connection to the conditions that can be observed in the Gregarinida. Two individuals of the generation of gamonts with the same form, yet sexually (biochemically) differentiated, become united; we can truly say that they copulate or pair without developing an intimate contact; they each mutually encyst the other. The gynogametes are produced after multiple divisions by one individual which functions as a female, and androgametes by the other individual which functions as a male. They become "free" even if they remain within the wall of the cyst and are in this way separated from the environment. Here the gametes can meet in masses to copulate and to produce zygotes. Yet in this way the whole mass of the cytoplasm of the gamonts is not used up. A considerable part of it remains as a remnant which is destined to die. The zygotes naturally become finally free. It should also be mentioned that in the case of a typical oögamy, one gynogamete only can be developed by way of meiosis by a gamont or by a gametocyte which can be produced by a gamont (in this case the gamont actually becomes a praegamont), while the number of androgametes can be very large.

The hermaphrodite state emerges at the first sight quite unexpectedly among such animals that had originally adopted the system of two different sexes. It appears, it seems, without a true motivation. This phenomenon, however, can be more easily understood if the generally valid and well-founded theory of a potential bisexuality is taken into consideration (Hartmann *et al.*). Less easily understood are the immediate reasons which can lead in individual cases to an introduction or to an omission of the hermaphrodite state. It is well known that in each individual which is normally gonochoristic (dioecious) the sexual biochemistry of one sex only is prevalent, while the biochemistry of the opposite sex remains inactive. An initially indifferent gametocyte can become divided by way of heterocyclic (not equivalent) divisions, and under special circumstances it can thus develop into units with two sexually opposed orientations. Such a development must be supposed to have taken place during the transition from the polykaryonic Zooflagellata to the primitive Ciliata. One of the great advantages of the polykaryonic theory, if compared with the colonial theory, an advantage which must not be underrated, is that it makes possible for us to understand the hermaphroditism not only of the Platyhelminthes, as the lowest Eumetazoa, but also of the numerous groups of Ameria (especially of the Mollusca), and of other larger or smaller groups which have reached a higher level of evolution. It can be stated quite generally that almost everywhere among the Eumetazoa an active inclination towards hermaphroditism can be observed.

Even if among the recent Protozoa no transitional forms can be found from the polymastigous and polykaryonic Zooflagellata and the lower Euciliata, there can still be no doubt that the Infusoria had evolved from just such Flagellata. The circumstances have been the reason that the endoparasitic poly- and hyper-mastigous species of Flagellata, which are partly equipped with the polymerized nuclei, have only been preserved till now, or that such species only have become known. They are certainly strongly specialized, and thus greatly modified. The Opalinidae have been considered, wrongly, to be transitional forms; they were therefore placed under the name "Protociliata" at the root of the Ciliata. The Opalinidae are in reality strongly modified Zooflagellata and they lead, moreover, an endoparasitic way of life. In spite of this we find the Opalinidae to be very interesting here; first, because they include species that are mutually closely related which contain two, it seems equivalent, nuclei only; the completely round body is covered with cilia; and, secondly, because some of their species contain an increasing number of nuclei, yet their sexual phase is in spite of all this only slightly atypical (Wessenberg, 1961)*. They form freely moving and externally slightly differentiated (in their size) gametes which belong to both sexes and which move by means of cilia. It is certain that the syngamy takes place in the Opalinidae. Unfortunately,

* Wessenberg who has recently (1961) made a study of the Opalinidae proposes a special taxon for this group under the name Opalinata which should be placed between Flagellata ("flagellated Protozoa") and Ciliata ("ciliated Protozoa").

little is known about the sexual phase of other polykaryonic Flagellata. It was even thought that they have completely lost their sexual phase, a supposition which has now been proved wrong.

It could perhaps be expected that some transitional forms might be found among the Euciliata, a possibility which cannot be completely excluded. Thus the case of the *Glaucoma (Dallasia) frontata* Stokes was described some time ago by G. N. Calkins and by R. Bowling (1941). It has been reported that a copulation as well as a typical conjugation can be observed in this species of holotrichous Infusoria. Yet the very fact that the copulation and a simultaneous conjugation have been observed makes it improbable that we really have a copulation here. It is supposed that here two individuals which consist of two nuclei each, encyst with each other which finally leads to copulation. The true gametes, however, consist of one nucleus only and they must pass through one or two meioses. I believe that the case of the *Glaucoma frontata* can be set aside.

The Zooflagellata (with strongly polymerized and equivalent kinetids and nuclei which were gonochoristic and reproduced asexually, yet which propagated during the sexual phase by way of oögamy producing greatly unequal free gametes that copulated mutually, creating one zygote each time) can be imagined as the initial form for the evolution of the typical Euciliata as well as of the primitive Eumetazoa. These gametes were haploid, and the zygote as well as the vegetative generation diploid. It should be mentioned in passing that in this they differed greatly from *Volvox* which is frequently mentioned as a pattern of the ancestor of Metazoa: the zygote of the Volvox undergoes a reduction, a fact which was particularly stressed by E. D. Hanson (1958 : 27).

There were in all probability two processes which played a major role during the transition from the polymastigous and polykaryonic Zooflagellata that had thus been developed by way of polymerization: (1) the emergence of the hermaphroditism, and, (2) the internalization of gametogenesis. The intermediate form, which was equipped with both these new properties, developed in all probability at the point where the two lines of evolution separated. Evolution then pursued two diverging directions, on one hand the line of evolution of Ciliata, and on the other the line of evolution of the Eumetazoa, with the acoelous Turbellaria at its very beginning.

Let us first make a closer study of the lines which were pursued by the Ciliata in their evolution. The following characteristics were decisive in connection with their lines of evolution: (1) the prevalence of oligomerization; it did not influence the vegetative (somatic) nuclei only whose number has thus been reduced to the possible minimum, i.e. to the so-called *macronucleus* which cannot be considered in spite of its singleness as a homologue to the originally single nucleus; oligomerization has now also been extended to the internal sexual phase and as its consequence we find one sexual karyon preserved. This development has led to (2) a further internalization of the gametes themselves so that finally one andro- and one gyno-gamete only are formed; copulation also becomes internal. Somewhat later, oligomerization was extended to ciliation; this has led, according to the rule, to a differentiation of the cilia into the ciliary organelles. This evolution had also led to a new form of copulation which is externally invisible because of its internalization and which is therefore better protected against the external influence. At the same time, it had determined the destiny of Ciliata since they could never develop into larger species; they have remained microscopic Protozoa with the ability to develop intensive differentiations, particularly if we take into consideration the range of dimensions within which they can change. A part of these properties (which was not really a very small part!) had been inherited by the Eumetazoa, because even before the separation of the two lines of evolution a comparatively high level of organization had already been reached within the frame of their small dimensions.

It is actually not very important to know in connection with our task, the evolution of Infusoria after their separation from the line pursued by the Eumetazoa. Still it may prove useful if we make a closer study of their sexual phase; in this way we could make it clear that the form of conjugation ot the sexual phase is not essentially different from a typical copulation. This will finally enable us to propose homologies of the two forms without any greater difficulty. We suppose quite naturally that the descriptive part of the process is well enough known. At the end we intend to touch very briefly on a few final stages of the process of conjugation which as extreme cases, diverge so far from oögamy as the typical sexual form, that a proposed homology might appear less probable if we do not take into consideration the whole development.

We will first characterize (define) the Ciliata (Infusoria) as they appear if viewed from our standpoint. This definition will agree, I believe, better with the actual facts than do the currently accepted definitions. Infusoria are hermaphroditic, polykaryonic Protozoa whose two karyons are already differentiated during the vegetative phase, without free gametes during the sexual phase; the generation of gametes is reduced to a possible minimum; it is at the same time also transferred into the interior of the generation of gamonts (praegamonts) which has made a pairing of the equally sexualized gamonts necessary. The so-called micronucleus represents during the vegetative phase a homologue to the sexual potency of the hermaphroditic primitive sex cell; the micronucleus is equally divided during the vegetative reproduction by means of transverse division; during the sexual phase, however, at a certain moment it divides heterocyclically (unequally) which leads to the formation of gametic karyons of the two sexes, the so-called pronuclei, i.e. the stationary and the migrating nuclei. The gynogamete with its cytoplasm merges totally with the cytoplasm (the plasmodium) of the gamont (the paternal animal) which leads to an internalization of the zygote. The androgamete remains moving actively and it can secondarily readopt the form of a sperm cell. A new set is developed by way of postgamous divisions which are again heterocyclic; their result is usually a vegetative, complex, or polyploid karyon (macronucleus), and a primitive, sexual, diploid karyon (micronucleus).

Scholars such as, Jennings, (1939) have tried to interpret the Infusoria *(Paramecium)* as gonochoristic animals. According to such an interpretation, the two so-called pronuclei (actually the gamete karyons) which frequently do not differ externally from each other, are supposed to belong to the same sex, they are supposed to be both androgametes or gynogametes. If this were true, then only two individuals which belong to the opposite sexes would be able to conjugate. Such a case, though theoretically not impossible, is completely improbable. In numerous hermaphroditic species of Eumetazoa with a uniform hermaphroditic gonad (e.g. in the Roman snail *Helix pomatius*, as well as in some Protozoa, e.g. in the Heliozoa) we can observe that the sexual cells of the two sexes can be developed by way of a heterocyclic division from an "indifferent" primitive sex cell. This can lead in special cases, e.g. in numerous Euciliata that have adopted a sessile way of life, that—under the influence of a strongly developed sexual dimorphism of praegamonts—the microgamont which becomes free begins to function as a male, and the sessile macrogamont as a female; yet in spite of this we can observe in both of them a clearly hermaphroditic nature.

J. P. Turner (1941, in *Protozoa in Biol. Research:* 617) expressed his opinion that conjugation cannot be considered as a propagation or a reproduction, but rather as a reorganization only. I believe this interpretation to be wrong, it agreeing only with the external superficial appearances. It has already been stressed that conjugation completely corresponds to a propagation or reproduction, combined with the sexual act; the only difference is that it is rather modified and somewhat concealed. Not even the usual consequence of the fertilization which takes place during conjugation is missing; it is manifest in Protozoa with free and numerous agametes in the postgamous divisions of zygotes which occur frequently *en masse*. The postgamous divisions of the still enclosed zygote (the zygote karyon) are strongly reduced in the conjugating Ciliata because of their general oligomerization; yet there still occur regularly, special divisions of the zygote karyon which succeed each other quickly and which are also followed by the divisions of the whole body. Numerous experiments have shown that the exconjugants divide more rapidly. This shows that during the conjugation the animals also become reorganized (or, as we frequently hear, rejuvenated). An essential difference between the genuine Ciliata and all the Eumetazoa lies in the fact that in the latter each zygote is regularly developed by way of divisions into a new polykaryonic individual which finally leads to an embryonic development. It is worth mentioning that much later this situation finally evolves in numerous animal groups, including man himself, into the phenomenon where simultaneously, or even generally, one gynogamete only is developed while the number of androgametes remains very large, a situation which can be easily understood if we take into consideration the function of the spermatozoa.

Other facts that have been observed and described under various names in connection with the sexual karyons of Infusoria, such as endomixis, hemimixis, reorganization, etc., can not only be compared with the similar developments in the "normal" Protozoa if we view the organization of Infusoria from our point of view; they can even be declared as simply homologous to self-fertilization and to parthenogenesis. A detailed study of these problems, however, would pass the limits of our present task.

A sexualization of the generation of gamonts takes place also elsewhere among the Protozoa as this can be seen in the case of Eugregarinida where the syzygy can be observed; from the Protozoa it was clearly transferred to the Eumetazoa. The question arises whether something similar could not also be found among the Acoela? As far as I know no sexualization of the vegetative phase has yet been observed in the Acoela.

This, however, does not mean that it does not actually occur since we are still far from knowing much about the biology of the Acoela. No extensive and planned experiments in their culture have been made so far. Many more precise investigations have been made in connection with the Infusoria. In these we can find a clearly developed progressive evolution towards a sexualization which has led to an explicit sexual dimorphism. During the early stage of this development the individuals do not show any morphological difference whatever, in spite of the fact that they are already physiologically differentiated. Here we can find an analogy to hologamous isogamy. The behaviour of individuals with different biochemical polarizations is similar to the behaviour of males and females of the gonochoristic or dioecious Eumetazoa. The individuals with the opposite "signs" are mutually attracted, and this leads to a union, to a pairing. In the actual sexual generation, in the gametes, the differentiation can take place in two directions only (bipolar: + and —), if we disregard the indifferent middle, the 0-point (e.g. the worker bees, and other similar cases), so that two sexes only can be developed. In the generation of gamonts of Euciliata, however, development has led, as it is well known, to the formation of several "mating types." In the species of Infusoria we could correspondingly expect several morphologically different forms which would answer the several "mating types." It is not known to me whether anything of this kind has been observed till now. Yet we find in the Infusoria, above all in their sessile species, sexual dimorphism further developed, in spite of their hermaphroditic state. On a lower level the difference is mainly of a quantitative nature, as is shown by the frequently quoted example of the *Opisthotrichium janus.* We speak in this connection of macro- and of micro-conjugants which are developed by means of a division that takes place before the conjugation. This division, however, should not be called—as it usually is—a progamous division; the true progamous division takes place during the conjugation in the gametic karyons and it is unequal. In this species the essential difference between the two sexes is not morphological, but rather physiological (biochemical). While its true microconjugants (any macroconjugants) are still able to conjugate mutually, the microconjugants when they meet are unable to do the same.

Sexual differentiation has pursued another direction in the species *Metopus sigmoides* (according to Noland, 1927). The two sexes do not differ morphologically, yet their destinies are different. One of the conjugants loses its individuality due to conjugation, and it is destroyed. Both these elements, the sexual dimorphism and the unequal destiny of the two conjugants can also be observed in the sessile Peritricha. The macroconjugant remains sessile; it functions mainly as a female even if it shows hermaphroditic inclinations because it is only its gynokaryon which becomes fertilized and which continues to develop. Its androgamete passes over into the free and swimming microconjugant which has taken over the role of a male; it produces one functioning androgamete only while all the rest get lost and they are resorbed by the luckier macroconjugant. This situation reminds us to some extent of some fish species that inhabit the deep sea whose dwarfed males live as parasites on their larger females. Two important differences must naturally not be forgotten in this connection: these fish are gonochoristic animals and their males are not resorbed.

Instead of speaking about the macro- and micro-conjugants we could also speak of the gyno- and andro-conjugants, parallel to the females and males of the gonochoristic Eumetazoa; yet these conjugants of Infusoria are hermaphrodites. The process of conjugation (as a secondary sexual process) becomes so one-sided that during the same process the androconjugant loses his life. This, however, cannot be observed among the Eumetazoa, but we can also mention the Rotatoria whose males can become strongly degenerated, or rather they can evolve one-sidedly and in this way retrogress so that finally they do not even appear! The females, however, which have become in this way their only representatives, do not develop into true hermaphrodites; they reproduce parthenogenetically having become unable to reproduce by means of division or of budding.

The consequences of the total internalization of gynogametes (which are changed into karyons)—which forms the main difference between the genuine Infusoria and the Eumetazoa—have been radical and remarkable. We must therefore call special attention to them. They had clearly evolved only after the lines of evolution of the Infusoria and of the Eumetazoa had become separated. In opposition to the conditions that can be observed in the Eumetazoa where not only the androgametes but also the gynogametes as such or even mature embryos which have developed into young forms leave the maternal body, we find in the Infusoria that their gynogametes remain in the maternal body, their cytoplasms merge with the cytoplasm of the maternal body without any distinct line left between the two. This phenomenon can be observed in the Infusoria only. The zygote is preserved even after completed insemination and fertilization, and the *Anlagen* of the prospective infantile individual which had developed by way of divisions, are now merged in the maternal body by means of the cytoplasm; in this way the maternal organism is not only rejuvenated (reorganized), it becomes almost eternal; the maternal form does not die, it continues its existence even if it suffers a partial death due to the loss of its macronucleus. The final result is a new complex animal which consists of the maternal and infantile parts that constitute its whole nuclear apparatus as well as parts of its cytoplasm. Thus it is not the maternal organism which continues to exist here as a whole; we rather have, in effect, a double being, while at the same time there is also no real corpse. These unusual conditions have become possible only in combination with an extreme reduction of karyons.

The evolution of the Eumetazoa has pursued an entirely different direction. The gametes of the two sexes have remained free; the polykaryonic state has also been preserved. The rejuvenating sexual process, a warrant of continuity, has remained connected with the gametes. The maternal body—inasmuch as it is not saved by an asexual reproduction—is exposed to an unavoidable ageing which ends every time with the death of the individual. Yet this has also made possible, as it has been frequently emphasized, the progressive evolution of the transitory sexual phase which has finally led to the formation of important and extremely differentiated species.

There are still other paths that were pursued in the evolution of complex species, i.e. such that lead by way of numerous biological units (in this case of genuine, primary cells), and thus of polycellular beings (Spongiae and frequently also Metaphyta). In many respects they have begun to resemble Eumetazoa, especially as regards their sexual phase and the ontogeny, a fact which we will later return to discuss in more detail. Still these forms have remained far behind the Eumetazoa, a fact that can be observed above all in the level which has been reached in their organizations, and in the uniformity, or in the wholeness, of their individuals.

The instance of the Ophryoscolecida to which Dogiel has called our attention shows that the nuclei of Infusoria had in reality earlier been independent cells, and in certain cases even true gametes. They had adapted themselves to a life in the stomach of the Ruminantia; they have thus become strongly specialized and they can in no way be considered as primitive forms. These remarkable minute animals have developed special armour-like formations which cover the whole surface of their body, with the exception of its terminal oral area and which protects the animal against the effects of gastric juices. The "bridging" during conjugation by way of cytoplasm has thus become impossible, while at the same time conjugation itself has been preserved. The contact of the two conjugants has been modified; the two individuals, which are usually dimorphous, touch each other with their terminal ends which are not covered with the armour-like layer. An intermediate space is developed in this way which is surrounded by the terminal ends and which is filled with a fluid. The androgametes (the migrating nuclei) of the two individuals must thus leave their maternal bodies and cross this intermediate space. Not only does a cellularization of these karyons take place, during which the cytoplasm which surrounds a nucleus becomes separated from the common cytoplasm of the conjugant, but also this cytoplasm develops into a spermatozoa which is similar to a flagellate. Thus equipped the androgamete which is now free (it deserves fully this term), crosses by swimming the intermediate space and penetrates actively into the cytoplasm of the partner in order to reach in this way the gynogamete which has kept the form of a karyon.

This androgamete of Entodiniomorpha is not a typical spermatozoan, its cytoplasmatic process which is similar to a flagellum is supposed to be developed at the anterior end of the cell and it does not correspond cytologically to the flagellum of a spermatozoan; yet in spite of this—and contrary to the interpretation proposed by Jägersten—it is an androgamete and it is a homologue to a spermatozoan. Nor can we suppose that it represents a line of evolution which had prepared the way to the formation of a spermatozoan. It is much more probable that we see in this special form of androgametes a new formation which has never led—and which will never lead—to the formation of a typical spermatozoan. According to Dollo's rule of irreversibility, the androgametes of Entodiniomorpha have not been able to recover the characteristic properties of the typical spermatozoa which they had previously lost; their androgametes have now been developed in a new way. In this way it becomes clear that I do not derive the spermatozoa of Eumetazoa from such androgametes that can be found secondarily developed in Ophryoscolecidae: in fact I derive the Eumetazoa from such infusorial ancestors that possessed free and typical androgametes. It is therefore unjust when Jägersten accuses me of treating the spermatozoa of the Eumetazoa in a similar way to the spermatozóa of these aberrant species, and when he states, "This is a pure conjecture with no basis in facts, but necessary for Hadži's view" (Jägersten, 1959 : 93).

I refuse to accept this accusation because it is completely unjust; at the same time I wish to emphasize that even if there were no case of Entodiniomorpha, my interpretation would still appear as more probable than the interpretation which was proposed by Jägersten, especially in those cases where he refers to the excellent research that was done by Åke Franzén (1956). The form, the structure of the spermatozoa, and the spermatiogenesis are so widely different not only when we compare different animal groups but also within the frame of one and the same systematic unit; we are therefore completely unable to develop on this basis a clear idea of the phylogeny of animals and we can also oppose on this basis a derivation of the Eumetazoa from some infusorial ancestors. It should suffice if we quote here the statement made by Franzén (1956 : 467) in the summary to his work; here he states that the spermatozoa of a "primitive type" can be found in such numerous and widely different animal groups as are, "*Cnidaria, Plathelminthes (only Xenothurbella bocki.)*, Nemertini, Aschelminthes (only Priapuloidea), Annelida, Echiuroidea, Sipunculoidea, Mollusca, Tentaculata (only Brachiopoda), Echinodermata, Enteropneusta, Tunicata, and Acrania."

It should not be taken too tragically that the spermatozoa of the Acoela do not belong to this primitive type. In the Acoela the spermatozoa had been able further to develop equally one-sidedly as their organs of copulation. In these and in their hermaphroditism they differ from the Nemertinea which have also reached a low level of evolution. The internal insemination and fertilization, which we believe that the Turbellaria had inherited from their infusorial ancestors, has been preserved in the side line of Platyhelminthes only (Trematoda, Cestoda). In numerous other side-lines of evolution, however, as well as in the main line that evolution had taken and which had finally led to the formation of the next higher phylum of Polymeria, we find that the separation of the two sexes had emerged, pairing had been abandoned, and an external fertilization had been introduced. No generally valid regularities or uniformities can be observed in this development. In the Mollusca, for example, we can find at least occasionally a very strong hermaphroditism reintroduced (species of snails with a uniform hermaphroditic gonad) which appears in combination with pairing, with the new formation of organs of copulation, and with an internal insemination and fertilization.

The example of Ophryoscolecidae with their individualized androgametes is not an isolated case among the higher Infusoria. The androgametes of the hypotrichous infusorian *Euplotes patella* which has a thickened pellicle assume, according to Turner (1930), during their migrations, the form of small amoebae and move actively by means of lobopodia. This is clearly a secondary phenomenon. This amoeboid androgamete of *Euplotes* is not a modified spermatozoon, as this is the case, for example, in Nematoidea or in numerous crayfishes; it is rather a new formation which had evolved from a state of a secondary karyon: in *Euplotes* no plasmatic bridge can be secondarily developed any longer; the "degenerated" (retrograded) karyonic androgamete has thus become reactivated, yet this time in a special way.

The early separation of somatic (vegetative) and sexual karyons is characteristic of the genuine, higher Infusoria from which we do not derive the Acoela. The two gametic karyons which bear the two opposite signs are developed by way of a heterocyclic division. We find also the macro- and micronucleus developed from a zygote karyon by way of an unequal division. This represents a very advanced specialization, and it has naturally been inherited as such by the Acoela. It must be assumed that the macronucleus is all powerful in spite of its limited function because it receives the complete number of chromosomes which are, moreover, frequently strongly polyploidal; yet a part of them, has become inactive. The experiment which was made by Horváth (1947) has shown that this is really so. This Hungarian zoologist suceeded in separating the micronucleus by means of ultraviolet rays. The animals remained alive. Parts of the old macronucleus which is normally lost, developed during the conjugation into a new micronucleus. I wish to mention in this connection that in the Acoela no early separation of the *Anlage* of a gonad takes place as far as we know about the early ontogeny of the Acoela. This is also true for other Turbellaria. We must consider it as a result of a secondary development if we find in other groups of Eumetazoa, e.g. in Nematoidea, an early developed "germ path." It seems to be very probable that in the primitive Infusoria—which alone can be taken into consideration as ancestors of the Acoela and which still have gametes that become free—no early separation of the somatic and generative karyons had taken place, a situation that can still be observed in the Opalinidae.

The Point of Separation in the Evolution of Infusoria and Eumetazoa

This deviation from the straight line of argument which investigates the origin of the Acoela, and thus of all the Eumetazoa from their infusorian ancestors, has led us to the more highly developed Infusoria whose complexity has been the main reason why it is so difficult to get the right interpretation of acoela evolution. It has been necessary to make this detour because with it we are enabled to determine with the greatest probability, the point where the two diverging lines of evolution had separated. I myself wavered initially on how to solve this question. I was inclined to believe—in view of the numerous peculiarities that are limited to the Infusoria only—that the Acoela had separated from the line of evolution that had been pursued by Infusoria even before the true Infusoria had developed, i.e. that the separation had taken place on the level of polykaryonic and polymastigous Flagellata (Hadži, 1944 : 160). I thought that this stage of the phylogenetic development should replace the planula as proposed by v. Graff. Later (Hadži, 1953 : 149) I became convinced that we must place this important point somewhat higher, and so I spoke of the "infusorial-like ancestors" of the Acoela. Due to a recent restudy of the whole problem I have now come to the conclusion—I will soon return to this point—that the separation of these two lines of evolution had taken place on the level of very primitive Infusoria which on the other hand had already ceased to be genuine typical Flagellata. These very primitive Infusoria had later developed on one hand into the typical Infusoria, and on the other into the Eumetazoa. It is much more probable that the definitive and total incorporation and internalization of gametes had taken place after the line of Eumetazoa had already separated from the line Infusoria. In the latter the development had led to conjugation as it is now known. This means that in the Eumetazoa the gametocytes have never lost their independence and that they have never united their own cytoplasm with the cytoplasm of the progamont. No cellularization of gametes has therefore in all probability been necessary. The sexual phase had become internalized; it was just at this point and in its transition to the hermaphroditism that this primitive infusorian—which was the ancestor of Eumetazoa—had differed from its equally polykaryonic and hypermastigous flagellate ancestors.

It should be mentioned in this connection when we refer to the Flagellata as direct antecedents of Eumetazoa that in this way we are easily able to understand, without being obliged to take refuge in the thesis of flagellate colonies, the numerous cytological peculiarities that can also be found in the Eumetazoa, and not only in sponges.

Yet before I begin an explanation of an outline of the probable organization the animal had at the point of separation of the lines of evolution of the Eumetazoa and of Infusoria (an outline which can now be made with a considerably greater precision) I would like first to call attention to the excellent and instructive work by Earl D. Hanson (Hanson, 1958).

I believe I am right when I state that Hanson has basically accepted my concept, even if he did not accept it at first. In his criticisms, expositions, additions, and ammendations Hanson refers, when he discusses my arguments, to the necessarily brief article only which appeared in the *Systematic Zoology* (Hadži, 1953). Hanson's leading idea is that my concept cannot be accepted in its present form, that it still needed some essential propping and complementing, above all the point where I discuss the deduction of the Acoela from the Infusoria. In his argument he states that, "The parallels between the Acoela and the Ciliophora may be illusory, in terms of demonstrating a phylogenetic relationship, if it turns out that the acoel has its counterpart only in a fictional amalgam of ciliate characters that has no more reality than the mythical Chimera." I believe that with such a formulation Hanson has gone much too far and that the formulation is inadequate. The fact which is called by Hanson somewhat ironically an "amalgam" or a "Chimera" is in reality a phenomenon which has been earnestly studied by modern phylogenetics where it is known under the name of the Mosaic theory, or Watson's rule, as it has been called (Sir Gavin de Beer, 1954). An "accidental" convergence of several characteristics of an existing type can lead by way of genetic regulations to new combinations (naturally with a simultaneous appearance of new mutations). It is in this way that new animal types which are able to live—and no chimeras—can develop and in all probability also have developed.

Moreover I wish to remind the reader that at the beginning of the present study I already said that I came to my concept (naturally not as the first zoologist, yet quite independently) neither by way of a study of Infusoria or of Turbellaria, but rather after a protracted study of problems connected with the Cnidaria. I am therefore happy when I see other zoologists who work in other special fields of interest, such as, Otto Steinböck, a prominent expert in Turbellaria, extend their interest in the direction of the present study. I am also very happy to see that Hanson wrote his study mainly from the point of view of an expert in Protozoa, even if we do not agree in every detail.

There are mainly three points in which Hanson tries to improve and perfect my concept in order to make it more acceptable, after he had submitted it to a detailed criticism.

Hanson wishes first that something more definite, more real, could be found instead of the too general name of the infusorial ancestors of the Acoela which were designated as "infusorian, or ciliate-like" animals. Hanson has selected the "pleurostomatous gymnostomes" from the group Euciliata which is rich in forms, more precisely from the subgroup Holotricha which even now possess the most primitive characteristics. These "pleurostomatous gymnostomes" are on one hand homogenous, and on the other hand they have remained most similar to the Acoela. Hanson selected as their representatives the two genera *Remanella* and *Dileptus*. It is quite natural that the two forms which are genuine (as well as recent!) Euciliata have all those similarities with the Acoela that can be generaly found among the Euciliata, even if they belong to the more specialized forms. We are therefore interested in those pecularities of these two genera of Euciliata which could justify us to suppose that they are more closely related to the Acoela than are the remaining Euciliata. Such peculiarities could be the un-differentiated character of cilia, the primitive conditions of the cytostome surrounding, and above all the plurality of nuclei, thus of karyons, whether they be somatic or generative.

It certainly is welcome and useful for my concept when Hanson called my attention to these forms of Euciliata which show some combined primitive characteristics, provided that the plurality of the two types of karyons be a primary phenomenon. This makes my thesis of the origin of the Acoela, and thus of the Eumetazoa generally, from some infusoria-like ancestors even more probable and more easily acceptable. Yet at the same time I do not think that it is of much importance. The two Holotricha are genuine Infusoria, and not some transitional forms. They suit the scheme of the Mosaic theory by way of which the characteristics that can be observed in one descendant can be attributed to different ascendants so that these characteristics become united and combined in a certain descendant which develops thus into a new type. It cannot be understood how our concept which derives the Acoela from the Infusoria could depend on this addition which was made by Hanson.

The second difficulty of the original concept which makes its acceptance hard or even impossible was formulated by Hanson in the following question, "Why is the macronucleus, one of the most important of all ciliate characters, absent in the Acoela?" (Hanson, 1958 : 33). This has in my opinion not been the most fortunate formulation of this question; its words should rather be, "what corresponds, what in the Acoela is homologous to the macronucleus of the Euciliata?" I was not able to discuss this problem in detail in my very short article which appeared in the *Systematic Zoology*, yet even from this article, and even more so from my other publications it appears clear that I consider the macronucleus to be homologous to the somatic, or vegetative ("indifferent") karyons. The macronucleus is therefore a result of a secondary oligomerization which succeeded during the evolution of Infusoria, the polymerization that had taken place in the Flagellata, the ascendants of Infusoria. The polymerization, however, was continued in the evolution of the Acoela, it was even further developed not only in the quantitative but even more so in the qualitative direction; the karyons had become differentiated in spite of their total potentiality after they had assumed a certain place in the animal body, a development which was of the greatest importance for the prospective destiny of the Eumetazoa. This is the reason why there is no macronucleus in the Acoela, this is one of the key differences between the higher Infusoria and the lowest Acoela. It must necessarily be supposed that formerly there had also existed intermediate forms between the stage with numerous vegetative karyons and the stage which has one karyon only and which is the final stage reached by way of this oligomerization. Not only in such stages was the number of karyons decreased, but even their behaviour was different (the type of origin, the subsequent divisions, etc.). The macronucleus, however, has lost its total potentiality and it has to be newly formed after each conjugation (combined with a copulation) when the final stage of the oligomerization has been reached and when everything has become concentrated in the macronucleus.

The case of *Remanella* which has been pointed out by Hanson is certainly very interesting because here the macronuclei are not developed by way of a division of themselves, but instead they develop continually from the micronuclei which themselves are also able to multiply. It is quite possible that a more primitive stage is represented in this case, even if a special development cannot be excluded either. The plausibility of my concept again does not depend on all this. Hanson states, "It can be seen that nuclear situation in *Remanella* provides a transitional form in a possible series going from that typical of the ciliates to the dispersed nuclei of the acoels" (Hanson, 1958 : 37). At the same time he adds that this series can also be reversed which, however, is not probable for other reasons. I confidently expect that new material evidence will come to light during the future studies of Infusoria which will support our thesis.

The third addition to my concept which was made by Hanson regards "The transition from ciliated protozoan to acoel." It consists in the suggestion that cellularization did not take place earlier than in the Turbellaria and that it can therefore not be considered as the decisive step in the evolution of Metazoa proper. The essential difference between the Infusoria and the Acoela, and thus the decisive step in the evolution of Metazoa, had been, according to Hanson, the fact that in the Acoela the karyons had become morphologically complex, in comparison with the Infusoria where they are physiologically "compound." A progressive organization had become possible because of this step. The variously placed karyons had become heterogeneous, and this heterogeneity was increased even more by a subsequent formation of cell membranes, by a visible cellularization or compartmentalization.

Hanson is certainly right when he attaches great importance to the differentiation of the somatic karyons. This, however, is not something entirely new because I too have thought of such a differentiation in the form of a regular distribution of karyons in all the three body layers. Neither have I attributed any primary role to the cellularization because it does not appear earlier than in the already "finished" yet primitive Acoela, and even then only partly. Moreover, I believe that it is a mistake to attribute a leading role to a single peculiarity in the creation of the Acoela ("crucial point" or "key step," according to Hanson). It seems to me much more probable that they had emerged because of a convergence of several important characteristics and moments, among which we must mention above all the internalization of the sexual phase combined with hermaphroditism.

After this discussion of Hanson's study on the primitive Infusoria I wish now to refer to the important work by I. B. Rajkov (1957). Rajkov discusses the problem of the origin of the bikaryonic state of Infusoria using in his study the discoveries that have been recently made in connection with the primitive Infusoria. Rajkov asserts that even now species can be found among the lower Infusoria which do not have a "nuclear dualism." As an example he mentions *Stephanopogon* Lwoff (1936) whose body has several equal nuclei which are not polyploid and which contain only little DNA. Quite bizarre is the case of *Trachelocerca phoenicoptera* (Rajkov) with its complex karyon which develops by way of a union of several macronuclei and which also encloses six micronuclei. This sounds very strange and it can be interpreted only as a lateral development from the main line that evolution had taken in connection with conditions that are typical of the higher Infusoria. In the conjugant of the same species we find a larger number of the so-called pronuclei (gamocyte karyons) from seven to twenty-two. They develop into three to six androgametic karyons (migrating nuclei). The fertilization is multiple, its result, however, is one zygote only which remains alive while all the rest is lost. Rajkov is right when he concludes that this is a remnant of a former multiple formation of gametes and that the conjugation of the Infusoria had therefore evolved from such sexual conditions that are characterized by the gametogenesis and by the copulation, a fact which several years ago I did not only maintain but also tried to prove (Hadži, 1950).

Trachelocerca belongs to the holotrichous Holophryidae which Rajkov believes to be the most primitive Infusoria. We can expect that many interesting facts will still come to light during the future researches.

The Origin of the Complex Hypercellular Individualities

We will now return to the problem of the cellularization which was so thoroughly discussed by Hanson. All biologists agree that the monocellular state with one cell nucleus, thus the primary independent monokaryon, represents an extraordinarily important stage in the evolution of life (Unicellularia, according to Rotmüller; Eunucleata, according to Moskovskij). The growth in size of an individual is necessarily limited by such a monokaryonik state. This limit was overcome several times during the subsequent phylogenetic evolution which, in agreement with a generally valid regularity, did not involve all the lines of evolution that had developed from one and the same origin. In the meantime a new bifurcation emerged; plants and animals. This bifurcation has also taken place in several lines of evolution. Complex and therefore easily enlarged bionts had evolved along the line which was pursued in the evolution of plants by way of the so-called formation of colonies; its reason was a strongly developed cell wall. The phrase "formation of colonies," however, which is so frequently used is not completely adequate. The monocellular individuals of one and the same species can also unite into a biological whole even if they belong to different colonies. Coenobia and polycellular algae are regularly developed from descendants of a zygote, more rarely from a vegetative cell (a spore). The products of division do not scatter, they rather remain together and develop into parts of a new unit which are organically connected, they develop into a complex individual. This process can be considered as a parallel to the process of the polymerization. The daughter cells are not only all powerful they are even primarily destined to develop into independent individuals. They lose part of their "sovereignty" by becoming members of a coenobium or of a colonial union, they become subordinated to the new unit or entity. This leads via practice, to a heterogeneity of originally equal and equivalent cells, to their differentiation. It can be observed above all in the development of the generative and of the somatic cells. Tissues, organs, and systems of organs are also developed in this way. The freely moving way of life is relinquished quite early by all the plant bionts (with a few exceptions, Volvocales!). They become permanently sessile beings which agrees with their type of feeding. Even androgametes which preserved their free mobility are now only active when they are transferred from place to place. This situation has finally become even more complicated because of an introduction of a remarkable alternation of generations.

In spite of a strong inclination of the plant cells to remain mutually separated they have nevertheless developed plasmatic connections which go through the cell walls, or they had even completely relinquished their cell walls and had developed in this way syncytia. The case of *Caulerpa* and of the whole group it belongs to is well enough known. Here a total polykaryonic stage had been reached. Among the higher plants it is not seldom that partial syncytia can be found.

The animals certainly pursued several lines in their evolution, yet it was one line only which succeeded in making essential progress while all the remaining lines had already come to a stop at the level of Protozoa. Another primitive line led to the formation of Spongiae. The evolution of animals has been much more vivid because of their heterotrophic type of feeding, because of their free mobility which is connected with the type of feeding, and—which is a very important fact—because of the very thin walls of their cells. The limitations of the monocellular and mononuclear state were overcome along at least three paths. One of these was, so it seems, a development which led to a slight increase of the cytoplasmatic mass which was subsequently divided half-way, first into two and later into several parts; its result had been the formation of considerably larger complex individuals. Yet this division into halves has not led to differentiation, it remained rather mechanical, and its result has only been an increased breathing surface. It was soon combined with a polymerization of the nucleus. This is how the comparatively large Foraminifera, e.g. of the type of *Nummulites*, evolved. Yet no genuine Metazoa had ever possibly developed along this way.

The second type of development of the complex individuals was similar to the one we have just described in connection with the evolution of plants. As in the case of plants we find now in the Flagellata an inclination to develop colonies. In the true colonies the products of division of the maternal cell remain only mechanically attached to each other (coenobia, colonies s.str.). This had finally led to the formation of cormi when certain cytoplasmatic connections developed between the members of the same colony. In this way the coordination, and finally the differentiation of partners became possible. This is how I imagine the evolution of Spongiae which begun characteristically from an already more highly developed and therefore more specialized group of Flagellata. I am supported in this suggestion by important factual arguments. These species of Flagellata were characterized by a cytoplasmatic collar which had developed around the basis of the flagellum (Choanoflagellata, Craspedomonadida). During this development the ability has not been lost either to abolish the collar form or even to assume an entirely amoeboid form and type of movement. Even if there were no species of *Proterospongia* (two such species have actually been described in the meantime) it would still be very probable for reasons that cannot be discussed here that the Spongiae had evolved from some originally freely-living cormi of Choanoflagellata after the latter had adopted the sessile way of life. Nothing can be changed in this connection by the fact that examples can occasionally be found among the Eumetazoa whose cells have a collar formation. The organization of Spongiae is in fact entirely different from that of all the Eumetazoa. Neither can this situation be changed by the fact that a sexual phase with an oögeny can also be found in Spongiae as well as in the Eumetazoa because we know that the same sexual conditions had also evolved in various plant groups. These are properties that had been inherited from the protistic ancestors of all the polycellular forms, in spite of the fact that we have here several lines of evolution. It may be emphasized that a formation of syncytia can also be observed in Spongiae, and not only in plants.

The embryonic development, the ontogeny, emerged as a necessary consequence of this state in all these lines of evolution, thus in Volvocidae and in various other polycellular algae, in Cormophyta, and finally also in Spongiae. It is therefore not surprising to see that there is a great difference between these ontogenies as a result of their separate lines of evolution; this is also true for Spongiae in comparison with the Eumetazoa. No other higher animal group has ever evolved from Spongiae. The further evolution of the animalic bionts had begun from another centre.

The most successful attack against the limiting influence of the monocellular state, an attack which has finally led to the formation of the most highly organized beings, of the polycellular animals and man, was made by way of polymerization, the plurality of nuclei in a cytoplasmatic or plasmodial body which preserves its individuality, and by way of a subsequent cellularization (Fig. 48). The way along which this development had taken place and how it occurred has already been partly discussed, but we will still return to this problem. The importance and the significance of the difference which exists between the development of multiple cells by way of a formation of colonies or cormi, and the development of such cells by way of polymerization can easily be understood. The first type of development is characteristic of plants, and the second of animals. The two types of development have in common (1) the growth in size; (2) the possibility of a differentiation; and (3) the sexual phase with the ontogeny at its end. Cellularity can also be considered as one of these common properties even if here there is one important difference. In the polycellular plants the cellularity is a primary element which is obstinately preserved; in the Eumetazoa on the other hand cellularity is a secondary development from a polykaryonic state. Cellularity is almost never completely carried through in the

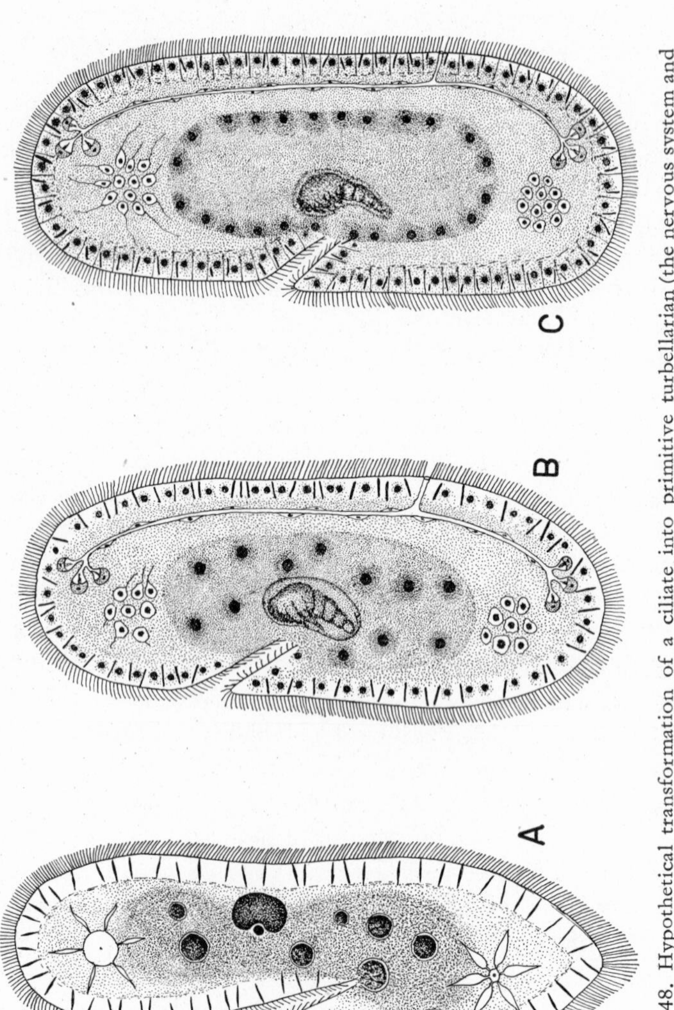

Fig. 48. Hypothetical transformation of a ciliate into primitive turbellarian (the nervous system and muscular system are omitted.) (After Hadži.)

Eumetazoa (which is particularly true for the middle body layer, the mesohyl!); their tissues show a strong inclination to a return into the plasmodial state which we usually call a syncytium.

An even more important difference between the polycellular plants and sponges on one hand and the Eumetazoa on the other, a difference which became evident above all during the subsequent destiny of the phyletic development, is the fact that such a degree of unity can never be reached by the polycellular bionts by way of a colonial formation, as is the unity that has been reached by the Eumetazoa. The latter had inherited from the very beginning a uniform and already comparatively highly developed organization from their protozoan ancestors, as far as such an organization could be developed within the framework of a mono- or paucinuclear state. The objections made by those scholars who adhere to the old interpretation which considers that all the polycellular organisms had evolved from colonies of cells—among these scholars we mention above all Sachwatkin (1956) and his intensive and extensive work—cannot deny the fact that a great difference exists between the organizations of Spongiae and of the Eumetazoa, even if we take into consideration the sedentary way of life only (e.g. a comparison with the Hydroidea). Neither can they abrogate the difference that exist between a sum of choanoflagellates where each member still continues to exist as an individual which must first become adapted to the "new conditions," and, on the other hand, an infusorian with various organelles and generally fine structures which evolves in a direct line into progressively higher Eumetazoa while at the same time the unity of the animal is constantly preserved.

There can be no doubt that a new form can develop by way a coenobium from originally independent "monocellular" protozoic or protophytic individuals; the development goes from the state of coenobium via a formation of a colony or of a cormus to that of the final form. Such a development can be observed in numerous Metaphyta and in Spongiae. Yet at the same time it can also be stated that great progress has never been made along this way towards a definite whole. The circumstances led to a change of exactly those metabionts that had evolved by way of colonial formations to the sessile way of life. This has proved an obstacle to a subsequent progressive development. A "blastuloid" organization *(Volvox)* represents the highest level reached in the evolution of the freely moving Metaphyta. Bypassing the immobile Metaphyta in which no central organs have been developed we see that the sponges have not come very far in their evolution either. They again have not developed any central organs or any devices which would unite the whole aggregation into a higher organic entity; they represent a very lowly-developed side branch of the animal world.

In the numerous, mainly sessile Eumetazoa which had frequently adopted a freely moving way of life (Siphonophora, Ectoprocta, Taliacea) and which had developed their own cormi ("colonies") higher units can be developed from several originally independent individuals. These new units represent a new organization, they have developed their own individuality, and it is not even easy to identify their original complexity. Siphonophora may serve here as the best and probably also as phylogenetically the oldest example. They have certainly reached the highest level of development in this direction. They excel in a highly developed external homogeneity, they show a considerable polymorphism both in their polypoid and medusoid "persons" (the formerly independent individuals), they have even evolved new impersonal and thus specifically cormic organs, e.g. a pneumatophore. Yet on the other hand they have not developed any centralized nervous system, neither have they been able to overcome the limitations of Hydrozoa and to develop in this way into a new animal type; this in spite of the fact that they have become at least slightly freely moving animals.

The quicker and higher development of the Eumetazoa was made possible by their animal type of feeding which is connected with a search for the living prey, and by the free mobility which is connected with their type of feeding, and finally by the direct transference to the Eumetazoa (of the type of Turbellaria) of an already plasmodial and polykaryonic unit which had already been enriched by all those elements that could be attained in a monocellular state. It has already been repeatedly stressed that quite a few zoologists already before me had taken into consideration the possibility that the Metazoa had evolved from some infusoria-like ancestors. Yet they were unable to develop a clear concept because they stood under the influence of the now still widely accepted interpretation that the Spongiae, the Cnidaria, and the Ctenophora, thus the so-called Coelenterata, are the lowest Metazoa (we will bypass the Mesozoa which are still very problematic). The only thing these scholars dared to do was make a few brief and vague remarks on the subject. The way to the new interpretation has become open only now after we have first developed a new concept of the evolution of the Cnidaria, after an exclusion of the Spongiae from the sphere of Eumetazoa, and after a removal of Ctenophora from a society with Cnidaria, and finally after we have bypassed the so-called Mesozoa. To this we must also add the recognition that the Acoela have the lowest organization that can be found among the Turbellaria, and that this simplicity is not a consequence of an eventual retrogression but rather a primary phenomenon. The situation became clear when the barrier that had artificially separated the polykaryonic and therefore plasmodial Infusoria from the equally plasmodial and polynuclear Acoela was dropped.

Is the Plasmodial State of the Acoela a Primary Element?

The antagonists of the new interpretation soon discovered its critical point; they believed that at this point they had the best chance to attack my concept. This point is the primary nature of the plasmodial state that can be found in the Acoela and in other Turbellaria. This was followed by a cellularization.

Erich Reisinger, endeavours to prove the faults of my thesis of the primary plasmodial state of the primitive Metazoa, the Turbellaria included. He believes that in a polykaryonic state we must always see secondarily developed syncytia. He tries to support his criticism not only by means of facts that he collected in some occasional observations, but also with experiments.

In order to make his interpretation of proposed facts all the more acceptable Reisinger initially makes an unproved statement in which he declares our concept to be "schon auf Grund der total verschiedenen Sexualverhältnisse der gamotogamen Ciliate einerseits und der gametogamen Metazoen andererseits als äusserst problematisch erwiesen."

Let us now consider those facts that were used by Reisinger as a basis of his conclusions, and above all the proof he obtained by way of an experiment. Reisinger pressed through a silk-gauze an already cellularized freshwater triclad *Planaria polychroa* O. Schmidt. In the separated rags of tissue Reisinger could see spheric complexes (the so-called "*Sphärien*") being developed in spots where cells ran together to form syncytia (with the exception of a few cells that remained amoeboid). Many parts became histolized. Thus syncytia similar to the central parenchyma (= endocyte, according to Westblad) of the Acoela (all the syncytia are actually similar!) have been developed from the cellular tissues.

Observations have shown that under the influence of the protozoic parasites (Sporozoa) of the species *Eucoccidium monoti* the cellular intestine of the species *Otomesostoma* can change back into a syncytial state. Such a development can take place, so to speak, normally in Planariae when they take too much food, a fact which is also mentioned by Reisinger. By means of some not too tender experimental interventions Reisinger succedded in leading a syncytial skin layer into a cellularized state (in *Gyratrix* and in *Koinocystis*); he used strong irritations in this experiment. Reisinger also succeeded in artificially stimulating the opposite process to the one first mentioned. He mentions the fact which he believes to be in itself a firm proof, that in all the ontogenies of the lower Turbellaria that have become known up to now, these ontogenies take place by way of a cellular development only ("rein zellig"), thus by way of cleavages.

On the basis of all these facts Reisinger comes to the conclusion that there are no primary plasmodia in the Turbellaria but rather secondary syncytia which show a constant inclination to return under certain conditions into their cellular components. He ends his discussion with the statement, "Die von Steinböck und von Hadži vertretene Ableitung der Metazoen von Ciliaten über polyenergide plasmodiale Stadien erscheint durch unsere Befunde weitgehend erschüttert" (Reisinger, 1959:641).

As regards the "totally different sexual conditions" that are supposed to exist between the Infusoria and the Eumetazoa, we have already shown that in this case we cannot really speak of such a total difference.

We cannot attribute the same conclusive power to the findings made by Reisinger as Reisinger himself would like to give them, in spite of the fact that they are very interesting. Reisinger goes even so far in his endeavours to deny the existence of a primary plasmodial state in the Turbellaria, that he calls Steinböck's opinion a "pure fiction" (Reisinger, 1959: 642) which is certainly unjust in view of the fact that Steinböck (Steinböck, 1954) too tried to prove his thesis of primary plasmodia in the Acoela (which he calls archhiston) by means of experiments.

It is unnecessary to discuss whether there are any true

syncytia; any experiments in this connection are completely superfluous. This is a phenomenon which can be found scattered in the whole animal world, a fact which has been recognized long ago. We even know that among algae which have reached a low level only in their organization (they are therefore certainly primitive organisms among the polycellular forms) there is a whole group, among the Siphonales, which shows a strong inclination to form syncytia, in spite of the fact that these are plants and thus colonial polycellular forms whose cells had evolved quite generally strong membranes. In the best known case, in *Caulerpa*, we find cellularity eliminated to such a degree that it appears only slightly during the phase of the formation of gonads while at the same time it has completely disappeared from the ontogeny. In spite of this *Caulerpa* has remained a lowly organized alga, and therefore a plant.

We are particularly interested in the cases that were observed by Reisinger during his experiments where a cellular state was developed from a syncytial (plasmodial) state. It should be mentioned in this connection that a trend must be taken into consideration by means of which the cellular tissue of the Eumetazoa developed from the plasmodia. Moreover, it is quite difficult, even if not impossible, to decide precisely whether in a given case we have a true primary plasmodium or a secondary syncytium. In the case of the more highly developed Turbellaria it must also be taken into consideration that their plasmodia have already reached a state of readiness to pass over into a cellular state; in these a slightly stronger irritation can be sufficient to produce a segregation of their karyons, and thus the formation of cells. Reisinger did not quote any example of artificial cellularization of the plasmodia Acoela.

As a contrast to all this we can find the very instructive experiments that were made by Steinböck in the most primitive Acoela *(Amphiscolops)*. Steinböck could prove with these experiments that all three parts of the archhiston, all the three body layers (which are called by Steinböck ecto-plasmodium, mesoplasmodium, and entoplasmodium) are all capable, that they are able to develop a new unit even if cut into the smallest dimensions (a minute-piece measuring 157 μ punched from the posterior end of the animal). They have therefore the character of a primary plasmodium. Where can we find a similar case in the whole animal world of the Eumetazoa that an entoderm can regenerate into a whole new animal even if it exists in a syncytial state?

The most important element among Reisinger's arguments against the existence of a truly primary plasmodium in the Eumetazoa (our thesis of a polykaryonic and plasmodial origin of the Eumetazoa loses every foundation if there are no such plasmodia) is, according to Reisinger, "Die ausnahmslose zellige Primärstruktur früher Embryonalstadien" (Reisinger, 1958: 642); or, in other words: the ontogenies of the Turbellaria. Among these, the Acoela begin with a cleavage, thus with a formation of cells which is only subsequently followed by a formation of syncytia. Steinböck has already given an answer to this observation. Above all, very little is known about the early ontogenies of the most primitive Acoela. We agree with Steinböck who does not think that species of Metazoa will be found with the oldest form of the early ontogeny (i.e. a plasmodial state) preserved. Evolution has led in the inactive sessile polycellular algae *(Caulerpa)* to a state where a division of karyons takes place as an obviously secondary phenomenon instead of a cleavage or of a division of the zygote.

Scholars have become used, under the influence of the colonial theory and of the blastula–gastrula, to see in the early development of the Eumetazoa by way of cleavage (the division of karyons that can be observed in insects was naturally immediately explained as a secondary caenogenesis) a recapitulation of the phylogeny which is supposed to repeat the primitive formation of colonies by the monocellular Flagellata. Scholars have begun only recently to analyse experimentaly, the early ontogeny taking into consideration the physiological viewpoint. On the basis of everything we now know about the very variable ontogenetic morphogenies it appears as improbable that the first, and thus the oldest, steps in the ontogenies—which had evolved regardless of the phyletic antiquity of total divisions of cells, with few exceptions that can be explained—could possibly represent a recapitulation of the oldest state in the evolution of the Eumetazoa. It seems *a priori* much more probable that physiological factors, above all the greatly increased need of oxygen as a consequence of a very intensive metabolism, had caused the cellularization to be adopted in the early ontogenies. The organism has thus endeavoured to evolve large surfaces for each active karyon for the sake of an increased gaseous interchange (the intake of oxygen, and the delivery of the carbon dioxide). This has caused the earliest cellularization which took place *ad hoc*. This trend had led occasionally to a temporary segregation, to really anarchic states of blastomeres even if the whole as such had not been lost. The state of the fully developed animal, the plasmodial state, has been recovered after this period of "Storm and Stress," and it can therefore be rightly considered as a primitive state.

Thus the initially reversible cellularization began in all probability in the earliest ontogenetic stages with cleavage as its very special form. It was much later that true cellularization combined with the formation of tissue, had evolved; it remained permanently without losing its ability to return under special conditions into the plasmodial state. Such a state is called a syncytium. Actual cellularization did not appear immediately and generally, but rather by degrees; this is proved by conditions that can be observed in Turbellaria. First it took place in the skin layer (the ectodermal epidermis), later in the intestinal wall (the entodermal intestinal epithelium), and finally in the middle layer where it has usually not been complete (the mesoderm s. l. or mesohyl, usually divided into the mesenchyme and the coelothelium).

An Attempt to Reconstruct the Initial State of the Eumetazoa

After all these criticisms, counter-criticisms, and discussions we will now try to reconstruct the initial state or the earliest state of the Eumetazoa. In this attempt I will correct and improve my previous suggestions which were necessarily vague. I am well aware of the hypothetical character of this construction, yet at the same time I believe that it is not simply a product of pure fancy as this has been maintained by some of its critics; it is based on critically selected facts and it can claim at least some probability, at least as much as can be claimed for those attempts that have been made so far by those who adhere to the colonial theory. It should be discussed critically and compared with the theory which is now generally believed to be true. From the very beginning I have expected that this interpretation would not find an easy acceptance because it requires that the old interpretation which is so deeply rooted and which at the first sight appears so bewitchingly clear should be given up. It cannot be expected that the numerous older zoologists could easily relinquish an opinion which they have considered true for such a long time. It is said that such a revolutionary idea will have to wait for the next generation to win its full success. My reconstruction of the origin of the Eumetazoa stands in opposition to the "belief" in the colonial origin of the whole animal world and to a number of other similar "beliefs" (e.g., the question of the relation between ontogeny and phylogeny, the significance of cleavage and of other ontogenetic mechanisms, the idea of germ layers, the "germ path," the general division of the animal world, the problems of the mesoderm and of the coelom, etc.). To this we must add the supposed difficulty which arises because I consider that the Metaphyta and the Spongiae have evolved out of the colonies of Protista, and thus in different ways to that which the evolution of the Eumetazoa had taken.

Instead of the vague and indefinite statement that the Eumetazoa evolved first as the Acoela, among the Turbellaria, from some Infusoria-like ancestors, we can now state with better justification that the Eumetazoa evolved first—contrary to the evolution of sponges and of all the polycellular plants—as polymerized Protozoa, thus as Protozoa that were equipped with a larger number of karyons and of kinetids (cilia); during that state they were no longer typical Flagellata, neither had they yet reached the state of the typical Infusoria; yet their ancestors stood closer to the Infusoria than to the Flagellata mainly because of the fact that their diploid and polykaryonic vegetative generation (the "indifferent" generation, according to Dogiel) had also become the bearer of the sexual, i.e. hermaphroditic, generation. These ancestors can therefore be called the "Urciliata" (Protociliata) (the primitive Ciliata).

The gamontized generation therefore also includes the sexual generation which had remained cellularized (it has by now already changed into a phase). This sexual generation develops its maturity in the interior of the maternal animal and it becomes free in the form of gametes after or during pairing. The zygotes which are formed in this way, the fertilized egg cells, develop during ontogeny into a new generation. Thus the progamic subphase of the sexual phase has been internalized and this has led to the formation of gonads. These gonads represent therefore from the very beginning a *corpus separatum* in the body of the Eumetazoa and they cannot be considered as a genuine gland.

The earliest Eumetazoa have taken over all the organelles as well as the finer and specialized cytoplasmatic structure of their protozoan ancestors. For reasons that are so far unknown, the direction of division changed just at this moment from a longitudinal to a transverse division via an oblique division. This change occurred during a transition which is at the same time one of the most crucial transitions in the whole evolution of the living world. The change may perhaps stand in a causal connection with the longitudinal rows of cilia.

From this reconstructed form we can deduce without any difficulty both the line which had been pursued in the evolution of the Infusoria with their characteristic mergings of the cytoplasms, the internalized sexual phase, and the conjugation; and the line which had been pursued by the Eumetazoa in their evolution with their gametes which become free.

The Origin of the Middle Body Layer—of the So-Called Mesoderm

The very large number of known characteristics common to both the Infusoria and the Turbellaria described by v. Gelei has been increased since the publication of his study. In this connection I would like to call attention to the fact that Remane himself, one of the most active opponents of the interpretation which suggests a direct relationship between the Infusoria and the Turbellaria and of its consequences, has stated that the numerous similarities that exist in the two groups could not be interpreted as a purely incidental phenomenon but rather as a proof of a closer relationship; and that they made any further proof i.e. transitional cases, patterns, etc., unnecessary. To this we could add that no facts have become known till now that disprove this close relationship. Furthermore, we must also mention a fact whose value should not be underrated, i.e. that many phenomena can be much more easily understood and explained if viewed from the standpoint of my thesis of the Prociliata as the ancestors of the Acoela, and therefore of the Eumetazoa, than when they are studied on the basis of the old interpretation which believes in a colonial origin of the Metazoa. I would like to mention in this connection the much discussed problem of the origin of the third, or of the middle, body layer, the mesoderm, and the coelom problem which is connected with it.

According to the old interpretation, the three body layers evolved successively one after the other, each after a long interval of time. This conclusion was reached mainly on the basis of the formative processes that can be observed during ontogeny. Yet on the other hand, these processes show a perplexing variety so that it was impossible to decide which of them represents the most primitive form. Haeckel proposed a special stage which contained no body layers and which he placed before the stage with one body layer. He believed he found support for this theory in the ontogenetic facts. He called this stage a morula. It did not actually suit the whole scheme he proposed and it has not been generally accepted. The one-layered stage which had according to his interpretation the form of a hollow sphere was given the name of a blastaea, after the ontogenetic blastula; it was thus believed to be recapitulated in the blastula. All the cells of the epithelium as the most primitive form of the tissue, are identical. The first differentiation had taken place by way of a separation of the vegetative and of the sexual functions, and, in connection with this, of their bearers. This is how the appearance of the "germ path" was also explained. The zoologists have not been too embarassed by the fact that no blastaea-like form can be found among the Metazoa. Haeckel, however, who found such an absence unpleasant, tried to track down such an animal form in the sea plankton. Thus a description was made of a certain "Magosphaera" which, however, had soon to be removed from the list of animal species because it was found to be nothing other than a colony of Flagellata. After this failure a blastaea-like form was borrowed from the plant world; this is the now famous *Volvox; Volvox* still continues to play the same role even in spite of the fact that we know that it has nothing in common with the origin of the Eumetazoa. It should serve as a pattern. *Volvox* is certainly a genuine green alga, and a particularly specialized fresh water alga. It emerged as a final product of evolution along a side-line. Many forms can be found among algae which show a transition from the monocellular species to the colonial polycellular forms. How can we be certain that the polycellular heterotrophic Eumetazoa evolved in the same way as was "invented" for an autotrophic regime? Scholars should refer in this connection only to developments that can be observed in ontogenies. Yet are these really recapitulations of some adult ancestors? Contrary to the widely accepted opinion which sees in *Volvox* pattern at least a plan of the primitive ancestor of the Eumetazoa, we consider such a suggestion as completely improbable.

Those who adhere to the old interpretation maintain that during the second stage of the phylogeny of Metazoa, a two-layered animal which was able to digest its food, the so-called gastraea, had evolved from the primitive one-layered hollow sphere whose members were able to perform, as epithelium cells, all functions with the exception of the sexual function. This two-layered form was called a gastraea, after the name of gastrula. Yet again no such animal exists. It was believed that the typical evolution of this diploblastic form had been similar to the development that can be occasionally observed in the ontogenies where the posterior half of the animal (i.e. the part of the animal situated opposite to the direction of swimming) invaginates into its anterior half. Thus with one action the animal succeeded in developing not only its two layers, the ectoderm and the entoderm, but also a digestive cavity and an oral opening which was unfortunately placed at the posterior end of the animal. The gastraea as we find it thus reconstructed is supposed to have lived as a planktonic animal and it was radially symmetrical. This gastraea descended later (partly simultaneously, according to Haeckel) to the sea bottom where it evolved into various "Gastraeadae." The latter were quite early given the unsuitable name of "Coelenterata." No gastraea ever existed among plants; it is typical of the polycellular animals. It possessed a skin and an intestinal layer and showed a corresponding difference in its tissue and in its cells.

It has later been found that there are no primary two-layered animals, except some forms which show traces of a strong retrogression due to their parasitic way of life. Haeckel himself showed a considerable uncertainty on this point; he wavered when he tried to find the actual division between the two-layered and the three-layered animals (the Coelenterata and the Coelomata, or the Diploblastica and the Triploblastica); he even suggested once that the Platyhelminthes should be classified among the Coelenterata. These animals had not evolved a genuine middle layer, an actual mesoderm, but only the so-called mesenchyme or the mesogloea.

Finally, it was established that a majority of Coelenterata posses a middle (the third) body layer and that they really represent a very motley group. Platyhelminthes were the first to have definitely left this group; they were followed by Spongiae (this, however, has not been accepted by all zoologists). The Cnidaria and the Acnidaria (=Ctenophora) have thus remained the last two groups which have still continued to be classified as Coelenterata. Yet even in connection with the Ctenophora it has become more and more clear that they do not really belong here. The Cnidaria have thus been the last group which have still been considered as Coelenterata, yet even with these it has been found that they possess the third (the middle) body layer even if it is only slightly developed. They are therefore no real Diploblastica either.

Evolution finally led, according to this interpretation, to the formation of the third layer. The difficulties which emerge together with it are even greater. The third body layer (actually its solid part only because the sparse mesenchyme is usually not considered as a part of the actual mesoderm) develops during the ontogenies (which should serve as patterns for the phylogenetic conclusions) in widely different ways. Two such developments are particularly conspicuous because they generally even if not completely, exclude each other. In one case the mesoderm is developed from the ectoderm (the ectomesoderm), or, if we are more precise, from the transitional area between the skin and the intestinal layers. In the second case the middle layer develops as a pure derivative of the primitive intestinal wall (the entomesoderm) usually by means of a formation of diverticula growing out of the intestinal wall. This formation of diverticula partly resembles the formation of lodges that are developed in anthopolyps together with their sarcosepta. Attempts have also been made to derive the formation of the ecterocoele from that of the enterocoele. This situation becomes even more complicated in the ontogenies of numerous higher animal groups, above all of the Arthropoda and of the Vertebrata; thus in the human embryo the mesoderm develops from not less than five different *Anlagen*. The human body is also developed during the ontogeny from four and even more layers.

These differences in the type of development of the mesoderm which lead to the formation of secondary body cavities (coeloms), and the differences that can be observed in the type of development of the intestinal orifices—they all occur in the ontogenies—even if they are not radical, have served as a basis for the general classification of the animal groups (Ecterocoelia or Protostomia, and Enterocoelia or Deuterostomia). We must consider this as an unfortunate solution. The point where this supposed separation or bifurcation of the two large groups had taken place is assigned characteristically by various zoologists into different levels.

The question must also be raised whether it can *a priori* be probable that the Eumetazoa, which are considered as a homogeneous group whose body layers are believed to be mutually homologous, can all have such a common basic part, as the middle body layer is supposed to be, and at the same time that such a part had evolved not only ontogenetically but also phylogenetically along two essential different ways, so that the same form is not even mutually homologous. It seems to us much more acceptable to consider that the middle body layer is the same everywhere, that it is therefore always a homologous formation, whose ontogenetic development, however, has been changed during evolution in the sense of a methodical rationalization or of a "technical" improvement. Such a development need not have been divergent, but rather successive: it was first ecterocoelic (teloblastic) and later enterocoelic; thus the formation of the "mesoderm" itself has never had anything in common with the formation of the intestinal diverticula, nor with the formation of lodges as they can be found in the Anthozoa.

The intestine too evolved according to the old interpretation as a new form along several lines; thus the Eumetazoa with their intestines are supposed to have evolved several times from a form that had no intestine (blastaea)! Can such an interpretation be probable? The development of a uniform intestinal cavity is one of the main characteristics of the Eumetazoa (therefore the name Gastrobionta, according to Rothmüller). We consider that this cavity evolved first in Protozoa as a transitional digestive vacuole; in the earliest Eumetazoa this had led to an *ad hoc* (i.e., for each swallowed piece) formation of a digestive cavity in their internal plasmodium; the final result of this development had been a permanent digestive cavity which is surrounded by a specialized epithelium that contains glands and which is able to resorb food. It had originally one permanent orifice, and finally two that are situated in the two opposite parts of the body. Nothing is changed in this connection by the fact that the ontogenetic type of formation had afterwards been repeatedly changed, similarly as in the case of the development of the *Anlage* of the middle body layer. The Metaphyta, however, have never been able to develop anything that could resemble an intestinal cavity. No new form has ever been evolved from the hollow sphere of the *Volvox*. In those cases where some plant species had begun to catch an organic prey (animals) and to digest the same we find this digestion to be purely external, limited to the surface of the plant.

What is then the situation with Spongiae? There can be no doubt that the Spongiae are genuine animals, yet at the same time they differ basically from all the other polycellular animal forms (Eumetazoa). Not only had they evolved into their polycellular forms from their protozoan ancestors along a completely different way, i.e. by way of some colonies of Flagellata, they also never developed a true digestive cavity which could be considered as a homologue of the cavity that occurs in the Eumetazoa: their chambers that are surrounded by choanocytes are not digestive cavities, i.e. they are not a multiplied intestine. The choanocytes are not gland cells, or intestinal cells; they digest in their own organelles, in the digestive vacuoles, in the same way as the solitary or colonial Choanoflagellata do. The Spongiae have neither an intestine nor an oral orifice. The choanocytes which are actually similar to the Choanoflagellata can only become amoeboid; as such they had been somewhat differentiated, yet they have never been able to develop a genuine tissue, and even less so an organ or systems of organs.

Under the influence of the old interpretation zoologists have tried to explain the internalization of an originally external digestive surface. It was supposed that the digestive surface had been originally situated externally on the body of the animal because the first colonies (blastaeae) had consisted, according to this interpretation, exclusively of individuals that gathered their food independently, which they digested each in their own vacuoles. These zoologists think that it was only secondarily and after the first differentiation had taken place, that the digestive surfaces were transferred into the interior of the animal body, which was subsequently covered with the skin cells. This transference into the interior was supposed to have taken place in different ways as this is shown by the patterns that can be observed in the ontogenies. The invagination of the posterior half into the anterior half was considered as the most primitive and typical way of the development of the intestine (the invagination gastrula). All this is extremely improbable and it is not supported by facts. These are pure reconstructions made on the basis of facts that can be observed in the ontogenies and under the assumption that they represent some kind of recapitulation. The development of a digestive organ by way of internalization, as was suggested by the old interpretation, can in reality be taken into consideration in connection with the Spongiae only; yet even in this case it did not lead to the formation of a genuine intestine.

The old interpretation meets great, insurmountable, difficulties when it tries to explain the subsequent evolution of organs, thus of the protonephridia, of the muscular system, of the nervous system, etc. All these "tasks" were already solved on the level of Protozoa. The way to all these differentiations had been prepared as early as in Infusoria. This is true not only as regards the size of the body, its form, its symmetrical conditions, the ciliation and the type of movement, but also for the type of feeding, the transverse division, the sexual phase together with the hermaphroditism and with the pairing, the triploblastic system and for all the peculiarities of the three layers.

The long list of similarities that can be found both in the Infusoria and in the Turbellaria (a list which was originally made by v. Gelei and which has now been enlarged) shows that these are obviously no accidental similarities, convergences, or parallelisms; they are instead true homologies which exist because they go back to a common line of evolution. These homologies are too numerous for us to consider them as accidental. The progressive evolution which began from a common basis continued especially as regards the middle body layer. We will later return to discuss this problem in more detail. It should suffice to state here that the function of the external or skin layer, which is usually called an ectoderm (the notion and the name have been originally created within the field of the older embryology of the higher Vertebrata), had only been to protect the animal and to maintain the contact between the animal and its environment; while the function of the entoderm had been on the whole to receive and to prepare the food; the middle layer (the mesohyl or the mesoderm s. l.), on the other hand, had taken over a large number of functions and it had later even participated in the formation of the skin and of the intestine (as a cutis layer of the skin or as a muscularis). The final result of this is that in an adult animal we can no longer find any sharply-limited system of layers; we only have a whole animal before us.

Two Difficulties of the Theory of Polykaryons

There are in the main two facts which seem to be the cause of considerable difficulties in connection with our interpretation, in spite of the fact that such a large number of similarities can be observed in the Infusoria and in the Turbellaria. One difficulty consists in the fact that I consider the plasmodial–polykaryonic thesis as probably more valid for the evolution of the Eumetazoa, while at the same time I admit that the colonial thesis seems to be much more justified for the evolution of the Metaphyta and of Spongiae. The second difficulty consists in the fact that in the ontogenies of the Eumetazoa as well as of Spongiae, the first steps are regularly made by way of divisions of cells or of cleavages and not, as one would expect, by way of a division or polymerization of karyons, which would take place in a permanently uniform cytoplasm, and by way of a subsequent cellularization. Or, in other words, why is the supposedly primary morphogenetic process not recapitulated at least in the lowest Eumetazoa, in the acoelous Turbellaria? I have already partly shown that it is possible to explain rationally both these difficulties.

Above all it is comparatively easy to overcome the first difficulty. I think that it is much more probable—in spite of the recent attempts (A. A. Sachwatkin) to place the Rhizopoda with their amoebae at the root of Protozoa—that the Flagellata are the most primitive Protista (Protophyta + Protozoa). In the recent Protista we can find active two trends to a higher development, i.e. the development by way of a formation of colonies, and the development by way of a polymerization of karyons and a differentiation of the cytoplasm. The situation in Protophyta is clear because they depend entirely on a gaseous food, salts dissolved in water and the sun rays that penetrate the exterior of Protophyta. Their units had soon developed firm cell walls and they had shown from the very beginning an inclination to form coenobia and colonies (cormi). It is certainly characteristic that in plants the transition from the monocellular to a polycellular state had occourred several times, as this is now generally believed by botanists. The *Volvox*-line which has been so frequently misused as a pattern must be mentioned here as a special case. *Volvox* is characterized by the fact that it has remained a freely-moving form even after it had begun to form special "colonies" and after it had made the first steps towards a differentiation. Something similar had also taken place in the Dinoflagellata.

The subsequent evolution of the polycellular plants had been very slow and it did not make any important progress in the direction of an integration (individualization) and of a differentiation (the formation of tissues and of organs). Still we should not attribute all these facts as being due to the colonial origin of plants. The whole regime of metabolism has also had an important role in this connection, as well as the immobility of plants (the fact that they are attached to their substratum). A local and partial mobility was achieved in a different way than in the case of the Protozoa and of the Eumetazoa; this was due to the fact that no muscles or nerves have ever been developed by plants in spite of their ability to contract and to conduct irritation.

It has already been mentioned that in Metaphyta a significant formation of syncytia can not infrequently be observed (*Caulerpa* and its relatives, some tissues of higher Metaphyta which function as vessels, etc.). The example of Siphonales shows that no special plant type has ever been developed by Metaphyta by way of secondary syncytia which would include new elements that could be considered progressive.

As in the case of Metaphyta, nobody (as far I know) has tried to derive the Spongiae from some polykaryonic ancestors; the colonial "spirit" of the Spongiae is much too obvious. The difference which exists in various interpretations of the origin of Spongiae are centred exclusively around the problem whether we can consider that Spongiae have a common origin with other Metazoa (Eumetazoa), or whether they evolved as a special type of polycellular animals from the colonies of specialized Flagellata, the Choanoflagellata. Originally, zoologists, who all came under the influence of ideas of Leuckart and Haeckel, were inclined to believe that the Spongiae do not represent an extra type, that instead they were genuine Gastraeadae. Numerous and important differences that exist between Spongiae and other Metazoa were noticed, yet again those differences were attributed to diverging evolutions which had started from a common origin (the primitive polyp). Scholars soon became perplexed when they found (Metschnikoff, Sollas, Delage, and others) that the greatest differences occur in just the earliest ontogenies; the interpretation has therefore been more and more widely accepted which sees in Spongiae a special case among the polycellular animals. In the system of the animal kingdom they were therefore separated as Parazoa (Sollas) or as Enantiozoa (Delage) not only from the Coelenterata but also from all the other Metazoa, the Eumetazoa. Nobody has found any objection to the fact that a cleavage occurs in the ontogenies of Spongiae in the same way as in the Volvocales and in the Eumetazoa.

This situation is definitely solved, when the derivation of the Eumetazoa from the colonies of Flagellata is generally accepted. Objections, even if not supported by any very important and convincing newly discovered facts (the supposed discovery of nerve cells in Spongiae by O. Tuzet and by her school cannot be considered as a sufficient proof) have suggested that the Spongiae had a common origin with the remaining Metazoa and that the differences which exist between the Spongiae and the remaining Metazoa were not absolute and that the same differences could be explained rationally.

As an instructive example I wish to quote here the interpretation that was proposed by Marcus (1958). He discusses the evolution of Spongiae in the following paragraph, "The oldest animals, the Zoomastigina, evidently gave origin to sponges and coelenterates, which are connected at their common root (Heider, 1885). Transitory forms between flagellates and sponges do not exist, as *Proterospongia* is a regenerating fragment of a sponge (Tuzet, 1945). As sponge larvae have ordinary flagellated cells, the Porifera need not have arisen from the Choanoflagellata. In any case, sponges and Cnidaria must have originated together, because both have germ layers. There exist other parallels between sponges and true Metazoa (Eumetazoa). The definitive layers of the Calcarea and simple Tetractinellida are achieved by a process similar to gastrulation by invagination. What previously had been described as inversion of the germ layers, is understood today as multipolar inwandering (Meewis, 1938). Spongillids show an "accélération embryonaire" (Brien and Meewis, 1938) like many limnic Eumetazoa. The alternations of shape in the blastula (pseudogastrula, stomoblastula, "plissement" of the coeloblastula of Halisarca) are intelligible as the result of the small space available for embryonic expansion in the body of the parent sponge. "The evolutionary line of sponges was divergent from the beginning and ends blindly." (E. Marcus, 1958:26).

All these arguments are supported by rather weak facts and they do not prove to be convincing enough. They could be complemented by two additional arguments which were mentioned by Tuzet; the supposed presence of nerve cells in Spongiae, and the fact that in some Eumetazoa, cells can be found similar to choanocytes. Yet all these objections cannot conceal the basic fact that the Spongiae do not possess an intestine (neither had they secondarily lost such an intestine), and in connection with this they do not have an oral or even less so an anal orifice. It should be mentioned in passing that a separate derivation of Spongiae from some cormi of Choanoflagellata can be considered to be more acceptable than a common deduction of all the Metazoa from some colonies of collar-less Zooflagellata. The former interpretation would appear more plausible even if the case that there were no *Proterospongia* were true, because no transitional form between the Flagellata and the Eumetazoa has become known up till now and in spite of this there are so many zoologists who "believe" nevertheless in the latter type of derivation. In the meantime another species of the *Proterospongia* has been discovered (we have already mentioned this in our study) and there can be no doubt about its nature.

And what can be said of the argument or even "proof" of the statement that the larvae of Spongiae possess ordinary flagellated cells which are only subsequently, by way of metamorphosis, developed into the choanocytes? This should prove, according to Marcus, that the Spongiae cannot be deduced from the Choanoflagellata! It seems as if the Spongiae were the only animals which had no right to evolve special early phases capable of swimming freely, and all zoologists can see in them an example of recapitulation. The spongulae are new forms like all the freely swimming larvae of the Metazoa; the animal does not need any collars of cytoplasm in order to be able to swim; these collars can rather be considered as a hindrance. The spongulae do not feed independently.

What can then be the value of the equation: germ layers = the same origin? It is even less convincing than in the case of flagella which have been just discussed. All the germ layers are a product of a rationalized ontogeny. There are no, and there never were any, germ layers in the Metazoa, not even in their lowest forms. If, in spite of this, we wish to talk about the germ layers (better, body layers) in analogy to the ontogenetic conditions that can be observed in the higher Vertebrata, we see that it is just at this point that there are radical differences between the Spongiae and the Eumetazoa. These differences cannot be simply dismissed with the nice phrase:

"the inversion of germ layers" which is so typical of Spongiae and which has been the reason that the name Enantiozoa has been given to them, is simply a "multipolar inwandering." In reality it appears also as an invagination and as a unipolar inwandering, thus in all the forms that we are used to find in a normal "gastrulation," yet it is usually reversely polarized! In the same way we could speak about germ layers in Metaphyta, or at least of something that is similar to this ontogenetic process. We are therefore not yet justified in supposing that there has been a common origin. Yet in spite of this, all the organisms represent a community, even if the complex organisms evolved several times. We must not forget that all the metabionts had originally evolved from the primarily solitary Flagellata. It is therefore not surprising that we find many common elements in them in spite of the fact that they evolved several times and invarious ways from these Flagellata.

There is no species of Spongiae—at least as far as I know—which begins its ontogeny with a division of karyons, thus without a simultaneous division of cells or without a cleavage. In the Eumetazoa on the other hand we can find such a development quite frequently even in such groups as the insects. We can rightly consider this type of development as a result of a secondary evolution. The larva (spongula) of *Mycale* passes subsequently, according to H. V. Wilson (1935), into a syncytial state. A formation of syncytia, however, can also be found elsewhere among the Spongiae, especially in those cases where we have a formation of macroscleres. We are therefore not allowed to conclude immediately that in all those cases there had been a polykaryonic phylogenetic origin where an animal type of a metaphyte can be found which forms syncytia. The well-known case can be mentioned here in passing where under the influence of a very simple saline solution a larva of Polychaeta was changed into a plasmodial animal (Lilly). It would be wrong to conclude on this basis alone that all the Metazoa had evolved from some plasmodial ancestors.

Can Egg Cleavage Be Really Considered as a Proof of the Colonial Theory?

We can now return to the question: can we conclude on the basis of the fact that the ontogenies of a majority of Eumetazoa begin with a cleavage, i.e. without a polykaryonic state, that the Eumetazoa also evolved (similarly as Metaphyta and Spongiae) from some colonies of the Flagellata? Those who adhere to the old colonial theory find this situation considerably simpler, especially if they believe in the validity of the "fundamental biogenetic law" and if they consider that the evolution proceeded in the direction Mono-, Di- and Triploblastostoidea. In this case one could expect in advance that the Eumetazoa also develop as postgamous individuals by way of polytomous or repeated divisions of cells, and secondarily and under special conditions plasmodially. This is the case when their zygote is overloaded with a reserve food while at the same time it is possible that a change in the type of breathing also plays an important role in this connection.

I think, in spite of the apparently greater probability of a generally colonial evolution of all the metabionts, that the Eumetazoa evolved from a plasmodial or polykaryonic state and that they adopted their cleavage as a result of a secondary development at a period when the older stages and the adult animal form had already become cellularized, even if we are well aware that we cannot offer any strict proof for this interpretation. We can make our interpretation only probable, and that on the basis of two "indications." The first indication which has already been mentioned could be the physiological necessity of the parcelling or of the cellularization just during the earliest ontogenetic stages because of the great consumption of oxygen and because of the need of large free surfaces which is a consequence of the increased consumption of oxygen.

The following objection can be made against this indication. If the cellularization had appeared at such early stages of the ontogeny, how is it then possible that this situation is not preserved and why does the internal structure return into the plasmodial state? To this we can remark that in all probability the physiological factors of the evolution as well as the inherited properties could be responsible for such a development. Moreover, we can call attention to the fact that even in Metaphyta and in (as we have just mentioned) Spongiae which both had certainly evolved from some colonies of cells, we can observe during a certain stage an inclination to form syncytia. This stage is again followed by a period of cellularization.

The second and even more important indication can be found in the long list of similarities that can be observed in the Infusoria on the one hand, and in the acoelous Turbellaria on the other. These similarities make it probable that the Eumetazoa had evolved from the polykaryonic Infusoria. We can therefore conclude that initially the postgamous divisions were limited to the karyons only, that the youngest embryos had a plasmodial character so that no recapitulations take place any longer in the early development.

Zawarzin (1945–1947) was not influenced, by the facts of cleavages, against the colonial theory. He placed the separation of the monocellular and polycellular animals far back into the remote geologic past, to a period when the separation of the animal and plant lines of evolution had taken place. The Metazoa had evolved, according to his interpretation, without any differentiation parallel to the Protozoa from the polyenergid plasmatic masses. This is a very radical concept which lacks probability because it presupposes that the sexual phase evolved in both lines (thus parallel to the plantal line) at least twice independently from each other and that it had led in spite of this to similar conditions. Neither does this concept explain the numerous similarities that exist between the Infusoria and the Turbellaria. How can we then interpret the not rare cases of the polykaryonic Protozoa?

The Basic Principles That Should Be Used in a Reform of the Whole Animal System

The necessity, or the unavoidable consequence, of changing the previous interpretations of the phylogenetic processes of the animal world becomes self-evident when we summarize the individual results of our study. They can be enumerated as follows:

(1) The evolution of Cnidaria had been mainly retrogressive (it was partly progressive in a specializing direction) because of their sessile way of life. This sessility of Cnidaria is a secondary phenomenon. The evolution of Cnidaria did not proceed in the direction Hydrozoa → Scyphozoa → Anthozoa as this has been believed till now, but just in the opposite direction.

(2) The Cnidaria are not the most primitive and thus the lowest Eumetazoa in spite of the fact that they have the simplest structure. The most primitive Eumetazoa are in reality the mainly plasmodial Acoela, among the Turbellaria.

(3) The primitive Eumetazoa had not been radially symmetrical animals; they were instead bilaterally symmetrical which was a consequence of their way of life; they were able to move actively over a solid substratum. The radial symmetry had been developed secondarily as a consequence of their sessile way of life which had been secondarily adopted by them.

(4) The Spongiae are a special group of Metazoa, they show a special structural type, they have their own way of feeding and their own form of development. They must be definitively separated from any connection with the other Metazoa, the Eumetazoa. They stand thus as Parazoa between the Protozoa and the Eumetazoa. They must be therefore excluded from the group of Coelenterata.

(5) The Ctenophora cannot be considered as Coelenterata. Like Cnidaria they had evolved from the Turbellaria, yet starting from their own root and parallel to the evolution

of Cnidaria. The Cnidaria had evolved from the rhabdocoeloid Turbellaria, and the Ctenophora by way of neoteny from the planktonic larvae of Polycladida.

It has been found that it has become necessary to submit the phylogenetic relationships of other animal groups to a critical revision in spite of the fact that all the findings made by me and the conclusions reached on the basis of these findings have been limited above all to the lowest groups of the Metazoa. This revision must be made from the same standpoint and under the application of the same working methods that have led me to a necessary reform of the interpretation of the evolution of Metazoa from Protozoa, and especially of the phylogenetic evolution of the Cnidaria. Thus a revision has become necessary of the genealogic tree and of the graphic representation of the phylogenetic connections of the large groups, as well as of the systematic–taxonomic classification.

First I will make a brief explanation of those principles which I used in my work on a reform of the animal system.

The comparative morphology of recent animals and of those animals that have been preserved as fossils was, is, and remains the main method that can be used in our work when we wish to construct a natural animal system and above all the genealogical tree of the animal world. It can be expected that in the future biochemistry will also make essential contributions to this field. All the facts should be taken into consideration by the comparative morphology, both those that can be observed by way of a general and of a detailed analysis and comparison of the adult forms, and of all the other stages of development, beginning with the gametes; while at the same time we must also take into account the physiological and ecological moments and the changes of the environment. In our morphological comparisons we pay special attention to the adult stage, and only in the second line to the ontogenetic stages; we have been led to this both by the experiences we have had so far and by the theoretical conclusions.

The historical circumstances have been the main reason why, since the days when the idea of evolution became accepted for the whole field of biology and above all for the field of phylogenetics—and in connection with this into the fields of systematics and taxonomy—scholars have relied too much on facts that can be observed in ontogenies. The wrong interpretation of the mutual relationship between the ontogeny and the phylogeny ("embryos–ancestors," according to de Beer) has played a particularly fatal role. It can never be repeated frequently enough that a basic mistake was made by the so-called "fundamental biogenetic law" as formulated by Ernst Haeckel which proposed that each ontogeny, even if it was secondarily more or less changed, was in principle a recapitulation of a phylogeny in the sense (which does not appear clearly in the formulation) that these were the earlier adult stages being recapitulated. At the first sight this difference does not appear to be too significant because recapitulations do indeed occur during the ontogenetic developments and they are also highly welcome in our phylogenetic operations. Even if we do not wish to discuss the whole problem, we will mention one typical example whose consequences have proved fatal.

This is the phylogenetic evaluation of a characteristic ontogenetic stage which occurs quite frequently, i.e. that of larvae. Any "proof" which could support the idea of evolution was highly welcome during the "storm and stress" period of biology when this idea still had to struggle for its final victory. The planktonic larvae of some sessile or parasitic animal types have not only proved to be of help in endeavours to determine the true nature of the corresponding adult forms which had been considerably changed. Peculiarities that are characteristic of a somewhat broader group of animals are preserved or recapitulated in larvae while at the same time these properties have been lost in their adult forms. Various zoologists, however, have gone further than this by stating that an ancestral form as such is recapitulated in larvae and that these ancestors were adult animals which lived in plankton. These scholars have not been satisfied with a recapitulation of individual properties or of whole stages (phases), they have believed instead that, in principle, the whole phylogeny can be recapitulated.

I have been accused of underrating those facts that can be observed in the ontogenies which could be used in the reconstructions of phylogenies. It is not difficult to show that it is the opposition which places so high a value on the same facts that they are actually in this way misinterpreted. As an example we can mention here in passing the development of the mouth in the ontogenies. The functioning oral opening of all the Eumetazoa is certainly a homologous form, i.e. it must have a common origin; yet in the ontogenies the same oral opening is developed during very different stages of development and in different ways (from the so-called primitive mouth, after the closing of this primitive mouth, and finally as a secondary intestinal opening while the primary mouth is changed into an anal orifice). It is true that these types of development have been observed in the ontogenies of several animal groups and that even if they are not a recapitulation of a common adult ancestral form (the old ontogenetic stages must naturally also be considered as ancestors) they can still be a common property which has been supplementarily acquired and they can still serve as a proof of a direct relationship. Should these conclusions be justified or at least probable then there must be no unexplainable exceptions, neither can a single peculiarity be decisive if it appears together with other common characteristics. In such cases the possibility must also be excluded that certain characteristics are not actual parallelisms, i.e. that they are not peculiarities that evolved after the separation of the lines of evolution had taken place, or that they had not emerged in completely different lines of evolution.

In our search for homologies, i.e. recapitulations of the morphological peculiarities of the adult stages, we must be very careful. Yet we should be even more careful when in this search we wish to identify the embryonic, post-embryonic, and above all the larval stages. Everything shows that the peculiarities of the not fully adult phases are even more subject to greater and special changes, regardless of the fact whether they live under the protection of the maternal animal or of protective hulls, or finally as free animals that feed independently; these phases can therefore not be considered as recapitulations in the old sense of the word. The changes and new formations which have a purely ontogenetic character have nothing in common with the peculiarities of the adult animal. It is therefore wrong to endeavour to show that such characteristics had already functioned in the ancestors of recent forms. This can be best seen in the attempt made by Boettger (1952) who tried to explain functionally the changes of the oral and anal orifices that can be observed in the ontogenies of the Eumetazoa (Protostomia–Deuterostomia). These and other similar changes can take place during the ontogenetic ontogenies only, thus during the non-functioning phase of the evolution.

This shows that generally we must be very cautious when we try to use the ontogenetic facts for our phylogenetic constructions (speculations). Other facts and methods must be also constantly taken into consideration. We must constantly distinguish between the material established in the non-functioning phases and that established in the functioning phases yet not in the sense of the adult stage, and between the final stages of development and those stages which directly precede the definitive stage, e.g. metamorphosis and the stage which frequently follows it. Metamorphosis emerged as a necessary phase of the ontogenies; it is a consequence of a widely different development of the larval phase. Such a metamorphosis can have really catastrophic proportions, or in other cases it can be considered as a non-functional ontogenetic event.

Those authors who try, too quickly, to conclude, on the basis of some similarities that can be observed during the larval stage, that there are some closer phyletic connections, will come in all probability to the wrong interpretation of the phylogenetic developments. This is the case with the interpretation proposed by Marcus (1958) regarding the Ectoprocta and Endoprocta. He tries to unite these two groups because of an accidental similarity that can be observed in their larvae (the trochophoroid larvae) in spite of the great difference which actually exists between these two animal groups, especially as regards the organization of their adult forms. These are clearly analogies only that occur in the adult forms and in larvae (cf. Hadži, 1958 and P. Brien, 1960).

The more probable interpretation seems to be that special larval stages were developed independently by each larger group of animals. The way of life of these larval stages is completely different from that of the adult animals. We can come to a more plausible conclusion regarding the relationship connection only if we also take into consideration other very important characteristics and peculiarities which are not limited exclusively to the larval stage.

Fortunately enough we find that recently zoologists have become more and more convinced that it is necessary to relinquish the erroneous "fundamental biogenetic law" which sees whole phylogenies repeated in the ontogenies, with a very small number of deviations (*"Fälschungen"*) which cover 10–0 per cent only of the total number; all the rest are, according to this interpretation, palingeneses, i.e. recapitulations. We get such an impression when we read the reports (both reviews and discussions) given at a special symposium of zoologists from Northern Germany, *Ontogenie und Phylogenie (Zool. Anz.*, 164, 1960). On the other hand we find scholars who still adhere to this quasi-law and who try to save what can still be saved (Remane and his school). They courageously defend Haeckel's definition, making only occasional retreats, while at the same time they miss the main point which is that this old concept is wrong in principle when it compares the ontogenetic stages of recent animals with the adult ancestral forms and when it even equates these two different elements. Remane would like to reach at least a compromise end so he proposes that the word "rule" should be used instead of the word "law" while at the same time he still continues to use the old word. Such a proposition, however, does not touch the main problem, above all because zoologists prefer to avoid the word "law" quite generally in the modern biology, and even more so the phrase "the basic law." Neither has the adjective "biogenetic" been very fortunately selected; it should be avoided because in the general biology the word "biogenesis" signifies the origin of life on our planet. And above all we can see how senseless it is to speak in this connection of a rule if we use the expression "the rule of the relation between the ontogeny and the phylogeny" (or even better: "between the ontogenies and the phylogeny") instead of the phrase "the biogenetic rule." We have actually here a biogenetic phenomenon which we still have to study intensively, and where we are still far from knowing its exact character. Would it not be sufficient if we simply call this biological phenomenon a recapitulation in order to characterize in this way a special case of repetition which probably takes place in each ontogeny and which is apparently a reiteration of characteristics and peculiarities that had originally belonged to the adult stages of the ancestral forms? This would then be recapitulations in a narrower sense of the word which can serve as best proof in our phylogenetic speculations. Yet there are also other recapitulations *(s. lat.)* which may also prove useful in our phylogenetic constructions which, however, must be used with considerable restraint. These are the ontogenetic repetitions of those characteristics and peculiarities which have nothing in common with the final stages of the ontogenies, with the fully adult functioning stage. Haeckel called them caenogeneses *(Fälschungen*, falsifications, deviations). If we look upon this problem from the point of view explained here then we must admit that theoretically such cases can exist where the whole ontogeny of a certain animal species or of an animal group had been changed so much that it no longer shows any trace of recapitulations *s. str.* We believe that it is completely improbable that cases could exist where up to 90 per cent of characteristics that can be observed in an ontogeny could be interpreted as true recapitulations. In this connection we can mention the important difference which can be found in the evaluations made by botanists regarding the frequency of recapitulations that can be observed in plants. Broman (1919) who studied this problem as an expert in genetics puts the maximum at 30 per cent, and Zimmermann (1943) even at 80 per cent.

In future the symmetrical conditions should be studied more critically than they have been till now, especially if we wish to use them in our phylogenetic and systematic–taxonomic constructions. Fortunately enough we can find that a considerable progress has now been made in this direction. The notion and the word Radiata and other similar names (Radialia, etc.) should be avoided from now on. We soon find, if we accept this suggestion, that the opposite symmetrical condition, the bilateral symmetry and the corresponding category Bilateria have also become unnecessary and that they should also be abandoned. These symmetrical conditions are very changeable. They depend entirely on the type of movement or on the kind of contact which exists between the animal and its immediate environment. Not infrequently, we can find different symmetries side-by-side in one and the same animal group (taken phylogenetically they naturally occur one after the other); some transitory forms have also become known.

Bilateral symmetry must be considered *a priori* not only as a characteristic but also as a primary property of animals which are able to move, in opposition to plants which are immobile. Radial symmetry, which in animals occurs only rarely, is therefore a secondary phenomenon. It is certain that a symmetry can be changed much more easily than the whole structure. A transition from a horizontal (parallel to the substratum) to a vertical attitude is sufficient to start a trend towards radial symmetry (towards the polypoid form). This change of symmetry can make a rapid progress regardless of the original form of structure when this induction is supported by an attachment of the animal to its substratum. It is obvious that the general type of structure nevertheless plays a certain role in this development. It is enough if we refer in this connection to the case of Aprocta–Euprocta. Radial symmetry can develop much more easily and fully in the aproctous type than in the Euprocta; in the latter the anal opening which was originally situated opposite to the oral opening must be first transplaced, and finally abandoned, before they are able to develop a perfect radial symmetry.

Recently, a significant tendency can be observed among zoologists to use the highest categories, especially that of the phylum, quite frequently when they classify larger groups of animals. Not infrequently, we can find systems which propose even up to forty different phyla, so that finally we could get an impression that there were the same number of completely different types of structures, and that the scholars are probably too subjective when they use the category of a phylum. It seems to me that in this way the true phyletic relationships only become blurred. It may be better for us to use the category "phylum" more carefully as long as we do not dispose of more exact methods of determining the antiquity of a certain structural form. The mistake will probably be less significant if we exaggerate in the opposite direction, even if in this way we expose ourselves to the accusation that we would like to take refuge in the old notion of a "progressive scale of all things," or of "*l'échelle animale*." Such an accusation is entirely unjustified as we will show later. We must pay our main attention to the classes, to their peculiarities and to their groupings which must not always be made from a purely formalistic point only. We can expect that in future many such uncertain problems will be clarified by means of biochemistry.

Evolution Generally Had a Progressive Trend

Quite generally and, as it seems to me, correctly it has been assumed that the evolution has generally taken a progressive course. This, however, should not mean that there had been no retrogressive evolution. Cases of distinctly retrogressive phyletic evolution are well enough known and it is therefore completely unnecessary for us to try to prove them in our study. Whole classes have emerged as a result of a retrogressive evolution; yet at the same time we must be aware of the fact that these retrogressions did not lead to reductions only, but also to some new acquisitions which appeared as a consequence of a specialized way of life. This was the same way of life which had caused a reduction of important organs or systems of organs. An internal parasitism and a completely sessile way of life have been the main cause of such a retrogressive development (cf. Cestoda among the Ameria, Rhizocephala among the Polymeria, and Tunicata among the Chordonia). The question arises here whether any limit can be found in such a development in the sense: what is the highest systematic category where such a generally retrogressive trend can still be observed? When we see that there are not only classes (Dicyemidea, Cestoda) that had evolved by way of a basically retrogressive development, but also subphyla as this is proved by the case of the Tunicata, we cannot exclude the possibility that even a whole phylum had eventually evolved by way of an evolution which shows a mainly retrogressive trend. Later we will return to discuss this problem more *in extenso.*

Among other factors which must be kept in view when we try to reconstruct the phylogeny of the animal world or its genealogical tree that could serve as a basis of a natural animal system, we must mention the various interpretations which have been proposed regarding the origin of large groups. It is by no means surprising to see how widely different opinions have been adopted by the zoologists on just this point. They all waver between the two extreme interpretations because they do not know of any exact method by which to determine the absolute age of individual animal types (frequently we cannot even determine their relative age), nor have they available any evidence in the form of fossils. One of these interpretations believes that there is no difference between the process of specialization, or the evolution of species by way of slight steps in the direction to such a differentiation, and the evolution of very large types of animals. According to this interpretation the "geologic age" can be considered as the only factor; the whole evolution had been uniform and gradual, yet it was not shared by all the species or all the lines of evolution.

The opposite standpoint has been defended above all by the palaeozoologists, and it is connected with the names of several zoologists; it believes in special, i.e. revolutionary, changes which had led to the formation of completely new animal types. We cannot find as many animal types as would be expected if evolution had constantly been strictly slowly evolutive, and never revolutionary, marked by sudden greater changes. The origin of the minor taxons is now already well enough known. Important sudden changes could also be observed in various cultures and experiments. It is therefore almost certain that the new types do not emerge in the way as was formerly thought, so that a young bird could suddenly emerge from an egg of a reptile. It is also clear that in the development and the preservation of a certain type of structure much can also depend on the external factors (the conditions of the environment). It is not my task to discuss here in detail the problem of macro-evolution versus micro-evolution. Still I wish to emphasize that I accept the standpoint as represented by neo-Darwinism combined with that of the genetics. As in the case of numerous other problems of biology we consider the phenomenon of the origin of new animal types to be a complex factor. It can be only approximately conjectured where the limit is between micro- and macro-evolutions. It is my opinion that the evolution of new types does not take place in one way only, and that the rapidity of these changes can be widely different, i.e. that there are species which are very old and conservative, and species which are very young, of which we can say they have just been developed.

The fortunate discoveries from the younger geological ages (e.g. that of the *Archaeopteryx)* can help us to get a clearer idea how the development of a new sub-type, let us say of a class, must be understood. De Beer (1954) has shown how in this case and probably also in many other cases within the frame of the Vertebrata, new mosaic-like combinations of characteristics that had existed individually and scattered within the frame of an older subtype (the peculiarities of a type, however, in our case those of the Vertebrata, are preserved) emerge as mutations parallel to the changes of the environment. They develop into new combinations and as such they become "new" peculiarities which win a predominant role due to the working of natural selection.

This type of formation of new animal forms which should be considered as representatives of higher taxonomic units is now known under the name of Watson's rule. It has certainly not been the only element which influenced evolution. It can be considererd also in connection with the evolution of other animal types and, so it seems to me, also with the evolution of the Cnidaria within the frame work of the turbellarian type. Later we will return to discuss this problem.

There can be no doubt that the descendants which show considerable variety and which therefore represent new animal groups can be developed by way of neoteny. The best-known case which has also been studied by way of experiments is that of *Proteus;* it could be established that in a not very remote past, a new subtype of tailed Amphibia had developed by way of neoteny; this subtype was given the rank of a family by the taxonomists. The geologically much older Appendiculata, among the Chordonia, were given at least the rank of an order. The Chaetognatha, which are considered by some zoologists as an extremely isolated group and which are therefore considered to represent a higher systematic category (e.g. Beklemischew), have even been given the rank of a special class. I have succeeded in showing (Hadži, 1958 c) that the Chaetognatha evolved by way of neoteny from some Brachiopoda.

In connection with the highest animal types, above all in connection with the high systematic category of phyla, it appears as very probable, (1) that there can be only few such categories; (2) that they must be very old taken from a geological point of view; and, (3) that they evolved as a consequence of a combination of a special genom, the change of the environment, the change in the way of life.

Finally, I must touch another problem even if I do not consider it to be of a very great importance. This is the question whether the phylogeny of animals had been mono- or poly-phyletic. I wish to mention this problem because some accusations were made against me that, in my attempt to reconstruct the phylogeny, I approach, the pre-Darwinian concepts ("*l'échelle animale*," and other similar interpretations). Quite naturally I must reject such an accusation because it is entirely unjustified. There can be in principle no linear or ladder-like evolution if we accept the standpoint of the neo-Darwinism. The alternative question of a monophyly versus a polyphyly is completely wrong. We can immediately see when we observe all the riches of the animal forms, and above all if we take into consideration also the palaeozoological forms, that the problem can only be of a monophyly and an oligophyly (yet not in an alternative sense). The few attempts to construct a genealogical bush instead of a genealogical tree have not been received favourably by zoologists. Something very similar has been proposed recently by Lemche (1958) who suggested four main branches or subordinate stems.

In order to avoid any misunderstandings I wish to mention that I think here of large groups only. We can see, if we make a survey of almost innumerable attempts to construct the genealogical tree of the animal world, that almost all these genealogical trees are based on the principle of the oligophyly. This is also true for my attempt. If we observe the best-known case of the Vertebrata, where we are not obliged to work with special phyla, we can see that in these evolution had proceeded concordantly with the principle of the oligophyly, and not of the polyphyly and there had been probably only one diphyly when the reptilian type evolved on the one hand into birds, and in the other into mammals. Yet even these two highest groups did not evolve in all probability from a common initial point as can be understood if we view the extremely schematized sketches of the genealogical tree.

G. S. Carter who sees in my attempt a similarity to "*l'échelle animale*" has in his own attempt taken into consideration the diphyletic development only of his superphyla which correspond roughly to my phyla. The "radiation" of his superphylum Annelida, however, does not issue from a single point, or from a single root, but rather from a very prolonged curve.

The example of the evolution of the Protozoa shows that we are not always able to use the concept of monophyly only. Here polyphyly seems to be the most probable form of the evolution. Yet even here the word polyphyly sounds an exaggeration because it seems that there were only two to three separate lines of evolution. The word oligophyly appears therefore to be more suitable also in this case. The same is true for the evolution of the Metazoa from the Protozoa; it is quite improbable that in the evolution of the Metazoa there were more than two separate roots or points of separation, i.e. besides those of the Parazoa and the Eumetazoa, that of the Mesozoa also, as the third root.

The question also arises of how those cases can be evaluated and named where two or several subtypes had probably evolved from one type, yet not by way of a radiation which had started from the same centre in the same geological age, nor from the same level reached by the primitive type. Such a development can be observed in the Turbellaria as the initial form for the evolution of Ameria with their numerous "side branches" or subtypes. Their developments had probably begun (this cannot be strictly proved) from separate "*Anlagen* of buds" (we cannot possibly speak here of roots).

This shows the relative character of the distinction between the "monophyly" and the "polyphyly." It frequently depends on the taxonomic rank we give to a certain animal group, above all whether this is a phylum in a narrower or broader sense of the word.

CHAPTER 4

THE NEW CLASSIFICATION OF THE ANIMAL WORLD AND THE NEW GENEALOGICAL TREE

The General Premises

The Limit Between the Plant and the Animal Worlds

A *general* revision of a system, which is already more than one hundred years old and which has therefore become very stabilized, has now become necessary above all in connection with the earliest Metazoa, because of the discovery that the Cnidaria do not represent the most primitive Metazoa, that their simple structures are a consequence of their transition to the sessile way of life, and that they had evolved from the Turbellaria (the turbellarian theory of the Cnidaria). To these discoveries we must add here also the interpretation which sees in Spongiae a type of Metazoa that had evolved completely separately, and which tries to explain the possible origin of the Ctenophora by way of neoteny from the planktonic larvae of the Turbellarian Polycladida. The notion and the taxon of Coelenterata have now become superfluous because they have lost their meaning. There can no longer be any Coelenterata, rather, they have really never existed. This group was built on erroneous interpretations. We see that the notion opposite to that of the Coelenterata, that of the Coelomata, also loses its justification as a consequence of the abolition of the Coelenterata. What can be done now in this situation?

I could have satisfied myself by selecting one from the unfortunately numerous animal systems, a system which would seem to me to agree best with the natural facts, and propose those changes which have now become necessary within the framework of the same system. This was done by the palaeozoologist A. H. Müller (1958:3) who has constructed a genealogical tree of the animal world mainly on the basis of the scheme which was originally outlined by L. Cuénot while at the same time Müller took into consideration my theory about the Coelenterata ("unter Zugrundelegung der Coelenteraten-theorie von J. Hadži"). Even such a change of the system is sufficiently radical and it can be expected that the zoologists will prefer to oppose it than to accept it favourably. This, however, can only be interpreted as a good sign because a certain amount of conservatism may not be amiss here.

Yet such a solution would be insufficient above all because of the fact that the Coelenterata have usually been considered as identical with the Diblastica. Thus the problem of the middle body layer (mesoderm or mesohyl) together with that of the coelom *s. str.* appears in a new light, a problem which itself is of great importance because of its significance for the main division of the animal groups. All these reasons have induced me to place my reform of the animal world on a broader basis so that in this way we can come closer to our ideal; to develop a natural, i.e. evolutional, animal system.

The first difficulties we meet with, however, emerge as soon as we try to determine the position of the animal world (regnum animalium, animalia, zoa, Zoaea,) within the framework of the world of living organism (bionta, organisms). It is not my intention to discuss in detail these difficulties. We can distinguish between three main types of organisms if we take into account the way they feed; the same three types also show certain morphological differences. For reasons that are purely theoretical, and in agreement with our interpretation of the first emergence of the organisms ("of life" as we usually say), we must give the first place to the primarily heterotrophic organisms. We consider them to be the first and phylogenetically the oldest type. It cannot be proved with certainty that such organisms still exist. In view of the fact, however, that in the main evolution there was regularly one part only that had further evolved while another part had remained on the same old primitive level (certainly with some smaller changes) we must admit the possibility that there still exist essentially unchanged descendants from the primary heterotrophic organisms that were neither plants nor animals. We can think here at once of viruses; it is even possible that not only viruses can be placed into this group, and moreover not all the organisms that are now known as viruses can be classified into this group. In the meantime the viruses have become strongly specialized, they live now mainly as endoparasites with animals and plants. By way of a purely logical thinking we can conclude that in the era of the primary heterotrophic organisms the latter had lived freely, feeding mutually on each other. Such an era, however, could not possibly have been of along duration because under such conditions life would necessarily soon come to an end if the producers of the "living substance" had not evolved in the form of organisms which were capable of chemosynthesis; such forms can already be classified among the bacteria. A new difficulty emerges here of how to distinguish these primitive organisms from the "younger" saprophytes which are usually classified as plants. All these organisms can be considered as a special group, and since it is necessary to name them, we could call them Anucleata after Rothmüller, or Monera after Barkley (the latter name, however, does not mean the same thing here as it was understood by Haeckel).

The Anucleata which were capable of chemosynthesis probably also evolved into the second main type of organisms which feed autotrophically or by means of photosynthesis. These organisms are plants (Phyta) regardless of whether they are mono- or polycellular forms. All plants can be divided practically and roughly into Protophyta and Metaphyta; yet such a division does not seem to have much sense if viewed entirely from the phylogenetic standpoint. It is more than probable that the Metaphyta had evolved several times from various protophytic lines. Neither is it sensible to bring together in our system of organisms, all the nucleate (monocellular) plants and animals into one group of Protista (Protobionta, according to Rothmüller, Unicellularia, Thaloidea, Protista, according to Barkley; yet not according to Haeckel). We are not justified in proposing such a group because its members had evolved in all probability polyphyletically and because it is obviously necessary to make a distinction between plants and animals. Rothmüller believes that such a distinction should be made on a higher level only, on the level of the polycellular beings, where he distinguishes between the Cormobionta (i.e. Phyta, according to Barkley) and the Gastrobionta (i.e. Zoaea, according to Barkley; Metazoa s. l. autorum).

The third main group consists of animal organisms which are secondarily heterotrophic (Zoa, Zoaea, according to Barkley). They feed at the expense of the autotrophic organisms. If we wish to remain consistent we must not classify as animals such Protophyta which feed either "occasionally" heterotrophically (while at the same time they lose their chromoplasts) or permanently in the same way as animals while at the same time they preserve characteristics that can be easily identified and which show that they certainly belong to the Protophyta. The fact alone that they are monocellular forms cannot be considered as sufficient reason for a classification of such a being as an animal. This is the case with the Cystoflagellata (with *Noctiluca* etc.) within the group of the Dinoflagellata. Because of such species or even whole groups we could think that there is no uniform group of animals. Zoologists should rather agree to exclude these forms from the animal world and thus to leave them to be studied by botanists or by protistologists who specialize in them. This would be the fate of the so-called Phytoflagellata which do not even constitute a uniform and taxonomically fixed group, of the so-called Mycetozoa (Myxomycetes, as they are called by botanists), and of the problematic Xenophyophora. If we drop the notion and the name of the systematic group Phytoflagellata then we are logically obliged to do the same with the Zooflagellata (as a name of a group). Zoology as well as the zoologists lose nothing if they transfer into the field of botany (Phytology) a number of Protista that had secondarily adopted the heterotrophic type of feeding. In fact they can win in this way a great deal because by means of such an exclusion a clear limit can be drawn between the world of animals and the world of plants. Moreover, a majority of "attempts" which were made by Nature to cross the limit between the autotrophic and the heterotrophic organisms soon came to a stop so that no new type of organism has ever evolved in this way. This is best illustrated by the example of the Cystoflagellata which consist of three monotypic genera only (among these *Noctiluca* is best known). Other descendants also have a completely isolated position from the typical Dinoflagellata that adopted the parasitic way of life.

Repeated attempts have been made to construct a system of Protista on the basis of their cellular structures. The Protista have therefore been frequently divided into the subcellular (without distinct cell nuclei: Protocytoidea, according to Naef), primarily cellular (among these are a majority of the monocellular Protophyta and Protozoa), hypercellular (with polymerized parts of cells, the cell nucleus included), and finally the polycellular and secondarily cellular forms. Such a classification does not seem to be very useful in our systematic and taxonomic work. It is not useful in connection with the animal world because the animals do not include any subcellular species; neither is it useful for the plant world because there are no secondarily nuclear plant species. Such a division, however, can be very good from a purely notional point of view, and within the broader frame of a general biology. Even the word "acellular," after Dobell, is usable as a notion in spite of the fact that it is formed in a rather negative sense: it is not uniform and it includes various categories (the subcellular, hypercellular, and actually also the primarily monocellular forms).

The System of the Protozoa

Now when we have drawn a clear limit between the Protophyta and the Protozoa we must also draw a limit between these and the higher forms. This does not seem to be such a difficult task because it has become clear that no corresponding transitional forms have survived till now. We can therefore still continue to use the name which was introduced some time ago, that of the Protozoa (Goldfuss, 1820) even if this word has not been most fortunately selected and in spite of the fact that in the meantime its exact meaning has been changed several times. The first sub-kingdom can therefore preserve its old name of Protozoa until it is changed by an eventual international decision. Few attempts only have been made to construct an animal system which do not include the taxon Protozoa (cf. the system proposed by Ulrich, 1951).

Scholars have usually been satisfied to give the rank of classes to the subdivisions of the Protozoa. Usually there are from four to five classes; this is dependent on the fact of whether we consider the Sporozoa *s. lat.* as one or as two classes (Telosporidia and Amoebosporidia, according to Doflein and Dogiel, 1937). The first scholar who proposed that the subregnum Protozoa should be divided into two larger subgroups was B. Hatschek (1888). He proposed in his famous *Lehrbuch der Zoologie* (unfortunately never completely published), that the first three large groups, i.e. Flagellata, Rhizopoda, and Sporozoa, should be included in the phylum Cytomorpha while each of these large groups should be given the category of a cladus (thus a higher category than that of a class). The phylum Cytoidea (i.e. "similar to the cells," now the "hypercellular forms") should consist of an independent cladus of Ciliata. Hatschek also united the two phyla into the division Cytozoa. In spite of the fact that Hatschek was the first zoologist who suggested such a classification we now find the same division generally used, yet under other names which were coined (quite unnecessarily) by Doflein (1901) as the Plasmodroma and the Ciliophora.

In many respects the Ciliata represent in fact an isolated group among other groups of Protozoa. The standpoint can also be defended that the climax of the progressive evolution of the Protozoa had been reached in the Ciliata. In spite of this it seems to be rather problematic that we should separate the Ciliata so thoroughly from the Flagellata by means of such a strict division into two large groups because it is quite certain that the Ciliata evolved from the latter. It may be better and more in agreement with the genetic conditions if for the present we avoid dividing the main groups of the Protozoa taxonomically into subgroups. In morphological practice, however, the notional pair Cytoidea and Cytomorpha may prove useful, as is also the case with the notion of the Undulipodia (Hadži, 1944) which includes the Flagellata and the Ciliata because of their undulipodia (flagella and cilia). In the literature we can frequently find that the division of Protozoa into two large subgroups has not been accepted (cf. Hall's *Protozoology*).

Some protozoologists, e.g. Bělař and others, may be right when they suggest that the taxon "phylum" should be given to those groups of Protozoa which have been given the taxon "class" so far, even if in the Protozoa the morphological differences (the structural forms) are not so conspicuous, owing to their acellularity and small dimensions, as in the geologically younger Metazoa. We must take into consideration here the fact that the Protozoa had at their disposal a much longer period for their evolution than the Metazoa. This circumstance has perhaps also been the reason why protozoologists are still so uncertain regarding the relationship and connections that exist within the sub-kingdom Protozoa. This uncertainty is met with as soon as we try to solve the question of which group of the Protozoa should be placed at the beginning. Naturally enough this question is also connected with the problem of the origin of the Protozoa.

If we bypass the earliest studies of the Protozoa we see that initially a majority of zoologists had considered the Rhizopoda and the amoebae as the most primitive Protozoa because they do not have a permanent external form and because they develop transitional pseudopodia only. These forms were considered as the initial forms for the evolution of the Flagellata and subsequently also of other types of Protozoa. Since about the time of E. A. Minchin (1912, cf. Hall), however, the Flagellata have usually been given the first place because they have been considered as a form that had developed from the Phytoflagellata. Pascher has later especially brought forward important arguments in favour of this new interpretation. This, however, did not mean that this difficult problem has been definitely solved. On the one hand there appeared Sachwatkin (1956) as an assiduous propagator of the older interpretation which believes in a priority of Rhizopoda and of amoebae. On the other hand Grassé (1948), an excellent and experienced researcher in Protozoa, has recently suggested that the two large groups of Protozoa should become united into a new group which he called Rhizoflagellata. These should represent a large uniform central group which had served as a starting point for the evolution of all the other groups of Protozoa. The main argument Sachwatkin brings forward to support his theory of the priority of the Rhizopoda is—besides the unpolarized character of these animals and a supposedly primary absence of flagella which Sachwatkin derives from the actinopodia of the Heliozoa—above all their primary heterotrophic type of feeding. He brings this fact in connection with Oparin's theory of the origin of organisms. The possibility cannot be excluded in principle that the primarily heterotrophic organisms (in all probability micro-organisms)—thus the organisms that had existed earlier than the eutrophic forms—had evolved into the animal Protista, thus into the Protozoa; yet at the same time such a suggestion cannot be made probable either. It must be assumed, if such a deduction be right, that the flagella had evolved at least twice, or we must suppose that the Protophyta had evolved from the Protozoa which does not seem to be probable at all. For all these reasons the interpretation which believes in the priority of the Flagellata appears to be more probable. The suggestion made by Grassé has one purely formal advantage because it avoids the problem which of the two groups should be given the priority. We could justify such a unification from a factual point of view only if we could prove that the common primitive form had both flagella and pseudopodia and that the separation of forms did not take place once only but several times. The suggestion for such a unification has perhaps been made too early and it is possible that in future it will be found that the suggestion has been justified. It seems to us that the Flagellata represent the central type of the Protozoa, that all the other types of Protozoa up to the Ciliata had evolved from the Flagellata, and that the Flagellata had played a role similar to the role of the Turbellaria, among the Metazoa.

Here we are not interested in any further and more detailed taxonomy of the Protozoa inasmuch as it has no connection with the evolution of the Metazoa. We would only like to point to the fact that the polykaryonic (plasmodial) states can be found developed by way of nuclear divisions—thus by way of a polymerization of nuclei (which, however, is not identical with the incomplete division!)—everywhere in all the large groups of the Protozoa, even in such that lead an entirely parasitic way of life; and that a process can afterwards be observed in the personal development cycles which is very similar to a cellularization. This process takes place in such a way that either the "young cell" is, so to speak, excised from the plasmodium (as we usually call the polykaryonic state), or so that the whole polykaryonic mass disintegrates into the monocellular, and thus simply cellular, parts or individuals.

On the other hand comparatively few cases can be found among the Protozoa *s. str.* where permanent unions (colonies, cormi) appear as a consequence of successive divisions (palintomy, according to Sachwatkin). If we exclude the Ciliata, we can find such formations of colonies among the more primitive Flagellata. As far as I know there does not occur even a single case among the Protozoa below the Ciliata where even a slightest trace of a polymorphism can be observed among the members (zooids or persons) of the colonies of Flagellata, neither can we find any differentiation into the purely vegetative and into the sexually active zooids. The Ciliata on the other hand can sometimes be found to develop colonies. In these colonies the zooids had developed mutual organic connections by means of stems, and here we can also find a slight differentiation of zooids even if it appears in their sexual characteristics only. So far nobody has ever thought of deriving the Metazoa from such "colonies" of Ciliata.

The Transition from the Protozoan to the Metazoan State

Thus it appears that the main line of evolution had in all probablity proceeded, as far as we can establish this on the basis of our present positive knowledge, from the Cryptomonada (according to E. C. Dougherty) by way of Chrysomonadina (Cuénot) to the Zooflagellata (Mastigophora) with the Bodonidea or quite generally Protomonadina (according to Cuénot and Grassé) at the beginning. Here a rich ramification can be observed. It had led to the emergence of the Rhizopoda or the Sarcodina, and the two parasitic groups which are usually united in our classifications under the name Sporozoa in spite of the fact that they had evolved at least diphyletically.

These Flagellata had afterwards evolved along at least four diverging lines: The first two lines ended "blindly" as Protozoa. The first of these lines is represented by the Flagellata. In this line we can observe a strong inclination to polymerization. The line ends with the Hypermastigina which now only live in other animals. The second line is very short, it consists of a

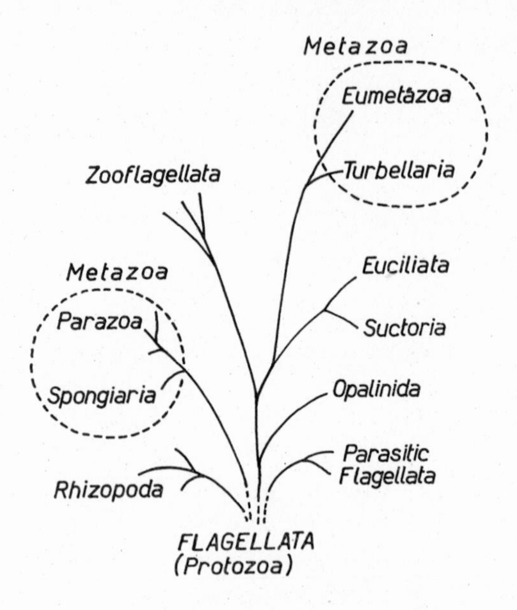

Fig. 49. Evolutionary relationship Flagellata–Metazoa; (orig).

few species only which belong to the Opalinidae (Opalinata, according to Wessenberg). These again live as parasites in the bodies of other animals. The third line had actually broken from the narrow frame work of the Protozoa, yet it evolved into a weak branch only of "polycellular" forms or Metazoa, i.e. into the Spongiae whose subsequent development had soon ended blindly (Fig. 49). It was the fourth line which had played a leading role; it had begun with the primitive Ciliata and it had continued to evolve all the way along the main line of the development of the Eumetazoa.

All these suggestions have a strongly hypothetical character. It is therefore not surprising if we find numerous other interpretations of this development. A majority of zoologists consider that the Ciliata represent a blind side branch of the Protozoa, and that the Metazoa had evolved directly from the colonies or aggregations of the genuine Flagellata. It is believed that this latter evolution had been either monophyletic (e.g. from the Choanoflagellata, according to Lameere) or diphyletic (once as Spongiae and the second time as Eumetazoa). We will not mention here all the other interpretations which are even less probable or which are occasionally quite bizarre. We can give here as an example only the interpretation that was proposed by Awerinzew (1910); he considers that the Metazoa did not evolve from the Protozoa, and that instead the two groups developed simultaneously along two parallel lines of evolution from some even more primitive ancestors. Franz, too, considers that the Protozoa and the Metazoa only had some common ancestors; these ancestors were algae which had already reached a somewhat higher level of development and which afterwards evolved on the one hand into the Protophyta and these into the Protozoa; the higher plants had evolved from the Protophyta parallel to the development of the Protozoa; the other line of evolution had gone from the algae by way of a "blastaea" towards the Metazoa. Fortunately enough, such extravagant interpretations have never been accepted by anybody.

It is generally considered that the Ciliata evolved (mono- or polyphyletically?) from the Zooflagellata; yet no recent transitional forms have ever been found, neither do we know of any transitional forms between the Ciliata and the Metazoa. Zoologists have tried to avoid these difficulties by referring to the pattern that can be observed in plants, yet at the same time they have completely forgotten that this is a pattern only, an analogy, which represents a possibility and which must not be interpreted as an indication and even less so as an evidence. There are a few facts only which take place in the ontogenies of Metazoa (cleavage, the "blastaea" stage) and which could eventually be interpreted as indications; yet there are also other possible interpretations of these same facts which are even more probable. It has already been emphasized that the only satisfactory evidence that can be found in the recent Protozoa point to the evolution of the Spongiae from the Choanoflagellata, while there are no facts available which could be used as evidence of the corresponding evolution of the Eumetazoa.

In my opinion there are three more or less probable ways how we can interpret the evolution of the Metazoa from the Flagellata. These three variants are:

(1) Spongiae Eumetazoa
↗ ↗
Flagellata → Ciliata

(2) Spongiae
↗
Flagellata → Ciliata → Eumetazoa

(3) Ciliata
↗
Flagellata → (blastaea) → Mesozoa → Spongiaria →
→ Eumetazoa

There is no great difference between the first and the third variant. It is only a question of the interpretation of the origin of Spongiae. We have already dealt sufficiently with this problem in our discussions and we have come to the conclusion that the Spongiae represent an isolated group. The diphyletic origin of the Metazoa (the variant No. 2) appears therefore to be more probable than the monophyletic evolution (the variant No. 3). There remain the variants No. 2 and No. 3 only if we disregard the variant No. 1 which seems to us be quite improbable. Here we do not take into account the inessential differences that appear within the framework of the third variant, i.e. whether evolution proceeded primarily by way of a blastaea, or a planula, or a parenchymella. Certain characteristics that are common both to the Spongiae and to the "genuine" Metazoa (the Eumetazoa) do not disprove the diphyletic origin of the two groups and the independent evolution of the Spongiae. The same properties (these common characteristics are generally the sexual phase and the ontogeny which follows this sexual phase, with its initial phases, the cleavage, the blastula, the gastrulation) can also be found in the plant world during the transition of plants into the polycellular forms, above all in the Phytomonadida or Volvocales. These similarities are therefore clearly parallelisms.

One more possibility can also be taken into consideration which, however, can also be considered as a variant of the pattern No. 3. This possibility is that all the Metazoa had evolved from the colonial Choanoflagellata. According to such an interpretation the Spongiae were the first which had evolved, while the remaining Metazoa, the Eumetazoa had developed from a very early phase of this phylogeny. We find such a variant, which can hardly be defended, quite unacceptable (Kemna has perhaps thought of some similar kind of development?).

Thus we find that contrary to the situation which exists in plants it is comparatively easy to divide the animal world into the Protozoa and the Metazoa inasmuch as we do not consider that the Protozoa consists exclusively of the heterotrophic monocellular (i.e. mononuclear) animal species. The limit between the Protozoa and the higher forms is also clear and I dare maintain that no transitional forms between the Protozoa and the Metazoa will ever be found among the recent species; such forms had probably died out long ago.

There Are No Well-Warranted Mesozoa

Before we begin to deal with the taxon Metazoa it may prove useful if we discuss briefly the problem whether the taxon Mesozoa, which is frequently used by zoologists, be justified or not.

Without any intention to go here into details we wish to state that we understand as "Mesozoa" only the Orthonectoidea (Orthonectida + Dicyemida). In all the other cases which were also considered as Mesozoa it has been possible to establish with considerable certainty that they were not real Mesozoa *s. l.* We will therefore not discuss them in this connection. So far the Mesozoa have been given various taxonomic evaluations; as a maximum they have been considered as a sub-kingdom (cf. *Zoological Names*, etc., published by AAAS, edited by A. S. Pearse, 1949); as a minimum they have been classified as an appendage only of the Platyhelminthes (e.g. by Cuénot). Moreover they have also been evaluated as a phylum (e.g. by L. H. Hyman, *The Invertebrates*, I., 1940) which is a middle-way found between the two extremes. So far the whole problem has remained unsolved. The most extreme solution can be found in Beklemischew (1958) who simply does not mention the Mesozoa at all in his systematic survey of the animal groups because of the uncertainty which exists regarding their systematic position. In this way he is not obliged to accept the auxiliary solution and to represent the Mesozoa as a kind of appendage. Beklemischew's solution is quite naturally purely formalistic. We must decide which interpretation appears at the present moment (on the basis of our present knowledge) as the most probable.

The main problem is whether the simplicity of the body structure which we find in these animals can be considered as a primary phenomenon, or whether it is a result of a secondary development which had taken place as a consequence of their parasitism. It appears as much more probable that it is a result of a secondary simplification (so-called "degeneration") because these animals are very specialized endoparasites which pass through a phase, even if short, of a free life. This, however, does not mean that there had been no partially progressive evolution, especially at the point of the development cycle; this can be observed in the Sporozoa among the Protozoa and in the Platyhelminthes (Trematoda). We will leave it undecided whether this was a case of the neoteny with the miracidium larva as the initial form, or something else.

This interpretation will appear *a priori* more probable to those who accept the theory that the Metazoa evolved from some colonies if they take into consideration the classical interpretation that evolution proceeded along the line blastaea–gastraea. Yet the planula thesis too seems to be now much less firmly rooted (Hatschek suggested the phylum Planularia, with the Planulozoa as the only cladus).

Those who accept the polykaryonic theory could derive the Orthonectidea directly from the Ciliata by way of a polymerization and of a partial cellularization which can be easily identified. There is, however, a large number of facts which completely disprove such a derivation. The equally numerous similarities appear as analogies, as a consequence of a retrogressive development which was caused by their endoparasitism. The Dicyemida seem to be much more reduced forms than the Orthonectida because they are built of a smaller and definite number of skin cells. It cannot be therefore expected (as this has been repeatedly emphasized) that anything essentially new could come to light with a discovery of those parts of the life cycle of these animals which have remained so far unknown. In all probability such a discovery will not help us to get a more precise knowledge of the origin of the Orthonectoidea, even if such a possibility cannot be completely excluded.

We come therefore to the conclusion that there are no Mesozoa in the sense as this word has been used till now. Neither had they ever existed, because both the Spongiae and the Acoela had in all probability passed quickly through the intermediate stages of evolution while there had been in all probability no third type of evolution. It is therefore completely improbable that any corresponding transitional forms will be found in the future. Even if such forms had existed in the most remote past they have certainly not left any identifiable traces of their existence.

Otto Steinböck (in his report at the symposium held in California, 1960) has recently made an interesting suggestion of considering the Ciliata as actual Mesozoa. This suggestion is in fact nothing more than an ingenious observation; the actual Ciliata are in reality genuine even if complex Protozoa, similarly as are, for example, the Nummulites, the Hypermastigina, and the Opalinidae. The evolution of the Metazoa had gone parallel to the evolution of these forms and there are the hypothetical Proacoela only which could be considered earnestly as "Mesozoa."

The Classification of the Metazoa

The Parazoa as an Independent Subregnum

In spite of the fact that the evolution of the complex "polycellular" forms had been so widely different in the plant and animal worlds we find that this difference does not have an absolute character. All the known facts if viewed objectively disprove that the evolution of these complex forms—which had made possible their differentiation and a larger size of their bodies—had been monophyletic within the sphere of animals and that it had been basically different from the evolution of plants. There are the Spongiae which have been given such widely different scientific names and which have been found to be problematic in several respects; in a certain sense they are more similar to plants than are the remaining polycellular animals. Originally they were considered as Zoophyta; the founders of the theory of Evolution, however, and above all Ernst Haeckel, had the unfortunate idea of classifying them as Coelenterata. A little later, before scholars succeeded in identifying the completely aberrant ontogeny of Spongiae, they were pronounced by Huxley (1875), Sollas (1884), and by other zoologists to be a form which stands completely apart from other polycellular forms. And what had been the main reason why the Spongiae with their special organisation and way of life have continued to be considered as Coelenterata in spite of the discovery made first by Metschnikoff of the special character of their ontogenies? It was again the fatal gastraea theory as it was proposed by Haeckel! Spongiae occasionally possess (as is also the case with the Eumetazoa) a freely swimming larva which has on the whole the form of a blastula. This form has therefore been considered as a recapitulation of the blastaea. It is followed by a gastrula-like form which again has been considered as a recapitulation of the gastraea. Is there anything else that could be desired?! Haeckel, as a master in this field, has also coined attractive names: *Olynthus* and *Ascon*. In his scheme he placed them possibly close to the *Hydra* and to the "typical" gastrula and the whole impression reached in this way was quite convincing. This idyll was not disturbed by an actually quite unpleasant fact that the "spongian gastrula" becomes attached by means of its primitive mouth, that it does not possess a digestive intestine, that it subsequently develops a new opening at its "aboral" pole whose function is rather that of an anal orifice than that of a mouth (thus the Spongiae would therefore be a special type of the Deuterostomata), and that the Spongiae show numerous orifices (pores) in their body wall where the sea water is drawn by means of choanocytes (they substitute here the digestive entodermal cells) into the internal system of canals in order to be finally forced out through a larger opening (the osculum) after it had gone through a special filtration system and after its oxygen had been removed. As far as I know there in not a single species of Spongiae which as such would consist exclusively of the sexually mature and solitary olynthi or ascons. It may be therefore better to speak of an olynthus stage which appears above all during the ontogeny (perhaps as an already sessile larva or as a kind of a postlarva) of the Calcispongiae. Complex individualities are soon developed by way of a further growth (budding or incomplete divisions) and in these it is frequently difficult to identify the single individuals or persons. A labyrinth of external and internal canals is soon developed. This complex can finally adopt a homogeneous form, it can become an individualized complexus (cormus). Most frequently, however, we find the olynthus stage not repeated at all. Larvae of benthonic or even sessile animals are not recapitulations of any ancestral forms, neither are spongulae anything of this kind. Their structures and forms show an equally rich variety as can be observed in the Cnidaria larvae.

The Spongiae have repeatedly been discussed in the present study, in which I have also tried to explain the phylogeny of the Spongiae as it appears to have taken place. I have also criticized the opposite arguments, above all those that were brought forward by Tuzet, which try to place the Spongiae as members of the large group of Metazoa. I definitely accept the thesis which considers that the Spongiae evolved quite independently of the main body of the actual Metazoa from the cormi of the Choanoflagellata, in spite of the fact that the Spongiae represent a polycellular animal type with a complex structure. Taxonomically the Spongiae must be considered without any doubt as something more than a phylum. We only have to make the decision whether we should place the Spongiae together with other polycellular forms (which evolved in all probability from a common root of protozoan ancestors) into one and the same subregnum of Metazoa, or whether it would be better to consider them as a special megataxon similar to that of a subregnum which could be inserted between the Protozoa and the Metazoa, or the Eumetazoa. In the second case we could use the already existing name of Parazoa Sollas 1884. It will be better for us to accept the view that each taxon should include one animal group only which had evolved monophyletically; we should no longer use as a taxon the notion and the name Metazoa, which should represent from now on a morphological notion only. Instead of the Metazoa we should rather use the name Eumetazoa when we speak of a special taxon.

The name Enantiozoa which was proposed by Delage is not only younger, it is also less fortunate; the question is not that in Spongiae the three body layers occur perhaps in an inverted sequence, i.e. that the skin is found in the interior of their bodies and that the intestine occurs externally, but rather that the Spongiae possess an external body layer which is not homologous with the skin of the Eumetazoa, and a non-uniform inner body layer which cannot be considered as homologous to a reversed intestinal layer. These are in reality morphological units which cannot be mutually compared, which are not mutually homologous. It is true that during the ontogeny we could get an impression as if a reversion of the two layers had taken place. Nothing can help here even if we try to save the old interpretation by printing pictures of spongulae, as has frequently been done, with the actual posterior end (posterior as seen when the animal swims, and quite generally during the polarization) turned upwards. This serves as a good example of how even the most difficult problems can easily be solved by means of a deliberate misrepresentation of facts in false pictures. This can lead, naturally enough, to apparent solutions only.

The name Porifera, which was introduced by R. E. Grant is also very characteristic of Spongiae. Nowhere else in the whole animal world (with perhaps the only exception of the Echinodermata) can pores be found which do not serve as openings through which the animal excretes its own products or the water that had been used for breathing, but rather as openings which serve for the intake of water that brings the necessary food to the animal. In spite of this we still prefer the name Parazoa because the word itself ends in *-zoa;* such an ending is much more suitable for the few subregna of the animal world and it should therefore be used in this sense only.

The Eumetazoa and Their Subdivisions

The Elimination of the terms Coelenterata: Coelomata. So far there have been no essential differences between our system of the animal world and the traditional and generally used systems. Yet the whole basis of the subsequent system necessarily becomes changed when we take into consideration the consequences of our interpretation that the real polycellular forms (the Eumetazoa, or the Metazoa s. str.) had evolved from the polynuclear (i.e. polykaryonic) or plasmodial Protociliata. From now on the organization does not develop anew from some independent units, from the protistic individuals which had been previously free, as had been the case with the "Metaphyta" and with the Spongiae. This kind of evolution leads, with a few "initial" exceptions (Volvocales), exclusively to the formation of sessile organisms. The evolution which had led to higher forms followed another principle: and in these the cells gathered to form a new individuality of a higher type, a new whole with a complex structure.

From the very beginning the genuine animal freely-living polycellular forms had taken over the higher organization which had been reached already on the level of the Protozoa (Ciliata). Thus, it was the eumetazoan organism which formed these cells and not conversely that the previously individual cells formed a polycellular organism, as was the case with the Metaphyta and with the Spongiae. This is the only way the development of an internal digestive organ can be rationally explained: thus neither by way of an invagination of a hollow sphere, nor by a wandering in of individual earlier skin cells into the interior of the same sphere. The names Enterozoa, according to Lankester, or Gastrobionta (animals with an intestine), according to Ulrich, which have also been suggested for the Eumetazoa are therefore very suitable.

We must not be led astray by the types of formation of the "body layers" which can be observed during the ontogenies; these types are mutually different and they change more and more during their subsequent development. These ontogenetic types of formation can even become identical in the two lines of evolution which are basically different (in the phylogenetic sense!); on the one hand in the evolution of the Metaphyta and of the Spongiae which alone are without an intestine, and on the other hand in the evolution of the Eumetazoa. We must liberate ourselves from the belief that the ontogenetic morphogenesis via blastula–gastrula were identical with the phyletic morphogenesis via blastaea–gastraea, as if the ontogenetic type of development were identical with a recapitulation of the phyletic (i.e. of the fully developed forms) development.

A digestive plasmodium existed even before there was any ontogeny of the Eumetazoa; it had been a substratum of the subsequent intestine in the interior of the proeumetazoon where the cyclosis of the digestive vacuoles had been stopped. There was no need of a gastrulation by way of a transference of the blastula epithelium into the interior of the animal. It was only due to the introduction of the ontogenetic morphogenesis (which finally became necessary) combined with an initial cleavage that the gastrulation processes finally began to take place. We can therefore still continue to use the notions gastrula and gastrulation even in this new situation, yet without any parallel idea of a blastaea or a gastraea. No Blastaeadae or Gastraeadae had in reality ever existed and no such forms can be found among the recent animals either, at least as regards the Eumetazoa.

Quite frequently we can see in some Cnidaria and Endoprocta how an intestine (the entoderm) develops from the "skin" (the ectoderm) during the ontogenies or during the so-called atypical budding. Experimental embryology, however, has shown that these processes are an instance only of an ontomechanism as this has been suitably named by O. Steinböck, or of the "morphogenetic technique" as I called the same process even earlier.

Viewed from our standpoint it appears as self-evident that the principle of a simultaneous emergence of the third, the middle body layer, or of the so-called mesohyl, with the second body layer has the same validity. All the Eumetazoa are without any exception three-layered animals if there is any sense at all of speaking about three layers in the adult animals, because there are frequently more than three layers present even as early as in the ontogenies. The Eumetazoa inherited all these three layers (zones, parts) from their prociliate ancestors, and these three layers had therefore not been newly developed by the Metazoa. The pair Diploblastica : Triploblastica is therefore completely superfluous. All the three body layers evolved continuously and parallelly without an internal struggle of the originally independent elements against the secondary centralization combined with the subordination, as had necessarily been the case with the evolution of the colonies of the Protozoa.

In connection with a general classification of the animal world and with taxonomy it is important that we call attention here to the subsequent evolution of these three layers. This is necessary because one can frequently hear the objection that too great an importance is usually attributed to the conditions of the middle body layer, i.e. of the mesohyl and of the coelom. As a matter of fact, however, we find that during the ontogenetic and phylogenetic developments the morphogeny is much more intensive in the middle layer than in the two remaining body layers. In order to be as brief as possible I wish only to mention that it is above all the duty of the external layer to "serve" as a means of protection (it is used as an organ of movement by means of cilia in the more primitive and small forms only; this property had been inherited from the infusorian ancestors); it also produces gland cells and the cuticular formations. And what is produced by the middle layer?

Both the skin and the intestine receive a mesohyl layer with muscles, nerves, etc. Later we will return to discuss again in detail the products of the middle body layer and their destinies. We are therefore fully justified in paying special attention to the conditions of the middle body layer in our attempts to construct a natural system of the animal world.

In opposition to the numerous attempts that have been made so far to construct a classification of the animal world on the basis of the colonial theory and in agreement with the hypothesis of an evolution along the line blastaea–gastraea where a bifurcation in the sense Coelenterata: Coelomata becomes necessary at the very beginning of the Eumetazoa, we find the classification of animals considerably simplified if we construct it on the basis of the plasmodium theory of the origin of the Eumetazoa in the sense of a development along the line Prociliata–Acoelia (Turbellaria). The adherents of the colonial theory have been unable to identify any well-founded and therefore probable phyletic relationship between the Coelomata and the Coelenterata. On the other hand it is possible to make a rational and probable interpretation of the phyletic, systematic, and thus also of the taxonomic conditions as they existed at the very beginning of the Eumetazoa and of their subsequent evolution if we view them from the aspect of the plasmodial theory and in combination with the new interpretation of the phylogeny of the Cnidaria. We can express the uniformity of the Eumetazoa both in their system and in their taxonomy if we abandon the opposing pair Coelenterata : Coelomata (which is actually identical with the pairs Diploblastica: Triploblastica, and Radiata: Bilateria) and if we place the Turbellaria at the beginning of the Eumetazoa. The symmetrical condition which as a property of the animal body has played so far an important role (which was unfortunately only a negative one) will lose from now on its importance. We have shown that in the Eumetazoa there has never been any primary radial symmetry; that this symmetry emerged more or less developed only in those animals which had adopted, for a long time, the sessile way of life. We have also shown that there is no justification in a distinction between the primarily two and three-layered Eumetazoa. We must therefore cease to use this supposed difference in the taxonomy.

There have been still other systematic attempts where a bifurcation was suggested at the very root of the Eumetazoa. Thus, for example, the Metazoa (s. l.) were divided initially by Hatschek into the Protaxonia and the Heteraxonia. This is thus a classification on the basis of a supposed difference in the axial conditions. Hatschek himself later abandoned this classification because it was soon found that the axial conditions are in reality very unreliable, that they have a role similar to that of the symmetrical conditions in the phylogeny and they are strongly changeable especially during the ontogenies.

A completely unacceptable classification was made by Colosi (1956: 505). He divided the Eumetazoa into the Perineura and the Epineura. It is only the Coelenterata that are included among the Perineura while even Ctenophora do not appear in this group. Colosi suggests that the Coelenterata consist exclusively of the Cnidaria. He naturally believed in the primary nature of the nerve-net system without a dorsal brain ganglion. On the other hand, he inclines strongly to a key-like dichotomy in the general classification of the Eumetazoa which he pursues for not less than eight stages up to the category of types (i.e. phyla).

Furthermore, I should like to mention those classifications which use the notion Coelomata while at the same time omitting the opposite notion of Coelenterata. Thus, for example, the groups Porifera, Ctenophora, Cnidaria and Planuloidea remain separate in the schematic survey which was made by J. Meixner and published in the *Handbuch der Biologie* (edited by L. von Bertalanffy and F. Gessner), Pt. III (The Genealogical Tree of the Animal World). In the text, however, we find nevertheless the word and the category of coelenterata used by A. Remane (*ibid:* 85) and by other collaborators (e.g. by

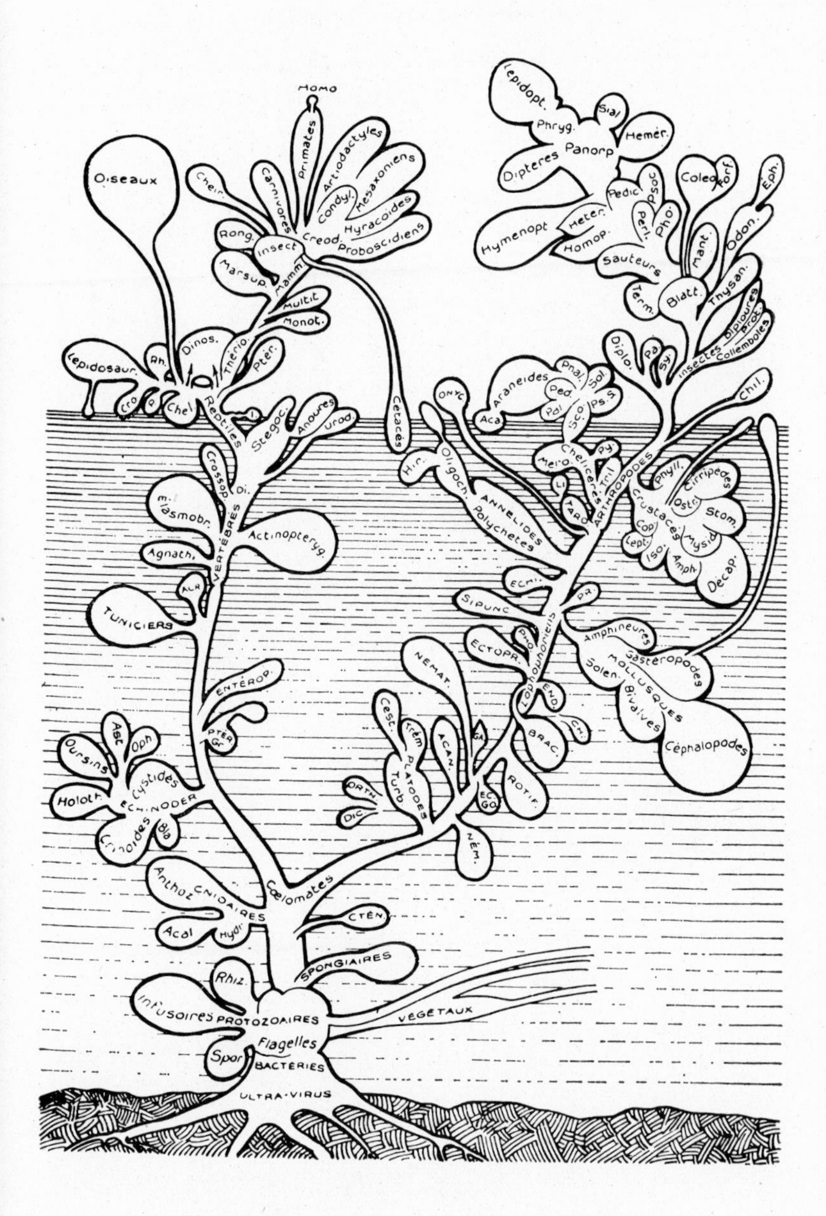

Fig. 50. Genealogical tree (After L. Cuénot.)

W. Marinelli, *ibid:* 311). It is possible that in the schematic survey the word Coelenterata was omitted due to a mistake only.

L. Cuénot *(Traité de Zoologie*, I., ed. P. Grassé, *Phylogénèse du règne animal*, *Árbre généalogique*, p. 2, cf. Fig. 50), too, would like to dispense with the taxon Coelenterata while at the same time he preserves the taxon Coelomata. Cuénot represents this graphically in such a way that he places two independent short branches on a very short common stem; the left branch which is longer represents the Cnidaria while the smaller branch which appears on the right side of the stem embodies the Ctenophora. In this way the scheme as proposed by Cuénot shows some similarities with my genealogical tree. Cuénot speaks of the Neuromyaria instead of the Eumetazoa. In the text, however (p. 25), he mentions the coelenterate stage ("Le Neuromyaire Coélentéré") which shows that he still preserves the notion of the Coelenterata even if it is used purely formalistically only and not taxonomically.

The palaeozoologist A. W. Müller (1958) has accepted to a considerable degree the general division of the animal world as it was proposed by Cuénot (1948), while at the same time he also takes into consideration the coelenterate theory as it has been proposed in my publications ("Unter Zugrundelegung der Coelenteraten-Theorie von J. Hadži" 1944, see Fig. 51). The taxons or notions Coelenterata and Coelomata do not appear in his graphic representation of the genealogical tree. The acoelous Turbellaria appear in the middle of the stem (Fig. 51); the Cnidaria and the Ctenophora are derived from the Turbellaria. A. H. Müller does not follow my suggestions in his subsequent interpretation of the evolution; he prefers to preserve the dichotomy of the Coelomata into the Protostomia and the Deuterostomia. Yet at the same time he is undecided where and how these Deuterostomia should be annexed. We can therefore see in his graphic representation the "left" branch hanging in the air. I think it is very important that A. H. Müller (1958:3) as a palaeozoologist finds that Hadži's theory (1944, 1949) does not stand in any opposition to palaeontology, that "sich keinerlei Widersprüche zur Paläontologie ergeben und mit deren Hilfe sich auch andere Erscheinungen zwanglos erklären lassen."

Attempts can frequently be found where the Coelenterata (these are usually understood as a group which includes the

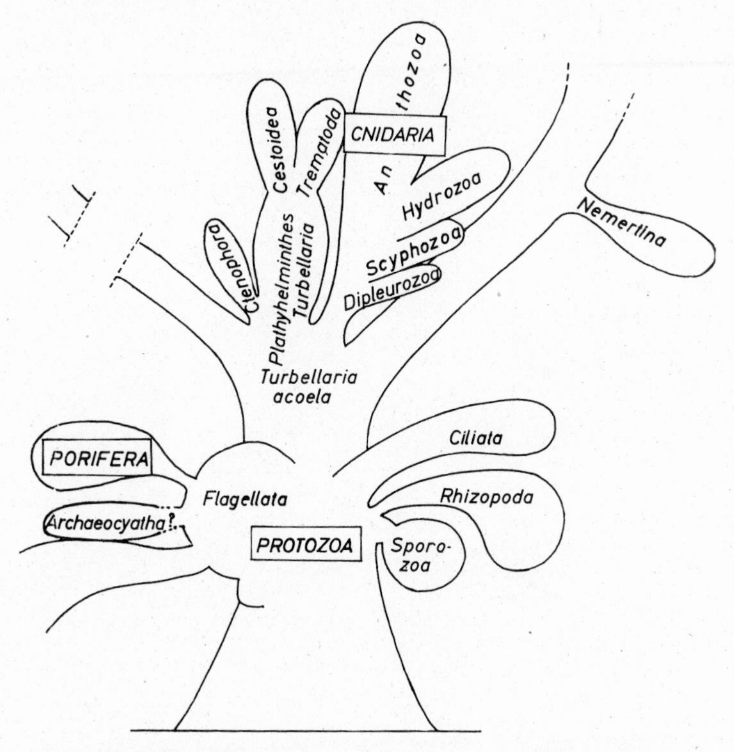

Fig. 51. The lower part of the genealogiel tree (after A.H. Müller), changed to agree with my turbellaria theory of cnidarians.

Cnidaria and the Ctenophora) do not appear on the geneological tree as a counterpart to the Coelomata but rather as an intermediate stage between the colonial Flagellata and the Coelomata (the Bilateria or even Vermes). This is, for example the case with the outline made by Schmalhausen (1947:411); in his graphic (Fig. 52) representation, however, we find the groups of Coelenterata indicated as a side branch so that finally we still get the impression of a bifurcation where the actual stem is represented by one of the two branches. The point in question is here a common, very primitive and perhaps planuloid ancestral form. Schmalhausen also goes his own

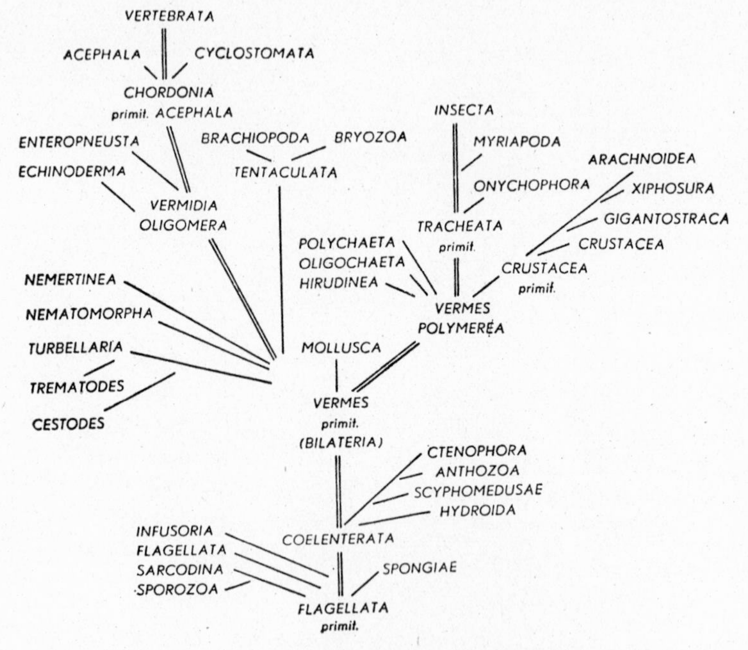

Fig. 52. Genealogical tree of animal kingdom. (After Schmalhausen.)

way in his interpretation of the phyletic conditions of the Bilateria; later we will return to this problem.

A very interesting suggestion was made by G. S. Carter (1940:482; cf. Fig. 53). In his construction of the genealogical tree Carter takes into account to a considerable degree the conditions that can be observed in larvae. We have already declared such a method erroneous. The classification of the animal world as it was proposed by Carter shows considerable simplifications which certainly is a welcome sign even if Carter goes in my opinion a little too far. Carter divides the Metazoa (these are actually the Eumetazoa, they do not include the Spongiae as the Parazoa) at their very root ("the ancestral metazoan") into two lines; these two stems were given the rank of superphyla, they are very

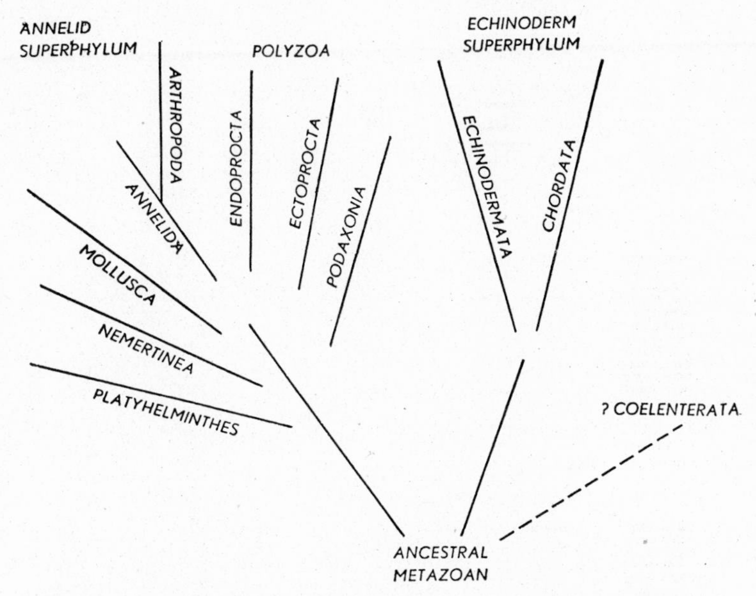

Fig. 53. "Evolutionary relationship of the invertebrate phyla" by G.S. Carter.

unequal, and they corespond roughly to the dichotomy Protostomia : Deuterostomia (the "Annelid superphylum" and the "Echinoderm superphylum"). As regards the Coelenterata Carter remains undecided; nevertheless he shows an inclination to derive them as an independent stem or as a third branch from the same "ancestral metazoan." A definite progress can be seen in his idea of a hypothetical ancestral form which had lived as a benthonic animal and was as such bilaterally symmetric, which had three body layers and did not consist of metameres (the amerous state), which showed a slight cephalization, and which possessed a ventral opening and even an anal opening and in all probability also protonephridia. We think that in this way too many requisites have been given to this hypothetical initial form. This can be seen above all when we try to derive the aproctous Platyhelminthes from it, while on the other hand it is not difficult to derive the Coelenterata from it because we can rightly maintain that some of these requisites had been lost due to the transition of these animals to a sessile way of life. As regards the Platyhelminthes, Carter must make some revisions; he must derive them from an even older primarily aproctous primitive form in which case he will be obliged to consider the Platyhelminthes as an independent branch—thus as the fourth branch—or he should go back to an already disqualified interpretation and consider the aproctous state as a secondary phenomenon, as a consequence of a degeneration.

We can easily understand that Carter does not assume a strictly negative attitude towards my interpretation. Carter discussed my suggestions twice. The first time in a very objective report which appeared in the review *Science Progress;* in this report he gives very adroitly all the essential points of my construction. Carter stresses judiciously that "it is not likely that zoologists will soon reach general agreement on them" (sc. my interpretations in the field of the "high phylogeny"). He mentions correctly the great interest which exists about these problems, and states as follows, "It is refreshing to read a discussion of these questions in which the results of recent zoology are taken into account. For this we have to thank Prof. Hadži."

In another detailed study (Carter, 1954) Carter took a critical attitude towards my suggestions as they appeared in the article which was published in *Systematic Zoology*. In this study Carter accepted, at least partly, my interpretations and expressed his opinion that it could be expected that my interpretations would not be accepted by many zoologists. Unfortunately enough Carter could not come to any conclusion concerning the derivation of the Cnidaria and of the position of the Cnidaria in the animal system; in his humility he considers himself not sufficiently competent to make any conclusions in this respect. Neither does Carter come to any conclusion regarding the origin of the Eumetazoa even if he admits that there are many points which seem to support the plasmodial theory, and that the old interpretation was based on the blastaea theory as it was proposed by Haeckel. I expect that in future Carter will come to some conclusions over these points, and that he will accept the idea that the Cnidaria evolved from some ancestors which they had in common with the Turbellaria, that he will accept the plasmodial theory, and finally that he will find that these interpretations agree best with the natural facts that have become known till now. It is a fortunate sign that such a large number of British zoologists have rejected the wrong interpretation of the relation embryos: ancestors. The only thing which remains to be accepted by them is the idea that the planktonic larvae must be interpreted as ontogenetic stages that had emerged secondarily as new forms which must not be compared with the adult ancestral forms but only mutually with each other. This is a necessary consequence of the right interpretation of recapitulations as they must be understood if they are not looked upon from the easily misleading standpoint of the "fundamental biogenetic law."

Among the more recent attempts to construct the animal system, mention should be made of the genealogical tree as it was proposed by Franz and Heberer (1943:291). From the standpoint of bifurcations this system is certainly the most extreme. The starting point is represented by the completely hypothetical and improbable gastraea. The pair Coelenterata: Coelomata is abandoned. The next lower stage, the Parazoa: the Eumetazoa are also abandoned. All the Metazoa are divided into two groups, the Protostomia and the Deuterostomia. The consequences of such a classification can rightly be considered as "horrible." Among the Coelenterata, which do not appear here under this name, the Platyhelminthes and the Bryozoa evolve almost together from one and the same point (we cannot speak here of a root or of a stem) which is also the starting point for the evolution of the Chaetognatha. The Annelida are placed above the Brachiopoda, Mollusca, Crustacea, and Arachnoidea, etc. It is really completely unnecessary to discuss here this system. The point of the bifurcation of the Eumetazoa can be found placed equally deeply in the system which was proposed by Steiner (1956).

This survey does not include all the attempts which have been made so far to find the correct position of the Cnidaria in the animal classification. Yet even this should suffice to show how many different opinions have been proposed so far and how little all these attempts are able to survive earnest examination. I suggest on the basis of the plasmodial theory of the origin of the Eumetazoa that the Cnidaria should not be separated from the remaining lower Eumetazoa. The dichotomy Coelenterata: Coelomata has in this way become superfluous. The same is also true for the two similar dichotomies, Diploblastica: Triplobastica (because there are no primary Diploblastica), and Radiata (Radialia): Bilateria. All the Eumetazoa have a primarily bilaterally symmetric structure, the radial symmetry being a secondary element caused by the transition to, and a longer preservation of, the sessile state. In this way we also achieve a simplification of the general system and of the genealogical tree.

The Coelomata as a Taxonomic Unit

On the basis of our study of the Cnidaria and of Ctenophora we have come to conclusion that the large taxon of Coelenterata has really no justification. The question necessarily arises in this connection what should be the destiny of its "counterpart," of the Coelomata, as that of a special taxon. The name itself indicates that those animal groups are included in this taxon which show a coelom in their internal structures. A new problem which emerges here is what should be understood as a coelom? This problem has already been sufficiently discussed in the present study. The name itself has been given to widely different body cavities which all appear in the middle body layer while at the same time they are of different origins. All these differences, however, can be reduced in the last line to two categories which are divided into several subcategories. We must distinguish between the coeloms in a wider sense of the word which are all the body cavities that are surrounded by the "mesodermal" cells that form their epithelia, and the coeloms in a narrower sense of the word, i.e. the body cavities which are developed around the intestine and which possess their own epithelium. The coelom is subject (which is very important!) to segmentation during a certain phase of the phylogenetic development. Whenever we speak of a coelom we usually think of this coelom *s.str.* for which I have suggested the word perigastrocoele to be used. This perigastrocoele played the most important role in the phylogeny of the Eumetazoa and it is therefore quite right if we take into consideration the development of this perigastrocoel when we propose larger taxons.

Just in the point of this coelom *s. l.* we can observe cleanly the great difference which exists between the two opposing theories about the origin of the Eumetazoa. Those who accept the colonial theory consider that all the body cavities of the Metazoa, the intestinal cavity included (in the last line this could also be considered as a coelom *s.l.*), are new formations which had evolved completely independently from each other and not all at the same time. The perigastrocoele, and this is mainly the coelom to be discussed, is usually derived from some sack-like outgrowths of the intestine, and the coelom cavity from the intestinal cavity. Such a type of development which can be observed directly and quite frequently during ontogenies would presuppose that a fundamental change takes place in the function of the sack-like outgrowths of the intestine.

An entirely different situation emerges if we view this problem from the standpoint of the polykaryonic theory, i.e. from the point of view which derives the Eumetazoa (the primitive Turbellaria) from the primitive Ciliata. All the "later" body cavities, the intestinal cavity included, had been developed, more or less clearly, in their initial stages as early as in the Ciliata, and that in the form of some permanent or transitory vacuoles, slits, or similar spaces that had appeared in their cytoplasm and that were filled with the cell fluid. They have not appeared anew in the Eumetazoa, they had only evolved, and differentiated in various ways. If we understand as a coelom *s.l.* all the body cavities, we can consider that all the Eumetazoa are actually Coelomata, at least primarily, because many coeloms or even all of them can get lost as a result of a secondary development. This is true both if we accept the one or the other theory about the origin of the Eumetazoa, because the coelenteron of the Coelenterata could be considered as the first stage only of the enterocoelic state of the "genuine" Coelomata.

We can therefore see that those who adhere to the enterocoelic version must necessarily meet with great difficulties as soon as they try to propose a major division of the Eumetazoa. They must propose such large taxons as the Acoela and the Pseudocoela, because there are no Eumetazoa earlier than the Annelida which had developed a coelom *s. str.*, (a perigastrocoele). At the same time they are uncertain whether the morphological conditions that correspond to these categories, such as the absence of an actual coelom, be a primary or a secondary phenomenon. This has been the reason why there are so many zoologists who would like to explain all the Eumetazoa of the Bilateria group, which show a simpler structure, as a product of a retrogressive evolution, an interpretation which has not been supported by any convincing arguments.

When we see that there are such widely different body cavities and systems of cavities—which are different not only in their forms but also in the ways that they are developed during the ontogenetic processes—even in groups which are otherwise obviously closely related, it becomes evident that it is better not to use the conditions of the coeloms as a basis for classification. Zoologists should therefore avoid such classifications as the Coelomata (because of the untenability of their counterpart, the "Coelenterata"), the Acoelomata, the Pseudocoelomata, etc. As an example, we mention here the lower "Coelomata" or the "Bilateria." The coelom cavities can be found as early as in the Turbellaria which we consider as the earliest Eumetazoa. These cavities occur in three forms if we do not take into consideration the digestive cavity. First of all we can frequently find a whole system of canals, often with a vesicle at its extreme end; this is the so-called protonephridium which functions as an emunctory–excretory organ. We derive this nephrocoele from the pulsating vacuoles of Protozoa.

There have been some zoologists who would like to consider this nephrocoele as an initial state for the evolution of the "genuine coelom" (the perigastrocoele; the nephrocoele theory which was proposed by Faussek). This is completely wrong because we can find this nephrocoele preserved as such up to the very end of evolution; it is quite natural that during the evolution it had been variously changed, especially after the appearance of the perigastrocoele. This nephrocoele was occasionally lost in the permanently sessile types whose size had been secondarily strongly diminished as has already been mentioned. In some other cases we find this nephrocoele changed beyond recognition (e.g. in numerous Arthropoda with the so-called mixocoele). Cases are also known where a combination of the nephrocoele with the perigastrocoele (which had developed much later), or with other coelom cavities (e.g. the gonocoele) have been observed.

The second coelom which appeared quite early during the phylogeny of the Eumetazoa is the gonocoele. It evolved completely independently and without any phyletic connection with the protozoan ancestors of the Eumetazoa. Earlier it was frequently called a "sack gonad" (Hatschek). There is no gonocoele yet in the most primitive Turbellaria which might be also true for the phylogenetically oldest Eumetazoa; these forms do not yet possess a regularly formed gonad but only an irregular aggregation of gametocytes which do not have any gonoducts. The gonocoele can be found highly developed in those animal groups which do not possess a perigastrocoele (our Ameria) as is the case, with the higher Mollusca. This gonocoele can again disappear secondarily, just as is the case with the nephrocoele; this takes place above all in those animal types which possess a perigastrocoele, yet it can also be observed in the Ameria. Not infrequently we can find gonocytes which do not form a hollow or a solid gonad and which become simply attached either to the skin (this can be observed in some Cnidaria), or to the intestinal epithelium (also in some Cnidaria), or even to other coelom cavities, above all to the perigastrocoele. At first sight this fact seems to support the gonocoele theory which maintains that the genuine coelom (the perigastrocoele) evolved from the gonocoele. Such a theory cannot be accepted from our standpoint.

The beginnings of the third coelom, of the haemocoel in the form of a haemocoelom system can also be found as early as in the Turbellaria. In these it appears occasionally as a system of blood vessels and lymphatic ducts; it can be found well developed first in the Nemertinea and in the Mollusca. It had been inherited by the Annelida as the lowermost Polymeria from some ancestors which stood closely to the Nemertinea. A pulsating centre of the haemocoele, a muscular heart, does not appear earlier than in the Mollusca.

There are some other special coeloms. Let us mention two such coeloms only; the rhynchocoele of the Nemertinea, and the cardiocoele (the pericardial cavity) of the Mollusca; these forms thus occur in the Ameria. All these coeloms and systems of coeloms evolved in the middle body layer, usually by way of a continuously progressive evolution from some slits and cavities filled with the "cell fluid." This is the case, for example, with the gonocoele of the Turbellaria with its different canals, side cavities, and not infrequently with a secondary polymerization (of gonads, of the terminal organs of nephridia). This is how a rich morphological differentiation became possible. It seems to me, however, that they do not represent a sound basis to be used in classification. These various coeloms and the morphological peculiarities which are connected with them enter into such a variety of combinations that it is impossible to develop on this basis any principle which could be used in the classification. Fortunately enough there have been only few attempts which have tried to construct a system on the basis of the conditions that can be observed in these coeloms. Among these we must mention above all the high taxons the Acoela and the Pseudocoela, or the Acoelomata and the Pseudocoelomata. To these we must add the Eucoelomata as the third subseries (according to Schimkewitsch, 1891). This classification was accepted by Hyman (1940) and by the AAAS *(Zoological Names*, edited by A. S. Pearse, 1949), obviously under the influence of Hyman. The category Acoelomata has only sense if we consider only the perigastric coelom as a genuine coelom; yet if we accept the broader definition and if we consider the coelom to be any body cavity which can be found in the middle body layer of the Eumetazoa and which is surrounded by its own cells, we see that the category Acoela becomes completely senseless because in this case there are no genuine and primary Acoela among the Eumetazoa. The notion of the Pseudocoelomata is even less justified and useful. There do not exist any Pseudocoelomata at all. A body cavity can either be a primary cavity, i.e. without a coelothelium; or it can be a genuine coelom if it has a coelothelium. The category Pseudocoelomata consists, according to Hyman, of the Aschelminthes and of the Endoprocta only. These Endoprocta are actually Aschelminthes that had adopted the sessile way of life but they do not differ essentially

26

as regards coelom conditions from the Acoelomata. It is even more erroneous to consider "the phylum Tardigrada" as a member of the Pseudocoelomata. In connection with this we could speak at the most of a myxocoele because in their ontogenies we can observe pairs of coeloms that are distributed metamerically like the enterocoeloms. The Tardigrada must therefore not be placed anywhere near the Aschelminthes. They certainly stand closer to the primitive Arthropoda.

The suggestion which was made by Colosi (1956:505) should be mentioned here as an example of an extremely one-sided systematization based on the conditions that can be observed in the coelom cavities. Among the taxons which are given various ranks we can find, in Colosi's suggestion, the Deuterocoelomata (including Mollusca, Molluscoida, Annelida, and Onychophora); instead of their counterpart the Protocoelomata or the Acoelomata we find the group ("stipite") Protonephridia which includes all the Ameria. A part of these (these are actually the Aschelminthes) can be found under the name Pseudocoelomata. All this refers to the Protostomia. The Deuterostomia are divided into the Archicoelomata (they include the Chaetognatha only!), and the Metacoelomata (the Hydrocoelomata and the Chordata). The Syncoelomata consist of the Tardigrada and the Arthropoda. The name Parenchymatosa appears twice; once it includes the Nemertinea and the Endoprocta, and another time the Gordiacea. I can hardly believe that any zoologist will ever accept such a classification, it is a purely personal affair.

There is according to my interpretation a basic difference between the various coeloms *s.l.* and the actual coelom *s. str.*, the perigastrocoele. The coeloms *s.l.* can be found in widely different groups of the Eumetazoa and it seems that they had evolved polyphyletically. They cannot be used as a sound basis of a high taxonomy, except in a negative sense, i.e. that all the Eumetazoa which do not possess primarily a perigastrocoele can be grouped together because they show a closer relationship also in other respects. They could therefore be called the Acoelomata; yet this name can be misleading because in all the subgroups of the Acoelomata we can find some kind of a coelom cavity. It will be therefore better to make the classification on the basis of the coelom conditions while at the same time another very important property is also taken into consideration (this in combination with many others!); this is the fact whether the metamerized perigastrocoelic sacks are primarily absent or present. In this way we can get the two groups, the Ameria and the Polymeria. We can see that the special coelom which surrounds the intestinal canal emerges, as it seems suddenly (this at least is the impression we can get now!), and from the very beginning in a metamerized or polymere form. In this way we meet here with an important gap which must be taken into consideration by the systematists and by the taxonomists. Later we will discuss this problem more in detail. Let us now first turn to the notion and to the taxon Ameria.

The First Phylum of the Eumetazoa: the Ameria

The Turbellaria are according to our interpretation the earliest Eumetazoa and as such they represent a starting point of an evolution that radiated into several directions. There are not less than fifteen distinct subtypes—we believe that it is sufficient if we give them the taxon of classes—which evolved from these Turbellaria, and these classes again evolved into numerous subgroups (ordines). We can notice some differences in the levels reached in the organization of all these classes of the Ameria which are due to the various ways of life the species belonging to these groups had to adopt. Here we can find forms which live in various environments as freely living animals, as parasites, animals which burrow in the sea bottom, semi-sessile and fully sessile (evolved even several times!) species. The extent of this difference can be best seen if we juxtapose, for example, on the one hand an acoelan or a hydropolyp, the males of various Rotatoria, the Cestoda, and the solitary Endoprocta, and on the other hand the Cephalopoda, the various higher Turbellaria, the Nematomorpha, etc.

It must be admitted, however, that certain very conspicuous common traits of the general organization and of the level of this organization can be found in all these animal groups which are otherwise so widely different. This proves that they do not only have in all probability a common origin, but also that they are mutually more closely related. The groups which are thus brought together under the phylum of Ameria show the following common traits if compared with the next higher phylum: (1) Not a single class of all these fifteen classes has a perigastrocoele, thus a coelom *s.str.* (2) We cannot find anywhere in this phylum a genuine segmentation and a formation of body regions which would appear in combination with this segmentation. (3) None of these classes has ever developed any extremities, and they have therefore not developed any articulated extremities. (4) Their protonephridia had developed into metanephridia only by Molluscs as a consequence of the union with the increased gonocoel. The first three characteristics represent negative values only, yet they can also be expressed in a positive way, i.e. (1) these classes possess only the coeloms *s.l.*; (2) their body is always homogeneous (the amerous state); and (3) they can move in various ways (by means of cilia or of body muscles), yet never by means of genuine extremities.

As could be expected there appear occasional characteristics, at least as *Anlagen*, scattered among the classes of Ameria which had played a very important role in the evolution of the Polymeria, the next higher animal type. As an example, we can mention the polymerization of individual organs (gonads, nephridia, etc.) or of whole parts of the body (Cestoda), an increased growth into length combined with a curving movement, etc.

The notion of Ameria which represents an unsegmented state of body and its use for the taxonomic purposes is not something entirely new. It is only the contents of this notion which are new. Houssay (quotation after Krumbach, 1937:13) came close to this notion by creating the notions and the names Paurometamera and Polymetamera which, however, are limited to the Enterocoelia only. Schneider (1902) seems to have been the first zoologist to have used the word Ameria, yet he used it for an entirely different notion, i.e. for the Echinodermata only which he included in the phylum Coelenteria. Much closer to our notion of Ameria stands the notion which was introduced by Bütschli (1910) under the name Amera and which has as a taxon other contents. Bütschli who was followed in this point by the editors of the *Handbuch der Zoologie* (Kükenthal–Krumbach) does not include among the Ameria either the Coelenterata or the Mollusca; he and the editors of the *Handbuch* still adhered firmly to the notion Vermes, which is used for practical reasons only, yet in no way as a taxonomic unit.

As regards the Coelenterata it has been shown that there is no such animal group, and that both the Cnidaria and the Ctenophora belong to the phylum Ameria because they had both evolved from the Turbellaria.

It is in agreement with our definition of the Ameria if we include among them the Mollusca in spite of the discovery of *Neopilina* by Lemche (1958) and in spite of his interpretations. In another work I have discussed *in extenso* the case of *Neopilina* (cf. Hadži, in press). For a long time scholars have endeavoured (and there are some zoologists who try to do this even now), to bring the Mollusca into a closer connection with the Annelida, and thus with the Polymeria; this was done in such a way that they have declared the Mollusca to be secondarily simplified animals (this was suggested especially by the older zoologists), or they have considered them as animals which have just reached the initial stage of the polymerous state. Those who believe in a closer relationship between the Mollusca and the Annelida have referred above all to the similarity that can be observed in their planktonic larvae of the trochophore type and to the spiral cleavage. We have already shown that neither an external similarity which can be found in larval forms nor a spiral cleavage can be used as firm proofs of a closer relationship between two animal groups. The situation is perfectly clear as regards the coelom conditions and the segmentation; a polymerization frequently takes place in the primitive Mollusca and in *Neopilina* (which is not a primitive mollusc but rather a primitive gastropod); this polymerization disappears in the higher subtypes and it is only partly preserved in the Cephalopoda (Tetrabranchiata). This, however, should not be interpreted as a remnant of a genuine segmentation but rather as a minimal polymerization. Zoologists have endeavoured to find by all means at least in the ontogenies a recapitulation of a formation of genuine metameres (of the perigastrocoele); they have even maintained that they have found something of this kind. Yet they actually saw something that does not really exist because that was what they wished to see. We can best see how much we are justified in classifying the Mollusca among the Ameria if we compare the lower and the lowest Mollusca—which differ only slightly from the probable initial form which stood close to the Turbellaria—with the other Ameria, and if we do not include first into such a comparison the highest Mollusca, the Cephalopoda.

H. Lemche went too far in his display of his scientific imagination (which can be quite useful if it is used within proper limits) when he tried to exploit the discovery of *Neopilina.* My opinion is shared by numerous other zoologists (cf. the discussion by C. Böttger and by others at the *XVI*th *International Congress of Zoologists).* There is no factual justification for a derivation of the primitive Arthropoda from the Mollusca, and above all of the articulated extremities from the ctenidia. In the primitive Mollusca we can find a somewhat stronger trend to the polymerization, just as is the case with *Nemertinea*, among the Ameria. This trend towards polymerization and to an organization in the direction of a polymerous type grew weaker and weaker during the subsequent evolution of the Mollusca; an evolution which was generally progressive even if it went in a special direction. The Mollusca must therefore be interpreted as a side branch on the stem of the Ameria. The Cephalopoda not only represent a climax in the evolution of the Mollusca, but also of the evolution of the Ameria as a whole. It does not seem that any new, higher animal type has ever evolved from Mollusca. We will also find very similar conditions in other main groups of the Eumetazoa.

Turbellaria Cnidaria Gastrotricha
Trematoda Ctenophora Kinorhyncha
Cestoda Nemertinea Endoprocta
Rotatoria Priapuloidea
Nematoda Acanthocephala
Nematomorpha Mollusca

We can see if we make a survey of the fifteen classes* which constitute the phylum Ameria that it is quite impossible to make subdivisions of this phylum where the classes that are more closely related with each other could be brought together into special subphyla or superclasses (Fig. 54). This is also true for the most widely accepted division into the Platyhelminthes and the Coelhelminthes (Aschelminthes), or into the Scolecida and the Aposcolecida, as well as for many other similar classifications which were suggested by various zoologists. Many of these notions can prove quite useful here and in comparative morphology—as is the case with the pair Aprocta : Euprocta—

* In all probability a sixteenth class will have to be added to these, i.e. that of the Orthonectoidea, as a side branch of the Trematoda (which were called Mesozoa by Beklemischew (he divided the class Trematoda into two groups: Monogenea and Digenea; in addition to these he also created an independent class Udonelloidea).

yet they cannot be used in taxonomy. They only lead to an unnecessary complication of the animal system and to differentiations which are, we can say, personally biased. The case of the antithetical pair Platyhelminthes : Aschelminthes where these two groups are understood as two parallel taxons, or

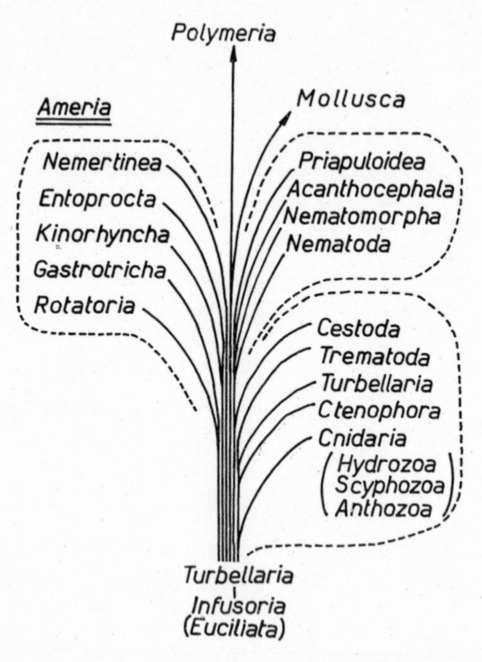

Fig. 54. Genealogical tree of the phylum: Ameria.

as two taxons where one stands above the other, shows the inadequacy of such a division because there is no real limit between these two groups, because the Nemertinea stand in the middle between them, and finally because not all the Turbellaria are really flattened animals. We do not even know which groups should be classified as Aschelminthes. According to Hyman the Aschelminthes consist of the following classes: Rotifera, Gastrotricha, Kinorhyncha, Nematoda, Nematomorpha, and Acanthocephala; yet they do not include the Priapuloidea, Nemertina, Endoprocta, and Mollusca (the first and the last classes are placed among the Coelomata).

It should be mentioned in passing that in our study of all these various animal systems we frequently get an impression that the pre-Darwinian custom of using a dichotomic determinative key in the construction of an artificial system still continues to work subconsciously even nowadays (cf. the attempt made by Colosi which has already been discussed above). The systematists must liberate themselves of this influence if they wish to construct a truly natural animal system. At present, it would be sufficient if these classes were placed into such a linear order, or indicated in the genealogical tree in such a way, that certain classes which are supposed to be more closely related appear close to each other. It is possible that after a certain time we will perhaps get a better knowledge of their mutual relationships and it will be only then that we will be able to begin with a more detailed work on these subdivisions. Important progress has recently been made just in this direction; as examples we can mention here the work made by Steinböck (the relationship connections between the Turbellaria and many other groups of the Ameria), Golvan (the closer relationship connections between the Priapuloidea and the Acanthocephala), and my own studies Cnidaria–Ctenophora, Turbellaria).

The Transition from the Amerous to the Polymerous State

We have seen that the phylum Ameria as the first phylum of the Eumetazoa does not possess a perigastrocoele. When we continue with our construction within the framework of one genealogical tree, we soon meet with the problem of how to explain the emergence of a perigastrocoele (coelom *s.str.)* and what its functional correlative could be. The problem is whether this perigastrocoele had originally evolved as a uniform cavity which had later become segmented, or alternatively that there had been originally a segmented perigastrocoele which had afterwards evolved by way of oligomerization into a uniform cavity. Both these types of evolution are *a priori* possible and probable.

A comparison of all the methods of coelom formation shows—we exclude here in principle all the tubular and cavernous formations which had evolved either by way of an infolding of the skin, as is the case with the tracheal system of the land-inhabiting Arthropoda, or by way of a folding of the skin layer, as is the case with the peribranchial cavity of the Chordata—that all these "hollow spaces" (tubules or cavities) emerge in those parts of the mesohyl where we can find either streaming of the fluid or rhythmic movements of the contractile organs. The first group includes the phenomena of the blood vessel system and the system of lymphatic and water ducts; the second group includes the rhynchocoele, the cardiocoele and, obviously, the perigastrocoele. A third group consists of the gonocoeles in the gonads together with their gonoduct, and the glands with central cavities and their secretory canals.

Thus the coelom cavities develop above all in combination with the frequently repeated or rhythmical movements of the internal muscular organs. We think that it was the peristalsis of the intestinal tube—after a mesenchymal muscularis had been added to the entodermal tubes—which led to the formation of a perigastrocoele. At the same time the intestine became lengthened as a consequence of a lengthening of the entire body. Another consequence of this lengthening of the body was also a radical change of the type of movement which now took place by means of wave-like zigzag contractions of the skin muscle tube which progressed from the front of the animal backwards. Such an interpretation has already been suggested by various other zoologists and it is therefore not an invention of my own.

We must now study as closely as possible the factual material and try to interpret it correctly in order to be able to determine which of the two possibilities is most feasible. So far we are still unable to present a strict proof which would definitely support the one or the other thesis. We cannot completely exclude the possibility that the perigastrocoele did not evolve once only; yet as much as we know and think now about the emergence of new types, this possibility does not seem to be very likely. The standpoint we take again depends heavily on the way we interpret the various phenomena that can be observed during the ontogenies. The interpretation of ontogenetic morphogeny has had a decisive influence on the way scholars have tried to solve the problem of the perigastrocoele and of its segmentation. The transition from the not-segmented to the segmented state must necessarily be recapitulated somehow in the ontogenies, yet this can be either a recapitulation of the ontogenetic development that had taken place during the phyletic past of an ontogeny, or it is partly a recapitulation of states that had existed in the adult (functioning) ancestors.

If now we first take a look at the conditions that exist in the adult recent Ameria we find that here there are no genuine transitory forms. This could actually be expected. Those forms that could eventually be interpreted as transitory forms between the state with a uniform perigastrocoele and that with a more or less segmented perigastrocoele give an impression of a secondary retrogression, of an oligomery combined with a change in the way of life or with a change in the type of movement (to a burrowing or semi-sessile way of life). Later we will again return to this same problem.

Among the recent Ameria, the Nemertinea are "the" group in whose organization we can find the greatest concentration of those elements that had probably led to the emergence of the type Polymeria. The Nemertinea show a strong inclination through their increased length combined with a sinuous type of movement, to a formation of various kinds of coeloms (the rhynchocoele, the gonocoele combined with the gonochoristic state and with a simplification of the auxiliary organs, the haemocoele, and the nephrocoele), to a development of planktonic larvae, and to a polymerization of various organs. One could even say that if the Nemertinea had not their characteristic proboscis and only slight indications of a perigastrocoele we could easily consider them as Archiannelida. These are not Polymeria, they are genuine Ameria which had probably evolved from some ancestors which stood close to the Turbellaria and which had served as a starting point for the evolution of the primitive Annelida and therefore of all the Polymeria. The perigastrocoele thus evolved, as did all the coeloms, from some "slits" that had developed in the middle layer, in the mesohyl (mesoderm), and which were filled with the cell fluid or with the body fluid; and not from some sack-like formations of the intestine. All connection (such connections are not numerous) of coeloms with the intestine are secondary phenomena. Those zoologists will therefore oppose my interpretation (and such zoologists are quite numerous) who firmly accept the enterocoele theory, in spite of the fact that they meet with difficulties which cannot be overcome as soon as they try to derive the conditions that can be observed in the Polymera (Ecterocoelia) from those that can be found in the Oligomeria (Enterocoelia).

It must be admitted that it is possible to imagine a state with a uniform perigastrocoele as the first step in the development towards a segmented perigastrocoele. Yet at the same time we see that among the recent groups of the Eumetazoa there is not a single group, at least as far as I know, which would represent such a state. Animals which show a state that is at least rather similar to that with a uniform, general perigastrocoele can be found on the periphery of the Polymeria only, and above all among the Oligomeria. As regards the reduction of segmentation we can find as early as in the Annelida, species which are more or less atypical, and therefore aberrant, and which clearly show a kind of a retrogression of the perigastrocoele system. Such a reduction is even more advanced in the Sipunculoidea and in the Echiuroidea. It is therefore completely wrong to place the Endoprocta close to the Ectoprocta as has been done by various zoologists (e.g. by Marcus and by Hyman) as if the "Bryozoa" evolved from the Kamptozoa parallell to a development of an undivided coelom cavity. This is clearly a case of a pure parallelism only, which took place as a consequence of a similar one-sided way of life at two entirely different levels of the general organisation. The polymerous Annelida can be considered as the direct ancestors of the Ectoprocta while at the same time they are genuine Oligomeria which show the extreme level reached in the retrogression of the perigastrocoele.

A clear trend towards a reduction of the segmented coelom system can also be observed in the evolution of the coelom conditions in the second large subdivision of the Polymeria, in the Arthropoda. These adopted movement by means of articulated extremities while at the same time the length of their body was decreased. As a final result of this reduction we find one undivided body cavity, the myxocoele, which is clearly a secondary element and which is also united with the primary body cavity. Something similar had also taken place in the Hirudinea, among the Annelida, where again it appears together with a change in the type of movement.

All the facts that can be found in the field of the comparative morphology of the adult Polymeria therefore support the interpretation that the perigastrocoele evolved first in the form of numerous pairs of small sacks, and thus as a segmented form. It was only due to a retrogression of this system (oligomerization) that the number of segments were decreased, or even that segmentation had completely disappeared. It is therefore quite improbable that the polymerization of the perigastrocoele had taken place step by step, thus by way of an oligomeric state (zoologists have usually thought here of a trimery).

At the beginning of our present study we have already discussed the problem of the relation between the ontogeny and the phylogeny. It is obvious that we must proceed very carefully when we consult the ontogenetic morphogenies as regards the conditions of the perigastrocoele. The fact must be taken into account that the destiny of the perigastrocoele had been closely connected with the destiny of the mesohyl (mesoderm). We have already repeatedly emphasized that in all probability the whole mesohyl—which is also a substratum of the perigastrocoele—of the Eumetazoa had been inherited by the Eumetazoa from their infusorian ancestors. Viewed from this standpoint we must reject the suggestion which tries to derive the mesohyl from the ectoderm (Ecterocoelia) or from the entoderm (Enterocoelia). Because of the monocellular initial state of each ontogeny (the fertilized egg cell), and because of the cellularization which takes place during the ontogenies, it became unavoidable for the ontogenies to develop gradually into a definitive three-layered state. This process can be understood quite generally as a recapitulation of the old adult state inasmuch as there is in these ontogenies first a monocellular state which is followed by a polycellular state. The same or even greater diversity that we can observe in the ontogenetic development of the entoderm (of the *Anlage* of the intestinal tube) can also be found in the development of the third body layer, the mesohyl. It is in principle wrong to try to find special recapitulations of the adult states. We cannot therefore accept a systematic division into the Ectocoelia and the Entocoelia. We could speak on an ecterocoelic and an enterocoelic type of development of the perigastrocoele if we had worked exclusively within the field of the comparative ontogenetics. Yet we must refuse to accept such a use of the type of development of the perigastrocoele during the ontogenies for taxonomic purposes because we know that among the Ecterocoelia we can find species or even smaller groups (e.g. the Tardigrada) which develop their perigastrocoele in the enterocoelic way.

Consequently, we must consider a derivation of the perigastrocoele sacks from the "lodges" of the Anthozoa as wrong. This is obvious already for the very fact that we consider the Anthozoa as the most primitive Cnidaria which evolved only into other classes of Cnidaria and not into any other form of the Eumetazoa. We think that the formation of the coelom (we think here always of the perigastrocoele only) had originally nothing in common with the intestine. The cases, however, where the coelom sacks develop during ontogeny as a result of an outgrowth of the intestinal wall (enterocoely)—a phenomenon which can be regularly observed among the higher Eumetazoa and occasionally also among the lower Eumetazoa—must be understood as a type of development which had evolved secondarily, as a rationalization, as a special "mechanism" which had developed from the phylogenetically older ecterocoelic type of development. Frequently, it is neither the ectoderm nor the endoderm which serves as a basis for the development of the perigastrocoele, but rather the transition area between the two. In the Polymeria the perigastrocoele develops, with few exceptions that have already been mentioned, without a participation of the *Anlage* of the intestine, yet in widely different ways. Very frequently we can find the *Anlage* of the segmented perigastrocoele developed in the form of a pair of the so-called primitive mesodermal cells which change into a pair of cell strings that finally develop into pairs of sacks that grow frontwards. This can be observed above all in the polychaetous Annelida, among the lowest Polymeria. Thus we cannot find here an intermediate preliminary stage with a uniform perigastrocoele. On the other hand we can frequently find in the derivative Annelida, *Anlagen* of coelom sacks which later grow together forming a secondary uniform perigastrocoele.

The ontogenetic type of development of coelom sacks had been necessarily strongly modified because of the planktonic larvae, the trochophores, which had been evolved by the benthonic Annelida. This suggests that we cannot make any conclusions regarding the original type of development by means of a comparison between the development of the mesohyl and of the coelom sacks in recent species; in this point there can be no recapitulation in the narrow sense of the word. The temporary development of a few pairs of coelom sacks that can be observed in the larvae of Annelida has nothing to do with the tetramerous Cnidaria. We must therefore resolutely reject the idea of a derivation of polymery from oligomery (Ivanov; we usually think here of trimery),

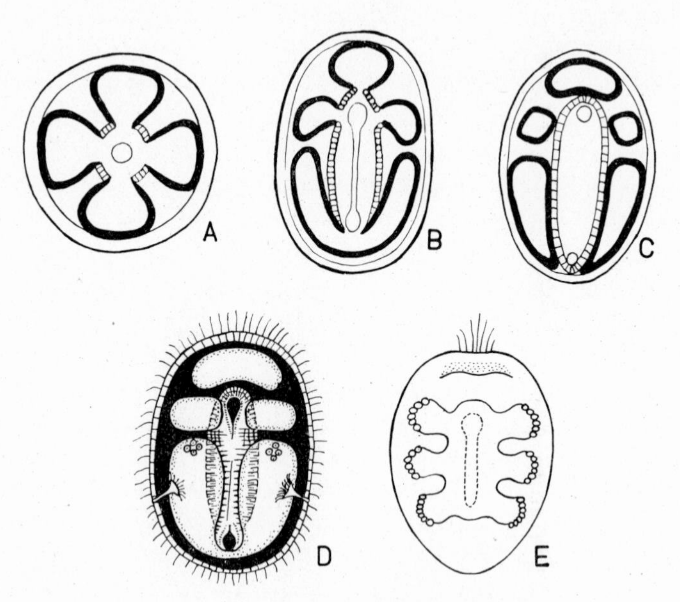

Fig. 55. Derivation of bilateral symmetry with "larval segmentation" from tetraradial symmetry of supposed primitive cnidarian by A. Remane (A-C). D, Remane's construction of a primitive segmented metazoon. E, Jägerstens "bilaterogastrea."

as well as of a derivation of polymery from cyclomery (Sedgwick, and many other zoologists after him, e. g. Remane and Jägersten cf. Fig. 55).

In our system the Polymeria must precede the Oligomeria, and the primitive Oligomeria, the so-called Tentaculata, cannot be interpreted as a transitional form between the unsegmented and the polysegmented Eumetazoa. This is a necessary consequence of the fact that we derive the Polymeria from an amerous state by way of a polymerization of several organs, and by way of an intensive growth in length combined with a sinuous type of movement, under the presupposition that the perigastrocoele had consisted from the very beginning of several segments. I wish to emphasize that for ecological and physiological reasons it is improbable that the polychaetous Annelida evolved from such animals as the semi-sessile or completely sessile Tentaculata. The facts such as the existence of transitional forms between the Annelida and Phoronoidea, suggest that there had been an opposite line of evolution.

Besides the interpretation which has been proposed in the present study, and the interpretation which we have rejected, there is one more theory which tries to explain the origin of the polymerous state. We can mention it only briefly. There have been besides older zoologists such as Haeckel, some modern scholars (e.g. Steinböck) who have believed that the so-called zooidal hypothesis could be the most acceptable interpretation. According to this theory a kind of a chain-like complex develops from an oözoöid, or a primary person, by way of an incomplete transverse division which can easily pass over into a budding. This complex had afterwards been changed by way of a subsequent complete integration into a uniform polymerous state. It must be admitted that many facts can be referred to by the adherents of the zooidal hypothesis. Thus above all the not so rare phenomenon of an initially incomplete repeated division which can be observed among the Turbellaria (the chain-like formation of the microstomous species). This is certainly a case of an only slightly modified asexual reproduction which could never possibly have led to any permanent polysegmented state. The case of the Cestoda which is also frequently mentioned in this connection belongs, I think, to the completely different category of morphogenesis than the development of a polymerous state.

The evolution of the Cestoda stands entirely under the influence of their endoparasitic way of life which has a very specific character: here the anterior part of the animal evolved into a scolex by means of which the animal becomes attached to the intestinal wall of its host while the remaining part of its body swims freely in the fluid and nutritive contents of the intestine. It is therefore not surprising to find in these animals an oppulent growth which is followed by a polymerization that can be observed above all in their complex hermaphroditic genital apparatus, especially since we can also quite frequently find a polymerization in the ancestors of the Cestoda, in the Turbellaria. The development of proglottides as a kind of a superstructure, a regulated segmentation of the body where the individuality is preserved in spite of a secondary separation of individual segments or of groups of segments, are all purely results of a further adjustment to such a specialized way of life. Yet even in this way no polymerous animal had ever been able to evolve. The state of "strobila" had evolved in an entirely different way and under completely different circumstances than did the genuine polymery (segmentation). The Cestoda are a blindly ending side branch of the Ameria which could never have been able to evolve into a higher form; they can therefore not be used as a pattern by means of which we could explain the evolution of a new higher type of segmented animals. They represent a very interesting special case only of polymerization; yet it must be mentioned in this connection that not every polymerization led to a segmented state.

As regards the "indications" that can apparently be observed in the ontogenies we can clearly see if we view this problem from our standpoint that they cannot be used as proof in favour of the zoöidal theory. Ontogeny has been considerably changed since the days when the primitive and regulated segmentation first evolved from the primitive Ameria with a scattered polymerization. This change is characterized by the emergence of a larval stage which remains a longer time in plankton. We cannot therefore expect to find recapitulations here any longer. Especially great were the changes which emerged as a consequence of the fact that true metamorphosis had been introduced. The institution of teloblasts and the introduction of zones of proliferation are two such new elements of the ontogenetic process.

The Problem of Justification of the High Taxons: Protostomia-Deuterostomia

Before we continue with our attempt to construct a new animal classification we must first discuss the problem of a justification of a division of the "Coelomata" into the two high taxons, the Protostomia and the Deuterostomia. This dichotomy has been widely accepted since the days of Hatschek and Grobben as a consequence of a belief that there had been a bifurcation of the two lines of evolution. There are few systems only which did not incorporate such a dichotomy. We therefore get an impression that this dichotomy must be supported by solid basic facts and interpretations. As is well known, the name itself has been given due to a phenomenon which can be observed in the ontogenies of numerous Eumetazoa, and even among our Ameria, where a definitive oral opening, i.e. the mouth of the adult form, appears as a continuation of the embryonic primitive mouth (gastrostoma). We must add immediately that among the species or subgroups which are classified as Protostomia there is either no mouth whatever, or a so-called primitive mouth only. During the subsequent evolution the primitive mouth grows together while at the same time a real "definitive" mouth is newly formed, instead of the "primitive mouth" in the same place more or less where the primitive mouth would be expected if it had been preserved. In numerous other Eumetazoa we can find a development which at first sight seems to be rather surprising and where an embryonic primitive mouth does not develop into a definitive mouth but rather into an anal opening, while at the same time the actual mouth is newly developed in a place where we would actually expect an anal orifice. Something similar has also been observed in one species of the Ameria, in *Gordius* (Švabenik, 1925).

These differences are certainly conspicuous and need an interpretation. First it should be stated that all our Ameria and Polymeria are usually considered as Protostomia, and all our Oligomeria and Chordonia as Deuterostomia. There is, however, an uncertainty among the adherents of the dichotomy Protostomia: Deuterostomia (also if these taxons appear under other names) on how they should classify the so-called Tentaculata (a part of our Oligomeria). Hatschek and Grobben placed them resolutely among the Protostomia (i. e. Ecterocoelia, according to Hatschek); the same was done by Hyman (as a part of the Schizocoela), Beklemischew (as Podaxonia which, however, include also the Brachiopoda!), etc. Frequently, the Tentaculata are also considered as an intermediata or transitional group between the Protostomia and the Deuterostomia (e. g. by Cori) because on the one hand they have a definitive mouth which develops from the primitive mouth (yet in the same place if the primitive mouth grows together in due time), and on the other hand because their perigastrocoele develops partly in the enterocoelic way which is quite an inconvenient fact for those who believe in the dichotomy discussed here.

After everything we have said about the evalution of the ontogenetic facts and their exploitation in a natural system of animals it becomes clear that we must proceed very carefully when we wish to use these facts for some taxonomic purposes. We must therefore assume not only a critical but also a negative attitude towards a division of the Eumetazoa as the Coelomata into the Protostomia and the Deuterostomia. We must take this stand not only towards those attempts which seek to represent the various types of oral and anal openings that can be observed during the ontogenies as if they were recapitulations of some adult states (cf. the desperate attempts made by Boettger (1952) and Steiner (1956) who tried to explain these differences on a functional basis) but also towards those zoologists who consider correctly that these are morphogenetic processes which are typical of the ontogenies only and which are therefore not recapitulations of some adult ancestral form. I have discussed this problem extensively in another study (Hadži, 1948).

It should be mentioned here that this high division of the Coelomata does not depend exlusively on the destiny of the primitive mouth during the ontogenies. It is usually combined with other pairs of opposite characteristics, above all the type of development of the perigastrocoele (the Ecterocoelia and the Enterocoelia, according to Hatschek, which have already been discussed), and the position of the cerebral process along the body axis (Epineuria–Hyponeuria). Even if there are some differences in special points between all these classifications we must nevertheless admit that there really exist such groupings of characteristics. The origin of these differences, however, can also be interpreted with the same justification in another way by means of which we can create an even more probable construction of the genealogical tree where the "function" of the so-called Tentaculata can be seen even more clearly. Those who accept the thesis of an evolution of the two main branches of the Coelomata from a common root run into great difficulties as soon as they try to explain why the protostomial state on the one hand and the deuterostomial state on the other had evolved with all the other differences which appear together with them. They have therefore been obliged to take refuge in a very hypothetical and therefore improbable construction as has already been shown here.

Both the facts as well as the working method show that it is much more probable that the two taxonomic units which are known under the names of Protostomia and the Deuterostomia had not developed side by side, i. e. parallel or diverging from a common root, but rather one after the other, so that first the Polymeria evolved from the amerous Eucoelomata (they are both grouped together as Protostomia), and the

Oligomeria afterwards evolved from the Polymeria. It was within the framework of the Oligomeria that a perfect deuterocoelic–enterocoelic state had been reached. A perfect hyponeuria, however, did not develop earlier than in the Chordonia.

It is even easier to pursue the enterocoelic type of development of the greatly reduced system of the perigastrocoele in the Oligomeria than it is to study the deuterostomic state. It is again a clear case of a rationalization of the ontogenetic morphogeny, a simplification of its mechanism. The formation of the perigastrocoele is brought closer to the *Anlage* of the intestine. This takes place in such a way that first some cells migrate from the epithelium of the primitive intestine into the middle layer where they subsequently gather to form the perigastrocoele sacks. This agrees well with the interpretation which had already been suggested some time ago and which considers the oligomerous state as a secondary phenomenon which had evolved from the polymerous state by way of an oligomerization. The deduction of the perigastrocoele from the "lodges" of the anthopolyps which has been from the very beginning a completely improbable suggestion, becomes herewith superfluous. This is also true for the entirely artificial construction of a bilaterogastrula and for many other similar things.

The fact that various *Anlagen* of the basic parts of the adult organization begin to develop first in rather different ways while finally they all become considerably uniformized (rationalized) can be considered as a general regularity of the ontogenetic morphogeny. This can be clearly seen in connection with the formation of the intestine (cf. the various modi that occur in the Cnidaria alone), of the perigastrocoele, of the segmentation, etc.

Thus we come to the conclusion that the categories Protostomia–Deuterostomia do not exactly express the actual facts, nor do they stand in agreement with the correct interpretation of the same facts. This result is therefore similar with our findings in connection with the high taxons the

Coelenterata–the Coelomata, the Radiata–the Bilateria, the Ecterocoelia–the Enterocoelia. The categories Protostomia and Deuterostomia must be therefore abandoned. We find it completely satisfactory if we use the simplified classification of the primarily polymerized animal groups (classes) as members of the phylum Polymeria. We emphasize explicitly that we speak here of the primarily polymerized animal classes only, because there are also secondarily polymerized animal classes which belong, as we shall later see, to the phylum Chordata.

The Classes of the Phylum Polymeria

Just as in the case of the phylum Ameria we find in the Polymeria that the evolution of their basic structural (Fig. 56) type had spread radiating into several different specialized directions. The system and the taxonomy of the groups of Polymeria which have emerged as a result of these various lines of evolution have been treated variously by zoologists. The study of these various groups of Polymeria has been made difficult by the fact that the same animal groups were placed into various categorical levels by various authors. There is a considerable unanimity among scholars about the general sphere of the high group of the Polymeria; it corresponds roughly to the old notion of the Articulata as it was proposed by Cuvier.* The word Articulata can be met with not infrequently even now as a name of a high taxon, e.g. in Beklemischew. In this case the two notions and high taxons Articulata and Polymeria correspond exactly to each other. Yet I prefer the name Polymeria because it agrees better with the names of other groups with a similar rank, the Ameria and the Oligomeria, and because it expresses better what it represents; the Oligomeria are finally also "articulated" animals while at the same time they had evolved separately from the typical

* Not in the sense of the "Articulata" Huxley (1869) as a subgroup of the Brachiopoda!

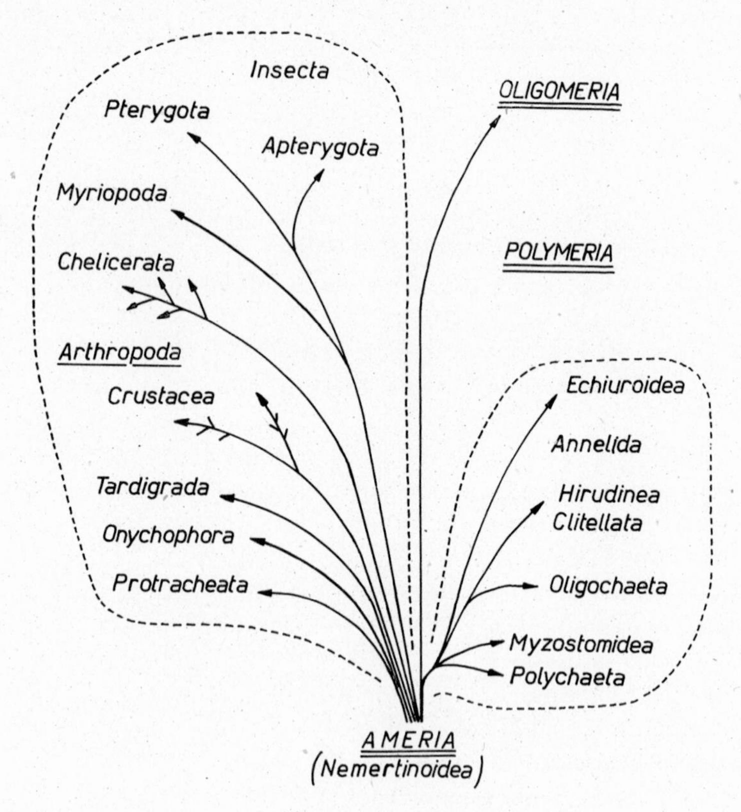

Fig. 56. Genealogical tree of the phylum: Polymeria.

"Articulata," and they must be therefore clearly separated from the latter.

Contrary to the situation which we have found in the geologically much older Ameria, we see that it is quite easy to identify the two main lines of the evolution of the Polymeria which have been used for a long time already as high taxons. We will consider them as subphyla and use the names Annelida and Arthropoda. It is quite easy to classify all the classes of the Polymeria into one of these two subphyla. Beklemischew, on the other hand, distinguished here five subphyla, i.e. Annelida,

Tardigrada, Pentastomida, Onychophora, Arthropoda. Such a classification can be well defended as well as a classification into three subphyla. In this classification we place an intermediate group which has stumps only as extremities (Tardigrada, Onychophora, Pentastomida) between the Annelida which have no extremities at all, and the Arthropoda which are equipped with the articulated extremities. The question remains open whether we can consider these forms as a primary element or whether they had emerged as a result of a secondary development. We think that it is sufficient to divide the Polymeria into two subphyla, the Annelida and the Arthropoda (this is true at least for the recent Polymeria) because we find that the stump limbed Polymeria do not only show closer relationship connections with the Arthropoda but also because they do possess extremities even if these extremities are very simple or if they are remains only of such extremities (Pentastomidea).

The dichotomy corresponds well, as this has already been mentioned, to the two main lines of the evolution of the Annelida which have remained more primitive animals. From these we derive the Oligomeria, i.e. the next higher phylum which is as such the third phylum of the Eumetazoa. The situation of the Annelida resembles that of the Turbellaria, among the Ameria. In these the polymerization had reached its highest development. On the other hand, we can soon observe a trend to a sessile way of life and its necessary consequences, a shortening of the body length and a reduction of the polymerous state. The Arthropoda on the other hand, the second main branch which had a much more exuberant evolution, played a role similar to that of the Mollusca among the Ameria. At the same time they far surpassed the Mollusca because they solved much better, not only in water but above all in the sea also (Crustacea), the problem of transition to a life on dry land by developing a tracheal system. Just as in the case of the Mollusca, among the Ameria, we find that the Arthropoda have still remained within the sphere of the type of the Polymeria in spite of their progressive evolution combined with a strong specialization.

The suggestion to use the Spiralia as a systematic notion and the group of the Protostomia as a part of the same must be resolutely rejected. Such a suggestion was made, for example by Kaestner (1954) and by others. Such a group would include besides some clear Articulata (Annelida, Echiuroidea) also many groups of our Ameria, above all the Mollusca, Nemertinea, and the Platyhelminthes. The spiral type of cleavage appears in widely different animal groups and it is in no way connected with the problem of the closer relationship. It belongs exclusively into the sphere of rationalizations of the mechanism of the early ontogenies. Or in other words, the spiral type of cleavage can appear in all those cases where similar conditions of the egg structure appear together with the mechanism of cleavage which is connected with the former. Attempts have also been made to justify the existence of the Spiralia as a natural group by referring to the similarities that can be observed in their larvae (Kaestner, 1954:13). Such an argument has already been sufficiently discounted in our present study.

It would be in no way difficult to show the unacceptability of the division of the groups which are covered by the notion and the taxon Polymeria into several (six) phyla as we find this in the *Zoological Names* (edited by A. S. Pearse). The classification which comes closest to the system which we consider as the best one is the system which was proposed by Beklemischew. It has already been mentioned that his characterization of the whole high phylum Articulata (the seventh high phylum, according to Beklemischew) corresponds exactly in its sphere with our Polymeria. The main difference exists in the fact that Beklemischew divides his high phylum into five subphyla (Annelides, Tardigrada, Pentastomida, Onychophora, Arthropoda) while we believe that a completely sufficient subdivision can be made by means of two subphyla (Annelida, Arthropoda). We consider that the three remaining groups

(Tardigrada, Pentastomida, and Onychophora) do not "deserve" to be given the category of subphyla. All these three groups can be considered as very specialized Arthropoda. Beklemischew has also given the rank of an independent subphylum to the Sipunculoidea (he calls them Prosopygia) as well as to the Kamptozoa. He places these two subphyla after the Arthropoda which is certainly quite unusual. In this connection we can also dispense well enough with the category of superclasses even if it is true that among the classes of the Polymeria there are some groups which are phylogenetically more closely related, similarly as has been the case with the Ameria. It seems that we will probably come to a generally acceptable scheme of the system of the Polymeria if we abandon these unnecessary subdivisions.

The subphylum Annelida can be well enough subdivided into three classes, the Polychaeta, Clitellata, and the Echiuroidea. The class Polychaeta is the main one whose ancestors had evolved into all the other subtypes as well as into the Arthropoda and into the next phylum Oligomeria. Several zoologists have given the rank of a class to the group Myzostomida; I myself have done this in my proposed genealogical tree of the animal world (Hadži, 1944:179); this, h wever, is really not necessary. The Myzostomida can be considered as specialized Annelida of the type of the Polychaeta; this is also the way how they are treated in the system proposed by Beklemischew. It is almost a question of personal taste whether we unite the Oligochaeta and the Hirudinea, the two groups of the Annelida, into a new group Clitellata, or whether we consider each of them as an independent class. There is no disagreement among zoologists that the Arthropoda evolved from some Annelida-like ancestors. Yet we are still uncertain about the way along which this evolution had proceeded, whether the Arthropoda evolved once only or after repeated similar attempts made by Nature. The systematists of the Arthropoda show in this point a considerable variety of opinions. For the present we can again avoid the obligatory intermediate categories in our system of the Arthropoda such as the superclasses. All the recent Arthropoda can therefore be subdivided directly into the corresponding classes. The number of these classes varies, if we take into consideration the recent animals only, between thirteen (e.g. according to Comstock), eleven (e.g. according to Beklemischew), and five. I believe that five classes are sufficient because there are many suggested classes here which can be easily considered as subclasses. These five classes are, the Onychophora (with the Protracheata and the Tardigrada), Crustacea, Chelicerata (among these are also the Xiphosura and the Pentastomida), Myriapoda (here are also included the Symphyla, Pauropoda, Diplopoda, and the Chilopoda with the old root of the Hexapoda), and the Insecta (with the two subclasses, Apterygota and Pterygota).

We can easily see how well-founded is a reduction of the number of classes if we study the classification as it was proposed by Comstock who suggested that there should be thirteen classes of the Arthropoda (yet without the Trilobita; his classification goes back to the year 1925!). He considers the Onychophora and the Tardigrada as two separate classes; separate classes are also the four groups of the Myriapoda (this can be found quite frequently even in modern zoologists because of the differences which exist in the relationship connections between the four groups). The Palaeostraca *(Limulus)*, Pycnogonida, and the Pentastomida are also considered as independent classes which in reality must be grouped together with the Arachnida into the class Chelicerata. Comstock separates, quite unnecessarily, a part of the Apterygota as Myrientomata from the remaining insects as Hexapoda, a classification which is no longer in use. In this way we find that five classes sufficiently represent all the major subdivisions of the Arthropoda. I will not discuss here the still open problem of how the Arthropoda had actually evolved from the Chaetopoda, and how the present classes evolved from the primitive Arthropod, because I cannot propose any new ideas here which would clarify these points. The Arthropoda probably evolved on the sea bottom and along several radiating lines. The hypothesis proposed by Giljarov about the origin of the youngest (and in spite of this very old) group Hexapoda from some ancestors similar to the Myriapoda wich had lived in the soil seems to me to be very probable. The Arthropoda left the sea several times to live on land; and this is also true for the Polymeria as a whole.

The number of subtypes is smaller in the Polymeria if we compare them with the situation which can be found in the Ameria. There, in one subclass only, which consists entirely of species that live as parasites, are the Pentastomida among the Chelicerata; on the other hand we find among the Ameria three classes which consist exclusively of the parasitic species. At the same time, however, we can identify parasitic species or even whole subgroups in other classes of the Arthropoda also (with the exception of the Onychophora and the Myriapoda). Among the Cirripedia we can find endoparasites whose form had been simplified beyond recognition so that it is their freely swimming larva only which shows their arthropodal provenance.

Among the Polymeria we cannot identify a single class of fully sessile species while on the other hand there exist two such classes among the Ameria (Cnidaria, Endoprocta). The reason for this is the fact that a fully sessile way of life can exist in a fluid medium only because a majority of the Polymeria are now terrestrial animals. There is one group only among the sea, inhabiting Polymeria (the Cirripedia among the Entomostraca) which includes fully sessile species; yet again these Cirripedia do not form any colonies (cormi) because they have completely lost the ability to reproduce asexually. It is noteworthy that forms similar to cormi have been developed by the Polychaeta which reproduce by way of division and of budding.

There is, however, another point which we find most interesting in connection with the way of life of the Annelida and which is important for the correct solution of the problem of the origin of the next "higher" phylum. These are two phenomena which are mutually closely related. One of these phenomena is connected with the way of life, above all with the type of feeding and of movement, and the other phenomenon with the evolution in the direction polymerization → → oligomerization. We find in this connection an interesting and revealing survey of the development trends such as they appear within the phylum Polymeria which had finally led to the emergence of the next "higher" phylum.

The starting form of the evolution of the Polymeria had been, contrary to the situation which we find in the Ameria, a bilateral richly segmented and therefore elongated eumetazoan which had moved over the surface of the sea bottom by means of a sinuous type of locomotion and which fed as a predatory animal. The polymerization took place in a part of their subline of evolution which developed progressively; its consequence are species which can reach a length of several metres, which consist of hundreds of segments, and which are either equipped with parapodia (Polychaeta errantia), or not at all (Oligochaeta). In the shorter side lines of evolution, however, the animals have actually preserved their free mobility while at the same time the size of their body was considerably decreased and the number of their segments reduced. They had thus been subjected to oligomerization. This development had taken place both in the Polychaeta and in the Oligochaeta. There have also been some instances of neoteny.

Another part of the freely moving Polymeria also developed progressively; they changed their type of movement by developing lateral excrescences which evolved into active extremities. Here the number of segments had been reduced (oligomerization) in several sublines of evolution, even in those whose representatives had begun to live on land; this reduction was usually combined with a differentiation of various parts of segments which led to a regionalization of the body, and above all to the cephalization of the foremost segments, the acron included. In several sublines we can observe a parallel development towards a stabilization of the number of segments, e.g. in the Crustacea where the number was fixed at twenty. Yet even in these lines the oligomerization can continue to have an important role, above all in the side lines with a specialized way of life (e.g. the Pentastomida), or with a strongly diminished size of the animal body (e.g. the Acarina).

The part of these Polymeria which evolved progressively reached its climax in several groups of the Polymeria that live in water and on land and whose evolution has always ended blindly. It should be mentioned in passing that during this development the conditions of the perigastrocoele and of the other coelom cavities had also been considerably changed and that this development led to the formation of a secondary myxocoele. Among the Arthropoda that live in the atmosphere we find the "worm-like forms" still preserved in the Protracheata (Onychophora) and in the Myriapoda *s.l.*, as well as in the larvae of numerous insects.

Now, we must return to the primitive Polychaeta among the Annelida. A part of these had given up the mobile way of life and predatory macrophagy and had begun to live as sessile and microphagous animals. This transition was made by freely moving species which had developed temporary protective tubules. Such species have been preserved down to the present day. The tubicolous way of life is different from the truly sessile way of life where the animal becomes directly attached to the substratum after metamorphosis had been completed. In this line of evolution we can also find formation of regions (e.g. *Chaetopterus*) and a diminution of the size of the body which had also led to a reduction of polymery, yet no special new type ever emerged as a consequence of this development. It has always remained a blindly ending side branch.

The radiating lines of evolution which started from the prototype of the Polychaeta proceeded even further. A part of these abandoned life on the free surface of the sea bottom and penetrated partly into its soft sediments where they burrow, eating sediments that are rich in organic substances, or they try to find protection in cliff fissures, empty shells of snails, etc. The parapodia and the sinuous type of locomotion became superfluous to these animals; this again led to a considerable reduction of their organization which had even reached the internal polymerization. The consequence of this development had been the loss of the dissepiments and of the

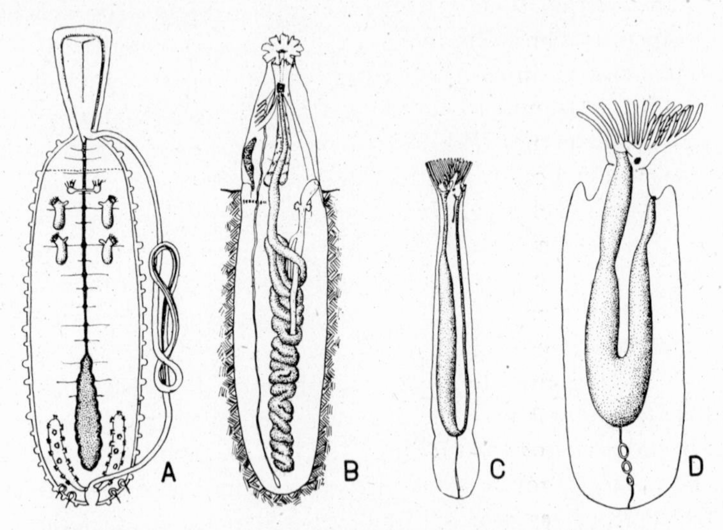

Fig. 57. Schemes illustrating the transition from Polymeria to Oligomeria: A, echiurid; B, sipunculid; C, phoronid; D, ectoprokt.

chaetae. Even among the recent species we can observe all the stages of this reduction which finally led to the emergence of a new animal type. These stages are well represented by the following forms: *Arenicola–Sternaspis* (with the disintegration of the dissepiments)–*Echiurus* (the segmented perigastrocoele can be found in their embryos only)–*Sipunculus–Phoronis* (Fig. 57). We will later return to discuss the Sipunculoidea in more detail. The elongated worm-like form had been preserved by all these animals in spite of the loss of an external and of an internal segmentation. We frequently hear in this connection of modified trochophores; this, however, does not have any sense if viewed from the phylogenetic point of view. Greater differences can be observed during the embryonic development.

The most important conclusion we can reach on the basis of our present discussion is that the polymerous state of the perigastrocoele must be considered as a primary, primitive phenomenon, and that the oligomerous state had only evolved secondarily due to a reduction of the segmentation. This reduction had been caused by a changed way of life. This development had finally led to a complete uniformity of the perigastrocoele.

The Phylum Oligomeria and Its Classes

We come now to a point of the construction of the natural animal system and the formation of the phylogenetic tree. This is considered quite generally as disputable but it can easily be solved if viewed from our standpoint. All zoologists agree that the Arthropoda represent a climax in a generally progressive evolution of the animal world and that for this reason no further evolution had been possible along this line. We must therefore presuppose that the evolution which led to the emergence of the Chordonia and of the Vertebrata, had started from a lower level than that reached by the Arthropoda. It has already been indicated how various zoologists believed they found the point of separation of the two lines of evolution in various parts of the genealogical tree. In the scheme of the genealogical tree we can find this evolution represented by two strong branches, the protostomic and the deuterostomic branches. As a typical example we can mention here the genealogical tree as proposed by Cuénot (see Fig. 50). Without any intention to deal here in detail with all the attempts that have been made so far to represent the phyletic relationship between the Protostomia and the Deuterostomia (also when treated under other names which we have already mentioned) I wish only to point here to the suggestion made by palaeozoologist Müller (1958). Here we can find a combination of the scheme as it was proposed by Cuénot—which Müller obviously considers as the best among the now available schemes—and of my diagram. The uncertainty Müller feels regarding the point where the left branch (the Deuterostomia) should begin, according to the interpretation proposed by Cuénot and by a number of other zoologists, is characteristic. A small operation only is needed here to reach a well-founded conclusion. The left branch which is hanging loose in the scheme proposed by Müller can be extended so much that it reaches the right branch at a point above that spot where the Mollusca branch off, and below the point where the Annelida branch off. In this way the two main branches are changed into a stem, and the Annelida–Arthropoda are represented as one of the main branches. It is true that in this way we expose ourselves to the accusation that we try to revive the old, long obliterated idea of an "*l'échelle animale*" or even of a general stage-like sequence. I consider such an accusation as unjust because in my attempt there is neither a simple gradation, nor only one uniformly progressive line of evolution. My construction represents a true genealogical tree, and not a ladder, with the only difference that this tree has a real trunk (as this is normal in all the trees) and only one main top. The new element which can be found in my attempt, however, is the fact that in my interpretation of natural facts I have come to the conclusion that there has been a long era of a retrogressive evolution. I have endeavoured to make this suggestion as feasible as possible.

During the transition from the phylum Ameria to the phylum Polymeria, as well as from the phylum Oligomeria to the phylum Chordonia, evolution always began at a somewhat lower level of the earlier type, yet it immediately continued in a progressive direction. This evolution led to the emergence of a new type whose organization reached another higher level afterwards. Due to various specializations this new type again evolved into various subtypes. Here we can find only a few side lines that led to a simplification of the organization because of a retrogressive trend in their evolutions (Tardigrada, Pentastomida among the Chelicerata, Acarina, the parasitic Cirripeda; among these there may also be some cases of neoteny). Several classes and subclasses have reached a very high level of organization, especially among the Arthropoda, with the Insecta as the highest point of this development. Had there been no further evolution, first in a retrogressive direction (Oligomeria) which was followed by a progressive evolution (Chordonia); the Arthropoda with the Chelicerata and the Insecta would be the two groups representing the climax and the end of all the evolution of animals.

The Sphere of the Phylum Oligomeria

Those who believe in a dichotomy of the "Coelomata" into the Protostomia and the Deuterostomia meet with great difficulties as soon as they try to draw exact limits between these two main subdivisions of the Coelomata. This could not be the case if these two subdivisions really stood clearly in opposition to each other, as was originally believed. Above all there should be no such combinations as protostomy on the one hand, and enterocoely on the other, or vice versa; yet such combinations do actually exist. We can avoid these and many other difficult and unpleasant facts if we interpret these apparently conflicting phenomena by means of the mosaic theory; if we consider that both the deuterostomatous and the enterocoelic states evolved from the protostomatous and ecterocoelic states. For the sake of a more easy understanding of these processes we will find it helpful, as this has repeatedly been emphasized, if we take into consideration the changes in the way of life and if we exploit more critically the ontogenetic facts.

The fact has already been known for some time and it has been accepted by many zoologists, that there exist several small groups of worm-like animals which somehow represent the transition from the Annelida to the Eucoelomata which consist of few segments only. These intermediate forms are partly enterocoelic, partly ecterocoelic animals. Earlier this group was frequently called the Gephyrea (the bridging animals). This grouping, however, was out of agreement with the facts because it includes animals which clearly belong to the Annelida; these animals were called now the Gephyrea chaetophora (Echiuroidea). These Echiuroidea have been classified quite generally and rightly among the Annelida, usually as one of their independent groups (as a class or even as a phylum which is certainly an overvaluation).

As regards the system of the remaining small groups which are not at all or only partly segmented, and which possess at the same time a perigastrocoele, we find above all that the group Molluscoidea corresponds least to the natural facts, and that its name has been least fortunately selected. We can see that according to Grobben, the Molluscoidea (which are also called Tentaculata in the parenthesis) consist of three classes, i. e. the Phoronidea, Bryozoa (Ectoprocta), and the Brachiopoda. These Molluscoidea appear immediately after the class Mollusca within the phylum Protostomia (Zygoneura, according to Hatschek). All these three classes have in reality nothing in common with the Mollusca. This is a grouping which has been introduced because of a lack of a better solution. Neither is the correct position given to the Mollusca in this system; the Mollusca are clearly primarily unsegmented animals, while at the same time the unsegmented character of the Molluscoidea must be considered as a secondary phenomenon. Fortunately enough we find that this name "Molluscoidea" has fallen into disuse.

A much better name has been proposed for this animal group by Lang. He called them Prosopygia. The members of the group which have thus become united under this name do really show a characteristic phenomenon; in these animals the anal opening was transferred to the anterior part of the bodies as a consequence of their semi-sessile or fully sessile way of life. Lang has therefore classified among his Prosopygia the Sipunculoidea which are usually placed close to the Annelida; the Sipunculoidea are, as a matter of fact, prosopygous "worms." Few zoologists have accepted these suggestions proposed by Lang (e.g. Haeckel). Beklemischew, on the other hand, has gone very far in the opposite direction; he limited Prosopygia to the Sipunculoidea only.

The word Tentaculata has been much more widely accepted as a name of this group. There have also been some other suggested names, e.g. the Podaxonia and the Vermidia (Delage and Hérouard), yet their spheres have been slightly different. All these attempted groupings have one thing in common; they include a part only of the Eumetazoa which possess few segments only and which are therefore classified among the Protostomia. In this way they are sharply separated from the remaining groups with few segments which are classified among the Deuterostomia. Few zoologists have tried to escape this magic circle attempting to reach better solutions on the basis of other concepts.

The attempt which comes closest to my suggestion both as regards its sphere and its name was made by Krumbach within the framework of his "Vermes" (Vermes Polymeria). Yet they do not include either the Sipunculoidea (in spite of the fact that his characterization of the Oligomera suits to the Sipunculoidea, with the exception of the number of their segments) or the Echinodermata which actually belong to the Trimeria. Schneider (1902) unites his Ameria (with the Echinodermata as their only cladus) with the Trimeria (Enteropneusta and Tentaculata) into the type Coelenteria; they are thus "Metazoen, deren Mesoderm vom Entoderm stammt und phylogenetisch als Enterocoel auftritt" which, however, does not correspond with our concept. Lameere united all the groups which we classify as Oligomeria—with the exception of the Sipunculoidea—under the name Dérosomes, yet he placed them within the framework of "Les Vers." Ulrich (1950) has also united, as we have done, all these groups (with the exception of the Sipunculoidea) but he used here different names (Tentaculata for three of our classes, and Enteropneusta for two of our classes); at the same time we find in his work the Chaetognatha accompanied by a question mark as a sign that Ulrich could not come to any decision regarding the classification of this truly aberrant group. The Sipunculoidea are also equipped by Ulrich with a question mark. The frame work, however, of this group is in Ulrich entirely different from the sphere of our Oligomeria. All these groups are placed under the name Archicoelomata (as a counterpart to the Neocoelomata which again are equipped with a question mark) at the beginning of the Bilateria (Coelomata). This must be interpreted in such a way that Ulrich believes that all these animal groups have primarily few or no segments; correspondingly we find the Platyhelminthes with the Nemertini, Endoprocta, and the Priapulida placed at the end of the system, together with the Protostomia which are preceded by the Deuterostomia. It is noteworthy to see that Ulrich inclines to judge "die Evolution des heutigen Cnidarenmaterials nicht als progressiv, sondern als regressiv." In his text Ulrich makes a good observation regarding the widely accepted division of the Coelomata into the Protostomia and the Deuterostomia. He states, "sie (sc. this division) wird jedoch der tatsächlichen Mannigfaltigkeiten nicht gerecht, tut den Dingen mancherlei Zwang an und gedenkt die im einzelnen ungeheuer heterogenen, bruchstückartigen Producte einer unermässlichen Evolution bereits mit einem intimen Einzelmerkmal regieren zu können." Ulrich stands clearly too much under the influence of the ideas that had been proposed by Remane.

We have not accepted the division of the Eumetazoa into the Protostomia and the Deuterostomia as such a division could not represent an actual phyletic development. We are therefore not hindered in uniting all the groups of the Eumetazoa which show an impoverished or reduced segmentation (yet not individual species!) into a large group which we call the Oligomeria. We think that this large group actually represents the natural facts. Here we include those groups which do not show a clear segmentation of the perigastrocoele, as well as those which have three pairs of the perigastrocoele. The following nine classes are therefore included in the phylum Oligomeria:

(1) Sipunculoidea.
(2) Phoronoidea.
(3) Pogonophora.
(4) Brachiopoda.
(5) Chaetognatha.
(6) Ectoprocta.
(7) Echinodermata.
(8) Pterobranchia.
(9) Enteropneusta.

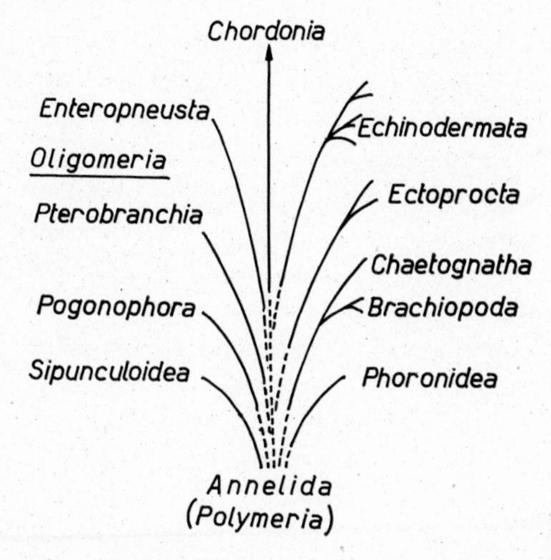

Fig. 58. Genealogical tree of the phylum: Oligomeria.

The phylum Oligomeria consists thus of nine classes which usually represent few species only, in comparison with the fifteen classes that belong to the Ameria, and the eight classes which belong to the Polymeria (Fig. 58). There are two classes only of the Oligomeria which represent a larger number of species. They are the Ectoprocta and the Echinodermata. All these species live without any exception in water, and there are few exceptions only (among the Ectoprocta) which do not live in the sea. With the exception of the class Chaetognatha—which is also otherwise an aberrant group—we find that all the groups of the Oligomeria live on the sea bottom. Lameere (1931) and Hadži (1958a) have shown that we can best explain the organization and the place where the Chaetognatha live, which is quite unusual for the Oligomeria—the free water zone—if we consider that the Chaetognatha evolved by way of neoteny from the planktonic larvae of the Brachiopoda. There is no other class or even a lower systematic category among the recent Oligomeria whose species have also become adapted to a life in plankton. Individual species can only be found among the Echinodermata which had also evolved into planktonic animals (*Pelagothuria* and a few other species), a fact which could be least expected because of the internal skeleton which had also been developed by these same animals. On the other hand we find a rich variety of planktonic larvae developed by these Oligomeria, a fact which could easily be expected; these larvae show widely different forms and structures which are of little use as material used in our phyletic speculations.

The fact that among all the recent nine classes of the Oligomeria there are only two with a richly developed asexual reproduction combined with a formation of cormi (Ectoprocta and Pterobranchia), shows the limited plasticity of the Oligomeria. Polymorphism can be observed quite generally among the Ectoprocta. A very surprising circumstance is the fact that even a dully sessile class such as the Brachiopoda are no longer able to reproduce asexually. We can understand this if we interpret the Oligomeria as secondarily simplified and specialized animals which had evolved from the Polymeria by way of a retrogressive evolution.

On the other hand, widely different trends in evolution can be found within the group Oligomeria itself; the situation here is very similar to the one we have been able to observe in the

Ameria. In the Echinodermata a secondarily emerging progressive trend is most clearly noticeable; this has been the reason why the Echinodermata have been treated so frequently by the systematists as a special type or as a phylum. The Echinodermata had developed, apart from a hypodermic skeleton, new systems of coeloms and special organs of movement also which are a consequence of their secondarily acquired free mobility. The Echinodermata certainly represent the climax reached in the progressive evolution within the phylum Oligomeria. They have even become indirectly able to reproduce asexually by way of an intensified regenerative ability. They also show a conspicuously rich development of various subtypes, many of these have died long ago.

Among the sessile Oligomeria we notice a progressive evolution in the Ectoprocta too. Yet as regards the condition reached in the organization of their individuals (we can speak here almost of subindividuals) they have preserved a low level, or they had sunk in this respect to an even lower level. A progressive trend can be observed in the formation of their cormi (colonies) which are frequently regularly built and polymorphous.

There are not less than six classes of the Oligomeria, i.e. Sipunculoidea, Phoronidea, Pogonophora, Brachiopoda, Chaetognatha, and Pterobranchia which all include a few species only (only the Brachiopoda possessed numerous species during their geological history), which represent "insignificant" side branches of the evolution that are of little use in our phylogenetic speculations, and which do not play any significant role in the life of the sea.

Special attention must be paid to the class Enteropneusta even if this class does not appear very important from the ecological viewpoint or with regard to the number of species it includes or the living mass. The species which belong to this class (ca. seventy-five) are some of those Oligomeria which had partly won the ability to move freely; they are therefore semi-sessile animals which do not live in tubules built by themselves but rather burrow into the soft floor of the sea. They also show a considerable morphological–physiological specialization in this direction which can be observed above all in the anterior end of their bodies. The trend to preserve a "worm-like form" is clear in the Enteropneusta (there are even species which can be several metres long). Even more important, however, is the fact that they show a strong inclination to a polymerization which re-emerges in these forms. This polymerization involves several systems of organs (the sexual, respiratory, digestive, etc., systems) along the third body region which is quite large in these animals. A very important fact also is the circumstance that in the Enteropneusta the maximum number of segments of the perigastrocoele sacks is still preserved. There are still other properties which must be mentioned here such as the presence of a ventral and of a dorsal nerve cord which are equipped with canals, the inclination of these animals to develop an endoskeleton and to form a pair of body folds for the sake of protection, of openings which are used as breathing organs, an inclination of their intestinal tubes to form skeleton-like outgrowths and glands similar to a liver as well as a cavity resembling a pericardium. The absence of metanephridia is conspicuous.

Thus we come to the conclusion, which has actually been also expressed by many other zoologists, that the recent Enteropneusta must be considered as considerably changed (because they are specialized) descendants from an oligomerous ancestral form, which had been at the same time the starting point of the evolution of the next higher phylum Chordonia, that had developed from this ancestral form during a very remote geologic past. This derivation of the Chordonia from some ancestral form, which they had in common with the recent Enteropneusta, is certainly more probable viewed from my standpoint than is the other variant which has also been repeatedly suggested by various zoologists and according to which the Chordonia had evolved from an even more primitive ancestor.

Finally we must not completely bypass the Graptolitha, an extinct class of the Oligomeria, in spite of the fact that in the present study we take into consideration the recent groups only. There can be no doubt that these Graptolitha must be classified among the Oligomeria and not among the so-called Coelenterata. They obviously represent a case parallel to that of the Siphonophora, among the Hydrozoa, i.e. a type with polymorphic cormi (colonies). We will not further discuss these Graptolitha because they represent a blindly ending side branch of the Oligomeria, and because they are now completely extinct.

The Problem of the Inclusion of the Sipunculida Into the Phylum Oligomeria

Following the interpretations suggested by many zoologists, and among them many specialists, I considered earlier that the Sipunculida should be classified among the Polymeria and that they should be looked upon as closely related to the Echiuroidea and the Annelida. After a thorough and critical revision of the actual facts, however, I have now come to the conclusion that some older zoologists had suggested correctly —among them especially Arnold Lang who was followed in this respect by Haeckel—that the Sipunculida must be more clearly separated from the Annelida and that they should be classified among the Prosopygia.

As regards the conditions of their perigastrocoele we can find that the Sipunculida show even more oligomerous properties than all the remaining classes of the Oligomeria. They have even lost last traces of an intestinal and of an external segmentation; their perigastrocoele has become a completely uniform organ. They show neither mesenteries nor dissepiments, a fact which is clearly connected with a change in their intestinal conditions. Their anal opening was transferred to the anterior part of the animal body, and their intestinal tube is not only U-shaped as in Phoronidea but it is also coiled. They live as semi-sessile animals in canals which they burrow in the sea floor. At the same time, however, they have also preserved some traces of a free mobility; animals have been observed that swam over short distances by means of sinuous movements, a fact which I wish particularly to call attention to.

The standpoint which can be defended here is that the conditions that can be observed in the Sipunculida represent the final stage of an evolution which led from the freely moving Annelida by way of the tubicolous and burrowing Annelida to the Echiuroidea and finally to the Sipunculida. The simple conditions that can be observed in the Sipunculida are therefore not a primary phenomenon. In the Echiuroidea we can still find several peculiarities of the Annelida clearly developed, thus above all the polymery and the neuromery which are temporarily recapitulated in their ontogeny, as well as the metanephridia and the remains of a parapodial apparatus, etc., while at the same time all these peculiarities of the Annelida have been lost in the Sipunculida. There is clearly a sharply-cut limit between the Echiuroidea and the Sipunculida which becomes even more clear if we liberate ourselves definitively from the notion of "worms" ("Vermes") as a systematic category which has now completely lost its significance.

The Sipunculida which have remained to a lesser degree freely moving animals had evolved as such from a simplified structure into a specialized direction; during this evolution they had developed many new properties, and this is the reason why they have been considered, correctly, as an independent higher systematic category (a class, frequently even as a phylum which seems to me an overvaluation). They also show more and more clearly, besides the prosopygy which is a consequence of their burrowing and sessile way of life, another peculiarity which is characteristic of all the Oligomeria; the division of their bodies into two regions (the prosoma and the metasoma). The anterior region which is frequently divided into two parts shows the strongest development in the most primitive groups of the Oligomeria, and above all in the Sipunculida. As an introvert it can even be longer, at least in some cases *(Phascolion, Aspidosiphon, Onchosoma)*, than the length of the actual body, longer than the postsoma. This proboscoid introvert had developed in the fully sessile Ectoprocta into the so-called polypid; the postsoma on the other hand is called here a cystid.

A polypoid develops from a "worm;" one of the most remarkable features of this development is a radially-symmetric circle of tentacle-like bodywall extensions which had evolved around the oral opening and which show in some groups of the Oligomeria a more bilateral arrangement (in the shape of a horseshoe, Phoronida, Brachiopoda, a considerable part of the Ectoprocta). A group of tentacles arranged approximately in the shape of a horseshoe can be found already in some species belonging to the Sipunculida.

The fact seems to me to be very important that as early as in the Sipunculida we can find a kind of an initial formation of a calcified exoskeleton as this is best shown by the case of the *Aspidosiphon speciosus* (according to Hyman). On the one hand we can find here a "posterior shield" secreted at the posterior end of the postsoma which can be compared with an ectocyst, and on the other hand there appears another protective layer at the basis of the introvert, at the place where a protective plate (operculum) can be found in the Ectoprocta, and which corresponds to the collar region, or rather subregion, of many Oligomeria. The introvert of the Sipunculida evolved into a very important organ which is no homologue to the proboscis of the Echiuroidea. To this we must also add the strongly developed retractors that can be frequently found in the Oligomeria. The introvert is frequently covered with various protuberances, even spines, which can be considered as a specialization of the Sipunculida.

A characteristic peculiarity of the Sipunculida is the fact that the place of their anal opening, which had been transferred frontwards, has not been completely stabilized. It usually occurs dorsally at the upper end of the postsoma; in the *Onchnesoma squamatum*, however, it can be found considerably farther forwards, on the introvert itself. Their skin which is generally cuticularized and which is closely connected with the skin muscle tube shows a rich differentiation, it is richly equipped with sensory organs, and it contains numerous skin glands; even coelom canals can be found growing through this skin.

As regards the adult form of the Sipunculida it can be stated that we can notice here some similarities with the Annelida which is by no means a surprising fact, because the Sipunculida had evolved in all probability from some ancestors which they had in common with recent Annelida. They also show some peculiarities that can be observed in the Oligomeria as well as some characteristics that can be found only in the Sipunculida.

As regards the properties the Sipunculida have in common with the Annelida, mention has most frequently been made of the structure of their central nervous system; this is rightly so in spite of the fact that they have preserved the last traces only of a neuromerism as an irregular arrangement of the pairs of side nerves. This circumstance is important because it serves as good evidence that here we do not have an initial state in the development of the neuromerism but rather a discontinuation of the segmentation. The emergence of sensory organs must be evaluated as a progressive and a prospective phenomenon which is closely connected with the cerebral ganglion (the supraoesopheageal ganglion).

Less significance should be attributed to the supposed similarities which the Sipunculida share with the Annelida in their ontogenetic morphogeny because here we find traits which are much more characteristic of the Sipunculida. It is true that the Sipunculida are Protostomia inasmuch as their oral opening coincides locally with the anterior end of a very elongated blastopore, yet here it is formed anew after the blastopore had first grown together. It has repeatedly been emphasized that in my opinion too great a phyletic significance has been attributed to the formation of the oral opening during the ontogeny.

The question has been widely discussed whether there were at least some temporary traces of a segmentation in the *Anlage* of the perigastrocoele which develops from a pair of teloblasts. Hatschek (1881) could find no trace of a segmentation in the embryos of *Sipunculus nudus*. Gerould (1906) on the other hand described and depicted from three to four pairs of coelom sacks which he believed to have found in the embryos of *Golfingia vulgaris*. Gerould has later revoked these facts; he considered these phenomena later as a consequence of a folding which is due to a strong contraction. Gerould made this statement in a letter only, which is quoted by Hyman. Those who prefer to see in the Sipunculida a preliminary stage of an evolution in the direction towards the Annelida will find the state of things, such as it appears now after Gerould's revocation of his findings, as very important and favourable to their interpretation. I, on the other hand, consider that it is much less important whether in fact a segmented state is still recapitulated in the perigastrocoele of some species belonging to the Sipunculida. It is not impossible that during the future researches forms will be discovered among the more than 250 species of the Sipunculida, which differ considerably from one another, where such recapitulations will be found preserved. Yet even if no such traces of a segmentation are actually found preserved in any of the recent species, there are still other numerous properties which seem to support my thesis that the Sipunculida evolved as a result of a secondary simplification and of a specialization of their way of life.

I wish finally to mention here the urns which are so characteristic of the organization of the Sipunculida. The structure and the ontogenetic development of these urns are well enough known. Yet there exists a considerable uncertainty about their function, and even more so of their origin, of their phylogeny. These urns remind me—by the whole line of their development: the freely swimming urns, the attached urns, the coelothelium cells which are strongly covered with cilia; by the fact that they collect material to be excreted; and finally by their visible function as motors of the coelom fluid, of the circulation—of the so-called rosettes that can be found in the Ctenophora which I (Hadži, 1957) have tried to explain as remains of the terminal organs of the protonephridia that had grown together with the gastral epithelium. These could thus be some kind of analogous formations. The ancestors of the Sipunculida possessed many pairs of the metanephridia that evolved from the protonephridia. These metanephridia have generally become superfluous as a consequence of a greatly changed way of life. It is the anterior pair only or a few individual metanephridia (in one species of the Sipunculida we can even see that all the metanephridia have been lost) that have been preserved in a somewhat changed form in order to serve above all as gonoducts. The sexual cells are soon freed in the Sipunculida from their gonads, they circulate in the coelom fluid which functions at the same time as blood, and it was in this way that the metanephridia had been changed into gonoducts. This change had actually taken place as early as in the Annelida. The nephrostomes of the remaining metanephridia had undergone a considerable transformation; they evolved first into the "sitting" and later into the freely swimming urns. At the same time the individual cells have preserved a strong ciliation. This seems to me to be a very probable interpretation which can also be used as a working hypothesis.

The richly developed net of canals are either of the coelomatic or of a schizocoelic origin and which serve as a "hydraulic machine" of these remarkable animals must be considered as a special "invention" of the Sipunculida.

Finally, we must not leave unmentioned the fact that solid forms can be found in their "coelom blood." Baltzer (1931:269) wrote about these forms as follows, "Die Mannigfaltigkeit aller dieser Zölomgebilde gibt dem Leibeshöhleninhalt der Sipunculiden eine erstaunlich hohe Komplikation, eine Kompliziertheit, die von keiner anderen Tier-Gruppe erreicht wird." I mention this circumstance because it again supports my thesis of an evolution of the Sipunculida from the ancient Annelida. It does in no way corroborate the opposite thesis which was formulated, for example, by Hyman (1959, Vol. V., 690) with the following words, "The Sipunculida are therefore to be conceived as protostomatous coelomates placed along the main line of the Protostomia that leads to Annelida, Mollusca, and Arthropoda."

The Oligomeria as the Initial Form for the Evolution of the Chordonia

One of the characteristics of the Oligomeria is the fact that they do not include even a single subgroup (class) whose species would lead a life considered as characteristic of the Eumetazoa. There is one class only which includes exclusively freely moving species (the partly inert *Spadella* does not disturb this general picture); these are the Chaetognatha. We have already stated at the beginning of the present study that life in free water cannot be considered as a primary and normal way of life. I have tried to solve the problem of the Chaetognatha together with Lameere by attempting to derive them by way of neoteny from the planktonic larvae of the Brachiopoda. This type of derivation corresponds best with the known facts. The Chaetognatha, as strongly specialized Oligomeria, cannot be taken into consideration as a possible initial form for the evolution of the Chordonia. The similarities that can be observed between the Chaetognatha and some small fishes are a purely external phenomenon. The structures, the ontogenies, and the types of movement, however, are entirely different in these two animal groups.

Free mobility has been attained secondarily by the Oligomeria in two other instances. We find, however, that in spite of a prolonged evolution the Echinodermata have still preserved traces of an original radial symmetry that evolved from an even older bilateral symmetry. This can be seen even in the burrowing Echinoida where new signs of a bilateral symmetry can be observed re-emerging. The adult forms of the Echinodermata (we state this explicitly), however, can hardly be taken into consideration as possible ancestors of the Chordonia as this is the case with the Chaetognatha. We have emphasized the statement "the adult Echinodermata" because attempts have been made, even by scholars who must be taken seriously, to represent the planktonic and at the same time bilaterally symmetric larvae of the Echinodermata as the initial forms for the evolution of the Chordonia type.

The second attempt which was made by the subtypes of the Oligomeria to achieve secondarily a free mobility can be observed in the small group Pterobranchia. The case is interesting because these are clearly primarily tubicolous animals. No type of the Eumetazoa could or did ever develop from these forms. Their organization had been strongly and irreversibly reduced. Quite remarkably we can find in the Pterobranchia —in these only and in the Enteropneusta—an open connection between the anterior intestine and the external world. This connection, however, which is supposed to be used by the animal in its respiration, was not invented by the Pterobranchia; it can also be found in some older types, even among the Ameria (Gastrotricha). This branchiotrema has been the main reason why zoologists have tried to bring the Pterobranchia into a closer connection with the Enteropneusta which are even better equipped with the gill slits. I believe that zoologists have gone too far with these attempts and that these two groups of the Oligomeria developed independently from each other in a very remote geological past. It seems to me that the Enteropneusta had never really lived as tubicolous animals and that they are therefore the only group of the Oligomeria which possess a primary free mobility that has been preserved by them down to the present day. The possibility cannot be completely excluded, however, that the Pterobranchia—which are now represented by few remaining forms only—had evolved from some burrowing ancestors which they had in common with the Enteropneusta. Their evolution proceeded from this ancestral form towards a tubicolous way of life and it had therefore been separate from that of other tubicolous Oligomeria.

A derivation of the freely moving Chordonia from such tubicolous Oligomeria as the Phoronida and the Pogonophora seems to be rather improbable. These two subtypes are clearly specialized, the Pogonophora even more so than the Phoronida. A complete loss of the digestive system in a non-parasitic animal type can certainly be considered as a unique case. It is clear that nothing could ever have possibly evolved from such specialists; they represent blind side alleys of evolution which are so numerous in the animal world. It is unnecessary to argue and prove that no evolution in the direction towards the Chordonia with the Brachiopoda and the Ectoprocta, two completely sessile classes of the Oligomeria, as initial forms had been possible. The situation as it appears from our standpoint—which we consider as the best founded point of view—is such that the Enteropneusta only can be taken into consideration as a possible initial form for the evolution of the Chordonia. Even if it is unnecessary, I nevertheless wish to state explicitly that quite naturally I do not see in the recent Enteropneusta the ancestral forms of the Chordonia; these ancestral forms were in reality at the same time ancestors of the present-day Enteropneusta and lived as such in the remotest geological past. From these ancestors had evolved divergingly (or I could also say in parallel) on the one hand the burrowing Enteropneusta, and on the other hand the Chordonia which had returned to a freely moving life. From these freely moving Chordonia a new subtype (class) had again evolved, in no way accidentally, of the sessile Chordonia which are represented by the blindly ending side branch of the Tunicata.

When we try to derive the Chordonia from the primitive Enteropneusta, among the Oligomeria, we meet with apparently the greatest difficulty—besides some other problems which can be solved more easily—of how to explain the evolution of the polymerous state of the Chordonia from an oligomerous state with three segments at the most and with the same number of pairs of the enterocoele (the anterior pair can also be found grown together).

We must include here first a general observation before we try to solve this difficult problem. The number of the main types of life and of the corresponding main forms of life is very limited. We can therefore see them repeated again and again within the framework of all the higher groups. The products of evolution, however, show as parallelisms considerable differences in spite of frequent analogies and external similarities; this is due to the fact that they always start their evolution from different initial points (levels of organization). Because of these similarities and analogies it is frequently difficult to identify the initial point of evolution. In our attempt to solve the problem of the origin of the Chordata we meet with one of the most important repetitions, the repetition of the body segmentation. It first took place by way of an irregular polymerization finally, to reach a regular polymery during the transition from the Ameria to the Polymeria; it was a consequence of a rapid type of movement by means of a curving of the entire body. Polymery was subsequently reduced to an oligomery within the framework of the Oligomeria. During the transition from the Oligomeria to the Chordonia we can again observe an irregular polymerization which led to polymery. And again this had been caused by an active type of movement. In this case, however, we can hardly speak of a sinuous type of movement; here the waves of contractions are very low, and the segments of muscles involved in this movement very short, following each other closely; they are limited to the dorsal side. The effect of these contractions had therefore been greatly increased. Later we can again observe in the Chordonia a secondary reduction of the number of segments, above all among the Tetrapoda where the reduction was caused especially by the evolution of their extremities. This had again been followed by a (third) polymerization and by a more sinuous type of movement which is typical of snakes. Among other changes and innovations that can be found in the Chordonia we must mention above all the formation of an internal axial skeleton, with the *chorda dorsalis* at the beginning.

In the recent animals we unfortunately find a deep gap between the Oligomeria and the Chordonia. This transition had taken place in the remotest geological past. The transition was made by animals whose soft consistency had little chance of preservation as a fossilized form. The speed itself of the evolution was also in all probability increased. Finally, it also seems that it was just this transitional stage which had lived not in a pure sea but, at least partly, in a brackish or fresh water and this again is an unfavourable circumstance for the preservation and for the discovery of such fossilized remains. We have therefore no other alternative but to take refuge in the comparative morphology of the recent adult forms and of the developing stages and at the same time to use our imagination within proper limits.

The Fourth and the Last Phylum of the Eumetazoa; the Chordonia

It is in no way surprising in view of the available material to see how many different ideas, hypotheses, and theories have been proposed so far in various treatises and even books about the origin of the Chordata, and thus also of the Vertebrata. Only little additional material has recently come to light, such as the discovery of the fossilized remains of the extraordinarily old chordate *Jamoytius*. It would transcend the limits of the present book if we discuss in detail this problem here. It does not even belong to the sphere of my own research. I will therefore limit myself to show only how this problem could be solved if studied from our standpoint and under the application of our working method; I will therefore exclude from this account all those elements which could be too hypothetical.

The situation has become slightly better now because there is hardly any living zoologist who would still be willing to accept a suggestion to derive the Chordonia either from the Nemertinea (Hubrecht, 1883), or from the Arthropoda of the type of the *Limulus* (Gaskell, 1895–1910, and Patten, 1912). The interpretation which derives the Chordonia directly from the Annelida (Dohrn, 1875; Semper, 1875–6; Minot, 1897; Delsman, 1922; and many others) finds recently less and less acceptance, though earlier it was frequently put forward; the interpretation itself was actually based on a fantastic idea that had been proposed by Hilaire (1818). The same interpretation (it is in reality only a minor hypothesis) has recently been revived in a somewhat changed form, when the Oligomeria have been suggested as a possible starting point of the evolution of the Chordonia. The Oligomeria themselves, however, can easily be derived, as we have already shown, from the polymerous Annelida. Yet even within the limits of a general theory which derives the Chordonia from the Oligomeria there exist several possibilities which can claim various degrees of probability. There exist therefore several interpretations of this kind which were suggested, e.g. by Bateson (1884–6), Brooks (1893), Willey (1894), and Garstang (1894–8) whose interpretation has been accepted by Sir Gavin de Beer and recently by N. J. Berrill (1955) in a special book he wrote on this subject.

I do not intend to begin here with a detailed analysis of these hypotheses about the supposed annelidan–arthropodan ancestors of the Chordonia; we will agree on this point with the critical discussion written by Berrill (Berrill, 1955:2–5). I wish only to state that the peculiarities which the Chordonia have in common with the Annelida (for example the solenocytes, the close connection between the sexual organs and the nephridia). These peculiarities have been discussed above all by Boveri (1892) and by Goodrich (1902) and do not seem to disprove the interpretation that the Chordonia did not developed directly from the ancestors of the recent Annelida and that instead this evolution was indirect, by way of the Oligomeria. This is how we can explain the reactivation of certain elements in the Chordonia while the same elements have been lost in the recent Oligomeria.

We can divide all the hypotheses which derive the Chordonia from the Oligomeria into two groups. According to one group of these hypotheses the Chordonia evolved from the larvae of the Oligomeria, thus by way of neoteny; the second group of these interpretations derives the Chordonia from the adult forms of the Oligomeria. It is by no means rare to meet the former type of interpretation. It corresponds to the widely accepted method of solving various phylogenetic problems by means of larval forms. Personally, I am not *a priori* opposed to use neoteny in various phylogenetic speculations. I myself have used the phenomenon of neoteny twice when I tried to explain the origin of new animal types. First, in connection with the suggested derivation of the Ctenophora from the planktonic larvae of the polyclad Turbellaria, and secondly, in connection with the derivation or the Chaetognatha from the planktonic larvae of the Brachiopoda. I am also firmly convinced that in several other cases new forms, which emerged during the phylogenetic processes, evolved by way of a neotenization. This type of development has to be taken into consideration in connection with the evolution of the Larvacea or Appendiculata, among the Tunicata, and with the Proteidae, among the Urodela, etc.

Yet at the same time I think that we must not go too far in this direction, and that we should use an explanation by means of a neoteny in those cases where all the other types of evolution appear as completely improbable. It has already been mentioned how the numerous attempts that have been made to interpret the origin of all possible groups by means of neoteny (or paedomorphosis) have been looked upon by many zoologists with a considerable degree of, partly justified, suspicion.

In connection with a derivation of the Chordata from some larvae of the Oligomeria or even of the Tunicata, I again think that such a derivation does not appear to be well founded and that it can therefore claim little probability even if it is not in principle impossible.

First, we will mention here the attempt made by Berrill (1955), whose views from our standpoint must be considered as completely erroneous. Berrill's derivation starts with the planktonic larvae of the Tunicata which he calls tadpoles. We must above all reject the usage of this word for the planktonic larvae of the Tunicata. These larvae are a very specific form which had been developed by the Tunicata and they have nothing in common with the tadpoles of the Anura, with the exception that they are both larval forms that occur in the Chordata. The remote external similarities can be considered as pure parallelisms.

In the Tunicata we can observe a process which we have already frequently met in the Invertebrata, i. e. because of their secondary transition to a sessile way of life, the Tunicata developed in their ontogeny a planktonic juvenile form, a larva. This certainly is a very illuminating phenomenon. Berrill (1955 : 11) also considers that the Ascidia are "primarily a primitive sessile, marine group of organisms." The Ascidia, however, are considered quite generally and correctly, together with the Tunicata, as lower Chordata which evolved into secondarily sessile animals. The important problem of the origin of the Tunicata is solved by Berrill very simply with the following words, "...which may or may not be related to the hemichordates." It is quite natural that Berrill who derives the Vertebrata from the planktonic "tadpoles" of the Tunicata does not find it interesting to try to solve the problem of the origin of these Tunicata. Yet what can be done if we find that it is quite improbable that any new form had ever been able to evolve from the larvae of the Tunicata? The important discovery made by Kowalewski who succeeded in proving that the Tunicata, which nobody knew how to place into the animal system, are in reality genuine even if retrograded Chordonia, has again shown the phyletic significance of these larvae. These larvae have been used as a representative example which could prove the theory of recapitulation. These larvae do indeed recapitulate or repeat something which is not, however, the adult ancestral form but only its ontogenetic stage that has also preserved numerous characteristics of the adult ancestral form.

The whole organization of the Tunicata larvae is specific and one-sided—we can mention here the fact that in them the notochord occurs in the tail only, a body region which had been newly developed by the Chordata—that there is one form only which had evolved from them by way of neoteny (similarly as has been the case with the Ctenophora and the Chaetognatha), i. e. the Larvacea, and nothing else. This subtype of the Chordonia which exists as an ontogenetic stage only points to an early existence of a general type of the Chordata. Berrill (1955:3) good-humouredly mentions a statement regarding the book by Delsman that the book should be confiscated and burnt; we can say on the other hand about Berrill's book that it would be better if it had not been published at all in spite of a number of sound interpretations which appear in it, because of its basic idea which is certainly wrong. The Vertebrata certainly did not evolve from the planktonic tadpoles but rather from the benthonic "worm-like" Oligomeria.

Neither can we consider as fortunate those suggestions which try to derive the Chordonia from the planktonic larvae of the Oligomeria, or directly from the so-called Ambulacralia (Echinodermata and Enteropneusta). Like the larvae of the Tunicata, these are again very specialized larvae of the Oligomeria which could serve, at the most, as a starting point for the evolution of some other planktonic form of the Oligomeria, a development which in all probability never actually took place. It could not be considered as a case of neoteny if this larval form evolved into a new type after its descent to the sea bottom, thus after a metamorphosis. The Chordonia, if they evolved in this way, would have a planktonic larva similar to the so-called dipleura. Something of this kind, however, is unknown to us. The interesting proposition made by Garstang to derive the central nervous system and the endostyle of the Chordonia from an immersion of ciliated bands of the Echinodermata larvae must be considered as an entirely erroneous concept, as a purely artificial construction. Where is here the origin of a secondary metamerization, of the notochord, of gill slits, etc.? Such a suggestion could perhaps be taken into consideration if there were no longer any such animals as the Enteropneusta. The adult Enteropneusta are comparatively less specialized than the planktonic larvae of the Ambulacralia. It is therefore easier to derive the Chordonia from the Enteropneusta than from the planktonic larvae of the Echinodermata. Such a derivation is also, therefore, much more probable. The suggestion that the hypothetical immersion of ciliated bands could be the starting point for the evolution of new organs is somewhat similar to Krumbach's attempt to derive the protonephridia from an immersion of the swimming plates of the Ctenophora.

Even less probable than a derivation of the Chordonia from the planktonic larvae of the Echinodermata seems to be a derivation of the Chordonia from some very ancient, armoured, adult forms of the Echinodermata. Such a suggestion was made by Gieslén (1930) on the basis of a comparison between the carpoidal echinoderm *Cothurnocystis elizae* and the Ostracodermata in which he took into consideration above all their armour. Such a derivation does not seem to be much better than is a derivation from *Limulus*. These are clearly cases of parallelisms or similarities which are not based on any closer relationships. Berrill (1955:5) has correctly criticized such interpretations, adding at the same time a very proper observation that we must search for the origin of the Chordonia much farther back in the geological past than in the now extinct carpoidal Echinodermata and in the equally extinct Ostracodermi, i.e. much earlier than in the Lower Silurian. In my opinion the Echinodermata cannot be taken into consideration as ancestors of the Chordonia either in their larval forms or as adult animals. The Echinodermata represent the largest and the most ramified branch that evolved from the stem of the Oligomeria. Yet this branch ends blindly, it did not lead to the evolution of a new subtype, and above all it did not lead to the emergence of a new type: the Chordata.

The Probable Origin of the Chordonia

It is most probable that the Chordonia evolved as the most recent and highest animal type from the Oligomeria. The recent subtypes of the Oligomeria, however, in which we can observe a greater or smaller degree of specialization cannot be taken into consideration as possible ancestors of the Chordonia; they had in the meantime too long a geological period at their disposal for their own evolution. It must nevertheless be admitted that the Oligomeria which evolved during this period in several directions, reached various levels of organization, while at the same time the Chordonia also went through a rich evolution which finally reached its climax in the human species. There still exist some forms of the Oligomeria which are similar to this early form. Animals with radial symmetry which adopted the sessile way of life became strongly simplified and their evolutions have ended blindly, even in those cases when they secondarily readopted free mobility, e.g. several groups of the Echinodermata and several other groups of the Oligomeria. We find then that there remain few slowly moving groups only, and even among these we must exclude the tubicolous forms, especially the very specialized Pogonophora (together with the extinct Graptolitha) as well as the Phoronidea. The only group which therefore remains to be taken into consideration in connection with our problem are the Enteropneusta. And even now we can really find in the Enteropneusta the greatest number of the so-called prophetic characteristics in spite of the repeated specializations which they underwent "in the meantime." The Enteropneusta move slowly yet they are nevertheless freely moving animals, they usually burrow in the ground and they have therefore an anterior part of the body which had evolved much later in the Chordonia into the head of the Vertebrata by way of a cephalization.

It is possible that the process which had taken place in the evolution of the Chordonia was similar to the process we have presupposed in connection with the evolution of the Polymeria from the Ameria, and of the Oligomeria from the Polymeria. The evolution of the new type started in all probability somewhere close to the root of the next lower type. In its evolution it had followed Watson's rule; it was due to a "fortunate" combination of several characteristics that had existed scattered in the next lower type and to the emergence of new characteristics which led to the formation of the new type under a simultaneous radical change in the environment and in the way of life.

We must suppose (and we have good enough reasons to) that something unusual had taken place in the period of transition from the Oligomeria—from a primitive form of the Oligomeria which is no longer preserved in recent animals and which it seems had resembled most closely the present-day Enteropneusta of all the recent Oligomeria—to the Chordonia. The transition of an oligomerous animal similar, perhaps, to a *Balanoglossus* into a new animal form resembling approximately the recent *Amphioxus (Branchiostoma)*, or the fossil *Jamoytius*, must have taken place in all probability in the soft shallow ground of estuaries, or even in fresh water. This supposition is based on the fact that *Jamoytius*, the most ancient fossil remains belonging to the Chordonia, has been found in the sediments which had been deposited by fresh water. The second necessary presupposition is that during the phase of transition the ancestors of the Enteropneusta which had evolved into the Chordonia had begun to move more intensively as freely moving animals. This change was probably connected with an adaptation of these animals to a life in firmer and coarse-grained sand sediments after they had left the soft mud and the fine sand. The inclination to swim which had never been completely lost, now became reactivated. Simultaneously, we can observe a rich secondary segmentation in the dorsal side of their oblong bodies which had become strengthened due to these changes; this segmentation had taken place above all in the body muscles and in the nerve trunk which had already become extended along the dorsomedian line. Other organs placed more or less dorsally, as the previously uniform perigastrocoele, the gonads, and the nephridia afterwards also participated in this segmentation.

The consequence of the special type of swimming which had been developed more and more progressively by the freely moving Chordonia—with the exception of the Tunicata which had secondarily returned to a sessile way of life—had been a special new formation which had developed at the end of their bodies. Here a new zone of growth emerged whose consequence was a new body region, that of the tail. The more active type of movement led to a progressive development of the two systems which had been inherited from the enteropneustan ancestors, the breathing system and the system of blood circulation. The trend to develop folds in the region of the breathing organs, which can also be observed in the Enteropneusta, had been continued in the lower Chordonia (the atrial cavity for the protection of the gill apparatus); yet this cavity later became more and more retrograded in fishes, etc., because of the completely freely swimming way of life which these animals had adopted.

The new type of movement of the primitive Chordonia led to a formation of an elastic inner skeleton staff, the *chorda dorsalis*. Numerous discussions have been conducted on whether the so-called cephalochord of the Enteropneusta can be considered as homologous to the genuine *chorda dorsalis*, or not. I think that these discussions are completely superfluous. The anterior outgrowth of the intestine which can be observed in the Enteropneusta is certainly not a "notochord" *s.str.*, it is certainly not a *chorda dorsalis*. It belongs to a group of forms that had been developed by the intestine and which appear repeatedly even if in various ways in the Eumetazoa. These are the intestinal diverticulae which originally have a lumen and which function as a periphery of the intestine. The lumen is later lost, the diverticulae become solid, and they change at the same time their function by their development towards an inner skeleton. The best known instance of this development are the tentacles of the Cnidaria which had secondarily evolved into solid forms. In some species we can even find that some other parts of the intestine also evolve into an elastic inner skeleton (the *Tubularia* species). Forms similar to the "cephalochord" of the Enteropneusta can occasionally be found in the Turbellaria (Ax, 1957), etc. (Fig. 33). During the ontogenies we can see the *chorda dorsalis* developed from the "*plafond*" of the intestinal *Anlage*, and this can be clearly observed in the lower Chordonia. The "notochord" of the Enteropneusta and the *chorda dorsalis* of the Chordonia originate therefore in one and the same trend of the intestinal tube to develop first some "hollow" outgrowths, i.e. outgrowths which have a lumen that later becomes solidified. Here we are not interested in the subsequent destiny of the *chorda dorsalis* in spite of its interesting character. This chorda is stubbornly preserved and it is recapitulated down to the end of the evolution even if it does not have any function in the adult animals. Its *Anlage* must clearly have an important morphogenetic function during the ontogenetic development.

This may be the best place to call attention to a fact which has been, it seems to us, too much neglected till now. It is well known that a planktonic larva appears during the ontogeny of the Enteropneusta which is typical of these animals; this is the so-called tornaria, one of those larvae that had been developed by the Echinodermata and which have been given various names. Zoologists have therefore considered that there is a probability of a closer relationship between these two groups of the Oligomeria. All these larvae, as well as the various planktonic larvae of the Ameria and the Polymeria belong to the category of the primary larvae, as has already been emphasized, i.e. they appear in a form with a lower level of organization. Very frequently we can find the phase of these larval forms transmuted from a freely living phase of the development of an animal and incorporated into an embryonic phase of the ontogeny. It should be sufficient if we call attention here to conditions that can be observed in those crustaceans that live in fresh water.

This tornaria can now be identified as the last primary planktonic form of its kind. The institution of a primary planktonic larva had been abandoned during the comparatively short phase of the phylogenetic evolution when the first chordate evolved from its oligomerous ancestor. It was changed into an embryonic stage, a development similar to that of the nauplius in the evolution of the crayfish *(Potamobius)*, among the decapod crustaceans. It seems easy to attribute this change to a transition to a life in the fresh water; it is considered that a reduction of a freely living larval stage regularly takes place when the animal relinquishes its life in the sea.

There are, however, some exception where this rule does not seem to be valid (e.g. in connection with the *Dreissensia polymorpha*, a species of bivalve molluscs which had probably penetrated late into the fresh water, and with the phylactolaematous Ectoprocta with their considerably changed larvae that develop forms similar to cormi).

The planktonic larvae had in all probability again been developed after the animal had returned to a life in the sea. Yet this planktonic phase of the ontogeny now reached a much higher level of organization, and we are therefore fully justified to speak here of a secondary larval form. Such a larva shows the structure of a chordate, and not of an amerous animal as is the case with the trochophores and with the dipleurulae. It is wrong to see in the primary larvae (the various trochophores and dipleurulae) a recapitulation of an adult ancestral form; the same is also true for those larvae of the Chordata that can be justly called tadpoles. Viewed from this standpoint we must reject any attempt (e.g. the attempt made by Berrill) to derive the Chordonia from some kind of planktonic larvae. The evolution of the Larvacea from the "tadpole" of the Ascidia belongs as a clear case of neoteny in a completely different chapter.

A Comparison of the present Attempt to Derive the Chordonia from an Ancestral Form Resembling the Present Day Enteropneusta with the Similar Attempt Made by Hans Steiner

Hans Steiner has also tried to derive the Chordonia from the Enteropneusta in a very interesting study, *Geschichte der Initialgestaltung der Chordaten* (1956) where we can find numerous correct observations. In this study he takes into consideration the comparative morphology and the way of life of these animals. As regards the derivation itself there is a considerable agreement between his and my interpretation; and in this point Steiner therefore does not show in principle anything new. There is, on the other hand, a great difference in the way we interpret the evolution which led to the emergence of the Echinodermata and of the Enteropneusta. Steiner tries to suggest something which I must consider as completely impossible, he correctly rejects the opinions proposed by

Remane as well as all the other attempts to derive bilateral symmetry from a radial symmetry with the "Coelenterata" as the initial form of this evolution, and above all the attempts to derive by means of the enterocoelic theory, a trimetamerism from the gastral diverticula of a tetraradial polyp of the Cnidaria. At the same time he wishes to preserve the division of the Eumetazoa into the Protostomia and the Deuterostomia, and in this respect he goes so far that he tries to place this unfortunate bifurcation back into the "gastraea" stage (he completely disregards here the Spongiae as well as the Cnidaria and the Ctenophora). Steiner has made here, I think, two basic mistakes; first, when he describes the youngest Metazoa as animals that live in plankton, and, secondly, when he interprets the larval forms as representatives of their adult ancestors. Steiner took great pains to make probable the early bifurcation of the two lines of evolution; the Protostomia and the Deuterostomia, and to provide this thesis with a solid foundation. This attempt, however, must be considered as completely unsuccessful, similarly as has also been the case with a not very different attempt made by Boettger. His construction, the Neurenterica, is, I think, unable to live.

Even the apparently fortunately suggested line of evolution, plankton—benthos—nekton is unable to stand an objective analysis. The benthos represents the starting point and the main type of life from which both plankton and nekton evolved.

It is also wrong to use the ecotypes, even as an auxiliary method, in high taxonomy. All the main types of life (of feeding), e.g. the predatores, turbellores, and the fossores (according to Steiner), can be found as early as in the Protozoa (the numerous benthonic Rhizopoda are fossores). In the Metazoa they do not follow each other in the way suggested by Steiner. We can find in the Cnidaria all these types of life represented perhaps with the exception of the burrowing animals (ceriantharia) if we do not wish to consider as such the species that stick in the soft sea bottom, e.g. *Branchiocerianthus giganteus*. There also exist, however, other types of life which can be frequently met with and which have not been taken into consideration by Steiner. We can mention here the parasitic way of life (which can hardly be found among the "Deuterostomia"), and the various types of movement and feeding which can be observed in the benthonic animals (from good swimmers such as the Cephalopoda and down to the fully sessile animals that can be found above all among the Oligomeria).

Steiner takes a correct attitude regarding the relation, ontogeny versus phylogeny. He considers that the ontogenies of the ancestral forms are only recapitulated in the ontogenies of the recent species; yet at the same time we can frequently find in his scheme of the genealogical tree pictures of larvae instead of the pictures of the corresponding imago forms; this gives an impression that the ancestors could be recapitulated in these larvae, as if these larvae could be a kind of representatives of some ancestral forms. We also get such an impression because Steiner simply transfers some purely ontogenetic processes—such as the morphogeny of the spinal chord by way of a secondarily closed "feeding canal" which finally leads to the formation of the canalis neurentericus and neuroporus—into changes that take place during the adult stage.

We cannot accept Steiner's interpretation when he suggests that the enterocoely and the triple metamery evolved as new forms because of the burrowing way of life of the Enteropneusta. If Steiner had found a correct interpretation, then there could be no homologies in the conditions of the coeloms in the Annelida and in the Echinodermata (the Protostomia and the Deuterostomia). We must conclude that in spite of all the endeavours made by Steiner to explain rationally these differences, the idea of a branching of the Eumetazoa into the two main lines of the Protostomia and the Deuterostomia still remains highly improbable.

Steiner does not mention my works which had appeared before the publication of his treatise; it is possible that either he did not know them or that he did not consider them as worthy of consideration.

The Genealogical Tree of the Chordonia

The mutual relationship connections that exist within the phylum Chordonia among the tetrapod Vertebrata can now be considered as sufficiently clarified; the same, however, can not be said for the numerous lower groups of the Chordata, from the Acrania and up to the bony fishes. Since I have not made my own researches in this field, I preserve here the system of the Chordata that was suggested by Vandebroek (1949) at the *XIXth International Congress of Zoologists* at Paris while at the same time I take into consideration the progress which has recently been made in the field of the paleozoology. If Tunicata had not existed we could divide all the Chordonia into two superclasses, Pisces and Tetrapoda; at the same time, however, we cannot recommend a division of the Chordonia into three greatly unequal superclasses, the Tunicata, Pisces, and the Tetrapoda. The term Vertebrata which is generally so widely used, and which will certainly continue to be used even if not as a taxonomic notion, finds no place in the system proposed by Vandebroek; neither can we find in this system the group Pisces as a name of a class, or the Acrania and the Cyclostomata (the former at least not as an independent class).

The Tunicata should definitively follow the primitive Chordonia, the Agnatha. There can be no doubt that the Tunicata must be considered as Chordonia which secondarily adopted the sessile way of life. It can be said that this was the last opportunity the animals have had to develop a sessile group with all the consequences which we have so frequently observed in the whole animal world, beginning with the

Protozoa. The starting point of this evolution were the free living primitive Chordonia which, however, had already lived partly as sessile animals that burrowed slowly in the sea bottom making stops from time to time, just as can still be seen in *Amphioxus*. The Tunicata evolved in all probability in the sea; they had developed their own larval form which is slightly similar, as this has already been emphasized, to the tertiary larva, to the tetrapodic tadpole. The entirely planktonic Larvacea have been the only form which had ever evolved from these larvae; they represent a small side branch whose evolution led no further, just as in the case of the Ctenophora.

The Ostracodermata represent a blindly ending side branch of fish-like Vertebrata which, however, remained in the benthos and became very specialized; they are now extinct. Because of them the displaced comparison with *Limulus* has been attempted. It is very probable that the class Agnatha (here in a very wide sense) was followed by the Protichtya with their two subclasses, the Acanthodea and the Arthrodira. We know less about the sequence of the Chondrichthya and the Osteichthya, whether they evolved in two parallel lines, or one after the other.

The phylum Chordonia would thus include nine classes (Fig. 59), the same number as the phylum Oligomeria and the phylum Polymeria (quite "accidentally"); only the first phylum of the Eumetazoa, the Ameria, must be subdivided into fifteen classes. The question remains open whether all these groups which have been given the rank of classes are really mutually equivalent. Thus, for example, such classes that evolved in all probability by way of neoteny, as such the Ctenophora, Chaetognatha, and the Larvacea, and other classes as the Turbellaria, Mollusca, Polychaeta, Insecta, Echinodermata, Mammalia, etc., to mention a few only.

The main emphasis, however, must not be placed on the size of each group. A smaller number of subordinate categories, down to the species, can be reached along widely different ways. The small size of a group can be due to the fact that it evolved by way of neoteny (this is true for the Chaetognatha, Ctenophora and the Larvacea), or it is a consequence of an ageing of the line of evolution and thus an indication of a decaying phase which can finally lead to a complete extinction.

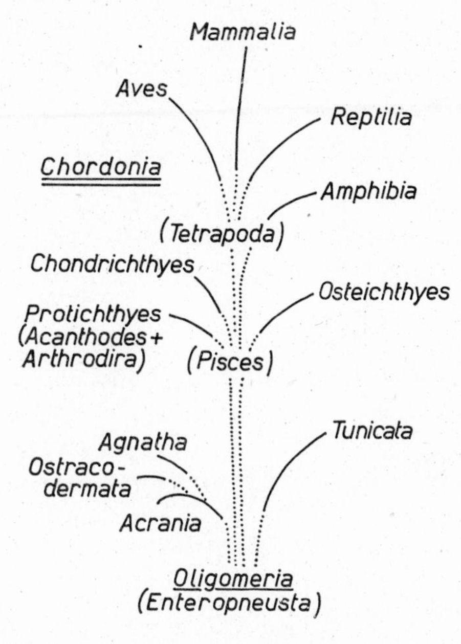

Fig. 59. Genealogical tree of the phylum; Chordonia.

Such a case is probably represented by the Brachiopoda. The small size of a group can also be a consequence of a hyper-specialization, as is the case, for example, with the Pogonophora.

The Genealogical Tree of the Entire Animal World

After we have constructed partial genealogical trees which show the individual phases in the phylogeny of the animal world we still have to bring them together and to construct a general genealogical tree (Fig. 60). The following special characteristics can be mentioned as typical of our construction if compared with the numerous other similar attemps:

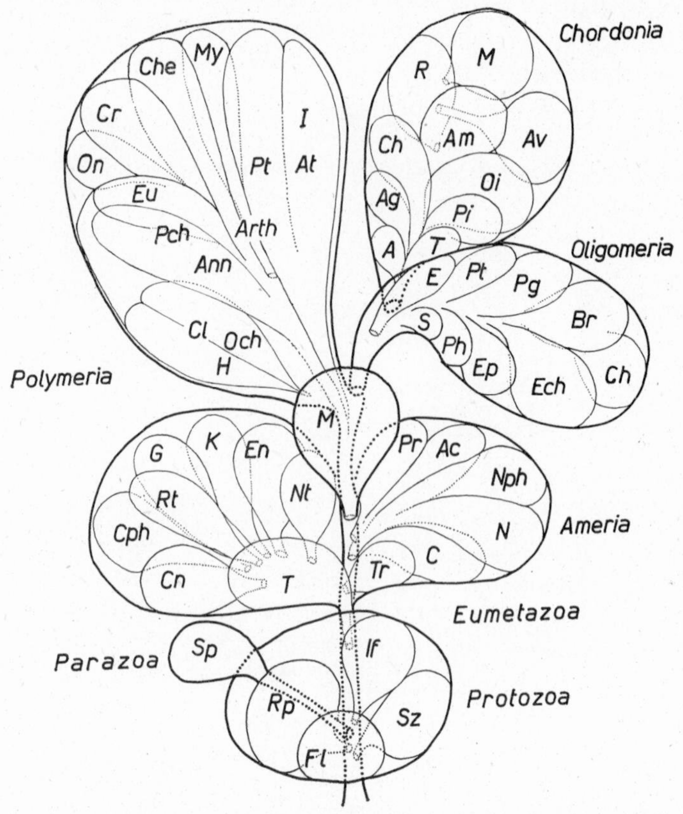

Fig. 60. Genealogical tree of the entire animal kingdom; the monograms used in these diagrams are explained in the list of phyla and classes (see p. 460–61)

(1) Our genealogical tree begins with the animal Flagellata which evolved on the one hand into the Rhizopoda, Sporozoa, and the Ciliata, as well as (by way of the Choanoflagellata) into the Parazoa (Spongiaria), and on the other hand (by way of the Ciliata) into the Eumetazoa. The Parazoa evolved as individualized colonies of the Choanoflagellata.

(2) The Eumetazoa do not begin, as has been generally believed so far, with the two-layered Coelenterata, but rather with the three-layered Turbellaria and are connected downwards with the primitive polynuclear Ciliata (the plasmodium theory or the polykaryonic theory).

(3) The evolution of the Eumetazoa took place without a bifurcation, thus in a direct line and by way of four main phases or stages which should be classified as phyla: the Ameria, Polymeria, Oligomeria, and the Chordonia (actually: secondary Polymeria). This whole evolution shows clearly a progressive trend which, however, had gone through a stage of retrogression during the phase of the Oligomeria. The scheme of our genealogical tree shows therefore one top only, and not two; in spite of this it must not be considered as a revival of the old type of "*l'échelle animale.*"

(4) The Mollusca have been treated in our study without any hesitation as a class of the Ameria.

(5) The Cnidaria and the Ctenophora are derived from the Turbellaria; they are therefore treated as classes of the Ameria.

(6) The Sipunculoida have been separated from the Annelida, and thus from the Polymeria; they are now classified among the Oligomeria.

(7) It has been suggested that the Chaetognatha had evolved by way of neoteny from the Brachiopoda.

Our first suggestion of the genealogical tree of the animal world (Hadži, 1944:179) is thus slightly modified now (Fig. 60 and the list of the phyla and classes of Eumetazoa; monograms in parenthesis). A mistake was made by the person who made the drawing of my suggested scheme of the genealogical tree as it was reproduced in my article published in the *Systematic Zoology* (the starting point of the Oligomeria line occurs at the top of the Polymeria line together with the Insecta, and not, as it should, in the Annelida line). This mistake was later corrected (Hadži, 1959b). It can be clearly seen that this is a mistake of the draftsman only if we compare this scheme with the sense of the text.

Herewith we have also reached a welcome simplification of the whole animal system and of the scheme of the genealogical tree. This simplification can be clearly seen if we compare our scheme with other schemes which are now usually proposed. This simplification is purely a side result of our research and it was not explicitly intended.

A List of the Phyla and Classes of Eumetazoa

PHYLUM		CLASSES
		Turbellaria (T)
		Cnidaria (Cn)
		Ctenophora (Cph)
		Trematoda (Tz)
		Cestoda (C)
		Nemertinea (Nt)
I. Ameria (15)		Rotatoria (Rz)
		Gastrotricha (G)
		Kinorhyncha (K)
		Entoprocta (En)
		Nematoda (N)
		Nematomorpha (Nph)
		Priapulida (Pz)
		Acanthocephala (Ac)
		Mollusca (M)
		Polychaeta (Pch)
	Annelida (Ann)	Clitellata (Cl)
		Echiuroida (En)
II. Polymeria (8)		Onychophora (On)
		Crustacea (Cr)
	Arthropoda (Arth)	Chelicerata (Ch)
		Myriapoda (My)
		Insecta (I)

III. OLIGOMERIA (9)	SIPUNCULIDA (S) PHORONIDA (Ph) POGONOPHORA (Pg) ECTOPROCTA (Ep) BRACHIOPODA (Br) CHAETOGNATHA (Ch) ECHINODERMATA (Ech) PTEROBRANCHIA (Pt) ENTEROPNEUSTA (E)
IV. CHORDONIA (10)	ACRANIA (A) TUNICATA (T) AGNATHA (Ag) PROTICHTHYA (Pi) CHONDRYCHTHYA (Ch) OSTEYCHTHYA (Oi) AMPHIBIA (Am) REPTILIA (R) AVES (VOLATILIA) (Av) MAMMALIA (M)

(42) CLASSES

An Attempt to Unify the Animal System

There still remain numerous suggested systems even if we disregard those suggestions which are now completely antiquated or clearly aberrant. There can be, however, one only truly natural system. We still have a long way to go to reach this ideal solution, even if we are coming closer to this ideal. We can be helped here by new discoveries of some recent species which have remained unknown till now, or of some corresponding fossilized remains. New facts and ideas can also be obtained by way of more detailed investigations of the already known animal species and of their ontogenies. Finally new viewpoints and methods of research can also be found useful, especially those offered by the biochemistry. All these elements combined can help us essentially to improve our present animal system. Even now we can see the important progress made within this sphere if we divide all the available systematic suggestions into two main groups, i.e. a larger group of systems which proposes a bifurcation in the evolution of the Eumetazoa, and a smaller group of systems where such a bifurcation cannot be observed.

This state of affairs has been the main reason why I have tried to make a corresponding suggestion before a competent forum, the *XIVth International Congress of Zoologists*. At this congress I (Hadži, 1956a) proposed that a uniform systematic scheme should be worked out which will be necessarily a result of a compromise and which could serve well enough in our practical didactic and operative work. Such a provisional scheme reached as a result of a compromise must quite naturally not prove to be an obstacle to our subsequent attempts to establish a definitive natural system. The subsequent destiny of my suggestion was entrusted to a special international committee which is headed by a well known zoologist—yet for reasons unknown to me this has been all that has been done in this connection. A standardized system could also serve as a basis for a review of all the valid animal names which was scheduled for publication at the occasion of the *XVth International Congress of Zoologists*, to take place in London (1958) simultaneously with a bicentenary of Linneus' work *Systema naturae*.

Let us compare now two selected systems which can represent the two previously mentioned main groups. I choose in this connection on one hand the system proposed by L. H. Hyman (1948, part I:38, cf. Fig. 61)—this system was made, according to a statement by Hyman, partly with the collaboration of Professor W. K. Fischer—and on the other

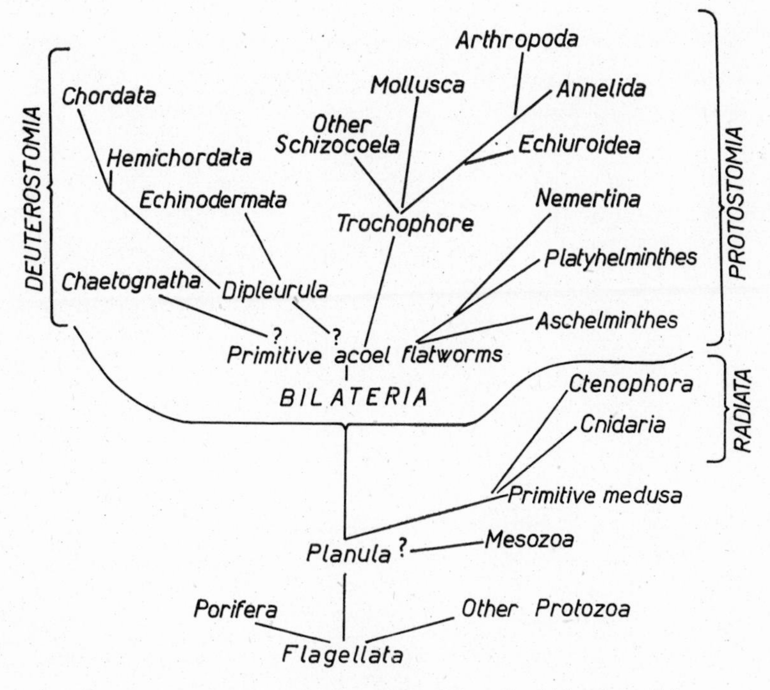

Fig. 61. Evolutionary relationships of the animal kingdom. (After Hyman.)

hand my own system. At first sight the differences between these two systems appear to be very great. We will now try to show that these differences are not actually quite so great, and that they can easily be overcome if only we have a little tolerance and good will. I will therefore enumerate here all those changes which can help us to overcome these differences. Such changes are actually not quite so numerous.

In order to solve first major problems we must abandon above all the two large groups of the Bilateria and Radiata; all the Eumetazoa are actually bilaterally symmetric animals, and there remain the Cnidaria and the Ctenophora only as members of the Radiata. The Echinodermata are quite correctly excluded from this group; there are few purely radially symmetric Cnidaria whose radial symmetry is actually a secondary phenomenon; the Ctenophora finally do not show a radially symmetric structure at all. For reasons which we do not wish to repeat here we should also abandon the division of the "Bilateria" into the Protostomia and the Deuterostomia. This is the change which will be least easily accepted and which is at the same time also the most important one that has to be made. All the remaining changes that must be made in the diagram as proposed by Hyman have a minor character only and they are actually "quite painless." First of all we must cancel in this system larval names (planula, dipleurula, trochophore) because they do not belong in such a diagram for reasons which we have sufficiently discussed. Furthermore we must also omit the Mesozoa, a group which is already now accompanied by a question mark. This especially must be done because we do not find indicated in the same diagram the adequate categories of the Protozoa, Metazoa, and the Eumetazoa, even if these groups are used in the linear enumerations.

The "primitive medusa" which has really no justification, must be abandoned as the initial form of the Coelenterata. Neither should the Coelenterata be indicated as such (in the enumeration they can appear together with the name Cnidaria, thus with the exclusion of the Ctenophora!). We must also cease to divide (this is actually not even done in the diagram here discussed) the Eumetazoa (they are indicated here as a "branch") into the Acoelomata, Pseudocoelomata, and the Eucoelomata (they are all written with capital letters only); the same should also be made with the division of the Eucoelomata into the Schizocoela and the Enterocoela, a division which is indicated once only ("other Schizocoela") and which is represented in the linear survey with numbers only. Such a division does not correspond to the well known relationship connections, a fact which is particularly true for the group Schizocoela, yet it is also valid for the group Enterocoela (e.g. the separation of the Brachiopoda from the Chaetognatha,

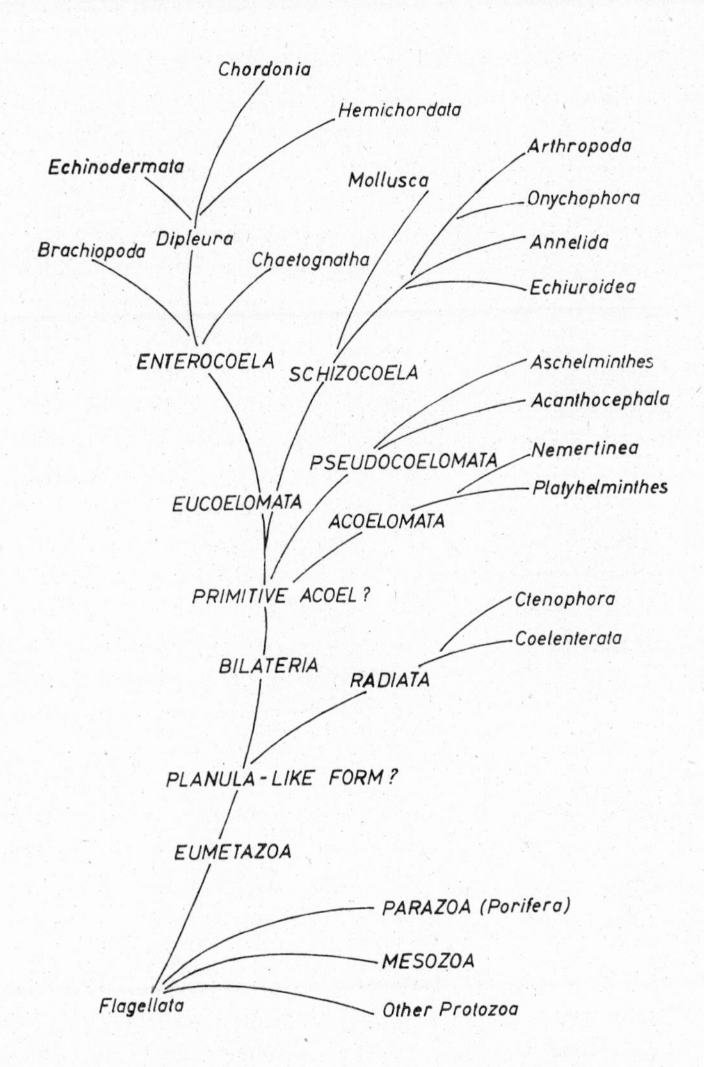

Fig. 62. Genealogical tree constructed by M.J. Guthrie and J.M. Anderson, following the ideas of Hyman.

the position of the Mollusca, etc.). If we represent the left-hand main branch as a continuation of the right-hand main branch—and this is actually the main change we have to make—we must necessarily also make some other minor changes in order to reach finally a clear separation of the Ameria, Polymeria, and the Oligomeria.

All these differences appear even slighter if we simplify the diagram proposed by Hyman in the way this was done, for example, by Guthrie and Anderson (1957:219, Fig. 73, Fig. 62), and if we do something similar with my attempt to construct a genealogical tree of the animal world.

Thus it appears to me that in spite of the apparently great differences of opinion which presently still exist regarding the true course of the evolution of animals we will nevertheless reach a general accord between all the zoologists in a not very distant future. The spectrum has certainly become now considerably narrowed. The main difference can be found in the fact—which appears clearly in my discussion and in my systematic survey—first, that I consider the Turbellaria as the starting point of the whole evolution of the Eumetazoa, and secondly, that I suggest that we must discontinue to use in our taxonomic concepts the difference which is found at the basis of the two groups, the Protostomia and the Deuterostomia; these two parallel lines of evolution must now be abandoned. It will not be difficult to solve all the remaining problems.

BIBLIOGRAPHY

ALVARADO R. (1953). On the origin and evolution of the coelomatous Metazoa. *Proc. XIVth Internat. Congress of Zool., Copenhagen.*

ALVARADO R. (1960) La evolucion morfologica del reino animal. *Rev. Univ. Madrid* **8.**

AWERINZEW S. (1910) Über die Stellung im System u. d. Klassifikation d. Protozoa. *Biol. Zbl.* **30.**

AX P. (1957) Ein chordoides Stützorgan bei Turbellarien. *Z. f. Morph. Ökol. Tiere* **46.**

BAKER J. R. (1948) The status of the Protozoa. *Nature, Lond.* 161.

BALTZER F. S. (1931) Sipunculida. In *Handbuch* der *Zoologie*, edited by KÜKENTHAL–KRUMBACH.

BATHAM E. J., PANTIN C. F. A. and ROBSON E. (1960) The nerve-net of the sea anemone *Metridium senile. Quart. J. micr. Sci.* 101.

BEER DE G. (1954) Archaeopteryx and evolution, *Advanc. Sci., Lond.* **42.**

BEER DE G. (1954 a) The evolution of Metazoa. *Evolution as a process* (edited by HUXLEY *et al.).* Allen and Unwin, London.

BEER DE G. (1958) *Embryos and Ancestors,* – 4th ed. Clarendon Press, Oxford.

BEER DE G. (1959) Paedomorphosis. *Proc. XVth Intern. Congress of Zool. London,* 1958.

BERG S. E. (1941) Die Entwicklung u. Koloniebildung bei *Funiculina quadrangularis* (Pall.). *Zool. bidrag, Uppsala* **20.**

BEKLEMISCHEW W. N. (1958) *Grundlagen d. vergl. Anat. d. Wirbellosen. I.* VEB, Berlin.

BERRILL N. J. (1955) *The Origin of Vertebrata.* Clarendon Press, Oxford.

BERTALANFFY V. L. *Handbuch d. Biologie.*

BEUERLEIN K. (1955) Biolog. Systematik u. Phylogenie *Zool. Jahrb. Anat.* **74.**

BIOCEA E. (1956) Schema di classificazione dei Protozoi e proposta di una nuova classe. *R.C. Acad. Lincei* **21,** No 6.

BOETTGER C. R. (1952) Die Stämme des Tierreiches in ihrer systematischen Gliederung (The classification of the different branches of the animal kingdom). *Abh. Braunschweig. wiss. Ges.* **4.**

BOETTGER C. R. (1955) Beiträge zur Systematik der Urmollusken (Amphineura). *Verb. Deut. Zool. Ges., Erlangen.*

BOETTGER C. R. (1959) Discussion upon lecture of H. Lemche, Molluscan phylogeny in the light of *Neopilina*. *Proc. XVth Internat. Congress of Zoology, London*, 1958.

BÖRNER C. (1925) *Die nat. Schöpfungsgeschichte, als Tokontologie.* Ein Entwurf. Leipzig.

BRESSLAU E. (1909) Die Entwicklung d. Acoelen. *Verh. dtsch. zool. Ges.*

BRESSLAU E. and REISINGER E. (1933) Turbellaria. *Handbuch. der Zoologie* (edited by KÜKENTHAL–KRUMBACH)

BRIEN P., and RENIERS-DECOEN M. (1950) Étude d'*Hydra viridis* (L.). *Ann. Soc. roy. zool. Belg.* **81**.

BROCH H. (1924) Hydroida. – *Handbuch der Zoologie* (edited by KÜKENTHAL–KRUMBACH)

BROMAN I. (1919) *Das sogenannte Biogenetische Grundgesetz und die moderne Erblichkeitslehre*, München and Wiesbaden.

BROOKS J. L. (1954) *Evolution as a process. Syst. Zool.* **3**.

BURNET A. L. and LEUTZ T. (1960) The nematocysts of *Hydra*. III. *Ann. Soc. roy. zool. Belg.* **90**.

BÜTSCHLI O. (1921) *Vorlesungen über vergl. Anatomie.* Berlin.

CAIN A. J. (1959) The postlinnean development of taxonomy. *Proc. Linn. Soc., Lond.* **170**.

CALKINS G. N. and BOWLING R. (1928/9) Studies on *Dallasia frontata* Stokes. I-II. *Arch. Protistenk.* **66**.

CALKINS G. N. and SUMMERS F. M. (1941) *Protozoa in biological research.* Columbia Univ. Press, New York.

CARLGREN C. (1904) Kurze Mitteilungen über Anthozoen. *Zool. Anz.* **27**.

CARLGREN C. (1918) Die Mesenterienanordnung d. Haleuriiden. *Lunds univ. Arskr.* NF, **2**, 14. No 29.

CARLGREN C. (1945) Further contribution to the knowledge of the cnidom in the Anthozoa especially in the Actinaria. *Lunds univ. Arskr.*, NF. **2**.

CARTER G. S. (1940) *A General Zoology of the Invertebrates.* Sidgwick and Jackson, London.

CARTER G. S. (1949) The turbellarian theory of the Cnidaria, *Sci. progr.* **14**.

CARTER G. S. (1954) On Hadzi's interpretation of phylogeny, *Syst. Zool.* **3**.

CHATTON E. (1914) Le cnidocystes du peridinidien *Polykrikos schwartzi* Bütschli. *Arch. zool. expér. génér.* **52**.

CHESTER W. M. (1913) The structure of the gorgonian coral *Pseudopleura crassa* Wright and Studer. *Proc. Amer. Acad. Sci.* **48**.

CHUN C. (1883) Verwandtschaftsbeziehungen zwischen Würmern und Coelenteraten. *Biol. Zbl.* **2**.

CHUN C. (1892) *Die Dissogonie.* Festschr. Leuckart, Leipzig.

CLAUS C. (1864) Bemerkungen über Ctenophoren und Medusen. *Z. wiss. Zool.* **14**.

CLAUS C. (1878) Über Halistemma tergestinum n. sp., nebst Bemerkungen über d. feineren Bau d. Physophoriden. *Arb. Zool. Inst. Wien–Triest.*

COLOSI G. (1956) *Zoologia e biologia generale.* Ed. Unione tipogr. Torino.

COMSTOCK, J. M. (1925.) *An Introduction to Entomology.* Ithaca.

CORI C. I. (1937) Tentaculata. *Handbuch der Zoologie* (edited by KÜKENTHAL–KRUMBACH).

CUTRIES E. E. (1955) An interpretation on the structure and distribution of cnidae in Anthozoa. *Syst. Zool.*, 4.

D'ANCONA U. (1939) *Lezioni di Biologia e Zoologia Generale.* Milano.

D'ANCONA U. (1955) Considerazioni critiche sul sistema di classificazione zoologica. *Bol. lab. zool. gen. agr. "Filippo Silvestri". Portici,* **33**.

DAWYDOFF, C. (1903) Hydroctena Salenskii etc. *Mém. Acad. imp. St. Pétersb.* (8) **14**, No 9.

DAWYDOFF C. (1928) *Traité d'embrylogie comparé des invertébrés.* Masson, Paris.

DAWYDOFF C. (1953) Contribution à nos connaissances de l'Hydroctena. *C. R. Acad. Sci. Paris.* **257**.

DELAGE Y. and HÉROUARD E. (1896–1903) *Traité de Zoologie Concrète.* Paris.

DELSMAN H. C. (1913) Der Ursprung der Vertebraten. *Mitt. Zool. Stat. Neapel.*

DELSMAN H. C. (1922) *The Ancestry of Vertebrates.* Amerfort.

DOBELL C. C. (1911) The principles of protistology. *Arch. f. Protistenk.* **23**.

DOGIEL V. (1925) Über d. geschlechtl. Prozesse bei Infusorien (speziell bei Ophryoscolecidae). *Arch. Protistenk.* **50**.

DOGIEL V. (1947) *Zoologia bespozvonoinih (Zoology of Invertebrates).* Moscow.

DOGIEL V. (1954) Oligomerizacija homologičnyh organov (The oligomerization of the homologous organs). *Izd. Leningr. Univ., Leningrad.*

DOHRN A. (1875) *Der Ursprung der Wirbeltiere und das Prinzip des Funktionswechsels.* Leipzig.

DOLLO L. (1893) Les lois de l'èvolution. *Bull. soc. geol.* III.

DOLLO L. (1922) Les Cephalopodes deroulés et l'irréversibilité de l'évolution. *Bijdrag tot de dierk.* **22**.

DOUGHERTY E. C. and ALLEN M. B. (1959) Speculation on the position of the Cryptomonads in protistan phylogeny. *Proc. XVth Internat. Congress of Zool., London,* 1958.

DUBININ V. B. (1959) Heliceronosnije životnije (Chalicerate animals). *Zool. zh.* **38**.

DUDICH E. (1957) Ein System des rezenten Tierreiches *Opus. Zool.* Budapest. II. 12.

EBERL-ROTHE G. (1950) Über das Zwischengewebe der wirbellosen Tiere. I. Spongien. Thalassia jugoslavica, II. 1.

FAUROT L. (1913) Développement et symétrie des polypiers coralliers. *Proc. IXth Congess Internat. Zool., Monaco, Rennes.*

Franz V. (1924) *Geschichte der Organismen.* Jena.

Franz V. (1943) Geschichte der Tiere. (Edited by Heberer G. *Die Evolution d. Organismen.* Jena.)

Franzén Å. (1956) On spermogenesis, morphology of the sperm., and biology of fertilization among Invertebrates. *Zool. bidrag, Uppsala* **33**.

Franzén Å. (1960) Monobryozoon limicola n. sp., a stenost. bryozoon from detritus layer of soft sediments *Zool. bidrag, Uppsala* **33**.

Gardiner E. G. (1895) Early development of *Polychoerus caudatus. J. Morph.* **11**.

Garstang W. (1922) The theory of recapitulation: a critical restatement of the Biogenetical law. *J. Linn. Soc., London* **35**.

Garstang W. (1946) The morphology and relations of the Siphonophora. *Quart. J. Micr. Sci.* **87**. II.

Gaskell W. H. (1908) *The origin of Vertebrates.* London.

Gélei V. J. (1939) Ein Vergleich d. Ciliaten und d. Strudelwürmer. *Sborník prací vyd. k* 90. *naroz. F. Vejdovského.* Praha.

Georgevich J. (1898) Étude sur le développement da la *Convoluta roscoffensis* Graff. *Arch. zool. expér. génér.* **7**.

Gerould J. (1906) The development of *Phascolosoma. Zool., Jahrb. Anat.* **23**.

Ghilarov M. S. (1956) Soil and the environment of the invertebrate transition from aquatic to the terrestrial life. *Proc. VII Congrès de la Soc. du sol, Paris,* III, 51.

Ghilarov M. S. (1960) Nekatorije obščije zadači evolucionoj morfologiji bespozvonočnih (Some general tasks of the evolut. morphology of invertebrates). *Uspehi sovrem. biol.* **49**.

Gislén T. (1930) Affinities between the Echinodermata, Enteropneusta and Chordonia, *Zool. bidrag from Uppsala* **12**.

Goette A. (1887) *Entwicklungsgeschichte d. Aurelia aurita u. Cotylorhiza tuberculata.* Hamburg und Leipzig.

Goette A. (1907) Vergl. EntwGesch. d. Geschlechtsindividuen d. Hydropolypen. *Z. wiss. Zool.* **87**.

Goette A. (1912) *Entwicklungsgeschichte d. Tiere.* Berlin–Leipzig.

Golvan Y. J. (1958) Acanthocephala. *Ann. parasit. humaine et compar.* **33**.

Graff v. L. (1878) Berichte über fortgesetzte Turbellarienstudien. *Z. wiss. Zool.,* Suppl. **21**, 3.

Graff v. L. (1882) *Monographie der Turbellarien.* I. *Rhabdocoelida.* Leipzig.

Grassé P. (Ed.) (1948). *Traité de zoologie.* Masson, Paris.

Grobben C. (1908) Die systematische Einteilung des Tierreiches. *Verh. Zool.-bot. Ges. Wien* **60**.

Grobben C. and Heider C. Das zoologische System. *Verh. d. Zool.-bot. Ges. Wien* **61**.

Grobben C. (1923) Theoretische Erörterungen betreffend d. phylogen. Ableitung d. Echinodermen. *S. B. Akad. Wiss. Wien,* Abt. I. **132**.

GROBBEN C. and KÜHN A. (1932) *Lehrbuch d. Zoologie.* Marburg/L.

GRÖNTVED J. (1956) Planctological contributions. II. *Meded. Danmarks fis.-og havunden* **1**, No 12.

GROŠELJ P. (1909) Über das Nervensystem d. Aktinien. *Arb. d. Zool. Inst. Wien–Triest* **17**.

GUTHRIE M. and ANDERSON J. M. (1957) *General Zoology* John Wiley, New York.

HAACKE W. (1893) *Die Schöpfung d. Tierwelt.* Leipzig and Wien.

HADŽI J. (1906) Vorversuche zur Biologie von *Hydra. Arch. Entw. Mech. Org.* **22**.

HADŽI J. (1907) Einige Kapitel aus der Entwicklungsgeschichte der Chrysaora. *Arb. d. Zool. Inst. Wien–Triest* **17**.

HADŽI J. (1907a) Über die Nesselzellwanderung bei d. Hydropolypen. *Ibid.* **17**.

HADŽI J. (1908) Über das Nervensystem von *Hydra. Ibid.* **18**.

HADŽI J. (1909) Die Entstehung d. Knospe bei Hydra. *Ibid.* **18**.

HADŽI J. (1909a) Bemerkungen zur Onto- und Phylogenie d. Hydromedusen *Zool. Anz.* **35**.

HADŽI J. (1909 b) *Ontogeneza i filogeneza hidromeduze (Ontogenesis and phylogenesis of the hydromedusa)* 179. knjiga "Rada" Jugoslav. akademije znanosti i umjetnosti, Zagreb.

HADŽI J. (1909 c) Rückgängig gemachte Entwicklung einer Scyphomeduse. *Zool. Anz.* **34**.

HADŽI J. (1911) Haben die Scyphomedusen einen ektodermalen Schlund? *Zool. Anz.* **37**.

HADŽI J. (1911 a) Bemerkungen über d. Knospenbildung bei Hydra. *Biol. Zbl.* **31**.

HADŽI J. (1911 b) *Razmeštaj i selidba knidocita u hidromeduza i hidroida. (Distribution and migration of the cnidocyts of* Hydromedusae *and* Hydroida*)* 158. knjiga "Rada" JAZU, Zagreb.

HADŽI J. (1911 c) Über die Nesselzellverhältnisse bei den Hydromedusen. *Zool. Anz.* **37**

HADŽI J. (1911 d) Die Reduktion d. Scyphopolypen u. d. Ephyra von Chrysaora. *Verh. d. VIII. internat. Zoologenkongresses in Graz* 1910.

HADŽI J. (1912) Über die Stellung der Acraspeden (Scyphozoa s. str.) im Systeme. *Zool. Anz.* **39**.

HADŽI J. (1912a) Über die Symbiose von Xanthellen und Halecium ophiodes. *Biol. Zbl.* **51**.

HADŽI J. (1912 b) *O podocistama u skifopolipa (Chrysaora) (The podocysts of the scyphopolyp Chrysaora)* 190. knjiga "Rada" JAZU, Zagreb.

HADŽI J. (1912 c) Über die Podozysten der Scyphopolypen. *Biol. Zbl.* **32**.

HADŽI J. (1912 d.) *Još o ontogenezi i filogenezi hidromeduze (Once more on the ontogeny and phylogeny of the hydromedusae)* 190. knjiga "Rada" JAZU.

HADŽI J. (1913) Allgemeines über die Knospung bei Hydroiden. *C. R. du IXe Congrès internat. de Zool. à Monaco*, 1913; *Rennes*, 1913.

HADŽI J. (1913 a) *Poredbena hidroidska istraživanja.* I. *Hebella parasitica* (Ciam.) *s dodatkom: Hebellopsis brochi g.n., sp. n., Hebella gigas* Pieper. *(Comp. studies on Hydroids.* I. *H.g. (Ciam.), with addendum (H.b. g.n., sp. n. H. gigas Pieper)* 198. knjiga "RADA" JAZU.

HADŽI J. (1913 b) *Poredb. istraž. hidroid.* II. *Perigonimus corii sp. n., P. georginae sp. n.* 200. knjiga "Rada" JAZU.

HADŽI J. (1914) *Poredb. hidroid. istraž.* III. *Haleciella microtheca g.n., sp. n., Georginella diaphana g.n., sp. n., Halanthus adriaticus g.n., sp. n. Campanopsis clausi (Hadži) i o porodici Campanopsidae.* 202. knjiga "Rada" JAZU.

HADŽI J. (1915) *O regeneraciji (renovaciji) hidranata u tekatnih hidroida (On the regeneration (renovation) of the hydranths in hydroids)* 208. knjiga "Rada". JAZU.

HADŽI J. (1915a) Rezultati biol. istraživanja Jadranskoga mora. Hidroidi. I. Camella vilae-velebiti g.n., sp. n. (Results of biol. researches of the Adriatic sea. I. C. v.-v.). *Prirodoslovna istraživanja Hrvatske i Slavonije*, **7**.

HADŽI J. (1917) Rezult. biol. istraž. Jadr. mora. Porifera, Calcarea. I. Clathrina blanca (Mikl.-Makl.), gradja i razvoj s osobitim obzirom na opća pitanja o spužvama (Results of biol. researches of the Adriatic sea. Spongiae, Calcarea. I. Cl. bl. M.-M., Study on morphol. and development with special regard of the general problems of the sponges). *Prirodosl. istraž. Hrv. i Slav.*, **9/10**.

HADŽI J. (1918) *Shvaćanje sifonofora (The status of the Siphonophora)* 219. knjiga "Rada", JAZU, Zagreb.

HADŽI J. (1919) Rezult. biol. istraž. Jadr. mora. Hidroidi. II. Halocoryne epizoica g.n., sp. n., Lefoëina vilae-velebiti sp. n. (Results of biol. research. of the Adriatic sea. Hydroida. II. H. e. g. n. sp. n., L. v-v. sp. n.). *Prirodosl istraž. Hrv. i Slav.*, **11/12.**

HADŽI J. (1919 a) Rezult. biol. istraživ. Jadr. mora. Hidroidi. III. Monogonija s pomoću kompleksnih propagula (kladogonija) u nekih halecija, uz opća razmatranja o stologoniji nižih životinja (Cladogony of the Hydroids and the stologony of the lower animals in general). *Prirodosl. istraživ. Hrv. i Slav.* **14**

HADŽI J. (1922) *Teorija gdje Moser o prameduzi (Theory of the primordial medusa of Mme Moser)*. Spomenica o 50-god. rada S.M. Lozanića. Beograd.

HADŽI J. (1923) Prividna pobočna neomorfoza na stabaocetu tubularije (The apparent lateral neomorphosis on the hydrocaulus of Tuburaria) 108. knjiga "Glasa" SAN, Beograd.

HADŽI J. (1923 a) O podrijetlu, srodstvenim odnosima is sistematsko poziciji ktenofora (On the origin, relationship and systematic position of the Ctenophorae) 228. knjiga "Rada" JAZU, Zagreb.

HADŽI J. (1925) Variation des Gattungscharakters bei einem thekaten Hydroiden. *Z. wiss. Zool.* **125**.

HADŽI J. (1928) Knidariji bučate i slatke vode The Cnidarians of brackish and fresh waters) 234. knjiga "Rada" SAZU, Zagreb.

HADŽI J. (1929) Einige allgemein wichtige Resultate meiner Untersuchungen über Coelenteraten. *Proc. of the Xth Internat. congress of zool., Budapest*, 1927.

HADŽI J. (1944) *Turbelarijska teorija knidarijev. Filogenija knidarijev in njihov položaj v živalskem sistemu (The turbellarian theory of the Cnidaria. The Phylogeny of the Cnidaria and their position in the animal system)*. SAZU (Slov. acad. of sci. and arts), Ljubljana.

HADŽI J. (1946) Pripombe k van Beneden-Lameerovi inačici enterocelne teorije (Remarks on van Beneden-Lameere variant of the enterocoelic theory). *Zbornik Prirodosl. dr. v Ljubljani, IV*.

HADŽI J. (1948) Problem celoma v luči turbelarijske teorije knidarijev. (The problem of the coelom and mesoderm in the light of the turbellarian theory of the Cnidaria). *Razpr. IV. raz. SAZU; knj.* 4., *Ljubljana.*

HADŽI J. (1949) Die Ableitung der Knidarien von den Turbellarien und einige Folgerungen dieser Ableitung. *(C.R. du XIIIe congrès de zool., Paris*, 1948.

HADŽI J. (1950) *Uporedjivanje spolne faze infuzorija sa spolnim plodjenjem kod turbelarija (A comparison of the sexual phase of Infusorians with the sexual reproduction of the Turbellaria)* 280. knjiga "Rada", JAZU.

HADŽI, J. (1951) Ali imajo ktenofore lastne ožigalke (Have the Ctenophores their own cnidae). *Razprave IV. raz. SAZU, knj. 4.*

HADŽI J. (1951 a) Izvajanje knidarijev iz turbelarijev in nekatere posledice tega izvajanja (The derivation of the Cnidaria from the Turbellaria and some consequences of this derivation). *Razpr. IV. raz. SAZU, knj.* 4.

HADŽI J. (1952) *Novi pogledi u filogeniju metazoa (New views regarding the phylogeny of the Metazoa)*. JAZU, Zagreb.

HADŽI J. (1953) An attempt to reconstruct the system of animal classification. *Syst. Zool.* **2.**, No 2.

HADŽI J. (1953 a) Bemerkungen zur Hardy's Hypothese über die Abstammung der Metazoen. *Bull. sci., Yougoslav.* I. 4.

HADŽI J. (1954) Morfološki značaj pnevmatofora pri sifonoforah (The morphol. significance of the pneumatophor of Siphonophora). *Razprave IV. razr. SAZU, knj.* 2.

HADŽI J. (1955) Eine Hypothese über die morphologische Bedeutung der sogenannten Wimperrosetten der Ctenophoren. *Bull. sci. Yougoslav.* II, 3.

HADŽI J. (1955 a) Odnos med scifomeduzo in scifopolipom (The relation between the Scyphomedusa and Scyphopolyp). *Razpr. IV. razr. SAZU, III.*

HADŽI J. (1955 b) Kritične pripombe s stališča turbelarijske teorije knidarijev, zlasti Remanijevim izvajanjem o razvoju živalstva (Critical remarks from the standpoint of the turbellarian theory of the Cnidaria and some considerations on the evolution of the animal kingdom with special regard to the Remane's view). *Razpr. I V. razr. SAZU*, III.

HADŽI J. (1955 c) K diskusiji o novi sistematiki živalstva (Remarks to the discussion of a new system of the animal kingdom). *Razpr. IV. raz. SAZU*, III.

HADŽI J. (1956) Zur Abschaffung der zoologisch-systematischen Gruppe: Bryozoa Ehrenberg, 1823. *Bull. sci. Yougoslav.* III, 1.

HADŽI J. (1956 a) Vorschlag zur Ausarbeitung eines Standardsystems des Tierreiches. *Proc. XIV-th Congress Internat. of Zoology, Copenhagen, 1956.*

HADŽI J. (1956 b) Das Kleinsein und Kleinwerden im Tierreiche. Ein weiterer Beitrag zu meiner Turbellarientheorie der Cnidarien. *Proc. XIVth Internat. Congress of Zoology, Copenhagen.*

HADŽI J. (1957) Die morphologische Bedeutung der Wimperrosetten der Ktenophoren. *J. Fac. sci. Hokkaido Univ.*, ser. VI., zool., 13. Prof. T. Uchida jubilee vol., VIII.

HADŽI J. (1957 a) Zur Diskussion über die Abstammung der Eumetazoen. *Verh. dtsch. zool. Ges. Graz.*

HADŽI J. (1958) Za opustitev sistematske zoološke skupine Bryozoa Ehrenberg 1823. (For the abolition of the zool. syst. group of Bryozoa Ehrbg 1823). *Razpr. IV. razr. SAZU*, IV.

HADŽI J. (1958 a) Über die Verwandtschaftsverhältnisse der Chaetognathen. *Bull. sci. Yougoslav.* IV, 2/3.

HADŽI J. (1958 b) *Hydroctena salenskyi* Dawydoff 1902. *Bull. sci. Yougoslav.* IV., 2.

HADŽI J. (1959) Zum Problem der Knidarienabstammung. *Bull. sci., Yougoslav.* IV., 4.

HADŽI J. (1959 a) Izvor in sorodniški odnosi hetognatov (The origin and relationship of the Chaetognatha). *Razpr. IV. razr. SAZU*, V.

HADŽI J. (1959 b) Štiri knidariološke študije (Four cnidariological studies). *Razpr. IV. razr. SAZU*, V.

HAECKEL E. (1874) Die Gastrea-Theorie, die phylogenetische Classification des Tierreiches und die Homologie der Keimblätter. *Jen. Natwiss.* 8.

HAECKEL E. (1896) *Systematische Phylogenie.* Berlin.

HALL R. P. (1953) *Protozoology.* New York.

HANSON E. D. (1958) On the origin of the Metazoa. *Syst. Zool.* 7.

HANSTRÖM B. (1928) *Vergleichende Anatomie d. Nervensystems d. wirbellosen Tiere.* Berlin.

HARDY A. C. (1954) Escape from specialisation. In *Evolution as a process.* London.

HARMS J. (1924) Individualcyclen als Grundlage f.d. Erschein··ng d. biol. Geschehens. *Schrift. Königsberg. geol. Ges.*, I. 1.

HATSCHEK B. (1884) Entwicklungsgeschichte von *Echiurus* u. d. system. Stellung d. Echiuriden. *Arb. Zool. Inst. Wien–Triest.* 3.

HATSCHEK B. (1888) *Lehrbuch der Zoologie.* Jena.

HATSCHEK B. (1911) *Das neue zoologische System.* Leipzig.

HEBERER G. (Ed.) (1943) *Die Evolution der Organismen.* Jena.

HEIDER K. (1914) Phylogenie d. wirbellosen Tiere. In *Kultur d. Gegenwart*, 1 Art, 3, Abt. 4.

HERIC M. (1907) Zur Kenntnis der polydisken Strobilation von *Chrysaora. Arb. d. Zool. Inst. Wien-Triest* 17.

HERTWIG O. and R. (1878) Der Organismus der Medusen. *Denkschr. Med. natwiss. Ges., Jena.*

HERTWIG O. and R. (1878) *Das Nervensystem u. d. Sinnesorgane der Medusen.* Leipzig

HERTWIG O. and R. (1879) *Die Aktinien...* Jena.

HERTWIG O. and R. (1882) Die Coelomtheorie. *Jena Z. Natwiss.*

HOFFMAN, H. (1937) Die Stammesgeschichte d. Weichtiere. *Verh. Zool.-bot. Ges.*

HORRIDGE G. A. (1956) The nervous system of the ephyra larva of *Aurelia aurita. - Quart. J. Micr. Sci. 97.*

HORVÁTH J. (1947) The question of the equality of somatic and germ nuclei in respect to heredity and survival on the basis of studies in soil protozoons. *Arch. Biol. Hung.*, **5**, II., 17. Tihany.

HUBRECHT A. A. W. (1883) On the ancestral forms of the Chordata. *Quart. J. Micr. Sci.* **23**.

HUXLEY T. H. (1875) On the classification of the animal kingdom. *Quart. J. Micr. Sci.* **15** (N.S.).

HUXLEY J. *Evolution, the Modern Synthesis.* Allen and Unwin, London.

HUXLEY J., HARDY A. C. and FORD E. B. (1954) *Evolution as a process.* London.

HYMAN L. H. (1940) *The Invertebrates.* McGraw-Hill, New York and London.

IMMS A. D. (1957) A *General Textbook of Entomology*, 3th ed. Methuen, London.

INONE IWAS (1958) Studies on the life history od *Chordodes japonensis...* I. *Japan. J. Zool.* **12**. No 2.

IWANOFF P. P. (1928) Die Entwicklung d. Larvalsegmente bei d. Anneliden. *Z. Morph. Ökol. Tiere* **10**.

IVANOV A. V. (1957) Materialy po embrion. razvitiyu pogonofor (Materials on the ontogeny of the Pogonophora). *Zool. Zh.* **36**.

IVANOV A. V. (1955) O prinadlezhnosti klassa Pogonophora k osobemu tipu vtorichnortikh — Brachiata (On relationship of the class. Pogonophora to a peculiar type of Deuterostomia — Brachiata). *Dokl. Akad. Nauk. SSSR.* **100**, 1–3.

IVANOVA-KAZAS O. M. (1959) K voprosu o proizkhozhdenii i evolutsii spiralnego drobleniya (To the question of the origin and evolution of the spiral cleavage). *Vestnik Leningr. Univ.* 9.

JÄGERSTEN G. (1955) On the early phylogeny of the Metazoa. The bilaterogastrea theory. *Zool. bidrag. Uppsala 30.*

JÄGERSTEN G. (1957) On the larva of Siboglinum. With some remarks on the nutrition problem of Pogonophora. *Zool. bidrag. Uppsala* **32**.

JÄGERSTEN G. (1959) Further remarks on the early phylogeny of the Metazoa. *Zool bidrag. Uppsala* **33**.

JODEAUX J. (1958) Contribution à la connaissance des Thaliaces (Pyrosoma et Doliolum). *Ann. Soc. Zool. Belg.* **88**.

KATSNELSON Z. S. (1948) Gastrulatsiya i obrazovanie endodermy (Gastrulation and formation of the endoderm). *Uspekhi sovrem. biol.* **25**.

KAESTNER A. (1954) *Lehrbuch d. speziellen Zoologie.* G. Fischer, Jena.

KEMNA A. (1908–9). Morphologie des Coelentaires. *Ann. Soc. roy. zool et malacol. Belg.* **43—44**.

KEPNER W. A. (1911) Nematocysts of *Microstoma. Biol. Bull.* **20**.

KOFOID C. A. (1940) Cell and organism. In : *The cell and protoplasm.* Lancaster, Pa.

KOFOID C. A. and SWEZY O. (1921) The free-living unarmored Dinoflagellata. *Mem. Univ. Califo.* **5**.

KOMAI T. (1935) *Stephanoscyphus* and *Nausithoë. Mem. Coll. Sci. Kyoto Univ.*, B., **10**.

KOMAI T. (1951) The nematocysts in the ctenophore *Euchlora rubra. Amer. Nat.* **85**.

KORSCHELT E. and HEIDER K. (1936) *Vergleichende Entwicklungsgeschichte d. Tiere.* Jena.

KRASIŃSKA S. (1914) Beiträge zur Histologie d. Medusen. *Z. wiss. Zool.* **100**.

KRUMBACH Th. (1928–1937) Scyphozoa, Ctenophora, Oligomera. In *Handbuch der Zoologie* (Edited by Kükenthal–Krumbach).

KRÜGER F. (1934) Untersuchungen über Trichozysten einiger Prorodon-Arten. *Arch. Protistenk.* **83**.

KRÜGER F. (1936) Die Trichozysten d. Ciliaten im Dunkelfelde. *Zoologica* **34**.

KUDO R. R. (1946) *Protozoology*, 3th ed. Springfield.

KÜHN A. (1910) Die Entwicklung d. Geschlechtsindividuen d. Hydromedusen. *Zool. Jahrb. Anat.* **30**.

KÜHN A. (1909) Sprosswachstum u. Polypenknospung b. d. Thecaphoren. *Zool. Jahrb. Anat.* **28**.

KÜHN A. (1914) Entwicklungsgeschichte u. Verwandschaftsverhältnisse d. Hydrozoen I. Die Hydroiden. *Ergebn. Fortschr. Zool.* **4**.

KUHN O. (1939) *Die Stammesgeschichte d. wirbellosen Tiere im Lichte d. Paläontologie.* Jena.

Kükenthal W. Anthozoa u. Octocorallia. In *Handbuch der Zoologie.* Edited by Kükenthal–Krumbach.

Kükenthal W. and Krumbach Th. (Edit.) *Handbuch der Zoologie.* de Gruyter, Berlin.

Lackey J. B. (1959) Morphology and biology of a species of *Protospongia. Trans. Amer. Microsc. Soc.* **78.** No. 2.

Lameere A. (1931) *Précis de Zoologie.* Bruxelles.

Lang A. (1880) *Die Polycladen (Seeplanarien) d. Golfes von Neapel.* XI. Monograph.

Lankester E. R. (1873) On the primitive cell-layers of the embryo as the basis of genealogical classification of animals. *Ann. Mag. Nat. hist.* **11.**

Laubenfels de M. V. (1955) Are Coelenterates degenerate? *Syst. Zool.* **4.**

Leloup P. E. (1929) Recherches sur l'anatomie et le développement de *Vellella spirans* Forsk. *Arch. biol.* **39.**

Lemche H. (1858) Protostomian interrelations in the light of *Neopilina. Proc. XVth Internat. Congress of zool., London.*

Lemche H. and Wingstrand K. G. (1959) The comparative anatomy of *Neopilina galatheae Lemche* 1957 (Mollusca, Monoplacophora). *Galathea Reports* **3.**

Lenhoff H. M. (1959) Migration of 14 C-labelled cnidoblasts. *Exp. Cell. Res.*

Levi C. (1956) Étude des Halisarca de Roscoff. Embryologie et systématique des Demonsponges. *Arch. zool. expér. génér.* **93.**

Livanov L. (1931) *Puti evolutsii zhivotnogo mira (The ways of evolution of the animal kingdom).* Moscow.

Löhner L. (1911) Zum Exkretionsproblem d. Acoelen. *Z. allg. Physiolog.* XII, 4.

Mackie G. O. (1960) The structure of the nervous system in *Vellela. Quart. J. Micr. Sci.* **101**

Marcus E. (1958) On the evolution of the animal phyla. *Rev. Biol.* **33.**

Martin C. H. (1914) A note on the occurence of nematocysts and similar structure in the various groups of the animal kingdom. *Biol. Zbl.* **34.**

Matjašič J. (1959) Morfologija, biologija in zoogeografija evropskih temnocefalov (Morph., biol. and zoogeogr. of the European Temnocephala). *Razprave IV. raz. SAZU, knj.* 4.

Matveyev B. S. (1947) Rol' embriologii v izucheniyu zakonitosti evolutsii. (The role of the embryology in the study of evolutionary laws). *Zool. Zh.* **26.**

Mečnikov I. (1886) *Embryologische Studien an Medusen.* Wien.

Meixner J. (1923) Über die Kleptokniden von *Microstomum lineare* (Müll.) *Biol. Zbl.* **43.**

Meixner J. Baupläne der Tiere. In *Handbuch der. Biologie* (edited by Bertalanffy).

MIKINOSUKE MIYASHIMA (1898) Über das Nervensystem von *Hydra. Zool. Magaz.* 10 *(Japan)*

MORTENSEN Th. (1912) A Sessille Stenophore, *Tjalfiella tristoma (Mortensen)* and its Bearing in Phylogeny. British Association, sect. D., Dundee.

MOSER F. (1925) Siphonophora. In *Handbuch der Zoologie* (edited by KÜKENTHAL–KRUMBACH).

MÜLLER A. H. (1958) *Lehrbuch der Paläozoologie,* II. 1. Berlin.

NAEF A. (1931) Phylogenie d. Tiere. In *Handb. d. Vererbungswiss., Berlin.*

NOLAND (1927) Conjugation in the ciliate *Metopus sigmoides. C. J. morph. Physiol.* **44**.

OKADA Y. K. and KOMORI S. (1932) Reproduction asexuelle d'un actinie Boloceroides. *Bull. biol. France* **66**.

PALOMBI A. (1935) Eugymnantha inquilina nuova leptomedusa etc. *Pubbl. Staz. Zool. Napoli.* **15**.

PANTIN C. F. (1956) Origin of the nervous system. *Pubbl. Staz. zool., Napoli.* **28**.

PAX F. Hexacorallia In *Handbuch der Zoologie* (edited by KÜKENTHAL–KRUMBACH.)

PAX F. (1954) Die Abstammung der Coelenteraten nach der Theorie von Jovan Hadži. *Nat-wiss. Rundschau.*

PEARS A. S. (Ed.) (1949) *Zoological Names.* Durham, N. C.

PERRIER E. *Traité de Zoologie.* Paris.

PICARD J. (1955) Les nematocystes du *Euchlora rubra* (Köll.)., *Rec. Trav. Stat. mar. d'Endoum.* **15**.

PICKEN L. (1953) A note on the nematocysts of *Corynactis viridis. Quart. J. Micr. Sci.* **94**.

POLEJAEFF N. (1893) Sur la signification systématique du feullet moyen et da la cavité du corps. *Proc. Congrès Internat. d. Zool., Moscow.*

RAABE Z. (1948) An attempt of a revision of the system of Protozoa. *Ann. Univ. M. Curie-Sklodowska, Lublin,* 3.

RAYKOV J. B. (1957) Yadernyi apparat i yego reorganizatsiya v tsikle deleniya u infuzorii (Nuclear apparatus and his reorganisation in the division cyclus of the infusorians). *Zool. Zh.* 36.

RAKOVEC R. (1960) Beiträge zur Kenntnis der Art Parazoanthus axinellae Schmidt. *Biol vestnik* **7**.

REISINGER E. (1928) Amera. In: *Handbuch der Zoologie* (edited by KÜKENTHAL–KRUMBACH).

REISINGER E. (1931) Polymera. In *Handbuch der Zoologie* (edited by KÜKENTHAL–KRUMBACH).

REISINGER E. (1957) Zur Entwicklungsgeschichte u. Entwicklungsmechanik v. *Craspadocusta... Z. Morph. Ökol. Tiere* **45**.

REISINGER E. (1959) Anormogenetische u. parasitogene Syncytienbildung bei Turbellarien. *Protoplasma* **44**.

Remane A. (1936) *Monobryozoon ambulans* n. g., n. sp., ein eigenartiges Bryozoon d. Meeressandes. *Zool. Anz.* **113**.

Remane A. (1937) *Halammohydra*, ein eigenartiges Hydrozoon d. Nord- u. Ostsee. *Z. Anat., Morph. Ökol. Tiere*, A. **7**.

Remane A. (1944) Die Bedeutung d. Lebensformentypen für die Oekologie, *Biol. Gen.* **17**.

Remane A. (1950) Die Entstehung d. Metamerie d. Wirbeltiere. *Verh. dtsch. zool. Ges.*, Mainz, 1949.

Remane A. (1950 a) Theorie d. Coelomentstehung. *Verh. dtsch. zool. Ges.*, Mainz, 1949.

Remane A. (1954) Die Geschichte der Tiere. In *Evolution d. Organismen*, 2. Aufl., Jena.

Remane A. (1956) *Die Grundlagen d. natürlichen Systems, der vergl. Anatomie und der Phylogenetik* 2. Ausg., Leipzig.

Remane A. (1957) Zur Verwandtschaft u. Ableitung d. niederen Metazoen. *Verh. dtsch. zool. Ges.*, Graz, 1957.

Remane A. (1960) Die Beziehungen zwischen Phylogenie und Ontogenie. *Zool. Anz.* **164**.

Romer A. (1959) *The Vertebrate Body*, 2nd ed., Saunders, Philadelphia and London.

Rotmüller W. (1948) Über das natürliche System der Organismen. *Biol. Zbl.* **67**.

Sacarrão, da Fonseca (1952) Remarks on gastrulation in Cephalopoda. *Arquiv. do Museo Bocage* **23**.

Sacarrão, da Fonseca (1952 a) The meaning of gastrulation. *Arquiv. do Mus. Bocage.*

Sacarrão, da Fonseca (1952 b) La conception du stade gastrula et la gastrulation. *Rev. Fac. cienc.*, Lisboa, 2 ser., C-II, 1.

Sacarrão, da Fonseca (1953) Sur la formation des feullets germinales des Cephalopodes et les incertitudes de leur interprétation. *Rev. Fac. cienc.*, *Lisboa* 3.

Sachwatkin A. A. (1956) *Vergleichende Embryologie d. niederen Wirbellosen.* VEB Deutsch. Verl. d. Wiss., Berlin.

Salensky W. (1908) Radiata und Bilateria. *Biol. Zbl.* **28**.

Sato T. (1936) Über Atubaria heterolopha. *Zool. Anz.* **115**.

Savarsin A. A. (1945–47) *Ocherki evolutsionnoi gistologii krovi i soyedinitelnoi tkani (Sketches on evolutionary histology of the blood and of the connective tissue)*. Moscow.

Sedgwick A. (1884) On the origin of metameric segmentation. *Quart. J. Micr. Sci.* **24**.

Seidel F. (1960) Körpergrundgestalt und Keimstruktur. *Zool. Anz.* **164**.

Seilern-Aspang F. (1957) Die Entwicklung von *Macrostomum appendiculatum* (Fabr.). *Zool. Jber. Anat.* **76**.

Severcov A. N. (1935) Modusi filembriogeneze. *Zool. Zh.* **14**.

Sharp L. W. (1943) *Fundaments of Cytology*. New York, and London.

Snodgrass R. S. (1938) Evolution of the Annelida, Onychophora and Arthropoda. *Smithson. Misc. Coll.* **17**.

Stammer H. J. (1959) Trends in der Phylogenie der Tiere; Ektogenese u. Autogenese. *Zool. Anz.* 162.

Stechow E. (1923) Zur Kenntnis der Hydroidenfauna d. Mittelmeeres... II. *Zool. Jahrb., Syst.* **47**.

Steinböck O. (1924) Untersuchungen über Geschlechtstrakt-Darmverbindungen bei Turbellarien. *Z. Morph. Ökol. Tiere*, 2.

Steinböck O. (1931) *Nemertoderma bathycola* n. g., n. sp. In Ergeb. einer Reise nach Grönland. *Vidensk. Medd. Dansk nathist. foren.* **90**.

Steinböck O. (1936) Eine Theorie über den plasmodialen Ursprung der Vielzeller (Metazoa). Reading at the IV. internat. congress of cytology, Copenhagen, 10–15. VIII. Only the title was published and a summary in *Arch. exp. Zellforsch* **19**, 2/4, 1937, Jena.

Steinböck O. (1952) Keimblätterlehre und Gastreatheorie. *Pyramide*, **2**. Graz.

Steinböck O. (1954) Regeneration azoeler Turbellarien, *Verh. dtsch. zool. Ges.*, Tübingen.

Steinböck O. (1957) Zur Phylogenie d. Gastrotrichen. *Verh. dtsch. zool. Ges.*, Graz.

Steinböck O. (1957 a) Schlusswort zur Diskussion Remane-Steinböck. *Verh. dtsch. zool. Ges.*, Graz.

Steinböck O. (1958) Zur Theorie der Regeneration beim Menschen. *Forschung. u. Fortschr.* **4**.

Steinböck O. and Aussenhoffer B. (1950) Zwei grundverschiedene Entwicklungsabläufe bei einer Art (*Prorhynchus stagnalis* M. Sch. Turb.). *Arch. Entw. Mech.* **144**.

Stepanov D. L. (1957) Neotenicheskiye yavleniya i yikh znacheniye dlya evolutsii (Occurrence of neoteny and its bearing on evolution). *Vestnik Leningr. Univ.* **18**.

Steiner H. (1956) Gedanken zur Initialgestaltung der Chordaten. *Rev. suisse de Zool.*, **63**.

Swedmark B. and Teissier G. (1958) *Otohydra vagans* n. g., n. sp., hydrozoaire des sables... *C. R. Acad. Sci.* Paris **247**.

Swedmark B. and Teissier (1958) Armohydra janowiczi, n. g., n. sp. Hydroméduse benthonique. *C. R. Acad. Sci.* Paris. **247**.

Švábeník J. (1925) Parasitismus a metamorfoza druhu *Gordius tolosanus* Duj. (Parasitism and metamorphosis of the species G. t.). *Publik. Fak. Sci. Univ. Masaryk*, Brno **58**.

Schäppi T. (1898) Untersuchungen über das Nervensystem der Siphonophoren. – *Jen. Z. Natwiss.* **32**.

SCHIMKEWITSCH M. (1908) Über die Beziehungen zwischen den Bilateralia u. Radiata. *Biol. Zbl.* **28**.

SCHINDEWOLF O. H. (1930) Über die Symmetrieverhältnisse der Steinkorallen. *Z. Pal.* **12**.

SCHINDEWOLF O. H. (1950) *Grundfragen der Paläontologie.* Stuttgart.

SCHNEIDER K. C. (1890) Histologie von *Hydra fusca*... *Arch micr. Anat.* **35**.

SCHNEIDER K. C. (1896–1898) Mitteilungen über Siphonophoren. *Zool. Jahrb., Ont.* **9**, und *Zool. Anz.* **21**.

SCHNEIDER K. C. (1902) *Lehrbuch der vergl. Histologie.* Jena.

SHMALHAUSEN I. I. (1947) *Osnovy sravnitel'noi anat. pozvonochnykh zhivotnykh (Principles of the comp. anatomy of the Vertebrata).* Moscow.

THIELE J. (1902) Zur Coelomfrage. *Zool. Anz.* **25**.

TOTTON A. K. (1954) Siphonophora of the Indian Ocean. *'Discovery' Reports. XXVII.* Cambridge.

TUZET O. (1948) La place d. Spongiaires dans la classification. *C. R. XIIIe Congrès Internat. de Zool.*, Paris.

TUZET O. and PAVANS DE CECCATTY M. (1952) Les cellules nerveuses de *Grantis compressa penniger* Haeckel (Eponge calcaire). *C. R. Acad. Sci.* Paris.

TUZET O. and PAVANS M. (1956) Les cellules nerveuses des éponges. *C. R. XIVe Congrès Internat. de zool.*, Copenhagen.

UCHIDA T. (1929) Studies on the Stauromedusae and Cubomedusae, with special reference to their metamorphose. *Japan. J. Zool.* II.

ULRICH W. (1951) Vorschläge zu einer Revision der Grosseinteilung d. Tierreiches. *Verh. Dsch. zool. Ges.*, Marburg.

US P. (1932) Embrionalni razvoj ktenofor (Development of Ctenophora). *Razpr. prir. sekc. prirod. društva*, Ljubljana, I.

VANDERBROEK G. (1949) Revision des classes et souclasses de Chordonias inférieurs. *C. R. XIIIe Congrès Internat. de Zool.*, Paris.

WATSON D. M. S. (1951) *Palaeontology and Modern Biology.* Yale University Press, New Haven.

WEBER H. (1954) Stellung und Aufgaben der Morphologie in der Zoologie der Gegenwart. *Verh. Dtsch. zool. Ges., Tübingen.*

WEYGOLD P. (1960) Embryologische Untersuchungen an Ostracoden. Die Entwicklung von *Cypridina litoralis* (G. S. Brady). *Zool. Jahrb., Anat.* **78**.

WEILL R. (1925) Les nematocystes et spirocystes des Cnidaires. *C. R. Acad. Sci., Paris* 180.

WEILL R. (1930) Essai d'une classification du nématocystes des Cnidaires. *Bull. Biol. France-Belg.* **64**.

WEILL R. (1934) Contribution à l'étude des Cnidaires et de leur nématocystes. *Trav. Stat. zool. Wimereux*, **10—11**.

WEISSMAN A. (1883) *Die Entstehung der Sexualzellen bei den Hydromedusen.* Jena.

WESSENBERG H. (1961) Studies on the life cycle and morphogenesis of *Opalina. Univ. Calif. publ. in Zool.* **61**, No 6.

WESTBLAD E. (1948) Studien über skandinavische Turbellarien. *Ark. zool.* **4**.

WESTBLAD E. (1949) *Xenoturbella bocki* g. n., sp., n., a peculiar primitive turbellarian type. *Ark. Zool.* **41**.

WILL L. (1909) Die Klebkapseln der Aktinien und der Mechanismus ihrer Entladung. *S. B. Schrift. natfor. Ges., Rostock,* N. F., **1**. MacMillan London.

WILLEY A. (1894) *Amphioxus and the Ancestry of Vertebrata.*

WILLMER E. N. (1960) *Cytology and Evolution.* Academic Press, New York and London.

WILSON H. V. (1935) Some criticical points in the metamorphosis of the halichondrine sponge. *J. Morph.* **58**.

WOLF H. (1903) Das Nervensystem der polypoiden Scyphozoa und Hydrozoa. *Z. allg. Physiol.* **3**.

WOLTERECK R. (1940) *Grundzüge einer allgemeinen Biologie.* I.

ZALOKAR M. (1955) "Degenerate" Coelenterates. *System. Zool.* **4**.

ZENKEVICH L. A. (1945) The evolution of animal locomotion. *J. morph.* **77**.

ZIMMERMANN (1943) Die Methoden der Phylogenetik. In *Evolution der Organismen* (edited by HEBERER). Jena.

INDEX

(Numbers in italic refer to illustrations.)

Acalepha 79
Acanthocephala 78, 141, 147, 168, 395, 396, 397, 460
Acanthodea 456, 457
Acarina 272, 419, 423
Acellular state 356
Acnidaria 9, 19, 21, 78, 199, 227, 244, 324
Acoela 71, 139, 148, 172, 196, 210, 211, 223, 256, 271–277, 279, 281, 290, 291, 296–298, 301–304, 314, 315, 320, 321, 337, 368, 386
Acoelomata 78, 130, 227, 387, 390, 391, 464, 465
Acontiae 182
Acrania 296, 455, 457, 461
Actinea 89
Actiniae 73, 99, 168, 178, 183, 197, 223, 246
Actiniaria 101, 108, 117, 148, 149, 178, 179, 194, 206, 217, 228
Actinodactylus 70
Actinula 265
Aeginidae 152
Aequorea *64*, 119
Agametes 283, 289
Aglaophenia *110*, *220*
Aglaopheniidae 159
Agnatha 455, 456, 457, 461
Alcyonaria 232
Allman 53, 111
Alloeocoela 148, 211
Alternation of generationes 153, 154, 215, 219, 242, 307
Alvarado 2, 26
Ambulacralia 445
Ameria 14, 21, 27, 40, 41, 52, 72, 86, 192, 195, 253, 266, 285, 346, 388, 390, 391, 393, 399, 400, 408, 412–414, 417, 427, 429, 440, 448, 451, 458, 459
Amerous state 452
Amoebae 32
Amoebocytes 7
Amoeboid androgamet 297
Amoebosporidia 357
Amphibia 37, 457, 461
Amphioxus 56, 448, 456
Amphiscolops 316
An der Lahn 146
Anderson 465
Androconjugant 292
Androgametes 282, 284, 287, 288, 290, 292, 295, 307
Androgamont 283
Annelida 27, 32, 40, 41, 68, 123, 142, 212, 213, 251, 270, 296, 350, 384, 386, 390, 400, 401, 403, 405, 412, 415, 420, 424, 431, 432, 434, 437, 442, 454, 460, 463
Anoplocephala *58*
Anthocaulus 154
Anthocodium 154, *238*
Anthocyathus 154
Anthomedusa 10, 11, 67, 242
Anthophyta 49
Anthopolyp 98, 105, 112, 115, 116, 125, 147, 154, 164, *166*, 180, 207, 226, 410

Anthozoa 31, 71, 76, 87, 88, 90, 95–97, 100, 101–108, 110, 113, 122, 123, 129, 130, 133, 149, 163, 166, 171, 172, 179, 183, 185, 190, 195, 197, 198, 202–206, 208, 209, 211, 212, 215–219, 223, 229, 237, 238, 243, 252, 254, 255
Antimeres 10, 59, 79, 186
Antipatharia 122, 183, 232
Anucleata 354
Apolemia 121
Aposcolecida 395
Appendiculata 349, 443
Aprocta 78, 241, 224
Apterygota 416
Arachnactis *263*
Arachnoidea 384
Archaeocyathidae 31, 379
Archaeopteryx 68, 69, 348
Archiannelida 400
Archicoelomata 426
Archihiston 212, 315, 317
Architomy 215
Aristotle 13, 73
Armohydra 51
Arthrodira 456, 457
Arthropoda 387, 412–417, 419, 437, 460, 463, 465
Articulata 411, 412, 414
Artiozoaires 87
Aschelminthes 296, 389, 395, 396, 463, 465
Ascidia 68, *174*, 444, 452
Ascon 7, 369
Asexual reproduction 153, 154, 213–220, 258, 266, 278, 283, 294, 429
Aspidosiphon 433
Assymetry 134
Athecata 53, 237, 239
Atypical budding 218,
Ausserhoffer 211
Autotrophy 355, 356
Aves 457, 461
Awerinzew 363
Ax 174, 215, 450

Babić 217
Balanoglossus 174, 448
Balanophylia 170
Balfour 25
Baltzer 436
Barkley 354, 355
Bateson 442
Bathypelagic animals 141
De Beer, Sir Gavin 21, 23, 24, 33, 68, 82, 248, 300, 348, 442
Beklemischew 24, 78, 232, 244, 257, 271, 273, 274, 349, 366, 408, 411–412, 414, 416, 425
Bělař 358
Benthonic life 10, 36, 48, 152
Berrill 174, 442, 444, 445, 446, 452
Bertalanffy v. 247
Bigelow 221, 263
Bilateral symmetry 10, 14, 19, 22, 55, 102, 273, 344, 437, 453
Bilateria 85, 245, 270, 375, 380, 386, 411, 426, 463–465
Bilaterogastraea 103, 249, 250, 269, *404*
Biogenesis 343
Bisexuality 282, 284
Bisymmetry 10, 102
Blastaea 26, 229, 248, 250, 322, 326, 327, 363, 364, 375
Blastaeadae 373
Blastoderm 1
Blastopore 434
Blastostyl 159
Blastozooid 217
Blastula 322
Boas 40
Bodonidea 361
Boettger 341, 394, 408, 453
Bolorereoides 149, 219

Boreohydra 151, 227
Börner 76
Bougainvillea 64
Bougainvillinea 242
Boveri 443
Bowling 286
Brachiopoda 60, 196, 213, 296, 384, 408, 424, 427, 428, 457, 459, 461, 464, 465
Branchiocerianthus 243, 454
Branchiostoma 56, 123, 448
Branchiotrema 438
Bresslau 81, 119, 120, 148, 169
Brien 122
Broch 93, 161, 220, 242
Broman 344
Brooks 21, 160, 442
Bryozoa 32, 253, 254, 260, 384, 401, 424
Bubalocerus 70
Bucal diverticulum 173
Bud communities 162
Bütschli 79, 87, 393

Caenogenesis 35, 38, 204, 205, 317
Calcarea 332,
Calceola 184
Calcispongiae 3, 370
Calcoblast 196
Calkins 286
Calycophorae 161, 220
Calycozoa 234
Calyptoblastea 242
Campanopsidae 239
Campanularia 31, 92
Campanulariidea 242
Canalis neurentericus 454
Capitata 242
Carcinonemertes 147
Cardiocoele 388, 398
Carlgren 168
Carmarina 123
Carpobothrium 58
Carter 24, 41, 274, 350, 380, 383
Carybdaeidea 234
Cassiopea 157
Catenulidae 169
Caulerpa 307, 316, 330
Caulus 117
Cellularity 309
Cellularization 197, 229, 295, 299, 305, 309, 367
Cephalochord 450
Cephalization 132, 172, 418, 448
Cephalopoda 49, 392, 394, 454
Cerebratulus 200
Ceriantharia 101, 108, 148, 184, 194, 198, 206, 208, 209, 217, 231, 232, 264, 453
Cerianthula 264
Cerianthus 184
Cerinula 209, 263, 264
Cestoda 57, 72, 147, 192, 244, 346, 392, 395, 405, 460
Chaetognatha 60, 269, 270, 349, 384, 390, 426–429, 437, 438, 443, 445, 456, 459, 461, 463–465
Chaetopterus 419
Chatton 203, 222
Chelicerata 412, 416, 417, 423, 460
Chester 115
Chilopoda 416
Chlorella 222
Chlorohydra 224
Choanocyte 7, 327, 369
Choanoderm 3
Choanoflagellata 5, 6, 7, 308, 311, 331–333, 363–365, 370, 458
Chondrichthya 456, 457, 461
Chondrophora 67, 141, 160, 266
Chorda dorsalis 13, 173, 174, 180, 441, 450
Chordata (Chordonia) 14, 56, 67, 68, 107, 142, 167, 173, 192, 346, 349, 390, 437–459, 461, 463, 465

Chordonoid tissue *174*
Chrysaora *108*, 206
Chrysomonadida 361
Chun 18, 161
Cilia 52–54, 273
Ciliata 62, 277, 281, 284, 285, 287, 288, 290, 303, 315, 358, 360–364, 367, 368
Ciliate rosette *143*, 144,
Ciliation 276, 280
Ciliophora 300
Cirripedia 417, 423
Cladocoryne 63
Cladogony 214, *221*
Cladonema 63
Clark 124
Claus 25, 121, 168
Clava 92
Cleavage 7, 35, 206, 207, 279
Clitellata 412, 415, 460
Cnidae 9, 12, 66, 190, 191 ff.
Cnidaria 1, 8, 12–16, 19–21, 23–27, 30, 31, 38, 39, 44–47, 50, 51, 56, 57, 61–63, 66, 68, 70–75, 77–81 ff.
Cnidoblast 191, 202
Cnidocil 202
Cnidocyte 112, 114, 121, 199, 203
Cnidoid 203
Cnidom 202
Cnidosporidia 72, 199
Cnidotrichoapte 200
Coelenterata 1, 2, 4, 5, 8, 9, 21–23, 25–27, 46, 75–79, 86, 100, 145 ff.
Coelenteria 393, 425
Coelhelminthes 395
Coeloblast 12, 212
Coeloblastula 205, 207, 322
Coelocoela 26
Coelom 25, 270, 319, 325, 374, 385, 386, 392, 454
Coelom blood 436
Coelomata 23, 26, 76, 78, 85, 102, 137, 227, 244, 249, 252, 253, 256, 372, 375, 376, 380, 383, 384, 386, 387, 408, 409, 411 ff.
Coeloplana 85, *143*
Coelothelium 251
Coenenchynme 217
Coenobium 306, 308, 311
Coenosarc 219
Coenothecalia 232
Colonial theory 284, 335 ff.
Colony 308, 330, 387
Colosi 174, 376, 390, 397
Colloblast 12
Comatula 261
Compartmentalization 304
Comstock 416
Concha 170
Conjugant 295
Conjugation 280, 281, 286, 288, 289, 291, 294, 305
Copulation 146, 280, 286, 287, 303
Copulatory organs 145 ff.
Corbula *161*
Cori 41, 141, 408
Cormic organs 111
Cormidium 110
Cormobiouta 355
Cormogony 116, 234
Cormophyta 309
Cormus 104, 109, 195, 219 330 ff.
Cornularia 158, *233*
Coronal muscles 118, 124
Coronata 235
Coryninae 242
Cothurnocystis 446
Craspedacusta 241
Craspedomonadida 308
Craspedotella 66, *67*
Crustacea 44, 413, 416, 419, 451, 460
Cryptomedusoid *92*
Ctenaria 10, *11*, 80, 165
Ctenophora 8–22, 25–27, 44, 57, 59, 60, 63, 66, 70, 75–86 ff.
Cubomedusae 188, 234, 235

Cuénot 95, 353, 361, 366, 377, 378
421, 422
Cutries 202
Cuvier 56, 74, 86, 411
Cyclomery 253
Cyclosis 278, 373
Cyclospora 283
Cyclostomata 455
Cydippe stage 269
Cystoflagellata 356
Cytoidea 357, 358
Cytomorpha 357, 358
Cytopharynx 138
Cytostome 138, 278
Cytozoa 358

D'Ancona 87, 228
Darwin 260
Darwinism 74, 349
Dawydoff 9, 17, 18, 134, 212
Degeneration 45, 97, 367
Delage 1, 3, 78, 91, 233, 331, 371, 425
Delamination 206
Delsman 442, 445
Deltoid muscle 218
Derosomes 426
Deuterocoelomata 390
Deuterostomia 78, 325, 341, 369, 378, 381, 390, 408–411, 422, 423, 425, 426, 453, 454, 463
Diaphragma 239
Diblastica 26, 112, 353
Dichotomy 408, 413
Dicoryne 53, 194
Dicyemida 346, 366, 367
Didermique 26
Digestive system 163, 189
Dileptus 301
Dimorphism 109, 218, 279, 289, 291,
Dinoflagellata 65, 199, 203, 330, 355, 356
Diphyes 203
Dipleurula 452, 463, 464
Diploblastica 75, 78, 324, 374, 384
Diplopoda 416
Discophora 234
Discomedusae 234
Disconanthes 161
Diskyneta 77
Dissipiment 420
Dissogony 44
Dobell 276, 356
Doflein 357, 358
Dogiel 62, 78, 139, 282, 294, 320, 357
Dohrn 442
Dollo's rule 51, 53, 94, 95, 115, 141, 144, 295
Dougherty 361
Dreissensia 451
Dudich 78
Dyctylactis 209

Eberl 3
Echinodermata 10, 56, 61, 63, 74, 87, 104, 127, 184, 244, 261, 296, 393, 425, 427–429, 437, 445–447, 451, 461, 463, 465
Echinoidea 438
Echiuroidea 41, 296, 400, 414, 415, 420, 424, 431, 433, 460, 463, 465
Ecterocoelia 251, 325, 400, 402
Ecterocoelic state 423
type 403
Ectocarpa 112, 182
Ectocyte 140, 197
Ectocytium 128
Ectoderm 116, 117, 323, 324, 328, 375
Ectoepithelium 140
Ectoparasitic animals 257
Ectoplasmodium 317
Ectoprocta 123, 194, 214, 253, 254 264, 312, 420, 424, 427, 428, 433 439, 461

Edwardsia 168
Eimer 125
Eleutheria 62, *150*, *152*
Emunctorial organ 137, 278, 387
Enantia 195
Enantiozoa 1, 3, 78, 331, 334
Endocarpous gonad 184
Endocyt 314
Endomyxis 290
Endoparasitism 275, 285, 354, 367, 405, 417
Endoprocta 123, 141, 147, 194, 195, 253, 260, 266, 342, 373, 389, 390, 395, 400, 417, 460
Endosymbiosis 223
Endosymbiotic algae 222
Enterocoel theory 249, 250, 253, 400
Enterocoelia 103, 325, 400, 409, 464, 465
Enterocoelic state 386, 402, 410, 423, 425, 440, 454
Enteropneusta 173, 296, 425, 429, 430, 438, 439, 445, 446, 448–452, 454, 457, 461
Enterozoa 78, 372
Entocarpa 112, 181, 184, 185
Entodiniomorpha 295
Entomesoderm 39, 212
Entomostraca 417
Entoplasmodium 317
Entoprocta 14, 68
Ephyra 149, 157, 260
Ephyropsidia 149
Epineura 376
Euchlora 9, 12, 66
Euciliata 97, 138, 192, 215, 222, 228, 286, 301, 302, 362
Eucoccidium 314
Eucoela 271
Eucoelom 41
Eucoelomata 253, 389, 409, 424, 464, 465
Eudendrium *92*, *160*
Eugregarinida 290
Eugymnanthea *91*, *237*
Eumedusoid 92
Eumetazoa 1–4, 21, 23, 41, 78, 128, 129, 138, 143, 144, 149 ff.
Euplotes 297
Euprocta 244, 395
Evolutionary mechanics 35
Exconjugant 290
Excretory system 137
Excretory-emunctory organelle 138
Extremities 413, 441
Exumbrella 15

Faurot 178
Faussek 387
Fecampia 168, 253
Filifera 242
Fischer W. K. 462
Fission 50
Flagella 52
Flagellata 4, 7, 26, 32, 56, 62, 96, 144, 206, 214, 228, 248, 278, 285, 286, 299, 302, 317, 322, 331, 333, 357–364, 458, 463, 465
Flemming 212
Foraminifera 307
Fossores 453
Fragmentation 215
Franz 383
Franzén 296
Fundamental biogenetic law 25, 33, 37, 38, 204, 250, 252, 255, 260, 275, 279, 335, 339, 342, 383
Fungia 71, 105, 106, 154, *155*, 156, 215

Galeolaria (larva) *263*
Gametes 33, 151, 282, 283, 285–288, 299, 305
Gametocytes 150, 277, 284, 299, 305

Gametogenesis 33, 286, 305
Gamont 283, 284, 290, 291
Gardiner 212
Garstang 21, 34, 162, 204, 260, 442, 446
Gaskell 442
Gastraea 5, 7, 25, 38, 80, 96, 104, 111, 183, 205, 229, 248, 264, 323, 375, 453
 bilateralis 250
 theory 249, 250
Gastraeadae 26, 78, 87, 323, 331, 373
Gastrobionta 326, 355, 372
Gastroblasta 216, *217*, 221
Gastrocoel 402
Gastropoda 56, 65, 204, 213, 394
Gastrotricha 147, 198, 253, 254, 395, 396, 438, 460
Gastro-vascular system 164, 179, 182 ff.
Gastrozooid 162
Gastrula 206, 207, 327, 369, 373
Gastrulation 373
Gelei 276, 321, 328
Gemmatio 50
Genealogical tree 270–338, 376, 377, 380–383, 384, 412, 422, 454, 455, 457, 458, 465,
Genital system 145 ff.
Georgevitch 212
Gephyrea chaetophora 424
Germarium 147
Gerould 435
Gessner 376
Gieslén 446
Giljarov 417
Glaucoma 286
Goette 80, 93, 96, 167, 183, 189, 234
Goette-Müller's larva 210, 263
Goldfuss 357
Golfingia 435
Golian 397
Gonactinia 105, 153, 215
Gonads 44, 117, 149, 150, 181, 184, 389, 392
Gonangia 160
Gonionemus 109, *241*
Gonochorism 147, 149, 284, 286, 292
Gonocoel 387–389, 398, 399
 theory 249, 388
Gonocyte 112
Gonophore 160
Gonosoma 153, 161
Gonothyrea 92, *160*, *263*
Goodrich 443
Gordiacea 390, 406
Gorgonaria 232
Graff 25, 140, 167, 168, 196, 223, 271, 274, 277, 299
Grammaria 92
Grant 371
Graptolitha 431, 448
Grassé 359–361, 378
Gregarinida 283
Grobben 274, 408, 424
Gröntved 6
Grošelj 125, 130, 135
Guthrie 465
Gymnoblastea 242
Gymnoblastiques 242
Gynocaryon 292
Gynogametes 282, 284, 285, 287, 290, 293, 295
Gynogamont 283
Gyratrix 315

Haacke 99, 246
Hadži 5, 12, 18, 22, 23, 29, 52, 53, 65, 81, 82 ff.
Haeckel 7, 25, 33, 34, 37, 75, 80, 103, 165 ff.
Haeckelia 18, 66
Haemocoel 388, 399
Haimea 108

Halammohydra 53, 54, 94, 194
Halanthus 237
Halcampia 168
Halcampogeton 168
Haleciella 237
Haleciidae 221, 239
Halecium 220, *221*, *226*
Haleremita 241
Haliclistus 124
Halicornaria 110
Halistemma 121
Hall 281, 358, 359
Halocoryne 63
Hanson 24, 271, 279, 286, 300–305
Hanström 128, 129
Hardy 21, 85
Harms 7, 78
Hartmann 282, 284
Haswell 70
Hatschek 25, 41, 260, 357, 367, 376, 387, 408, 409, 424, 436
Hebella 187, *237*
Hebellidae 160, 239
Heberer 383
Heider 80, 176, 322
Heliozoa 289, 359
Helix 289
Hemichordata 178, 444, 463, 465
Hemimyxis 290
Heric 167
Hermaphroditism 145–149, 167, 271, 284–286, 288, 289, 291–293, 296–299, 304, 320, 328
Hérouard 91, 233, 425
Hertwig's 25, 112, 125, 126, 168, 184
Heteraxonia 376
Heterocyclic division 280, 289, 297
Heteromedusoid *92*
Heterotrophy 353, 356, 360
Hexacorallia 122, 217, 231, 232, 246
Hexactiniaria 100, 109, 122, 231, 242
Hexapoda 416, 417
Hilair 442
Hincks 242
Hirsch 277
Hirudinea 116, 401, 415
Hofstenia 148
Hologamous isogamy 222
Holophryidae 305
Holotricha 302
Horridge 134
Horváth 298
Houssai 393
Hubrecht 442
Huxley Th. 112, 369, 411
Hydra 2, 7, 9, 44, 92, 96, 107, 114–116, 124, 126, ff.
Hydranth 150, 187, 219, 238
Hydrocaulus 117
Hydrocoelomata 390
Hydrocorallia 196
Hydroctena 9, 15, *17*, 18, 81, 134
Hydroidea 53, 89, 93, 101, 107,161, 195, 236, 312 ff.
Hydromedusa 10, 17, 64, 78, 81–83, 89, 90, 92, 93 ff.
Hydropolyp 118, *160*, *166*, 175, 178, 226
Hydrorhiza 123, 131, 133, 136
Hydrosoma 117, 121
Hydrotheca 220, 238
Hydrozoa 8, 31, 52, 71, 72, 75, 87, 88, 91, 93, 95–97 ff.
Hydrula 265
Hyman 24, 25, 74, 78, 81–83, 89, 90, 92, 93, 100, 101 ff.
Hypercellular state 305, 356, 357, 358
Hypermastigida 62, 299, 362, 368
Hypogenetic development 17, 44, 210, 218, 219, 230, 236
Hypolitus 108
Hyponeuria 409

Infusoria 52, 54, 57, 140, 169, 274, 276, 278, 279 ff.

Insecta 456, 460
Internalization of gametogenesis 286, 293, 328
Interstitial cells 12, 112
Intestinal diverticules 12, 13, 14
Invertebrata 444
Isogamy 282
Ivanov 404

Jägersten 2, 5, 26, 101, 103, 246, 248–252 ff.
Jamoytius 441, 448
Jennings 289

Kaestner 100, 196, 231, 243, 246, 414
Kamptozoa 123, 141, 253, 260, 264, 401, 415
Kemna 365
Kepner 200
Kinetids 286
Kinorhyncha 395, 396, 460
Kleinenberg 115, 125
Kleptocnide 12, 66, 191, 199, 204
Kofoid 203
Koinocystis 315
Komai 143, 149, 235
Komori 219
Korschelt 176
Kowalewski 36, 178, 445
Krasińska 123, 187
Krüger 200, 203
Krumbach 79, 81, 137, 234, 246, 393, 425, 446
Kudo 281
Kühn A. 189, 212, 242
Kuhn O. 98, 100
Kükenthal 81, 100, 175, 196, 246, 393

Laceration 215
Lackey 6
Lafoëa 160
Lafoëina 237
Lamarck 74, 86
Lamarckism 34
Lameere 363, 425, 428, 437
Lamellibranchiata 213
Lang 82, 85, 140, 424, 431
Lankester 25, 26, 112, 205, 372
Lar 63
Larvacea 443, 452, 456, 457
Laubenfels 24, 110
L'echelle animal 345, 349, 380, 459
Leloup 162
Lemche 42, 349, 393, 394
Lemna 49
Lendenfeld 2
Lengerich 152
Lenhoff 122
Leptodiscus 66, *67*
Leptolida 206
Leuckart 7, 8, 25, 73, 103, 161, 164, 244, 331
Lévi 3
Lictorella 160, *161*, *220*
Lilly 334
Limnomedusae 240
Limulus 416, 442, 446, 456
Lineus 200
Living fossil 30
Löhner 140
Loxosoma 214
Lucernaria 124, *193*
Lucernariidae 88, 91, 123, 149, 158, 193, 218, 233, 234, 235
Luther 178
Lwoff 305

MacBride 82
Macroconjugant 291, 292
Macroevolution 45
Macrogamete 282
Macrogamont 289

Macronucleus 287, 289, 293, 297, 298, 302, 303
Macrophagy 169, 419
Madreporaria 31, 32, 98, 105, 154, 170, 215, 223, 232
Magosphaera 322
Mammalia 456, 457, 461
Manubrium 114, 124, 151, 171, 172
Marcus 41, 246, 254, 267, 270, 332, 333, 342, 401
Marinelli 378
Martin 204
Mastigophora 361
Mating type 291
Matjašič 192, 256, 257
Medusae 50, 52, 71, 73, 89, 127, 133, 189, 194, 209
Medusochloris 66, *67*
Medusoid 92, 103, 131, 156, 161
Medusom theory 93
Meiosis 283, 284, 286
Meixner 200, 376
Mesenchyme 112, 128, 181, 251, 368, 398
Mesenteries 148, 175
Mesoderm 117, 118, 121, 252, 264, 318, 321, 324, 328, 353, 385, 403, 425
Mesogloea 112, 117
Mesohyl 13, 112, 150, 198, 219, 264 311, 328, 353, 375
Mesoplasmodium 317
Mesozoa 87, 275, 313, 366–368, 463–465
Metabionta 312
Metagastraea 89
Metagenesis 88, 151, 155, 266
Metamerism 41, 64, 229, 251, 391,
Metamorphosis 37, 39, 208, 261, 262, 264, 266, 269, 311, 341, 419, 446
Metanephridia 142, 392, 430, 436
Metaphyta 294, 319, 326, 329, 331, 334, 354, 355, 372, 373
Metasoma 432
Metazoa 5, 7, 25, 38, 49, 54, 55, 87, 102, 103, 142, 205, 229, 251, 269, 307, 323, 331, 334, 350, 358, 391 ff.
Metschnikoff 1, 25, 26, 82, 85, 205, 206, 263, 331, 369
Microconjugant 291, 292
Microgamete 282
Microgamont 289
Microhydra 241
Micronucleus 288, 289, 297, 298, 303
Microphagy 169, 170, 188, 419
Microstoma 200
Microstomidae 169
Micrura 200
Migration of cnidocytes 203
Miles 107
Millepora 91
Milleporidae 196, 241
Minchin 358, 359
Minot 442
Minyidae 104
Miyashima 125
Mollusca 21, 41, 54, 65, 66, 72, 134, 137, 148, 168, 196, 198, 212, 285, 296, 384, 388, 390, 392–395, 413 ff.
Molluscoida 390, 424
Monera 354
Monobrachium 63
Monobryozoon 107, 214
Monocaryonic state 283, 305
Monocellular state 283, 307, 330, 357, 365, 402
Monodiscal strobilation 157
Monophylly 349, 351
Monopodium 162
Monoxenia 108
Morea 248
Morphogenetic technique 374
Morula 208, 322
Mosaic theory 300, 302

Mosaic-like evolution 68
Moser 93, 94
Moskovski 306
Müller H. A. 24, 353, 378, 379, 422
Müller's larva 20, 21, 82, 83, 269
Mycale 334
Mycetozoa 38
Myoneme 278
Myrientomata 416
Myriopoda 412, 416, 417, 419, 460
Myriothelidae 209
Myxobolus 199
Myxocoel 387, 390, 401, 419
Myxomycetes 356
Myzostomidea 412, 415

Naef 89, 250, 356
Narcomedusae 12, 15, 17, 18, 54, 66, 72, 88, 92–95, 152, 209, 221, 263, 265, 266
Natural selection 135, 140
Nauplius 36
Nausithoë 108, 117, 149, 151, 185, 186, 206, 235
Nectocalyx 266
Necton 453
Nematoblast 191
Nematobothrium 58
Nematoda 52, 57, 196, 395, 396, 460
Nematoderma 129, 196
Nematoidea 142, 297, 298
Nematomorpha 392, 395, 396, 460
Nemertinea 65, 66, 141, 191, 200, 250, 253, 254 ff.
Neocoelomata 426
Neodarwinism 28, 347 ff.
Neopilina 42, 393, 394
Neoteny 19, 21, 23, 49, 94, 274, 348, 349, 418, 443 ff.
Neoturris 123
Nephridial organ 139, 141, 142, 144, 389, 392, 449
Nephrocoel 387, 388, 399
Nephrocytes 143
Nerve-net 126
Nervous system 126 ff.
Neurenterica 453
Neuromerism 432, 434
Neuro-muscular-epithelial cell 115
Neuromyaria 378
Neuroporus 453
Noctiluca 355, 356
Notochord 450
Nuclear dimorphism 305, 385
Nummulites 307, 368
Nutation 111, 116

Obelia 64, 133, *187*
Ocellatae 134
Octactiniaria 108, 109, 122, 218, 231, 232, 238, 242
Octocorallia 158, 194, 196, 206, 231, 232
Oesophagostomum 58
Okada 219
Oligochaeta 415, 418
Oligomeria 14, 41, 64, 87, 142, 167 ff.
Oligomerization 10, 62, 64, 122, 139 ff.
Oligophyly 349, 350
Olynthus 7, 369, 370
Ontogenetic mechanism 319
Ontogenetic technique 35
Ontogeny 209 ff.
Onychophora 390, 412, 413, 415–419, 460
Oögamy 284, 286
Oözooid 108, 162
Opalinata 362
Opalinidae 285, 298, 362, 368
Oparin 359
Ophiuroidea 57, 87
Ophryoscolecidae 294, 295, 297

Opistotrichium 291
Ordovicium 185
Orthogon 128
Orthonectoida 366, 367
Osteichthyes 456, 457, 461
Ostracodermata 446, 456, 457
Ostroumovia 108
Otohydra 51, *95*
Otomesostoma 314

Paedogenesis 39
Paedomorphosis 444
Palaeostraca 416
Palintomy 361
Palmenia 169
Palombi 91, 237
Pantin 127, 130
Parabronema 58
Parallelism 65, 440
Paraphanostoma 140
Parapodia 270, 420
Parasitism 46, 192, 253, 339, 366, 454, 391
Paratomy 215
Parazoa 1, 2, 4, 8, 331, 337, 350, 362, 368, 371 ff.
Parenchyma 314
Parenchymatosa 390
Parenchymella 25, 26, 205, 365
Parthenogenesis 290, 293
Patten 442
Paucinucleata 312
Paurometamera 393
Pauropoda 416
Pax 24, 99, 100, 149, 175, 246
Pears 243, 244, 366, 389, 414
Pecten 135
Pegantha 221, *263* (larva)
Pelagia 137
Pelagic zone 48
Pelagothuria 428
Pennaria 63, 91, 110
Pennatulacea 109, 232
Pentacrinus 261
Pentamery 184
Pentastomida 413, 417, 419, 423
Pericardium 430
Periderm 107, 109, 195, 199, 233
Perigastrocoel 25, 26, 41, 130, 164, 249, 270, 392, ff.
Perineura 376
Perrier 78, 86, 87
Person (subindividuum) 116, 154, 312, 370, 405
Petrunkewitch 24
Peysonell 74
Phallonemertes 147
Pharynx 163, 183 ff.
Phascolion 433
Phoronoidea 405, 427, 429, 431, 433, 439, 448, 461
Photosynthesis 354
Phylembryogenesis 42, 44
Phylogeny 29, 35, 44, 52, 114, 185, 204 ff.
Phyta 354
Phytoflagellata 49, 355, 356, 359
Phytology 356
Phytomonadida 365
Phytoplancton 48
Phytozoaires 86, 87
Pilidium *43*
Pinacocyte 7
Pinacoderm 3
Pisces 455, 457
Placula 25
Planaria 215, 314
Planctonic way of life 10, 49, 60, 261 ff.
Planea 276
Planula 25, 38, 39, 80, 89, 158, 193, 206, 207 ff.
Planularia 367
Planulozoa 367
Plasmodial state 309, 311, 314–318

Plasmodial theory 278, 384, 459 ff.
Plasmodium 197, 212, 276, 288, 313, 361
Plasmodroma 358
Platyctena 85
Platyctenea 22
Platyhelminthes 78, 82, 137, 252, 258, 270, 285 ff.
Pleurostomous Gymnostomes 301
Plumularia *220*
Plumulariidae 110
Pneumatophorae 161
Pneumatophore 161, 162, 198, 312
Podaxonia 408, 425
Podocoryne *64*, 159, *160*
Podocyst 107, 158, 214, 218
Pogonophora 4, 168, 427, 429, 439, 461
Polycellular state 330, 368, 370, 402
Polychaeta 135, 334, 403, 412, 413, 417, 456, 460
Polychoerus 212, 223
Polycladida 14, 22, 54, 71, 81, 82, 85, 140, 148, 195, 263, 338, 352 ff.
Polycnidom 203
Polydiscal strobilation 218
Polyenergetic 72
Polygordius *40*
Polykaryonic state 294, 307, 309, 361
Polykaryonic theory 284, 290, 313, 329, 335, 386, 459
Polykrikos 65
Polymastigida 62
Polymeria 27, 52, 137, 257, 346, 388, 391–393, 399, ff.
Polymeric state 397, 405, ff.
Polymerization 9, 11, 63, 64, 142, 148, 170, ff.
Polymetamera 393
Polymorphismus 70, 109, 110, 153, 161, 214, 218, 236, 312, ff.
Polyp 189, 209
Polyphyly 349, 350, 351, 354
Polypodium 216
Polypomedusa 123
Polysegmented state 405
Polystylophora 174
Porifera 78, 79, 322, 371, 463
Porus excretorius 138
Postgamous division 289, 290, 336
Potamobius 451
Pouchetia 65
Praedatores 453
Praegamont 284, 287, 289, 294
Praesoma 432
Priapuloidea 296, 396, 397, 426, 460
Proacoela 308
Prochorda 180
Prociliata 321, 375
Poeumetazöon 273
Progamous division 291
Progressive evolution 45, 75, 98, 103, 111, 167, 259, 271, 329, 414, 449
Pronucleus 288, 289, 305
Prorhabdocoela 258
Prorhynchus 120
Prorodon 200
Prosopygia 415, 424, 425
Protandry 148
Protaxonia 376
Proterospongia 6, 7, 308, 322, 333
Proteidae 443
Protichtya 456, 461
Protista 33, 65, 66, 103, 138, 281, 282, 319, 329, 355
Proteus 348
Protobionta 355
Protociliata 285, 320, 372, 375
Protocoelomata 390
Protocytoidea 356
Protohydra 151, 216, *211*
Protomonadina 361
Protonephridia 22, 137–144, 328, 387, 390 ff.
Protophyta 65, 227, 354, 360, 363

Protosepta 98,
Protostomia 78, 271, 390, 378, 381, 408, 410 ff., 463
Protozoa 5, 23, 49, 52, 54, 56, 67 96, 149, 222, 258 ff.
Protracheata 412, 416, 419
Protrochophora 38,
Protrochula 81
Przibran 224
Pseudocerops 386
Pseudocoela 386, 389
Pseudocoelomata 64, 389, 465
Pseudogastrula 322
Pseudometamerization 64
Pseudoplexaura 115
Pseudopodia 359, 360
Pterobranchia 173, 427–429, 438, 461
Pterocorallia 32, 98, 185
Pycnogonida 416
Pycnothrix 159
Pyrosoma 66, *67*

Quinet 95

Radial symmetry 10, 19, 99–101, 135, 182, 273, 344 ff.
Radialia 78, 100, 222, 244, 245, 344, 463
Radiata 56, 73, 87, 185, 273, 344, 437, 447 ff.
Radiolaria 49, 60, 61
Rajkov 304, 305
Rakovec 264
Ratarula 162, 266
Recapitulation 25, 34, 96, 186, 205, 260, 264 ff.
Regeneration 272, 429
Regressive evolution 45, 110, 112, 116, 122
Reisinger 6, 81, 88, 120, 128, 257
Remane 2, 5, 24, 25, 26, 53, 66, 94, 107, 166, 247 ff.
Remanella 301, 303
Reniers-Decoin 122
Renovation 195, 219, 220
Repetition 440
Reptilia 457, 461
Retrogressive development 126, 132, 136, 140, 148, 149, 159 ff.
Rhabdites 66, 200
Rhabdocoela 10, 71, 172, 210, 222, 256, 258
Rhamnites 200
Rhiza 117
Rhizocephala 346
Rhizoflagellata 359
Rhizopoda 329, 351, 358, 361, 362, 453, 458
Rhopalium 133, 136
Rhynchocoel 398, 399
Rotatoria 147, 213, 272, 292, 395, 460
Rotmüller 306, 354, 355
Rugosa 185
Ruminantia 294

Sacarão 35
Sachwatkin 25, 26, 77, 206, 311, 329, 359, 361
Sack gonade 150
Saprophyta 354
Sarcosepta 31, 32, 102, 118, 122, 149, 150, 151 ff.
Saville-Kent 6, 276
Scappus 160
Schaudinn 283
Schimkewitch 389
Schindewolf 31, 32, 98, 245
Schizocoela 408, 463
Schmalhausen 379, 380
Schneider K. C. 119, 121, 125, 131, 393, 425
Schulze 215
Sclerosepta 31, 32, 180, 182, 184

Scolecida 395
Scolex 57, *58*
Scyphopolyp 118, 124, *166*, 198
Scyphomedusae 16, 31, 67, 88, 118, 124, 131, 133 ff.
Scyphostoma 90, 99, 156, 233
Scyphozoa 32, 39, 71, 72, 76, 90, 91, 95, 96, 97, ff.
Scyphyla 80
Sedgwick 103, 249, 253, 276, 404
Segmentation 385, 392, 399, 420, 427, 435, 449
Self fertilization 290
Semaeostomata 284
Semper 442
Semper' s larvae 208
Senna 263
Septa 231
Septal apparatus 122, 230
Sessil way of life 339
Sidonia 190
Siphonales 316, 330
Siphonanthes 161
Siphonoglyphe 102, 170, 230
Siphonophora 61, 67, 72, 73, 89, 90, 92–94, 101 ff.
Siphonosome 161
Siphonula 162, 262, 263, 266
Siphozooid 109
Sipunculoidea (Sipunculus) 271, 296, 400, 415, *420*, 425, 426, 429–437 ff.
Solenia 117, 164
Solenocyte 442
Sollas 1, 331, 369, 371
Spadella 433, 437
Spermatozoa 282, 290, 295–297
Sphaeries 314
Spiralia 35, 414
Spirocyte 202
Spongiae 1–3, 5–8, 21, 25, 52, 67, 124, 144, 164 ff.
Spongiaria 25, 255, 319, 333, 391
Spongicola 183
Spongilidae 322
Spongula 3, 7, 333, 370
Spora 306
Sporosac *53*
Sporozoa 53, 314, 357, 458
Statocyst 133
Stauromedusae 123, 235
Stechow 241, 242
Steenstrupia 64
Steinböck 24, 35, 120, 129, 181, 196, 210, 212 ff.
Steiner 384, 408, 452–455
Stephanoscyphus 108, 117, 149, 183
Stephanopogon 305
Stereoblastula 206
Stereogastrula 211
Sternaspis 420
Stolon 218
Stolonifera 194, 232
Stomodaeum 167
Stomotoca 64
Strobilation 128, 149, 156, 216
Stylasteridae 196
Styloid *92*
Subcellular state 357
Subepithelium 115
Suctoria 97, 215, 362
Suitcase theory 80, 249
Švabenik 406
Swedmark 95
Swezi 203
Symbionts 72
Symbiosis 225
Symphyla 416
Syncaryon 281
Syncoelomata 390
Syncoryne 63
Syncytial state 315, 317
Syncytium 197, 212, 213, 307, 309, 312, 314 ff.
Syngamy 280, 282, 285, 290
Synthetium 220
Syzygy 290

Tadpole 452, 456
Taeniolae 96, 117, 118, 180, 182, 188, 230
Taku Komai 12
Tardigrada 272, 390, 402, 412–414, 416, 423
Teissier 95
Telestacea 232
Teloblasts 326
Telosporidia 357
Temnocehala 14, 20, 70, 140, 192, 256
Temnocephala sp. 70
Tentaculata 270, 296, 405, 408, 409, 425, 426
Terminal budding 218
Tetrabranchiata 42, 394
Tetracorallia 184
Tetramery 184, 186, 404
Tetrapoda 440, 455, 457
Tetraposthis 146
Thaliacea 214, 312
Thaloidea 355
Theca 194
Thecata 110, 159, 195, 220, 222, 237, 239, 242
Thysanoplana 179
Thysanozoon 181
Tialfiella 85
Tiaropsis 134
Tornaria 451
Totton 160
Trachelocerca 305
Trachomedusae 92, 209, 236
Trachylina 90, 92, 123, 159, 189, 203, 236, 240
Trematoda 72, 147, 192, 244, 296, 367, 395, 460
Trichocysts 66, 199
Tricladida 71, 180
Trilobita 416
Trimeria 425
Trimetry 401, 404, 453
Triploblastic system 328
Triploblastica 75, 79, 324, 374, 375, 384
Trochophora 38, 39, 40, 60, 342, 421, 452, 463, 464
Tubularia 92, 174, 263, (larva)
Tubulariidae 89, 107, 172, 209, 242, 265
Tunicata 14, 36, 123, 196, 214, 296, 346, 439 ff.
Turbella 196
Turbellaria 9, 13–19, 22, 23, 31, 37, 41, 52, 62, 70, 71, 81, 85, 115, 119, 122, 123, 126, 128, 132–137 ff.
Turbellores 453
Turner 289, 297
Turritopsis 213
Tuzet 1–4, 124, 331, 332, 370
Typical budding 218

Uchida 108, 234
Udonelloidea 395
Ulrich 247, 357, 426
Umbrella 119, 133, 135, 188
Undulipodia 48, 52, 120, 142, 358
Unicellularia 30, 355
Urcoelenterata 83
Urna 436
Urodela 443
Us 82, 85

Vanderbroeck 455
Vanhöffen 235, 263
Veliger larva 41
Velum 119, 134
Vermes 379, 393, 432
Vermidia 425
Vertebrata 37, 49, 68, 69, 75, 145, 325, 328, 333, 348, 350, 421 ff.
Vesiculatae 134
Vitellarium 147

Volvocales 306, 365
Volvocidae 168
Volvox 2, 4, 7, 49, 279, 286, 322, 323, 325, 330, 372
Vorticidae 168

Wacke 70
Wandering of cnidocyts 15
of sex cells 151
Wattson's rule 68, 69, 70, 106, 300, 348, 448
Weill 202, 203
Weismann 114, 151
Wessenberg 285, 362
Westblad 140, 314
Wietrzkowski 193
Will 202
Wilson 334
Willey 442
Wolf 115, 125
Wulfert 263

Xanthellae 222
Xenophyophora 356
Xenoturbella 252, 296
Xiphosura 416

Zalokar 110
Zawarsin 336
Zenkewitch 52
Zimmermann 344
Zoa 355
Zoaea 355
Zoantharia 209, 232, 263, 264
Zoanthella 209
Zoanthina 209, *263*
Zoochlorellae 72, 222
Zooflagellata 49, 284, 285, 286, 333, 364
Zoomastigina 392
Zoophyta 74, 99, 246
Zooxanthellae 72, 222, 223, 224
Zygoneura 424
Zygote 284, 293, 305, 306, 320, 335

THE INVESTOR'S GUIDE TO UNDERVALUED ART & ANTIQUES

THE INVESTOR'S GUIDE TO UNDERVALUED ART & ANTIQUES

JIM POWELL

G. P. Putnam's Sons
New York

Published on the same day in Canada by General Publishing Co. Limited, Toronto.

Designed by Lee Ann Chearneyi

Library of Congress Cataloging in Publication Data

Powell, Jim.
The investor's guide to undervalued art & antiques.

Includes index.
1. Art as an investment. I. Title.
N8600.P68 1983 332.63 83-11109
ISBN 0-399-12692-9

Printed in the United States of America

To Madeline and Valerie

CONTENTS

	Introduction	*11*
1	*How to Buy Art and Antiques Like a Professional*	*14*
2	*English Neoclassical and Regency Silver*	*30*
3	*Oriental Flatweaves*	*45*
4	*English Porcelain*	*58*
5	*American Arts and Crafts Furniture*	*74*
6	*Classic Flower and Fruit Prints*	*85*
7	*American Brilliant Cut Glass*	*94*
8	*Chinese Snuff Bottles*	*104*
9	*American Illustrators*	*114*
10	*Nineteenth-Century French Sculpture*	*124*
11	*English Watercolors*	*133*
12	*American Pewter*	*143*
13	*Nineteenth-Century Chinese Hardwood Furniture*	*153*
14	*Twentieth-Century American Drawings*	*160*
15	*American Art Pottery*	*171*
16	*Antique Maps*	*180*
17	*American Quilts*	*190*
18	*Old Master and Nineteenth-Century Prints*	*200*
19	*How to Sell Art and Antiques for Top Dollar*	*231*
	Acknowledgments	*247*
	Index	*249*

THE INVESTOR'S GUIDE TO UNDERVALUED ART & ANTIQUES

INTRODUCTION

PAUL MAGRIEL, A SPIRITED SEVENTY-SEVEN-YEAR-OLD NEW YORK COLLECTOR of modest means, has a seemingly uncanny knack for discovering great art that other people overlook. He assembled a superb collection of American still-life paintings for as little as $1,000 apiece during the late 1950s. Mrs. Andrew Mellon persuaded him to part with one still life, and Mrs. John D. Rockefeller, Jr., pried away another. These paintings could be worth over $200,000 now.

Magriel acquired great Art Nouveau, Renaissance bronzes and American drawings for very little money, too, because art markets, like markets everywhere, are swept by fashion. While one style becomes the rage among critics, blessed by museum shows, widely sought after and high-priced, other styles are routinely ignored.

But taste changes. For instance, in the 1960s when Magriel was collecting Art Nouveau material, the critic Alan Gowans reflected prevailing opinion when he declared: "Art Nouveau summarized the essential sterility of all the late 19th century movements of which it was composed." Art Nouveau prices exploded tenfold during the 1970s, and critics express very different views now.

Back in the 1960s, few people dreamed that Oriental rugs, out of fashion for more than three decades, would become a booming market again. And back then, who could have imagined collectors paying more for a little black-and-white photograph than for a new Cadillac? Ornate Victorian furniture seemed sure to remain in the doghouse, yet it has become the darling of museum curators and art writers. Those long-reviled anecdotal, often sentimental nineteenth-century academic paintings were dusted off and now share wall space with revered Impressionists in our most prestigious museums.

Bargains abound when the crowd looks the other way. By becoming familiar with and taking advantage of market cycles, you can buy good things without spending a fortune. There's plenty that's satisfying for modest sums if you know how and where to look. The purpose of this practical guide is to give you specific recommendations. They're the result of reviewing dozens of collecting fields. I considered them with these thoughts in mind:

1. Are stars within your grasp? A field isn't any fun unless you can afford some of the best, most beautiful material. I look for those where top quality—not necessarily the greatest rarities—can be had for less than $5,000, often under $1,000.

2. Is the material decorative and useful? My selections include things you can hang on the wall, display on the floor, sit in, eat with. I avoided fields like coins and gems, which, though they can offer good values, usually stay hidden in a vault.

3. Is there an adequate scholarly literature? Some fields aren't supported by much reference material you can turn to for practical information, and I wouldn't recommend them to you.

4. Can the material be sold at a regional or international auction house that publishes descriptive, illustrated catalogs? Such catalogs give you a convenient way to gain perspective on a market, whether you are a buyer or a seller. You should visit dealers also, but that takes much longer to gain a reasonable overview, and, depending on where you live, it might be difficult. More important, if your interests change, if you need cash or if you decide to sell for any other reason, you deserve a choice of selling at auction or through a dealer.

5. Is the field comparatively straightforward for intelligent novices? While it's true that every field involves subtleties, some are much trickier than others. There are wonderful buys in Chinese paintings, but they can baffle even the experts. I wouldn't recommend that novices venture there.

6. Has the field had a big, recent boom? Steep price increases seldom happen in any field, since they involve the quirks of publicity and fashion. If a steep rise has occurred recently, a cooling-off period or perhaps a decline is likely.

So I have ruled out many fields that offer good buys for highly sophisticated, perhaps well-traveled buyers. But there are still abundant possibilities to choose from.

For example, there is elegant porcelain, handcrafted for aristocrats and available now at perhaps $100 a plate. A coffee service may cost under $1,000. Brand-new machine-made fine porcelain costs more than that.

Perhaps you would prefer original prints by important artists whose work appears in major museums: wonderful lithographs, etchings, woodcuts, engravings with prices ranging from $150 to $2,000. Some of these prints are over three hundred years old. You can't do any better with a highly promoted contemporary print.

Do you like silver? I will tell you about handcrafted silver that's treasured around the world for its classic, stylish look, yet it costs less than brand-new. You can buy many pieces under $1,000. It will embellish your dining room, and you can use it, too.

If you are drawn to the intriguing, colorful designs on Persian pile rugs but are put off by tags over $10,000, then you will want to read the chapter on a type of Oriental rug that can give you spectacular beauty at very reasonable prices—usually under $2,000.

It's difficult to find appealing antique furniture that doesn't cost a fortune. The finest eighteenth-century French furniture costs hundreds of thousands of dollars, eighteenth-century English furniture has had a steep rise, and eighteenth-century American furniture is prohibitive. I considered some very low-priced styles completely out of step with contemporary taste, then selected a category of lovely American furniture that's well documented and available, yet still offers many good buys.

That's not all. I will pinpoint nearly a dozen more areas where you can make tremendous buys, and maybe some will surprise you. In each field, I will pass on tricks and techniques that successful collectors use to buy and sell. You will learn:

What kind of material is really available.
How to recognize quality.
Important names to watch for.
Prices you can reasonably expect to pay.
How to avoid condition problems.
How to protect yourself against fakes.
Museums where you can attune your eye to quality.
Terrific sources for more detailed information.
Where you can buy.

As you will see, you don't have to be a millionaire to live like one. If you choose out-of-the-limelight, beautiful things carefully with your eye on quality, you can enjoy yourself and make a profit as well.

1

HOW TO BUY ART AND ANTIQUES LIKE A PROFESSIONAL

AN AFFABLE WHITE-MANED COLLECTOR KNOWN AS THE LONE RANGER boasted, "I've made a considerable amount of money in the art market, yet rarely do I pay more than $500 or $1,000 for anything. Of course, an art object of real merit is a different story—recently I paid $22,000 for a pair of eighteenth-century English picture frames. I've done especially well with so-called headache pictures, those by minor masters. I'm saving to buy my first 747 jumbo jet."

The Lone Ranger didn't have any formal academic training. "When I got into the art market nineteen years ago, I was a commercial pilot. I was about thirty when I decided to change careers. A man asked me for a nice living-room picture. I contacted a dealer I knew, and he sold me one for $400. The man liked it and asked how much. I said $1,000. He bought it. After he left with the picture, I looked into the mirror and said to myself, Why am I working for somebody else? I started to explore the art market."

The first essential, he explained, is to develop an eagle eye for quality.

Learning to Look

This may be easier for some people than for others, but in all cases it is cultivated by a lot of practice. Begin with a specific subject that interests you and see every possible example that you can find.

Museums try to illustrate standards of quality, so you can go to them and see what is considered good design. You'll need repeated visits to absorb the details and begin making comparisons. Edward Carter, chairman of Carter-Hawley-Hale Stores and an ardent collector, told me, "Almost wherever I travel, I set aside some time to visit local museums. This can add to your knowledge considerably over the years."

When you look at a work of art, give yourself enough time to become involved with it, to see it from all points of view. Ravish it with your eyes. Here's how Thomas Hoving, former director of the Metropolitan Museum, described his first encounter with the Bury St. Edmunds Cross, a masterpiece medieval ivory:

> I became enclosed in a pocket of silence. All light in the room seemed to fade except for a tunnel of yellow-white refulgence at the exact point where I stared—the circular center of the cross. Converging toward the center, vertically and horizontally, as if drawn to it, were two budding branches of a great tree. My mind seemed to fill with music, a rhapsodic, deep, tonal series of chords forming into words and eventually a visual image. . . . I kept looking, staring for at least half an hour. . . . I just kept staring at the ravishing work, turning it on its base one way and then another. The complexity of the sculpture and its simple harmony were awesome.

As you examine something that interests you, ask yourself questions like these—they are your keys to becoming a connoisseur:

1. What is your first impression? Does the work of art project grace, anger, sadness, power? Do the various parts contribute to a whole, or do they seem at odds with one another? Do you have a strong reaction to the work of art? Does the work of art seem honest and sincere?

2. What is the overall shape? Does it involve straight lines, jagged lines, curves? Is it about simplicity or complexity, harmony or conflict? Is it a shape that commands your attention or one that is easy to miss?

3. What materials were used and why? Why a painting on board instead of on canvas? Or watercolor instead of oil? Why oak for the furniture instead of mahogany, walnut or something else? Why a shiny glaze instead of a flat glaze?

4. How is it executed? Smooth brush strokes or slashing ones? Pale colors or rich colors? Smooth finish or coarse? A lot of decoration or a little? Does each of the artist's choices serve a purpose?

5. Why was the object made? To sit on, pray on, provide warmth, eat soup with, hold coffee? Did it play a certain role in religious ceremony or commemorate an event? Does a painting celebrate ideal beauty, extol working people, express agony, evoke nostalgia? Do the materials and method of execution make sense when you consider the apparent purpose of an object?

6. Who created the object? Was it a single individual or a number of people? Are there telltale signs to suggest who did it? Is there contradictory evidence? How important is it to know the creator?

7. When was the object created? How old is the latest technique evident in the object? Are the materials, techniques and style consistent with the era in which it was supposedly made?

8. What is the condition of the object? Do you see cracks, tears, dis-

coloration, missing pieces? Are there signs of wear in places that should be exposed to wear? Does wear look random or applied with the possible intent to deceive? Do you see evidence of prior restoration? If so, how extensive? Could the restoration be undone if it were found to damage the object?

Buy What You Can Sell

You never know when you might want to sell an antique or an artwork. Perhaps you become tired of it, or you need money, or you can afford to trade up and acquire better quality. Save yourself the headache of trying to sell what nobody wants by acquiring art and antiques that have a ready market. This means you should know several dealers who are interested in buying this type of object. When in doubt, ask. Call a dealer, describe the kind of material you are interested in and see if the dealer expresses a willingness to buy it from a collector like you. Listen for waffling. You will discover that many dealers are eager to sell but lack the capital or the desire to provide a resale market.

You will also want the option of an auction market, because the typical sales commission there is 10 percent as compared with the 100 percent markup that dealers need. Auction increases the likelihood that you will be able to sell and offers the prospect of a higher net for you. Ask several auction houses whether they accept material of the type you are interested in and how many times a year they sell it.

Unless you are an expert, avoid art and antiques that are exceptionally difficult to authenticate—Old Master drawings, for instance. Many artists made thousands, and only a fraction may be catalogued. There are few places you can turn to for authoritative information about a particular work, and the drawings are seldom signed. Students honed their skills copying work by masters, so there are plenty of look-alikes around.

You should also avoid markets rife with fakes and forgeries. For example, Pre-Columbian art prices soared during the 1960s, inspiring hungry craftsmen to produce a prodigious quantity of fakes. They scared away collectors, and the market remains comparatively depressed. It is only for those who really know what they are doing.

You can smell a problematic market when you discover wide spreads between offers to buy and sell. They reflect the difficulty of evaluating individual objects and determining current price levels. They also reveal the reluctance of buyers to enter the market except at a steep discount.

A coordinated collection will enhance the value of individual objects, so pick material that you like and form as rich a collection as you can afford. If the time comes to sell, you won't have much of a negotiating position with a single object, but a collection gives you considerable leverage. Objects that reveal the personal vision of a great connoisseur attract more attention and buyers than if they were offered individually. Consequently, auction houses are willing to offer quite a few breaks to land a major collection.

When to Buy

The greatest bargains—high quality at low prices—occur in fields few people are interested in. They're out of fashion. Few museums spotlight the material, though many museums may have it. Magazines don't write about it; major dealers don't handle the material; it doesn't get a big play at auction. When you discover a neglected field like this, one that seems to abound with good-quality material you enjoy, by all means pursue it.

If you are concerned about liquidity and financial safety, then you are asking for something else, because an out-of-fashion field can remain out of fashion for years. Oriental rugs, for instance, boomed during the 1920s and then crashed in the Great Depression, and by the end of the 1940s popular taste favored pastel wall-to-wall carpeting. You couldn't give away an average Oriental rug. Two decades later, the market revived. Since there is no telling just when an uptrend may begin, you are best off looking for a field where prices, while still low, have started to rise.

When there are few current books about a field, you can bet it is a sleeper. This is because many collectors are uncertain about their taste. They feel comfortable only buying a work of art that looks like something they have seen in a book which provides some information and a basis of comparison. Conversely, it is hard to arouse interest when the few books on a subject are thirty years old and out of print. The publication of expensive new books offers an obvious clue that times are changing, because publishers are very much aware of new trends.

A major museum exhibition can have an explosive impact on a long-dormant field. This was the case with "19th Century America," a show mounted by the Metropolitan Museum of Art in 1970. The show helped make nineteenth-century American paintings and decorative arts respectable, and it had a lot to do with rising Americana prices during the 1970s.

On the other hand, some museum shows mark a climax. In September 1979, the Museum of Modern Art's one-man show, "Yosemite and the Range of Light," generated tremendous interest in photographer Ansel Adams. The show coincided with publication of a $75 book by the same title. Adams appeared on NBC's *Today Show.* He was profiled in *Esquire, Reader's Digest, Newsweek* and *Time.*

Many people rushed to buy his photographs, and prices hit record levels. But anybody who had bothered to check his market knew that prices for his work were already in a strong uptrend. A little reflection would suggest that never again would so much attention be lavished on him. This was a classic market "top." Dealers weren't buying for stock—they were selling and cashing in on what they had acquired before the rush. Obviously, you have to interpret the possible impact of a museum show in terms of the current market.

Keep your eye on world events that might have an impact on the art world. For instance, since the reopening of relations with China, almost anything Chinese has become news. Decorating magazines feature Chinese motifs, scientific magazines talk about Chinese archaeological discoveries and Chinese medical practices. Tours are showing American sightseers a firsthand glimpse of the country. It's easy to find books about China. Museums have expanded their exhibition space devoted to Chinese works of art; best known, perhaps, is the Metropolitan Museum's Ming Garden. Until recent years, Chinese artists were known mainly for porcelains and bronzes, but now there are active markets for antique Chinese furniture, paintings and costumes as well.

Disasters such as a revolution can prevent buyers from making further purchases or force them to sell a portion of their holdings. A resulting oversupply can mean weak prices, a good buying opportunity if you like the material. For instance, in 1974 a coup toppled the Portuguese government. Some Portuguese bankers were heavy buyers of Chinese export porcelain made by eighteenth-century Chinese potters according to Western designs. After the revolution they couldn't get their money out of the country to buy more porcelain. Prices dropped as much as 50 percent and remained depressed for several years until enough new buyers entered the market.

Window on the Market

Since auction houses thrive on volume sales, they offer you a passing parade, a whole new assortment every week or two, according to the frequency of sales. Even though auction as well as dealer offerings represent what happens to be available and what sells, not necessarily what is good, you can quickly educate your eye by attending the presale exhibitions. Typically they last several days. You can touch things and educate your tactile sense, something usually not possible in a museum. Prospective bidders pick up porcelain and inspect it for cracks, examine the hallmarks on silver, rub fingers across the nap of a rug, pull out drawers and peer at the unfinished wood of antique furniture.

Illustrated auction catalogs with prices give you a convenient, armchair view of a market, showing you what is available at auction for how much. Moreover, after you have absorbed some survey books about a collecting field, you will notice what kinds of objects are not offered at auction and thus become aware of the rarities in a field.

You can learn a great deal from the descriptions provided, because they tend to be more detailed than what you will find in most dealer or even museum catalogs. The process of familiarizing yourself with terms is likely to help you notice more about the fine points they describe.

Moreover, auction catalogs enable you to see how various factors affect value. In many cases, side-by-side comparisons of similar-looking objects that brought very different prices will make you aware of the impact of an appealing subject versus a gruesome subject, plain execution versus elegant decoration, fashionable versus unfashionable style, a famous versus a little-known name, work from an artist's best period versus a less desirable period, and so on.

Of course, an auction catalog does not tell you everything you need to know. The details described are not enough to establish attribution. In furniture, for example, both fakes and honest reproductions copy the style of authentic pieces. You can identify authentic pieces by the quality and size of boards used, the woods that provide internal bracing, the color of unfinished surfaces, the type of joints, the quality of carving and other factors difficult to describe in a catalog. And this is true of any kind of art or antiques. The texture of porcelain, its hardness, the color of paper used for a print, the amount of restoration in a painting—these and a myriad other crucial details are omitted from catalog descriptions.

Reading Between the Lines

As you peruse a work of art, notice the standard terms used to describe it. Certain distinctions can have a tremendous impact on value. Often you will find terms explained in the front of an auction catalog.

A Chippendale chair, for instance, can be a period piece dating back to the eighteenth century, or an old chair in the Chippendale style, or a recent reproduction of a period chair. When the auction house identifies it as a "Chippendale style mahogany chair," be wary. The word "style" indicates the chair is not an original period piece, merely fashioned in the style of an earlier, authentic Chippendale period piece.

A description might read like this: "Chippendale block-and-shell-carved mahogany chest, Goddard-Townsend family, Newport, Rhode Island, 1755–85." Here is the translation of that entry: the piece is made according to a style associated with English furniture designer Thomas Chippendale. However, the famous Englishman did not make this particular chest. It is attributed to a well-known family of cabinetmakers who worked in the city of Newport, and it seems to have been made between 1755 and 1785.

If the entry reads: "Chippendale mahogany chest, mid-18th century," the piece could be either English or American, since the country of origin is not stated in the attribution. The phrase "mid-18th century" means that the chest actually dates from the Chippendale period, in the opinion of the auction-house specialist. "Chippendale-style mahogany chest" would mean that the piece was made later during the nineteenth or twentieth century. It would be a reproduction and thus worth only a fraction as much as a period piece of comparable quality.

Descriptions of art are similar. If a painting is described as being by "Giovanni Bellini," this means that the auction-house specialist believes Bellini painted it. "Attributed to Giovanni Bellini" means that stylistic analysis suggests Bellini did it, but that there are reasons to doubt this. "Circle of Giovanni Bellini" means that one of the artist's associates painted the picture. "Studio of Giovanni Bellini" means that the painting was done by somebody under Bellini's supervision. If the attribution says either "School of Giovanni Bellini" or "Follower of Giovanni Bellini," the painting is believed to be the work of a contemporary or near-contemporary of the artist. "Manner of Giovanni Bellini" means that the painting is a later work, created after the artist's death. "After Giovanni Bellini" means it is a copy of an authentic painting by the artist. "Bellini" means that the auction-house specialist believes anybody but the artist did the painting, and that the date of the piece is uncertain.

Especially with Old Master paintings, you will find that most of the time, when the artist's name is used, the code words indicate that he did not paint the picture. It could be costly if a would-be buyer does not realize this.

With an attribution for porcelain, you might find these words: "Fine Meissen cup and saucer, *circa* 1735." This means the two pieces were made at the Meissen factory (Germany) around 1735, they came from the same set, and they are in fine condition. The value probably is about $150. "Meissen cup and a saucer" means they were made at the Meissen factory but did not come from the same set; the date is unknown. Thus the value drops to $125. "German cup and saucer" means the pieces cannot be attributed with confidence to any particular factory; good-quality pieces, also from the 1700s, probably are worth $100 or less.

Regardless of the code words used, most auction houses do not guarantee the authenticity of an object—it is sold "as is." Of course, there is some pressure to describe property correctly, because a house that makes even a few bloopers will be ridiculed in the trade. People are still talking about the 1977 Mentmore, England, sale where a painting was attributed to the French eighteenth-century artist Carle Van Loo—not a very well-known or popular artist. London dealer David Carritt paid $17,000, did enough research to confirm his hunch that the painting was by Jean-Honoré Fragonard, a much more important artist, and sold it to the National Gallery of London, reportedly for a million dollars.

Auction catalogs say little about condition, since often this judgment involves a question of degree. Always expect some damage. Serious damage may elicit comments such as "scratches," "repairs," "arms braced" or "reduced in height." A scratch on the back leg of a desk might affect its value very little, but a scratch across the top or the front drawers and panels of inlay will sharply reduce the value of a piece. Often, though, major auction houses produce condition reports that provide far more information than what is published in the catalog. Ask about getting a copy for an item you are interested in.

Finally, the reproduction of color in an auction catalog—and in many books, for that matter—can be far off the mark, because precise color printing is a costly, time-consuming process that the auction houses cannot afford. Blue may appear as black, yellow as orange, green as blue, beige as dark brown. Despite these limitations, auction catalogs enable you to develop valuable perspective about a market. That is why astute collectors build a library of catalogs on the things they collect.

Where to Get Auction Catalogs

Current catalogs are available from the major auction houses for $3 to $30. The cheapest ones are simple mimeographed listings of items for sale, with one or two lines of description at most. They don't help you much. Higher-priced catalogs have extensive description with a lot of color illustrations. Painting and rug catalogs tend to be among the most expensive. Add several dollars for first-class postage when you purchase catalogs by mail rather than at the door.

You can subscribe to all the catalogs published in a field. At Sotheby's or Christie's, New York, for instance, a subscription of perhaps a half-dozen catalogs ranges from $20 to $135. A small additional fee will get you postsale lists of prices realized.

During the summer, the major auction houses sell extra catalogs from the previous season to book discounters like Barnes & Noble, New York, and they can be had for $1–$2 apiece. But not everything you might want is available. These catalogs come without prices. To get a price list, just give the auction house the sale number and date indicated in the catalog.

Buying at an Auction versus a Dealer

Dealers offer several important advantages. If a dealer specializes in a field, he is likely to have stock that you can peruse year round. An auction house might hold a sale in a certain field only a few times each year. Many dealers let you take a work of art home on a trial basis. This isn't possible when buying at auction.

In some markets, particularly those with a limited appeal, dealers tend to handle finer-quality objects. If you formed an opinion based on auction catalogs, you might not think the field was very interesting.

Reputable dealers guarantee what they sell—or your money back. The guarantee appears on the invoice: it should describe the work of art in detail, including such essentials as title, artist, materials used, date, any damage or restoration.

Most auction houses sell things "as is," and you proceed at your own risk. The biggest international houses offer carefully drawn guarantees. Sotheby's has a five-year guarantee and Christie's a six-year guarantee, but liability extends only to the bold-type headings in catalogs when the painting, drawing or sculpture was made since 1870. Thus, Old Masters and many nineteenth-century paintings come without any guarantee. However enticing the catalog description under the bold-type heading, nobody stands behind any of it.

Those willing to do their homework, though, can take advantage of auction prices which often are well below what dealers charge—dealers depend heavily on auctions to supply their stock.

When to Look for Auctions

In September, the auction season starts with warm-up sales of comparatively inexpensive property. Major American sales take place October through May. You can look for important print sales in

November on the East Coast, Americana sales in late January and Impressionist-painting sales in mid-May.

Spring and fall are the favorite times for big on-premises sales by the auction houses. The weather is warm, but buyers haven't scattered for their summer vacations. June is cleanup time in the United States, with sales of inexpensive property at most auction houses. But in England it is the month of the major annual sales. Country auctions thrive from June through autumn in most of the United States.

From time to time, a famous, highly publicized collection comes on the market. For instance, in 1977, Sotheby's sold the diverse Rothschild collections at Mentmore, England, for more than $10 million. The next year, Sotheby's auctioned exquisite works of art belonging to Robert Von Hirsch, and they realized an astonishing $25 million. In 1980, Sotheby's auctioned the Edgar and Bernice Chrysler Garbisch collection of Americana, French paintings, furniture and ceramics for $18 million. At the same time, Christie's brought in as much by selling ten paintings that belonged to Henry Ford II.

Such famous names and some fabulous things generate tremendous excitement, and many people mistakenly conclude that anything the famous person owned must be valuable. Well, the fabulous things might hold their own if offered for sale again within a few years, but lesser things are likely to be overpriced, and they would have a hard time making as much on their own, without the hoopla, for quite a while. Don't expect bargains at one of these sales.

You are more likely to find good buys at a sale offering a specific type of property from numerous owners. For instance, Americana sales, Chinese-porcelain sales, modern-print sales. Different auction houses like to schedule related sales close to each other so that they will attract more collectors. Many more American-furniture buyers, for instance, are likely to fly into New York when three sales are taking place during the same week rather than just one.

Other things being equal, the last sale in a series is likely to offer the best buys, because many collectors have already spent their budgets or acquired what they wanted by then. Quite a few casual buyers can be counted on to drop out, because auction-going involves a lot of sitting around and waiting while things they are not interested in go on sale.

Probably the biggest bargains occur at general sales, largely estate material. Only the most devoted, hard-core collectors show up when just a few objects in their area of interest are up for sale. These auctions are attended mainly by dealers whose business it is to pore through odd lots of silverware, lamps, glassware, tea sets, statuary, rugs, reproduction and antique furniture.

Inspecting the Property

Never offer to buy something you have not inspected thoroughly. This means looking at it from every angle. Bring along:

- A TAPE MEASURE. It will help alert you to unusual dimensions that might suggest a copy.
- A FLASHLIGHT. Any good one will do when you are in poorly lit places, examining details.
- ULTRAVIOLET LIGHT. This can reveal something like a fake signature added on top of a painting's varnish, or cracked porcelain that has been repaired. Portable ultraviolet lights are being advertised for $37. Powered by two AA-size batteries, they will fit into a side pocket and are effective in a darkened room. Write: Gal-Cam Corporation, Box 3, Freehold, NY 12431.
- A MAGNIFYING GLASS. Even though it magnifies things only about five times, this is enough to stamp details in your mind. With a magnifying glass you are more likely to take your time examining a work of art and absorbing the fine points. The most useful one I've found is a 5-inch size, the largest generally available. Bausch & Lomb makes one that sells in office-supply and stationery stores for about $25. It gives you a generous viewing area. A small magnifying glass can be frustrating because the viewing area is impinged by distortion around the edges.
- A CAMERA, preferably the instant type. You won't remember everything, but armed with a picture you can pore through reference books and see if a piece being offered is consistent with other known authentic examples.

Don't be shy. You deserve full knowledge about anything you are going to pay money for. Pull the drawers out of a chest (gently) and see what the inside surfaces look like and how the piece is constructed. Have a print removed from a frame so that you can examine it front and back. Feel porcelain for surface texture, a revealing clue to authenticity. Come back as many times as necessary to understand a piece.

You won't be able to judge everything on the spot, of course. Note signatures, hallmarks, labels, dimensions and other details, and consult appropriate reference books later. Inconsistencies will suggest additional points to check.

In the event that authorship is important, and you are not comfortable about evaluating it on your own, arrange to have an expert meet you at the auction house or the dealer's shop. This might be a university scholar, perhaps an appraiser in the field or a museum specialist. If you are contemplating spending a large sum, $50 for about an hour of an expert's time could save you grief.

If a piece has condition problems, do not buy it until you know whether they can be fixed and at what cost. Ask a museum for the name of a competent conservator who might meet you at the auction house or dealer and advise you about what's involved.

How to Establish a Bidding Limit

Once you have decided you would like to buy something, the next question is what bidding limit to set. This is important whether you are buying at auction or through a dealer. You want to determine in advance the maximum amount that it makes sense to pay.

At an auction you may become a victim of auction fever, the momentum generated by a skillful auctioneer and enthusiastic bidders. It can cost you dearly to become swept up in the crowd and decide you must have the property at practically any cost.

In their catalogs, many auction houses publish estimated price ranges for each piece or group of property, called a lot, that's offered. Overall, auction-house specialists do a fine job. But sometimes the estimates are unrealistically high or low. The reserve—the confidential minimum price a consignor is willing to accept—has something to do with this. It is nearly always 25 to 30 percent below the lowest published estimate. If the consignor insists on a high reserve, the published estimate will be higher. Obviously, you shouldn't pay more just because the seller wants more.

You are best off estimating value yourself or with the help of an appraiser. The basis for auction liquidation value, naturally, is recent auction sales. Check past catalogs for property as similar as possible to what you are interested in, keeping in mind that some important considerations cannot be evaluated from a catalog.

For paintings, drawings, watercolors, sculpture, prints and photographs, there are auction-sales indexes that can give you a quick idea of auction value. The most comprehensive one for paintings, drawings and watercolors is *Art Sales Index* (Pond House, Weybridge, Surrey, England, $140). It reports on about sixty thousand sales annually. To survey past prices and trends, you can check past volumes, which go back to the 1970–71 season.

Or you can consult Art Sales Index Ltd.'s "decade books," which give you 400,000 prices registered between 1970 and 1980. Out now are *Auction Prices of American Artists* (2 vols., $85), *Auction Prices of Impressionist and 20th Century Artists* (2 vols., $150), *Auction Prices of 19th Century Artists* (2 vols., $150) and *Auction Prices of Old Masters* (2 vols., $150).

Éditions Mayer (224, avenue du Maine, Paris) publishes *International Auction Records* ($150). It reports a limited number of paintings, watercolors, drawings, prints and sculptures. It is harder to use than the *Art Sales Index*. *Leonard's Annual Art Index of Art Auctions* (Auction Index, Inc., 30 Valentine Park, Newton, MA 02165, $165) covers paintings, drawings and watercolors sold in America. *Gordon's Print Price Annual* (Martin Gordon, Inc., 25 East 83rd Street, New York, NY 10028, $235) reports on European and American print sales. The *Photography Art Market* (Falk-Leeds International, 521 West 23rd Street, New York, NY 10011, $32) covers the photography market.

Since all these take many months to prepare, the indexes tend to be out of date by the time they are published. But they supply the background information on trends. You should use these references in conjunction with recent auction catalogs and your knowledge of dealer offerings.

Your Bidding Strategy

Before a sale, check with the auction-house personnel and make sure you are familiar with all the house rules. Many houses require bidders to register and to indicate the price range of anticipated purchases. For inexpensive items, you are most likely to be asked to show a driver's license and credit cards. With more expensive items, you will need bank references. The auction house might contact your bank to see how long you have had the account and whether in the bank's opinion you can make the kind of purchases you describe. Some houses will insist on advance cash deposits. Assume that personal checks won't be accepted.

Do not tell anybody your bidding limit. It can be used against you by the auctioneer or competitors who want you to pay more than you otherwise might.

More important, stick to your bidding limit, even when it means not getting what you want. You will probably acquire no more than 10 percent of the art and antiques you bid on, because the market exceeded your limits. But the pieces you acquire will be solid buys.

Familiarize yourself with the way an auctioneer conducts a sale. For example, advances tend to follow a pattern. When the bidding is below $200, an auctioneer is likely to call $10 advances over previous bids, then $25 advances up to $500, $50 advances up to $1,000, and so forth.

Most auctioneers sell about one lot per minute. Notice the pace, so that you can see how to time your bid. For example, some auctioneers start by calling a high bid. If nobody responds, they will call lower and lower bids until there is a taker. Then the bids rise. Obviously, with this style of auctioning, you should delay your bid until you see how low the bidding will start.

Opinions differ on the best time to join the action. Some buyers believe in entering fairly early, especially if the auctioneer proceeds at an irregular pace. You cannot always tell when the hammer will fall. A late bid, according to this view, is likely to attract attention and stimulate more bids—just what you don't want.

On the other hand, some buyers like to sit back and wait until most bidders have dropped out. Late bids can demoralize those who began to assume the property was theirs. Suddenly, they are forced to pay more money or forfeit the prize.

Whichever approach works for you, the smartest way to bid is a simple visual signal, like raising your hand. Once you have the auctioneer's attention, you might want to switch to less conspicuous head nods, minimizing the likelihood you will stimulate competition. Or when an auction house issues paddles to registered bidders, you might use your paddle to get attention, then flick it thereafter until you are through bidding.

Since voice bids tend to convey urgency, they might encourage other bidders. You should avoid them, except when an auctioneer has overlooked you.

Avoid fancy signals; holding your tie, touching your eye and similar ploys risk confusion. Since the auctioneer must watch fifty, a hundred or more bidders, it is easy for a mixup to occur, even though you explained your signals to him beforehand.

Where to sit? Front rows afford the clearest views of the auctioneer and the property. The auctioneer can see you easily, so you can use quiet bidding signals. The drawback is that you cannot see what else may be happening in the auction room behind you. You don't know whether the auctioneer is pulling bids "out of the air," running your price up—an all-too-common practice. This is why many auction-goers prefer to stand along the sides or the back of the room.

What if you suspect that an auctioneer is pulling bids out of the air or working with a shill—a hired hand who makes phony bids to stimulate action? Your best protection is your knowledge of what the property is worth. Assume you are ahead of the game if, despite phony bids, you acquire something for less than your limits.

Sometimes, though, shenanigans become blatant. You might then shout, "Where was that bid?" Or ask, "Whose bid?" Several such inquiries are likely to restrain the auctioneer. If he persists, walk out. Because there are many knowledgeable people in every auction crowd, this sort of exodus will encourage others to follow.

If you cannot attend a sale, ask about leaving a confidential order bid. This should be executed competitively in your behalf. Assume, for example, that your order bid is $600, the highest floor bid is $300, and the auctioneer advances in $50 increments. He should call your order bid at $350. In the event nobody goes higher, the property should pass to you at that price. It would be poor form, to say the least, for an auctioneer to pull bids out of the air and knock the property down at your $600 maximum.

Should you decide on making a phone bid, arrange this with the house in advance. They will phone you collect during the auction, shortly before your lot comes up. The person handling the phone will call your bids out to the auctioneer.

After-Sale Essentials

In the event you are the highest bidder, arrangements can be made for the auctioneer to pack and ship your property, if you wish. You will bear the costs. Make certain that your property will be insured. Some purchasers negotiate insurance and shipping charges before entering bids. What will the auction house do, for example, if somebody accidentally kicks a hole through a painting you purchased, before the auction house has turned possession over to you?

If you attend a country auction, you are responsible for removing your acquisitions immediately. Come prepared with bags, boxes and rope. You might be asked to pay for your purchase immediately after the bid, while the auction is still in progress.

In addition to the purchase price and costs related to shipping, you might have to pay a 10 percent buyer's premium. Not all houses add this to successful bids, but it is becoming standard procedure.

Once you receive your shipment, examine it to see that everything is in good condition. Don't accept the shipment until you have confirmed that everything is intact.

One increasingly common complaint of collectors is that a painting they buy has an expensive frame when the lot is brought to the auction block, yet it arrives later without frame. They did not receive all the merchandise they bid for. The problem is usually exacerbated by the absence of a description or picture of the frame in the catalog.

For this and other problems, contact the specialist you dealt with. Auctioneers will generally reach an agreement with you concerning repair work or adjustments necessary because a portion of the lot failed to arrive. If a dining table and set of chairs arrive with a chair missing, for example, your bill should be adjusted—if you still want what amounts to an incomplete set. You retain the right to refuse any property if it is "not as purchased." Any money you already advanced should be returned to you.

Will We Run Out of Fine Art and Antiques?

"When I got into this business two decades ago," the Lone Ranger told me, "an old Italian dealer warned me that everything good was found already. Well, it is tougher than it used to be, because more people go to auctions. You would be amazed how many business and professional people come to out-of-the-way sales.

"Despite increased competition, there are still plenty of opportunities for a good eye. The market will never be depleted. I could take you through New England farmhouses and churches with fabulous Dutch paintings, for instance. Gradually, they become available.

"A great thing about this business is the treasure hunt. I could never go to an office every day and work for a living."

2

ENGLISH NEOCLASSICAL AND REGENCY SILVER

PERHAPS NOTHING PROCLAIMS LUXURY LIKE MAJESTIC ANTIQUE SILVER. FOR some two thousand years, since the first silversmiths began hammering away, silver has set elegant tables and served as a practical store of value. In part, this is because silver stands for permanence. It doesn't burn, break or corrode. Silver recovered from sunken treasure ships has regained its brilliance after four centuries beneath the sea.

"There's joy in the collection of early silver," declared Irwin Untermeyer, who donated his splendid pieces to the Metropolitan Museum of Art. "Early silver displays a subtle and fluctuating bluish tinge that enhances the beauty of the material in contrast to the uncompromising aspect of modern work. . . . early productions, whether elaborate or simple, display great ingenuity and beauty of form."

The voluble Palm Beach collector Winston Guest quipped, "I think fine silver is more fun than racehorses or polo ponies."

Yet fine antique silver can be had for surprisingly modest sums, often less than you'd pay for brand-new. Your best bet is English silver.

During the eighteenth and nineteenth centuries, England enjoyed tremendous prosperity—the Industrial Revolution started there. English aristocrats and wealthy businessmen supported a large number of silversmiths who fashioned more table silver as well as ornamental pieces than anybody else. Consequently, you are more likely to find early English silver than American, and it tends to be less expensive, sometimes costing half as much. You can do very nicely for a few thousand dollars.

One of the most attractively priced styles is Neoclassical, so-called because it revived simple, elegant designs perfected by the ancient Greeks and Romans. When there's decoration, it tends to involve subdued forms like beading or swag. Neoclassical silver was fashioned from about 1770 to 1815. Then the elaborately decorated Regency style came into vogue, reflecting tastes of Britain's royal family. Regency silver gave way to exuberant Victorian silver after 1837.

Silver is alloyed, because in a pure form it is too soft. It damages easily. Most table silver was handcrafted from sterling—92.5 percent silver, 7.5 percent copper, the standard which has prevailed almost continuously since 1300. Silver was usually handcrafted in a shop that may have had several journeymen and apprentices in addition to the master silversmith. A large shop had as many as a hundred craftsmen.

A silversmith began with a silver ingot and hammered it into a sheet. Then he cut a piece about the size of the finished article, and he hammered it into the desired shape. Blow after blow made the silver brittle, so it had to be annealed to restore its malleability. This involved rotating it over a flame until red hot, then plunging it into cold water. Throughout the hammering, the silversmith had to be careful to avoid exposing bits of copper which, in the flame, could cause a discoloration known as firestain.

Since all this hammering roughened the surface, the silver was planished—hit with a broad, flat-faced hammer to make the surface smoother. Fine polishing was done with pumice, a soft and porous volcanic stone.

Small parts like feet, handles and spouts were commonly made from molten metal cast in molds. Temperature control was a must to avoid making the parts brittle, the surface pitted. Sterling-silver solder was used to secure these parts to the body.

Flatware

People who collect antique flatware prefer services with at least a dozen settings, not individual pieces. What we think of as fairly full services came along during the mid-eighteenth century, but they do not include knives. Cutlers, rather than silversmiths, made knives. Some knives had bone handles; others had hollow silver handles filled with pitch, the blade inserted into the pitch. Over the years, the blades tended to work loose. Silver-handled knives became a standard part of flatware services only after about 1820.

Old English is the pattern you are most likely to see. It is the least expensive, with simple lines that were popular between 1775 and 1830. Stems of forks turn up, while stems of spoons turn down. Spoon bowls taper to a point.

A number of patterns were introduced during the late eighteenth century, mostly with self-explanatory names: Feather Edge in the 1770s, Beaded Edge in the 1780s, Old English Thread in the 1790s, Fiddle around 1805. Altogether English silversmiths produced about a dozen patterns during the nineteenth century. Curiously, American silversmiths produced an estimated two thousand patterns, often with fancy names like Richelieu or Fontainebleau.

In the most desirable services, spoons and forks are by the same maker, same date. Knives have a cutler's mark. Each of the knives should be the same date. So-called same-maker, same-date services are scarce. They might average $300 per piece. Fancy settings might include nine pieces—two forks, five spoons, two knives.

If a service has utensils by several different makers, it might be worth 20 percent less than a service by one maker with one date. For instance, a service with a dozen table forks by one maker, a dozen dessert spoons by another maker and a dozen soup spoons by a third maker may be worth about $250 per piece.

In a mixed service with utensils by many makers, much depends on quality, for such mixed services tend to have many damaged pieces as well as pieces adapted to fit the pattern. In this situation, the price might be around $100 per piece, still very attractive and practical.

Coffee and Tea Services

The earliest tea services appeared around 1790. Besides the teapot, oval and drum-shaped being the most popular, a basic service includes a sugar bowl and a creamer. It might include a slop bowl and a coffeepot too. Coffeepots, much scarcer than teapots, are bigger, and they lack a sieve to prevent tea leaves from being poured into the cup. A good three-piece tea service runs $2,500 to $4,000. Add a coffeepot, and the price might go to $6,000 or $8,000.

Occasionally, you will find a chocolate pot. It is similar to a coffeepot of the same period, except that it has a hinged or removable top on the lid so that you can insert a rod for stirring up the tasty chocolate sediment. A chocolate pot may cost $2,000 or $3,000.

Check to see that the hallmarks on the lid match those on the pot. Different marks mean different origin and potential trouble if you wanted to resell the service later. Collectors prefer to have a silversmith's work intact.

Then there are tea caddies, containers intended to hold about a pound and a half of tea. They tend to be rectangular, oval, vase-shaped or boat-shaped. Most seem to be about 6 inches high. Collectors prefer pairs over a single caddy. Prices range $1,000 to $2,000 for a typical pair.

Kettles, which come with a three- or four-leg stand and a heating lamp, were made so that people could prepare tea right at the table.

These ensembles can be big—40 to 150 ounces. They were popular as centerpieces during the 1950s, but there isn't much interest in them now. If you want one, check that the kettle, the stand and the lamp have the same hallmarks. Many stands were lost, and new ones were made. Matching ensembles can be had for several thousand dollars, while assembled sets with hallmarks that do not match are worth a fraction as much.

Urns are not high on anybody's list today, either. Used to hold hot water for tea, an urn was meant to stand rather than be poured. The spout has to be horizontal, so that water can flow out easily. The shape cannot assume any of the upward curves that add grace to teapots, coffeepots and chocolate pots. Nor has anybody produced a design that makes a spigot look elegant. It seems destined to remain a clumpy little thing that interrupts clean lines. Urns can be large—perhaps 20 inches high and weighing over 100 ounces. But there are more impressive centerpieces, if that is what you are looking for. They sell comparatively close to their bullion value—$1,000 to $3,000, depending on size.

Trays, Salvers, Dishes

Neoclassical tea trays, typically oval, have simple rim decoration and a center area left plain for a coat of arms. Tea trays have two handles, weigh from 40 to over 200 ounces, and are priced from $2,000 to $5,000.

Salvers—trays without handles—come in pleasing circular or oval shapes, and often they have rather elaborate decoration around the rim. Many are raised on four feet. Salvers range from 20 to over 200 ounces and are priced from $1,000 to more than $10,000.

With meat dishes, the central area is depressed to contain juice. Some meat dishes have a well-and-tree so that juice will flow into one spot, and many have handles. Mean dishes run 15 to 30 inches long, weigh 40 to 180 ounces, and sell for $2,000 to $5,000.

Dinner plates are circular, about 10 inches in diameter. They weigh 17–20 ounces, and they are plain except for rim decoration. The later the plates, the more elaborate the rim decoration tends to be. They run $500 to $1,000 per plate.

Tureens

Soup tureens make splendid centerpieces. They are said to have originated with one Marshal Turenne of France who used his helmet as a serving dish for soup. In any event, soup tureens tend to be major pieces that weigh 100 to 250 ounces, with two rigid or movable ring handles. Often tureens became a silversmith's special project, and the craftsmanship lavished on them can send prices to $5,000–$15,000. Smaller ones, perhaps 50 ounces, can be had for about $2,500. Make sure the cover has hallmarks that match the tureen's.

Sauce tureens are quite attractive, too, with oval forms the most common. They weigh 15 to 30 ounces, and a pair might cost between $2,000 and $5,000.

Vegetable and entree dishes are somewhat bigger—50 to 75 ounces. They come in oval and rectangular shapes decorated around the rim. Prices run $5,000 to $12,000 for a pair.

Wine Coolers and Two-Handled Cups

Wine coolers belonged to wealthy families, and they represent fine-quality, large pieces of silver—50 to 60 ounces. Many were made with outturned rims and stand on a pedestal foot. To be very desirable, wine coolers must be in pairs with detachable rims and liners. Prices range from $5,000 to $20,000.

Two-handled cups are smaller, too small for a wine bottle. This is one reason they are less popular than wine coolers. Another reason: so many similar silver-plated things are awarded as trophies for every imaginable sporting event, the forms are commonplace. Two-handled cups sell for several thousand dollars. Even early-eighteenth-century pieces are inexpensive. To bring more than a few thousand dollars, a two-handled cup must have some outstanding features.

Neoclassical silver ewers, cider jugs and hot-water jugs, weighing 25 to 30 ounces, are simple pieces. You'll see vase, urn, barrel and spherical forms. They sell for $1,000–$3,000.

Candlesticks

Candlesticks are among the most popular kinds of silver, because everybody can use them. Usually collectors want sets of four or sets of two—there isn't much demand for a single candlestick. A two-light candelabrum commands a modest premium over one-light sticks.

The most distinctive part is the stem, which can be like a Roman column, vase-shaped, a tapered square or a baluster shape. The best candlesticks are cast. This means they are made with a good deal of silver and are durable. Turn a candlestick upside down, and if you see an open bottom the piece is cast. When an auction catalog gives the weight of a candlestick, that means it is cast. Good pairs run $3,000–$4,000.

If you see a solid bottom, the candlestick is filled with composition, commonly pitch. A catalog will say "weighted base," and it won't give a weight for the piece. The silver tends to be thin, particularly vulnerable to wear. These candlesticks sell for about $1,500 per pair.

A Potpourri of Silver

Cake baskets and breadbaskets, though small, are prized because many have delicate pierced decoration. Late-eighteenth-century pieces are thin, usually oval forms. After 1810 the forms became heavier, rectangular. Most baskets sell for $1,500 to $2,000. Elaborate decoration can double the price.

Tankards are popular pieces, too. They are a big hunk of silver, perhaps 25 ounces in a piece 7 inches high, usually tapered cylindrical forms with banded decoration. Tankards cost several thousand dollars.

Every once in a while, you will see an epergne, a spidery object with four to six branches that end in dishes for sweets or condiments. There is not much interest in these now. An epergne can weigh 100 ounces and measure 30 inches across—it takes a lot of room on a table. Since the branches invite damage, many are replaced or restored. If you are interested in an epergne, check that the centerpiece, the branches and the dishes have matching marks. An epergne can cost several thousand dollars, depending on size.

Under $1,000

Some pieces of silver are almost always under $1,000. Beakers, for instance. They are 2 to 5 inches high, light pieces decorated with a little engraving, and sell for $500 to $700.

Goblets are more interesting. They are 6 to 8 inches high and weigh about 8 to 10 ounces—more than twice the weight of beakers. For $600–$800 you can buy a goblet with handsome engraved or lobed decoration.

Small items like silver salts, wine coasters, cruet sets, toast racks, saucepans, chamber sticks, a dozen labels for wine and liquor bottles, all are under $1,000.

1

2

3

English silversmiths crafted more fine silver than anyone else. Consequently, you can acquire fine pieces for less than scarce, similarly-styled American silver. (1) Candlesticks. Height, 9½ inches; total weight, 39 ounces; $2,500–$3,500. *Sotheby Parke Bernet.* (2) Entre dishes by Robert and Thomas Makepeace, London, 1794. Diameter, 10⅜ inches; weight, 43 ounces; $1,000–$1,500. *Christie's, New York.* (3) Sauce tureens and covers by Benjamin Laver, London, 1782. Length, 8¾ inches; weight, 44 ounces; $3,500–$5,000. *Christie's, New York.*

Impact of Design

Design quality can account for a tenfold difference in value between two pieces. As you examine something you are interested in, ask yourself questions like these:

- How successfully has the silversmith served the practical requirements of a soup tureen, for instance, and made it appealing as a work of art?
- How pleasing are the proportions?
- Are the lines beautiful?
- Is the decoration crisp and clearly articulated?
- How well does it complement the form?
- Does the piece take advantage of silver's reflective properties?

These questions are easy to answer when you compare many pieces. A museum collection is a good place to begin, since it is likely to include superb examples of their type. Once you are familiar with them, you can evaluate what you see in the marketplace.

Two Famous Silversmiths

Two English silversmiths stand out above all others during the late eighteenth and early nineteenth centuries. Their work tends to be better designed and commands premium prices.

The best-known silversmith working in an austere, Neoclassical style was Hester Bateman. When her husband, John, a gold-chain maker, died in 1760, she resolved to hold the family business together. She started producing silver flatware, then turned to more ambitious domestic pieces. They are distinguished for understated elegance. She died in 1794, and her son Peter, daughter-in-law Ann and grandson William continued making attractive silver.

Two decades ago, after a biography had made collectors aware of her contributions, her prices had a steep rise. Her premium has declined since then as collectors concluded she wasn't so different from other fine Neoclassical contemporaries. Still, there is a premium. What you see on the market are mostly smaller pieces. For instance:

- George III small silver basket, vase shape, pierced with scrollwork and arches and chased with laurel festoons, twisted ropelike rim, openwork swing handle, pierced pedestal foot, 1784, 2 ounces, 5 inches high, $1,000–$1,500.
- George III silver waiter, plain circular form, the rim chased with a running band of husks below a beaded border, on three beaded

panel feet, base engraved with initials and date 1789, 7 ounces, 7 inches in diameter, $750–$1,000.

After 1810, people wanted to show off more, and Regency style came into vogue. It featured flamboyant sculptural shapes and decoration. It was created by hammering variously shaped punches into the back of a piece so that bold relief appeared on the outside surface—a technique called chasing. A complex design might involve dozens of punches. Often the silversmith hammered certain areas on the outside surface—a technique known as repoussé—to finish the design. Borders were enlarged; handles became elaborate affairs. Silversmiths mixed motifs from different sources such as Roman, Greek and Egyptian designs.

The greatest English silversmith of the early nineteenth century, a master of the Regency style, was Paul Storr. London-born, he began an apprenticeship in 1785, and eight years later he was on his own. He created well-proportioned pieces with restrained decoration. When a client was willing to pay extra, Storr revealed a gift for delightful flourishes.

In 1807 he accepted an offer to fill commissions for the royal silversmiths, Rundell & Bridge. He served more as a designer and production supervisor rather than an actual maker. Hence, a large variety of pieces bear his hallmarks, but few are from his hand.

He seems to have worked on large elaborate pieces. They secured his reputation then, and they are what collectors pay substantial sums for now. Storr created bold styling alive with movement. For instance:

- A Regency two-handled tray, oblong on four foliage feet, gadrooned border with shells and acanthus leaves at the intervals, with rising reed and foliage handles, the center engraved with laurel wreath cartouche, 1813, 22⅛ inches long, $14,000–$18,000.
- A Regency soup tureen and cover, oval, on spreading oval foot with fluted band, partly fluted body with gadrooned border and rising lion's mask, foliage-and-shell-capped reeded handles, domed cover with fluted band, and double-griffin's-head ring handle, body engraved with coat of arms in foliate cartouche, marked on body, cover and finial, 1816, 17⅜ inches long, $18,000–$25,000.

Fine Points of Silver

It is prudent to check whether a piece is compatible with the period when it was supposedly made. For instance, a surprising number of wealthy New York estates contain fake Paul Storr plates made in the 1920s and 1930s. Their size is the first giveaway. Most eighteenth-century English silver dinner plates are 9½ to 9¾ inches in diameter. Storr's tend to be bigger, about 10¼ inches. The fakes are about 11 inches. Moreover, the overall shape is not as elegant as Storr's. The plate borders and the coat-of-arms engraving are crude, too.

Certain kinds of pieces were faked a lot. Goblets were scarce during the eighteenth century, so be wary if a dozen appear at a time in an estate sale. However, the crude shape and coat-of-arms engraving should alert you. Forged hallmarks do not stand a comparison with the real thing.

Almost always, English silver has some kind of engraving that relates to the original owner, the most decorative being a full coat of arms. A simple crest is less interesting, and initials are the least interesting. If a piece lacks engraving, something may have been removed, leaving a thin spot vulnerable to damage. With your fingers, feel the areas that are commonly engraved—the center of the tray or the sides of a teapot, for example.

If you are satisfied that a piece represents authentic good design skillfully executed, then check the condition. Handles and spouts can be broken, fork prongs bent, knife blades loose in their handles, tankards dented. Look for replaced or added parts. Most often replaced are lids, spouts, handles. Look inside a coffee, tea or chocolate pot, because that is where a repairman applies solder. It appears grayish, sometimes black.

Quite a few people added spouts to silver tankards so that they would pour better, but collectors consider such pieces defaced. They are worth a fraction as much as an intact piece, and they are harder to resell.

By the same token, it is common to find florid Victorian engraving on what were plain, elegant eighteenth-century pieces. Added decoration is inevitably out of keeping with designs from an earlier era, as you can tell after spending a little time with a good museum collection.

What's in a Hallmark?

For about six hundred years, hallmarks have helped protect buyers of English silver. They were enforced through the London Goldsmith's Company and regional guilds. The typical piece of silver has four hallmarks.

First, there is a mark to signify that a piece complied with the established purity standard. Before 1697 and after 1720, it was sterling (92.5 percent silver, 7.5 percent copper), and the most common purity mark showed a lion viewed from the side, moving toward the left. It is called a lion passant, and a variety of designs appeared over the years. From 1697 to 1720, the era of the Britannia standard (95.8 percent silver, 4.2 percent copper), a seated female figure was the favored purity mark.

Second is the maker's mark. Before 1697, this was commonly a symbol. But records have disappeared, and only a few early marks can be attributed to a maker. With the return of the sterling standard, many silversmiths adopted marks showing initials from their first and last names. A statute made this practice uniform after 1739.

The date mark is third. In 1478, the London Goldsmith's Company devised a twenty-letter code that assigned a letter for each year. The code went through the alphabet except that *i* and *j* represented one year, *u* and *v* one year, and *w, x, y* and *z* weren't used. When a cycle finished, it started over with the letters marked in a different typeface. For example, if you consult a book of English silver marks, you will see that from 1736 to 1755 the letters were lower-case roman, from 1756 to 1775 Old English capitals, and so on.

The fourth mark is the tax mark. Kings were always searching for new things to tax, and periodically the English rulers turned to silversmiths. When a tax was paid on a piece, it was marked with the king's profile. Many citizens evaded this tax, and the absence of a tax mark does not detract from the value of a piece.

English silver was made in places besides London, and each has a similar, though somewhat different, set of marks. The main regional centers were Birmingham, Chester, Exeter, Newcastle, Norwich, Sheffield, York. If you are buying silver, you should consult one of the books of marks listed at the end of this chapter. The marks can be confused, so inspect details under a magnifying glass. Look at not just the letters themselves, but the symbols between and around the letters.

Satisfy yourself that a mark is authentic. Sometimes fakers removed a mark from a lesser piece, like a spoon, and applied it to a larger, more important piece like a tray or a teapot. Points to check:

- Do the surface characteristics of a mark match surface characteristics of the piece? For example, it would be suspect to have a bright shiny mark on a worn piece.
- Is the same craftsmanship that is evident in the piece also evident in the mark? It is the silversmith's signature, so the more skilled the craftsman, the sharper, clearer and more attractive the mark should be. Beware of blurred, stiff-edged, heavily scratched marks.
- Can you see a tiny solder line bonding a mark to a piece? Sometimes your moist breath on the mark will reveal that its color

is a little different from the color of the piece. They should be identical.

For More Information

Silver Auction Records (25 Van Zant Street, Norwalk, CT 06855) provides a broad overview of what is available for how much. It is issued every two years.

The best general book is Michael Clayton, *The Collector's Dictionary of Silver and Gold of Great Britain and North America* (New York: World Publishing, 1971). Lavishly illustrated, so you can see how each kind of silver evolved through different styles.

The standard reference for most eighteenth- and early-nineteenth-century English silver is *London Goldsmiths, 1697–1837: The Marks and Lives, by Arthur G. Grimwade (London: Faber & Faber, 1976).*

Marks from other silver-making centers can be found in English Goldsmiths and Their Marks, by Charles J. Jackson (New York: Dover, reprinted from a 1922 edition).

Judith Bannister's *Old English Silver* (London: Evans Brothers, 1965) provides a style history as well as profiles of Paul de Lamerie, Hester Bateman and Paul Storr.

For more detail about early periods, see:

Arthur Grimwade, *Rococo Silver, 1727–1765.* London: Faber & Faber, 1974.

J. F. Hayward, *Huguenot Silver in England, 1688–1717.* London: Faber & Faber, 1959.

Charles Oman, *Caroline Silver, 1625–1688.* London: Faber & Faber, 1970.

Robert Rowe, *Adam Silver, 1765–1795.* New York: Taplinger Publishing, 1965.

You'll find a spectacular series of black-and-white photographs, over two hundred pieces of silver plus hallmarks, in *English and Other Silver in the Irwin Untermeyer Collection* (New York: Metropolitan Museum of Art, 1969).

Museums

ALBANY, N.Y.
Albany Institute of History and Art
125 Washington Avenue
Albany, NY 12210
(518) 463-4478

BALTIMORE
Baltimore Museum of Art
Art Museum Drive
Baltimore, MD 21218
(301) 396-7101

BOSTON
Museum of Fine Arts
Huntington Avenue
Boston, MA 02115
(617) 267-9300

CAMBRIDGE
Fogg Art Museum, Harvard University
32 Quincy Street
Cambridge, MA 02138
(617) 495-7768

CHICAGO
Art Institute of Chicago
Michigan Avenue and Adams Street
Chicago, IL 60603
(312) 443-3600

CINCINNATI
Cincinnati Art Museum
Eden Park
Cincinnati, OH 45202
(513) 721-5204

CLEVELAND
Cleveland Museum of Art
11150 East Boulevard
Cleveland, OH 44106
(216) 421-7340

DETROIT
Detroit Institute of Art
5200 Woodward Avenue
Detroit, MI 48202
(313) 833-7900

HARTFORD
Wadsworth Atheneum
600 Main Street
Hartford, CT 06103
(203) 278-2670

INDIANAPOLIS
Indianapolis Museum of Art
1200 West 38th Street
Indianapolis, IN 46208
(317) 923-1331

LOS ANGELES
Los Angeles County Museum of Art
5905 Wilshire Boulevard
Los Angeles, CA 90036
(213) 937-4250

MINNEAPOLIS
Minneapolis Institute of Art
2400 Third Avenue South
Minneapolis, MI 55404
(612) 870-3046

NEW HAVEN
Yale University Art Gallery
1111 Chapel Street
New Haven, CT 06520
(203) 436-0574

NEW YORK
Metropolitan Museum of Art
Fifth Avenue at 82nd Street
New York, NY 10028
(212) 535-7710

PALM BEACH, FLA.
Henry M. Flagler Museum
Whitehall Way
Palm Beach, FL 33480
(305) 655-2833

PHILADELPHIA
Historical Society of Pennsylvania
1300 Locust Street
Philadelphia, PA 19107
(215) 732-6200

PORTLAND, ORE.
Portland Art Museum
1219 Southwest Park Avenue
Portland, OR 97205
(503) 226-2811

PROVIDENCE
Museum of Art, Rhode Island School of Design
224 Benefit Street
Providence, RI 02903
(401) 331-3511

ST. LOUIS
St. Louis Art Museum
Forest Park
St. Louis, MO 63110
(314) 721-0067

ST. PETERSBURG, FLA.
Museum of Fine Arts
255 Beach Drive North
St. Petersburg, FL 33701
(813) 896-2667

SAN MARINO, CALIF.
Huntington Library, Art Gallery and Botanical Gardens
1151 Oxford Road
San Marino, CA 91108
(213) 681-6601

SARASOTA, FLA.
John and Mable Ringling Museum of Art
5401 Bayshore Road
Sarasota, FL 33580
(813) 355-5101

SEATTLE
Seattle Art Museum
Volunteer Park
Seattle, WA 98112
(206) 447-4710

WILLIAMSBURG, VA.
Colonial Williamsburg
Goodwin Building
Williamsburg, VA 23185
(804) 229-1000

WINTERTHUR, DEL.
Henry Francis du Pont Winterthur Museum
Winterthur, DE 19735
(302) 656-8591

WORCESTER, MASS.
Worcester Art Museum
55 Salisbury Street
Worcester, MA 01608
(617) 799-4406

Where to Buy

Regular auctions including English silver are held in New York by:

Christie's
502 Park Avenue
New York, NY 10022
(212) 546-1153

William Doyle
175 East 87th Street
New York, NY 10028
(212) 427-2730

Phillips
406 East 79th Street
New York, NY 10021
(212) 570-4838

Sotheby's
1334 York Avenue
New York, NY 10021
(212) 472-3531

Among dealers:

BOSTON
Firestone & Parson
Ritz Carlton Hotel
Boston, MA 02117
(617) 266-1858

Gebelein Silversmiths
286 Newbury Street
Boston, MA 02115
(617) 266-3876

Shreve, Crump & Low
330 Boylston Street
Boston, MA 02116
(617) 267-9100

CHICAGO
Marshall Field & Company
835 North Michigan Avenue
Chicago, IL 60611
(312) 781-1000

ESSEX, CONN.
Robert Spencer
Essex Square
Essex, CT 06426
(203) 767-8655

HADDAM, CONN.
Hobart House
Middlesex Turnpike
Haddam, CT 06438
(203) 345-2525

LAKE FOREST, ILL.
Lake Forest Antiquarians
P.O. Box 841
Lake Forest, IL 60045
(312) 234-1990

LOS ANGELES
Beverly Antiques
8827 Beverly Boulevard
Los Angeles, CA 90048
(213) 271-8517

NEW YORK
James Robinson
15 East 57th Street
New York, NY 10022
(212) 752-6166

S. J. Shrubsole
104 East 57th Street
New York, NY 10022
(212) 753-8920

PALM BEACH
Hartmann Galleries
234 Worth Avenue
Palm Beach, FL 33480
(305) 655-6114

WASHINGTON
Martin's of Georgetown
1304 Wisconsin Avenue, NW
Washington, DC 20007
(202) 338-6144

3

ORIENTAL FLATWEAVES

FLATWEAVES EXPRESS THE FIERY SPIRIT OF THOSE WHO, DURING THE LATE nineteenth and early twentieth centuries, lived in the world's greatest melting pot. It stretched from the Himalaya Mountains to the Mediterranean. Over the centuries, Mongols conquered China and poured into Central Asia. Ottoman warriors conquered Persia. Turkomans swept through Anatolia, the equivalent of modern Turkey. Russian armies invaded Central Asia from the north.

Illiterate and poor but ever resourceful, the hardy people of these lands transformed utilitarian things into powerful works of art that proclaim strength, devotion, joy. Many weavings embellished a nomad's simple home. Salt bags, bedding bags, utility bags, water-bottle bags, decorative tent bands, tent door rugs, floor rugs—each was made with loving care. A horse or a camel was often a nomad's most valuable asset, so it is not surprising that many beautiful weavings were created to make an animal look dapper on special occasions like a wedding—saddle blankets, headpieces and knee trappings, for instance.

Nomads worked magic with the simplest materials. From wool or cotton they spun yarn. Many dyes came from materials around them: red from the madder root, blue from dried leaves of the indigo shrub, yellow from Persian berries.

The most basic flatweaves are called kilims. The entire design was made with wefts—yarn woven back and forth between alternate warps which run lengthwise. It is difficult to create curved lines with such a simple technique, known as tapestry weaving, and you seldom see curves in a flatweave. But flatweaves are ablaze with diamond patterns, hexagon patterns, concentric rectangles, horizontal bands, vertical bands, zigzag patterns, latch hooks, comb patterns. For special effects, weavers embellished their textiles with brocading or embroidery.

Until recent years, few collectors paid much attention to flatweaves. They are still the least expensive major category of Oriental textiles. Most flatweaves are under $1,000. For $4,000—about a fifth as much as you might pay for a fine antique Persian pile rug—you can buy a superb example.

The Wild Energy of Anatolian Flatweaves

More flatweaves come from Anatolia than from anywhere else. There's an incredible variety of Anatolian flatweaves, thanks to the ethnic stew of rug-weaving Armenians, Greeks, Kurds, Yoruks, Georgians, Lesghis, Azerbaijans, Turkomans, Cherkesses, Tartars and Tziganes. They projected tremendous energy in their flatweaves. Often six to eight colors were used, giving the flatweaves a dazzling effect. Anatolian weavers chose nervous jagged lines to define forms, and weavers created more tension by crowding together many different geometric forms. The flatweaves tend to have a wild look.

Many of the designs hark back to antiquity. For instance, during the 1960s, excavations at Çatal Hüyük, in west-central Anatolia, uncovered flatweaves, thought to be linen, which experts estimate were made around 6500 B.C. Moreover, wall paintings there depict the same concentric diamond designs that appear in nineteenth- and twentieth-century Anatolian flatweaves.

Among the most popular Anatolian flatweaves are those believed to have come from the Konya region in south-central Anatolia. They are loosely woven of wool, sometimes with cotton highlights, usually in two pieces sewn together. Many have brocading. A late-nineteenth-century Konya kilim, woven in rows of polychrome hexagons, interspersed by diamonds within a sand border of large multicolored stylized insect forms, cotton highlights, 12 feet by 5 feet 2 inches, would sell for $800–$1,000.

Northwest Anatolia, around Bergama and Balikesir, produced some distinctive designs with zigzag lines and interlocking latch-hook motifs. Reds and blues are the primary colors. The flatweaves are single-piece, some superb. A mid-nineteenth-century Balikesir, for example, brick-red background containing three ascending geometric designs, 7 feet 8 inches by 5 feet 1 inch, could be bought for $3,000–$4,000.

Some of the most easily recognized flatweaves come from southeast Anatolia around Aleppo. They are finely woven in two pieces with subtle colors, burgundy red tending to dominate. Borders have a white background and some kind of repeat pattern. An Aleppo flatweave, late nineteenth century, honeycomb design with stylized insects in dark brown, brick red, midnight and light blues, peach on a polychrome background, all surrounded by a border with leaf and floral sprays in the same colors on an ivory background, 11 feet 2 inches by 8 feet 8 inches, would sell for $500–$700.

Perhaps the most readily available flatweaves are from central Anatolia. They are referred to as "Rashwan" after the Kurdish tribes who wove them. Typical designs are based on a series of concentric diamonds. Warps are undyed wool, wefts are undyed cotton. For instance, a Rashwan flatweave, late nineteenth century, an interconnected diamond pattern worked in ivory, midnight blue, green, blue, brown, orange and magenta surrounded by a border with stylized leaf and floral sprays worked in the same colors on an ivory background, 10 feet by 5 feet 7 inches, would be worth $800–$1,200.

The most distinctive Anatolian design is the prayer rug. No other people made nearly as many prayer rugs. Devout Moslems pray several times daily by kneeling on a clean surface, and a small portable rug provides that. It has multiple borders enclosing an arched central field known as a mihrab, derived from the niche in a mosque. Like the niche, the mihrab is meant to face Mecca. It symbolizes the gateway to a better world.

A typical example is a Karaman prayer flatweave, late nineteenth century, brick-red niche containing a stylized tree-of-life motif ascending to lime-green spandrels, or corner designs, holding hooked medallions with similar motifs in the hexagons ornamenting the guard borders on ivory and sea-blue grounds, 5 feet 8 inches by 3 feet 8 inches, priced at $800–$1,000.

Earlier prayer rugs in superb condition bring more money, of course. A Ladik prayer flatweave, first half of the nineteenth century, dark-blue mihrab, red spandrels ornamented with rosettes, beige main border and brown guard borders with stylized flowers and wing motifs, 4 feet 11 inches by 3 feet 10 inches, might bring $4,000–$5,000.

With all Anatolian flatweaves, quality declined fast as weavers began aiming for a commercial market. The worst examples were woven after World War II. Weavers went berserk with synthetic dyes, making flatweaves in bright purples, oranges, lime greens, ultraviolet reds, hot pinks. They adopted rigid design elements that could be excecuted quickly but were not well formed. Nor were they aligned properly. They are simply poor handmade rugs and are not satisfying. Dealers offer them for about $300. Save your money.

The Boldest Flatweaves

The Caucasus Mountains, between the Black and Caspian seas, are among the roughest, most desolate regions on earth. Some 90 percent of the land is too steep to grow anything on. Much of the rest is rocky grassland good only for grazing sheep and goats. The borders of Turkey, Iran and Russia meet in the Caucasus, but it is really more of a no man's land, a wild frontier separating Europe from Asia, Christendom from the Moslem world.

Yet Caucasian weavers created magnificent flatweaves, including some that are the most popular now. They tend to have fewer colors and design elements than Anatolian flatweaves. Consequently, most Caucasian flatweaves convey a stronger immediate impact. Weavers gained more power by juxtaposing contrasting colors, especially red and blue. Symmetry rules Caucasian flatweaves, so that even when there are numerous design elements they pull together.

There are several main types that appear regularly on the market. They tend to be good quality and popular. There are the Kuba-type flatweaves commonly attributed to the northern Caucasus. They feature repeat patterns of geometric medallions. These flatweaves have one or two borders, usually with a continuous linear design such as a zigzag. For example, a late-nineteenth-century Kuba flatweave with wide polychrome bands decorated by large, stepped stylized spiders separated by thinner stepped bands and abstract running-dog borders, 11 feet 4 inches by 5 feet, might be priced at $2,000–$3,000.

Also attributed to the northern Caucasus, probably around Karabagh, are brocaded soumak rugs which involve some of the most intricate Caucasian designs, such as stars within crosses within octagons within diamonds. Most soumaks have squarish proportions, like one with a rust field containing three stepped medallions surrounded by human figures and floral motifs within running-dog and octagonal flowerhead borders, late nineteenth century, 5 feet 9 inches by 5 feet 1 inch. This would sell for $2,500–$3,000.

Many flatweaves attributed to the Shirvan region of the southern Caucasus have horizontal bands of alternating colors containing various geometric forms. Few Shirvan flatweaves have borders. These pieces run in fairly narrow proportions. For $1,000–$1,500 you could buy a late-nineteenth-century Shirvan piece with a polychrome ground composed of diagonally offset concentric stepped hexagons, each centered with cruciform and hourglass motifs within reciprocal borders, 11 feet 5 inches by 5 feet.

Then you will see flatweaves with rows of squares containing stylized birds and animals. Displaying long skinny necks and legs, a big beak and enormous wing feathers, the birds look like whimsical cartoon characters. Usually you will see red-and-white designs against a blue background. They tend to be brocaded. A Verneh flatweave containing a variety of parading animals, human figures, birds in colors of gold, green, ivory, red and blue, all surrounded by geometric design borders, 6 feet 7 inches by 4 feet 8 inches, would fetch $7,000–$9,000.

One of the most striking Caucasian designs is the Sileh, or dragon rug, consisting of large S or Z figures, believed to be stylized dragons. Most Silehs, attributed to the southern Caucasus, have four rows of figures lengthwise and four across. Almost all are two-piece. A Sileh flatweave, four rows of four geometrically stylized dragons in ivory and shades of blue on a brick-red ground, all worked in the soumak weft-wrap technique, two panels, 10 feet by 7 feet 1 inch, would sell in the $7,000–$9,000 range.

Since many nomads wandered between Anatolia or Persia and the Caucasus, it is often difficult to say just where a flatweave is from. You might argue plausibly for an attribution to eastern Anatolia or the western Caucasus. As a general rule, the warps of Caucasian flatweaves are natural brown wool or a mixture of brown and white wool. At each end of a Caucasian flatweave, threads are knotted together in bunches. Each bunch, in turn, is knotted to one next to it. Most Caucasian flatweaves are one-piece.

The Most Sophisticated Flatweaves

During the 1940s, an American civil engineer named Paul Case went through Bulamir, a small village in central Persia. He visited a chieftain's windowless mud home. "The outside of mud and sun-dried brick had hardly prepared us," Case recalled, "for the magnificent carpets, heavily upholstered chairs, hand-embroidered silk table scarfs."

Persia became famous for large, formal, city-made carpets, but some charming flatweaves blossomed in unlikely villages and hamlets like Bulamir. The most exquisite flatweaves you will find anywhere were made in northwest Persia by Kurds, a roisterous seminomadic people adept at eluding government troops.

Kurds around Senna (also spelled Sehna and Sennah) used a few traditional repeat patterns based on small, precisely woven stylized flowers. Colors are harmonious—beige, ivory, soft orange, yellow and blue, for instance. The sophistication of these flatweaves suggests an urban clientele. Sizes range from about 4 by 6 feet to 10 by 15 feet. For example, a flatweave produced during the first quarter of the twentieth century, central blue poled medallion on a red ground within a floral-wreath-design border, 6 feet 11 inches by 4 feet 1 inch, is worth $3,500–$4,500. Or a mid-nineteenth-century piece, midnight-blue prayer field with an allover floral boteh design beneath a rust arch of similar design, all within an ivory flowering lattice border, 6 feet 8 inches by 4 feet 7 inches, would sell for $7,500–$8,500.

Western Persia also abounds with less expensive, dramatic flatweaves made with cotton warps and thick wool wefts. The designs tend to be based on serrated diamonds and contrasting colors. A Bijar flatweave with an open ruby-red ground, three interconnected poled medallions, within blue spandrels, all within ivory, blue and saffron geometric guard borders, 18 feet 10 inches by 6 feet 5 inches, is worth $1,500–$2,500.

Durable, brilliant flatweaves came from the area around Veramin, a town in northern Persia. Some designs involve horizontal bands containing serrated hexagons, while other designs feature diagonal arrangements of interlocked squares or hexagons. Most of these flatweaves have borders only at the ends, not along the sides. Each end border includes a narrow band of brocaded S-forms. A Veramin flatweave, twentieth century, woven in a diamond pattern, colors including rust, sea green, blue, brown, peach, a geometric skirt at either end, 11 feet by 5 feet 8 inches, would be worth $1,000–$1,500.

In southwestern Persia, the large and powerful Qashqai (also spelled Gashgai) tribes produced flatweaves that look as if they were hit by lightning. They have geometric patterns formed by interlocked serrated squares of bright contrasting colors such as red, orange, light blue. They are among the most readily available Persian flatweaves. A late-nineteenth-century Qashqai flatweave, a forest-green background with repeating scorpion design within geometric borders, 8 feet 7 inches by 5 feet 4 inches, would sell for $2,500–$3,500.

Aristocrats of the Desert

Nomadic Turkoman warriors were the feared aristocrats of the harsh desert extending 9,800 miles east from the Caspian Sea, an area embraced now by Afghanistan and the Soviet Union. Temperatures hit 120 degrees Fahrenheit during the summer, plunge below zero in winter. Nomads plundered each other as well as their neighbors. Among the most sought-after prizes were women who created powerful weavings with repeat patterns of medallions called guls—the Persian word for "flowers." The weavers displayed their resourcefulness by working magic with just two colors: red and black. Sometimes you will see other colors such as yellow, but only as highlights.

Generally speaking, the older the weaving, the larger the guls and the farther apart. They have more breathing room and are full of little touches that add considerable interest. After about 1910, guls became smaller, simpler, crowded together into rather monotonous rows. Like weavers elsewhere, the Turkomans abandoned mellow handmade vegetable-based dyes in favor of convenient ready-made synthetic dyes with an unpleasant metallic quality. Turkoman-style rugs are being made and marketed now as Bokharas. A quick comparison with a fine older Turkoman rug, late nineteenth or early twentieth century, will demonstrate graphically why the older rugs are worth much more.

The more white there is, the more valuable the weaving. A rare flatweave with guls against a white background can be worth ten times more than a weaving with just a few white highlights.

Of the dozen Turkoman subtribes, only one—the Yomud—are credited with producing many flatweaves. A Yomud embroidered carpet, early twentieth century, red field with an allover design of hooked guls, within a complementary border and a starflower skirt at either end, 13 feet 8 inches by 7 feet 4 inches, is worth $1,000–$2,000. Or an early-twentieth-century piece with a field containing bands of directional connected ornaments and stepped geometric motifs, within a repeating geometric border, cotton highlights, 7 feet 5 inches by 3 feet 8 inches, might bring $1,000–$2,000.

Finally, if you are interested in something bright and cheery for the wall, take a look at late-nineteenth-, early-twentieth-century Suzani (Persian for "needle") embroideries from Uzbekistan, now a Soviet province. Suzani embroideries were made for a bride's dowry. Typically, they depict big red and orange stylized flowers together with green leaves against a white linen background. They consist of perhaps a half-dozen panels sewn together. A mid-nineteenth-century Suzani embroidery, 7 feet 6 inches by 5 feet 4 inches, would be worth $2,000–$3,000.

How Experts Estimate the Age of a Flatweave

Materials can suggest approximate age. For instance, cotton is cheaper than wool, and after about 1890, when some rug-weaving tribes started making flatweaves for export rather than just home use, often they substituted cotton for wool. Cotton is fairly common in flatweaves dating from the 1920s.

Machine-spun yarn usually means a later date than hand-spun yarn, though practices varied from tribe to tribe. Machine-spun yarn has a uniform look, while hand-spun yarn is marked by irregularities. It is a little thicker in some places than others.

For centuries, tribesmen gathered wool by shearing healthy living sheep. The fibers are bright and lustrous, nourished by natural oils. After about 1900, according to rug chronicler A. Cecil Edwards, more and more wool was purchased from town merchants who acquired it at tanneries. Called "skin wool," this product of dead sheep tends to be dull. Dyed, it yields rather muddy colors.

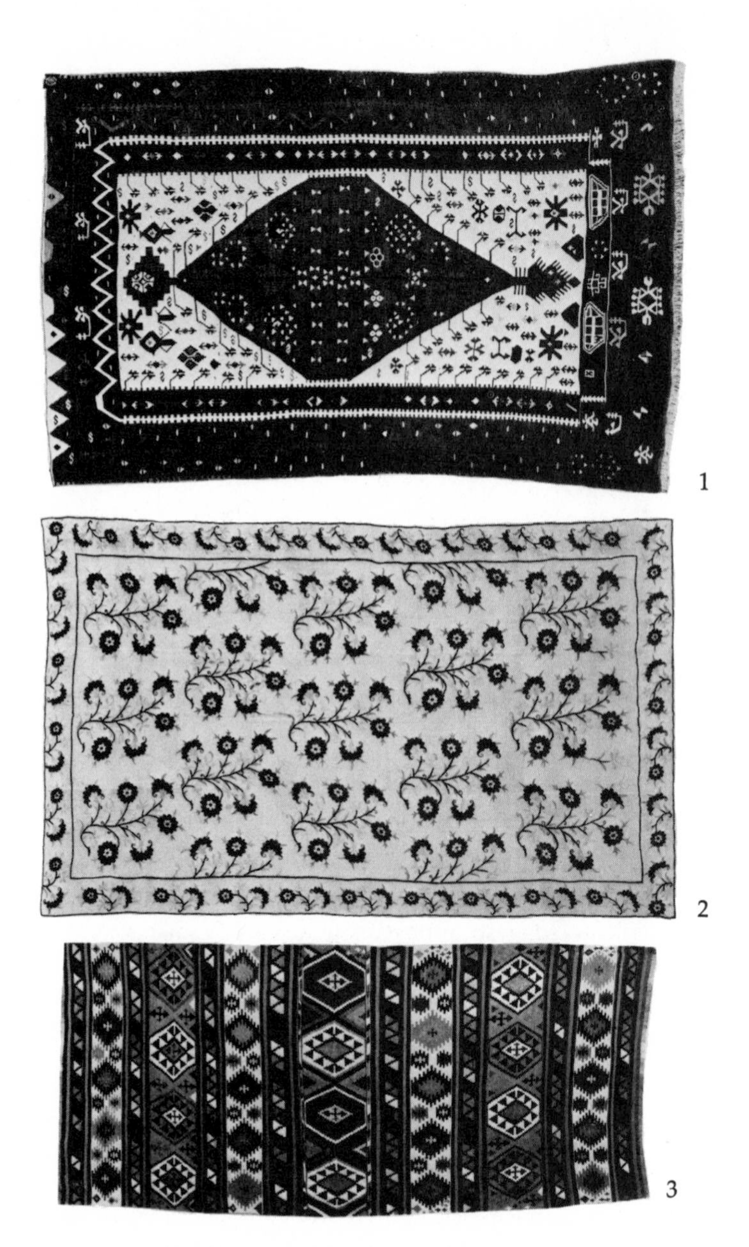

Fine antique oriental flatweaves were made by Turkish, Caucasian, Iranian and Afghani peasants to embellish tents or huts. (1) 19th-century Turkish flatweave. 4′10″ × 3′1″; $1,000–$1,500. *Edelmann Galleries.* (2) 18th-century Turkish embroidered curtain. 7′ × 4′4″; $3,500–$4,000. *Edelmann Galleries.* (3) Caucasian banded flatweave. 10′8″ × 5′1″; $2,000–$3,000. *Sotheby Parke Bernet.*

The presence of synthetic dyes means a rug cannot have been made before the 1880s, when they were introduced. Chemical analysis is the only sure way to identify a dye, but few collectors bother with it. You can do well enough by noting the typical look of the dyes. Most vegetable-based dyes mellow over the years, while synthetics either deteriorate into muddy colors or remain strong. Synthetic red was popular, for instance, and you will see rugs with mainly soft mellow tones except for some red highlights that stand out like a beacon. They are almost certainly synthetic.

However, the absence of synthetic dyes doesn't necessarily mean a rug is very old, because many weavers continued using traditional vegetable-based dyes long after other weavers adopted the more convenient synthetics. In other words, estimating age depends on many factors considered together.

How to Evaluate a Flatweave

While some collectors are willing to pay extra money for what they believe to be an especially old rug or a rare one from a particular region, other collectors do not care about these points. Quality is the main thing. "I'm interested in perfect weaving, perfect color and perfect condition," declared collector Arthur Jenkins, now president of the Textile Museum, Washington, D.C. "I never bothered with exactly where a rug came from. I looked at a lot of rugs and developed my eye."

Compare enough Oriental weavings until you know what good color looks like. Then insist on it for yourself.

Avoid flatweaves with important areas of color that became muddy over the years. A dirty blue or purple that turned blackish, for example. Avoid faded, washed-out colors such as a dirty-white-tinted pink that might have started out as red.

Some flatweaves are dreary-looking from the smoke inside tribal tents. This is especially true with Central Asian weavings such as the Baluch. There is no sure way to clean out the smoke without disturbing the dyes.

Be wary of colors that run. If it has happened once, it will probably happen again. Since some colors run in plain water, you might test a rug by dabbing it with a moist cotton ball.

Every once in a while, you will see a rug on which somebody used paint or a felt-tip pen to cover up wear. Discrepancies between these colors and surrounding colors are easy to spot. Examine carefully the entire surface of a weaving you are interested in.

Generally, collectors prefer single-piece rugs to two-piece. Single-piece looks better and does not involve the potential problem of halves separating.

Note any wear such as bare spots, frayed edges, ends fringing out, holes, moth damage, stains. These can be repaired, but it is difficult to find a good textile conservator, and often the work costs more than a rug is worth.

Check for signs of previous repairs like rewoven areas or a new fringe. Repairs are easiest to spot from the back of a rug.

Also check for brittle areas with your fingers. See how easily a rug can be folded. Sometimes salt water, accumulated dirt or dog urine can make a rug brittle, and there is nothing that can be done. Such a rug is vulnerable to cracking. Avoid it.

Many rugs have borders that run lengthwise but not around the ends. This is a sure sign the ends were removed, a common practice after they became seriously damaged. Such altered rugs are worth a fraction as much as an intact rug in good condition.

Dealers and auction galleries save space by displaying rugs on hinged wall racks. If you are interested in a rug on a rack, have it removed, so that you can see whether it will lie flat. A curling edge is unsightly, and it is likely to accelerate wear. You can sew a thin strip of leather or linoleum along the curling edge, but the problem will return if the strip is removed.

Watch out if you discover glue or wax on the back of a rug. These represent failed attempts to eliminate a curling edge, and they can damage the foundation.

There are enough fine flatweaves available that you should not burden yourself with condition problems. Check that you are buying a fine flatweave, and it can give you decades of pleasure.

For More Information

Majid Amini, *Oriental Rugs, Care and Repair.* New York: Van Nostrand Reinhold, 1981.

Cathryn Cootner, *The Arthur D. Jenkins Collection: Flat-Woven Textiles.* Washington, D.C.: Textile Museum, 1981.

Kilim. Milan: John Eskenazi, 1981.

M. G. Konieczny, *Textiles of Baluchistan.* London: British Museum, 1979.
Anthony N. Landreau and W. R. Pickering, *From the Bosporus to Samarkand: Flat-Woven Rugs.* Washington, D.C.: Textile Museum, 1969.
Yanni Petsopoulos, *Kilims.* New York: Rizzoli, 1979.
Rugs and Flatweaves of the Transcaucasus. (Pittsburgh: Pittsburgh Rug Society, 1980).
Valerie Sharaf Justin, *Flat-Woven Rugs of the World.* New York: Van Nostrand Reinhold, 1980.
The Undiscovered Kilim. London: David Black Oriental Carpets, 1977.
Daniel S. Walker, *Oriental Rugs of the Hajji Babbas.* New York: Asia Society and Harry Abrams, 1982.
William Ziemba, Abdulkadir Akatay and Sandra Schwartz, *Turkish Flat Weaves.* Vancouver, Canada: Yoruk Carpets and Kilims, 1979.

Museums

BOSTON
Museum of Fine Arts
Huntington Avenue
Boston, MA 02115
(617) 267-9300

CAMBRIDGE
Fogg Art Museum, Harvard University
32 Quincy Street
Cambridge, MA 02138
(617) 495-7768

CHICAGO
Art Institute of Chicago
Michigan Avenue and Adams Street
Chicago, IL 60603
(312) 443-3600

CINCINNATI
Cincinnati Art Museum
Eden Park
Cincinnati, OH 45202
(513) 721-5204

CLEVELAND
Cleveland Museum of Art
11150 East Boulevard
Cleveland, OH 44106
(216) 421-7340

DENVER
Denver Art Museum
100 West 14th Avenue Parkway
Denver, CO 80204
(303) 575-2793

DETROIT
Detroit Institute of Arts
5200 Woodward Avenue
Detroit, MI 48202
(313) 833-7900

FLINT, MICH.
Flint Institute of Arts
DeWaters Art Center
1120 East Kearsley Street
Flint, MI 48503
(313) 234-1695

INDIANAPOLIS
Indianapolis Museum of Art
1200 West 38th Street
Indianapolis, IN 46208
(317) 923-1331

LOS ANGELES
Los Angeles County Museum of Art
5905 Wilshire Boulevard
Los Angeles, CA 90036
(213) 937-4250

NEW YORK
Asia Society
725 Park Avenue
New York, NY 10021
(212) 288-6400

Metropolitan Museum of Art
Fifth Avenue at 82nd Street
New York, NY 10028
(212) 879-5500

OSHKOSH, WIS.
Paine Art Center & Arboretum
1410 Algoma Boulevard
Oshkosh, WI 54901
(414) 235-4530

PORTLAND, ORE.
Portland Art Museum
1219 Southwest Park Avenue
Portland, OR 97205
(503) 226-2811

SEATTLE
Seattle Art Museum
Volunteer Park
Seattle, WA 98112
(206) 447-4710

SPRINGFIELD, MASS.
George Walter Vincent Smith Art Museum
222 State Street
Springfield, MA 01103
(413) 733-4214

ST. LOUIS
St. Louis Art Museum
Forest Park
St. Louis, MO 63110
(314) 721-0067

WASHINGTON
Textile Museum
2320 S Street, NW
Washington, DC 20008
(202) 667-0441

Where to Buy

Among auction houses holding regular sales which include flat-weaves are these in New York:

John C. Edelmann Galleries, Inc.
123 East 77th Street
New York, NY 10021
(212) 628-1700

Sotheby's
1334 York Avenue
New York, NY 10021
(212) 472-3451

Dealers to check:

CHARLOTTESVILLE, VA.
Sun Bow Trading Co.
108 Fourth Street, NW
Charlottesville, VA 22901
(804) 293-8821

CHEVY CHASE, MD.
Mark Keshishian
6930 Wisconsin Avenue
Chevy Chase, MD 20015
(301) 340-6666

LOS ANGELES
Rugs Inc.
8687 Melrose Avenue
Los Angeles, CA 19151
(213) 657-6031

NEW YORK
Linda Miller
150 Thompson Street
New York, NY 10012
(212) 533-1677

Marian Miller
148 East 28th Street
New York, NY 10016
(212) 685-7746

Mark Shilen
185 West Houston Street
New York, NY 10014
(212) 989-8664

OAKLAND, CALIF.
Breema Gallery
6015 College Avenue
Oakland, CA 94618
(415) 655-0167

PHILADELPHIA
Dennis Dodds
2815 Queen Lane
Philadelphia, PA 19129
(215) 438-7873

J. M. Sorkin
P.O. Box 12509
Philadelphia, PA 91951
(215) 848-6600

PITTSBURGH
O'Bannon Oriental Carpets
5666 Northumberland
Pittsburgh, PA 15217
(412) 422-0300

PORTLAND, ORE.
James Opie Oriental Rugs
214 Southwest Stark Street
Portland, OR 97204
(503) 226-0116

SANTA FE, N.M.
Stephen A. Miller
212 Galisteo
Santa Fe, NM 87501
(505) 988-7366

4

ENGLISH PORCELAIN

A PROPER LADY, ACCORDING TO THE WITTY NINETEENTH-CENTURY ENGLISH historian Thomas Macaulay, valued fine porcelain "quite as much as she valued her monkey, and much more than she valued her husband." Fine translucent porcelain is as sensuous as marble or ivory, and the brilliant colors are like nothing else in the world. They do not dull or fade. They retain their scintillating radiance.

Long one of the most coveted ceramics, English porcelain is now surprisingly inexpensive. Elegant dishes can be had for as little as $100 apiece, and $1,000 will buy you a rarity, a major item like a fruit cooler or a coffee or tea service. Often, for less than for brand-new porcelain you can acquire lovely, durable designs by famous names like Spode, Coalport, Worcester. These old pieces are better quality than brand-new. They are hand-painted and hand-gilded. Many rich pigments were produced from costly materials like gold that are prohibitively expensive now. New, mass-produced porcelain is machine-stamped or stenciled with cheaper pigments.

Bone China

Fine porcelain is made from a clay called kaolin that contributes a plastic quality, and a dazzling white feldspar known as petuntse. Fused together at over 2,300 degrees Fahrenheit, with the right kind of flame, they produce a hard, durable, translucent ceramic referred to as hard-paste. It is decorated and protected with a glasslike glaze.

English potters drew inspiration from the Chinese, who invented translucent so-called hard-paste porcelain, and the Germans, who developed this porcelain in Europe. Both tried to keep secret the porcelain formula, the optimum firing conditions and the time.

During the mid-eighteenth century, English potters began making a soft-paste porcelain. It was not translucent, but it could be fashioned into a fantastic variety of sculptured shapes, the most popular modeled after vegetables, flowers, even fish. Then in the 1790s a more durable, translucent bone china was developed—the term reflecting the addition of bone ash to the paste formula. Bone china appeared in more standard, less flamboyant forms. It became a canvas to which decoration was applied.

Aristocrats and wealthy merchants ordered huge bone-china services running into hundreds of pieces. Over the years, most of these were divided among heirs or sold. Sets appearing on the market now are described typically as part services, even though they may include several dozen pieces—plenty for almost anybody's needs. You can buy pieces individually if you just want to decorate a room. Or you can buy a part service for actual use, and you will pay less per piece.

Dishes and Platters

A service with pieces that originally started out together is more valuable than a set assembled from odd lots, even though the pieces are the same pattern. Yet an assembled set can be quite attractive and practical. For instance, a Spode blue-ground assembled part dinner service, 1813–47: three rectangular serving dishes, liners and covers, a pair of covered circular muffin dishes, a rectangular liner and cover, a pair of lozenge-shaped dishes, a 14⅛-inch oval platter, three 11½-inch oval platters and twenty-nine plates in various sizes, each piece with a pale-blue border molded with white floral sprays between gilt bands on the rims, the circular dishes and covers also with gilt sprays in the center and on the rims, the covered serving pieces with twig handles and knops heightened in gilding, most pieces with Spode pattern number 2036. Altogether the forty-four pieces are worth $2,000–$3,000—less than $70 per piece.

Most plates from a major factory, made between 1800 and 1830, can be had for $40–$60 apiece. A Coalport "Japan"-pattern circular covered sauce tureen and set of twelve soup plates, 1810–15, each painted in underglaze blue, shades of red and gilding with a flower-filled vase within a blue-ground band on the cavetto and a border of leaves, flowers and gilt scrolls on the gilt-edged rim, the handles and knop edged in gilding, 6¼ inches high, 10⅛ inches in diameter, sells for $400–$600.

Or a Coalport "Japan"-pattern part dessert service, altogether fifteen pieces, *circa* 1805: a pair of shell dishes, a pair of lozenge-shaped dishes, a square dish and ten plates, each painted in underglaze blue, red and gilding with a central cluster of stylized Oriental flowers, the border with alternating panels of flowers and a red bird in a cartouche, range from $1,200 to $1,800.

Unusually fine early-nineteenth-century plates can bring as much as $200 apiece. For instance, twelve Derby "Japan"-pattern crested plates, *circa* 1810, each decorated in blue, red, green and gold with four panels of floral sprays alternating with a blue-ground stylized foliage scroll, crowned crossed batons and D marks in red, 9¼ inches in diameter, could bring $1,500–$2,500.

Earlier, scarcer, more sculptural porcelain tends to command premium prices. A Worcester plate, interior painted in shades of purple, red, yellow and green with a central bouquet and sprigs, the sides formed of interlocking circlets applied at the intersection of the pale-yellow exterior with turquoise-centered brown florettes, 6⅛ inches, would be priced at $350–$500.

Coffee and Tea Services

While coffee and tea services are more useful than individual pieces, they too cost less per piece. A Staffordshire porcelain part tea service, thirty-seven pieces, 1800–1810: teapot, cover and stand, milk jug, covered sugar bowl, waste bowl, two saucer dishes, twelve teacups, eight coffee cups, ten saucers, each piece printed in gray with figures at various pursuits in pastoral landscapes, the rims, spouts, handles and knops edged in brown, is priced at $300–$500.

Or a collection of Derby coffee and tea wares, late-eighteenth/early-nineteenth century: four fluted coffee cups and saucers, a fluted milk jug, an oval teapot and cover, coffee can and saucer, each with a pink border heightened in gilding with scallops, wheat sheaves or leafage, twelve pieces altogether, could be worth $200–$300.

A pair of Spode apple-green cream bowls, *circa* 1818, each painted in the center in yellow, rose and green with a sprig of peaches within a wide green border, the exterior with a similar border molded between the floral panels with sprays of white flowers, the sides with gilt butterfly handles, and the wide circular foot with a gilt-edged wide green border, one with Spode pattern number 2894 in red, 7⅛ inches wide, costs $150–$250.

A fluted tea caddy, Worcester, late eighteenth century, painted with an exotic bird with rose, purple, red and yellow plumage, perched on a grassy plateau amidst red and green shrubbery, the reverse with a smaller bird on a branch, 5⅛ inches, would be worth $400–$600.

A New Hall oval teapot, cover and stand, *circa* 1795, each piece painted in shades of brown and gilding with a fruiting strawberry-vine border within gilt bands, the teapot shoulder, spout and handle with gilt foliate motifs, 6¼ inches high, sells for $150–$250.

Serving Dishes

Everything that once belonged in a full service can be had individually. For instance, a pair of Worcester sauce boats, late eighteenth century, blue and white, each with a lightly ribbed body painted on either side and under the spout with floral clusters within foliate-molded cartouches, the interior with a large stylized tulip, open crescent marks in underglaze blue, 8 inches long, is worth $450–$650.

A Worcester tureen, cover and stand, late eighteenth century, decorated with gilt-scroll-edged cartouches enclosing brightly colored floral bouquets and sprigs, surrounded by gilt floral sprays, the twig handles terminating in yellow-centered white flowers and pale-green leaves, rims gilded, 8¾ inches high, could be priced at $750 –$1,000.

Large pieces can be stunning. For instance, a Derby fruit cooler and cover, *circa* 1800, cobalt-blue band border heightened in gilding with palmettes or scrolling leafage, the fruit cooler applied with shell-form handles, crowned crossed batons and D marks in purple and red, 11¾ inches, might bring $100–$200.

An unusual shape adds interest. A pair of English or Welsh porcelain "Japan"-pattern shell dishes, possibly Swansea, *circa* 1820, each painted in underglaze blue, red and gilding with an allover pattern of large floral sprigs and gilt trailing vines, the shell-molded handles and rims edged in gilding, 9 inches long, might sell for $350–$550.

A pair of Chamberlain's Worcester "Famille-Verte" lozenge-shaped dishes, *circa* 1805, each painted in red, green, blue, black and gilding with a central floral roundel within a blue border reserved on a field of flowers, leaves and gilt scrolls, then scalloped rim edged in gilding, 11¾ inches long, is $400–$600.

The more sculptural a piece, the more desirable and expensive. A Worcester leaf-molded sauceboat, *circa* 1765, formed by overlapping leaves edged in green and veined in puce, curling into a green stalk handle and painted on the exterior in puce, blue, red, yellow and brown with scattered insects and floral sprigs, on the interior with a green sprig of lily-of-the-valley, 9½ inches long, is worth $300–$500.

Scarce types of pieces bring comparatively high prices. For instance, a Chamberlain's Worcester four-piece covered crescent-shaped breakfast set on a fitted mahogany stand, *circa* 1812: each piece with a gilt-framed pictorial panel in shades of gray, salmon, brown, yellow and turquoise, the panels depicting exotic birds, in a river landscape, fruit, shells, pink and purple seaweed, yellow, blue, red and white flowers, the rims edged in gilding. Altogether six pieces, 12 and 10½ inches long; sells for $1,000–$1,500.

Assorted English Porcelain

A Derby large mug, *circa* 1825, naturalistically painted within a rectangular panel, showing a house in an identified landscape beneath a border of gilt scrolling leafage, crowned script Derby marks, and one inscribed "View of Switzerland," 4¼ inches high, costs $125–$175.

A Derby chamberstick, *circa* 1760, painted with scattered flower sprays in iron-red, brown, yellow and green, the dished base decorated with scrolls and affixed with a green stem handle terminating in florettes and leaves, surmounted by a petal-molded candle nozzle, 5 inches in diameter, is worth $200–$300.

A pair of Chamberlain's Worcester "Japan"-pattern covered vases, *circa* 1810, each hexagonal and painted in underglaze-blue, red and gilding with a central blue-ground panel reserved with a gilt foliage, flanked by panels of floral sprays, the rims, foliage and dolphin-molded handles and pod knops heightened in gilding, each cover with Chamberlain's Worcester mark in red script, 13⅛ inches high, is priced at $1,000–$1,500.

A pair of English porcelain bough pots and covers, Chamberlain's Worcester or Coalport, 1805–10, the D-shaped bodies with recessed panels enclosing colorful flowers in a basket, the sides decorated with red, rose, yellow and green flowers, the rims of the pots and covers with gilt foliate borders, the covers pierced with four gilt-edged small holes around three brown-edged bulb supports, and the pieces raised on four brown ball feet, 8⅝ inches wide, sells for $800–$1,200.

A Worcester reticulated circular basket, 1765–70, painted in pink, purple, red, yellow and green with a large floral cluster and small leaf sprigs, the sides formed of interlocking circlets applied on the exterior at the intersections with green-centered rose florettes, and the gilt-edged rim with green loop handles at the sides terminating in yellow flowerheads and green leaves, 8 inches wide, is worth $400–$600.

Versatile Spode

Porcelain-making on a commercial scale requires a sizable operation for storing the bulky materials, mixing them and firing them. Consequently, porcelain factories have become much better known among collectors than have individual craftsmen. Many collectors tend to settle on a style they like and acquire pieces mainly from a single factory. Connoisseurs relish learning about the top artists at a factory during its heyday.

While it is true that porcelain from a major factory, such as those we touch on here, will tend to bring more money than porcelain from a lesser factory or an unidentified factory, the quality of an individual piece has the greatest bearing on price. Depending on quality, a Spode might be more or less as expensive as Worcester, Coalport, Minton and so on.

Because he pioneered durable, attractive bone china, Josiah Spode became the first really famous name in English porcelain. Starting in the 1790s, he produced a fantastic variety of finely potted forms including such unusual things as chestnut vases, root dishes, turtle pans, asparagus trays, violet baskets.

Spode borrowed designs from practically everywhere. He was among the first English potters to use Japanese designs, and he copied from the Chelsea, Worcester and Meissen factories. More than anything else, he used Chinese designs. Best known perhaps is the blue-and-white Willow pattern which shows three people crossing a bridge, a willow tree, teahouses, two birds and a garden—a composite based on several Chinese designs. Spode introduced the Willow pattern about 1790, and it has appeared off and on ever since. Also popular were Spode's blue-and-white Mandarin, Rock, Two Temples and a variety of Chinese-landscape patterns. These appeared on all kinds of table wares.

Spode used many meticulously painted colors like apple green, canary yellow, gray, turquoise, red, brown, peach. Spode porcelain received colors well (not all porcelain does), and it has a rich velvety look.

Since Spode was a big successful factory, it represents both refined and gaudy taste—whatever would sell. Beginning around 1800, pieces were clearly marked. Spode died in 1827, and his son, Josiah Spode II, took over and continued to improve potting quality. He introduced a feldspar porcelain that is more translucent than bone china, and it enhances the brilliance of the colors. Ultimately, the company passed through many hands. Most pieces bear the name Spode and/or Copeland, the name of the man who bought the company from Spode's heirs.

Minton's Bright, Pure Colors

Thomas Minton, who worked for Thomas Spode before going into business for himself, is best known for bright pure colors such as red, purple and gold played against translucent porcelain. Like Spode's, Minton's designs weren't especially original, but he knew how to please.

Minton worked on transfer-printing, a process first developed at the Worcester factory. It cut the cost of decorating porcelain and involved printing an image from an engraved copperplate onto a nonabsorbent tissue paper and then transferring the ink to a ceramic surface. Skillfully done, the image is as sharp as a fine print on paper, as desirable as painted decoration.

In 1796 Minton started producing bone china like Spode's. The early pieces had a slight grayish tone with black specks. Minton pushed for better quality, and it improved. By 1815 Minton's porcelain was as good as any being made. A decade later it was hard to find porcelain as white and translucent as his.

Tea services are the most readily available type of Minton porcelain. Typically they include teapot, stand, sugar box, slop bowl, a dozen teacups and saucers, a dozen coffee cups, bread and butter plates. Minton's straight-sided oval teapots were followed by bellied forms, then canoe shapes from 1800 to 1810. Then more curvacious bellied forms appeared. The mid-1820s saw wider, lower teapots with more ornate handles and spouts.

Apparently few Minton porcelain dinner services were made before 1820. The factory concentrated on earthenware dinner services. So if you are looking for Minton porcelain dinner services, you will find them mostly in the ornate styles fashionable from the 1820s through the 1850s, though some simple designs appeared, too.

Minton porcelain dessert services date from about 1805. "The body of these services is mellow and soft, often showing *very* fine crazing of the glass," according to porcelain scholar Geoffrey Godden. Quality changed after 1824. "The porcelain body becomes harder and more compact, the glaze is clear, close fitting and free from crazing, the shapes become more rococo, with shaped edges and with relief molded panel work, and ground colors are extensively used."

Minton produced ornamental wares such as vases. By the 1830s, they featured flower-encrusted designs and made extensive use of ground colors and gilding.

Minton drew on many sources for his designs. There were blue-and-white transfer-printed Chinese patterns, and some designs involved seaweed and shell motifs, while others depicted landscapes, flowers, birds and animals, often in the style of Sèvres porcelain.

Minton's early marks combined the crossed *Ls* of Sèvres (France) with an *M*. Few pieces were marked during the 1820s and 1830s, probably because London porcelain retailers insisted on promoting their names rather than factory names. Scholars have attributed pieces by examining Minton's record books.

Derby's Landscapes and Flowers

Famous for porcelain figures, the Derby factory, started in 1755, made elegant practical wares. Among the most appealing are those decorated with flowers, fruit or landscapes. The best work is from the eighteenth century—pieces with vivid painted decoration were done during the 1780s and 1790s. After that, quality declined as the best painters moved to other factories. Derby introduced a paste formula with a slight greenish tone—you can see it when you hold a piece up to the light. It is a thin hard glaze that enamel could not sink into, so Derby porcelain lost the soft mellow look of enamel blending with glaze. Fine Derby pieces are marked variously "D," "Duesbury-Derby," "Duesbury & Kean."

Worcester's Elegance

Some of the most successful porcelain was made in Worcester. To compete with popular Chinese imports, Dr. John Wall, a druggist who contributed much to the factory's early success, made blue-and-white designs after Chinese styles during the mid-eighteenth century. His soft paste was unusually hard, and it has fewer cracks now than other eighteenth-century English porcelains. He concentrated on practical wares.

Around 1763, Dr. Wall decided to aim at a more affluent market. He produced porcelain in lush greens, purples, blues, reds. He adapted patterns from Japanese, French and German as well as other English porcelain factories. All kinds of natural forms appeared on Worcester wares, from flowers and birds to butterflies. Dr. Wall splashed his porcelain with gleaming gold leaf.

While Dr. Wall was busy producing these elaborate wares, he introduced inexpensive transfer-printed decoration. Portraits were the vogue—Frederick the Great, George II, William Pitt or William Shakespeare. These were printed in a single color such as black or red or purple—over the glaze.

Thomas Flight, a jeweler serving the royal family, bought the firm after Dr. Wall's death. Flight's paste has a slight yellow tone, and collectors prefer Dr. Wall's. With his connections, Flight got porcelain orders from the royal family. After the Queen visited the factory in 1788, Flight was granted permission to dub his porcelain Royal Worcester. A shrewd move, for it helped stimulate business from well-heeled buyers. Flight would not have attracted business if his wares weren't good quality. They were. A magnifying glass will show you the meticulous artistry of Worcester landscape decoration, for instance.

After Thomas Flight's death in 1793, his son Joseph and a partner, Martin Barr, ran the firm. It became Flight & Barr. Later it changed to Barr Flight & Barr (1807–13), then Flight Barr & Barr (1813–40). The firm started producing bone china with a grayish tone in 1799. Two decades passed before the firm attained a highly translucent, pure white porcelain.

The firm is known for large services emblazoned with coats of arms. Many pieces have raised molded borders, floral decoration and gilding.

Several dozen different marks were used on early Worcester porcelain. There was a *W*, a crescent, imitation Chinese seals, and marks imitating French and German factories. From the 1790s on, the marks are clear—"Flight Barr & Barr," for example.

Robert Chamberlain, Dr. Wall's first apprentice, rose to become head porcelain painter at the Worcester factory, and he could see the opportunities. He struck out on his own in 1786, opening a shop nearby. He painted white wares from the Caughley, New Hall, Lowestoft and Derby factories, and he prospered.

Soon after his death in 1798, his sons Humphrey and Robert opened a business making bone china very much like Flight & Barr's. The Chamberlains scored a hit with Regent's China—a highly translucent, clear porcelain. They favored a chain or net border. They made Japan patterns plus those modeled after Spode and Derby. Quality tends to be high. Pieces are marked "Chamberlain."

During the 1840s, these Worcester-area firms merged, forming Royal Worcester. It produced high-quality wares in the fashionable, ornate Victorian styles.

The Cornucopia at Coalport

Coalport is derided often as a mass-market, common-taste factory, but it was capable of just as good quality as any other. It owed its success to John Rose, a practical man who kept abreast of technical advances, producing fine wares at a cost people were willing to pay. His firm was a sort of General Motors which offered something for almost every taste and pocketbook.

Rose served his apprenticeship at the Caughley factory, an offshoot of Worcester, where he met fellow apprentice Thomas Minton. Caughley produced durable soft-paste transfer-printed wares like Worcester. In 1785 Rose set out for himself. He began making pottery near Jackfield. A decade later he moved to Coalport, nearer his clay supplies. He saw bone china as the wave of the future, so he switched to it. His was not very translucent, and it was marred by black specks, but it was less expensive and more appealing than most soft-paste porcelain. About half the wares decorated at Coalport are Japan patterns.

By 1799, he was doing well enough so that he bought the ailing Caughley factory. It had bucked the trend toward bone china, and sales of its soft-paste porcelain were in a slump. Rose converted the factory to bone china, and it produced wares for another one and a half decades. He closed it in 1814 and transferred operations to Coalport. The most common Caughley marks are a *C* and an *S*.

A Splash of Splendor

Starting in 1826, the Rockingham factory turned out some of the most lavish wares ever made. It was commissioned for a two-hundred-piece service upon the coronation of King William IV in 1830, highlighted by his coat of arms and swimming in gold leaf. Such lavish decoration may not be to your liking, but Rockingham did it in high style.

Rockingham is a hard white porcelain with strong ground colors. Apple green, deep blue, maroon, peach and canary yellow are perhaps the most popular. During the 1830s, nobody else surpassed its color quality, and there is plenty of gilding. Decoration was meticulously applied.

Rockingham produced enormous tea, coffee, dinner and dessert services. Their figures and animals too became popular, though here the enameled decoration is not always up to the graceful modeling.

Comparatively few Rockingham pieces are marked, thanks to London retailers who wanted to promote their own names, and many pieces—often slipshod—were attributed mistakenly to Rockingham. Scholarly research is revealing how fine Rockingham porcelain really is.

How to Evaluate English Porcelain

Overall, the potting quality of early-nineteenth-century English porcelain is high. It is stronger and more consistent than eighteenth-century English and most European porcelain.

Some factories mastered the fine points more quickly than others. Check for disfiguring specks on the surface. Hold a piece up to the light and determine whether there is an off-white tone you do not care for. See if the piece has enough translucence to suit you.

Decoration is a big variable. Generally speaking, the fancier the piece—the more colors and artistry in it—the more it is likely to be

1

2

3

19th-century English porcelain is beautiful for display, durable enough to use and inexpensive. You can acquire it for about the same price as new porcelain. (1) Dessert plates, hand-painted at the Davenport factory, about 1825; $500–$700. *Sotheby Parke Bernet.* (2) Part of a dinner service from the Coalport factory, circa 1825; $1,000–$1,500. *Sotheby Parke Bernet.* (3) Oval dishes, 11½ inches wide, from the Derby factory, circa 1820; $800–$1,000. Botanical dishes are prized because of the variation from one plate to another. *Christie's, New York.*

worth, if the design elements are well executed and complement each other.

Patterns that vary from piece to piece can make a set several times more valuable than a set in which every piece looks the same. For example, botanical services in which each plate features a different fruit or flower are much sought after.

The least popular pieces are austere Neoclassical designs fashionable from the 1780s through about 1805. They contain a few small design elements and large white areas. Also on the least wanted list are overcrowded, overdecorated designs that appeared after 1810 and became a little more overbearing with each passing year.

Fine early-nineteenth-century English porcelain is available enough that you should be picky about condition. Watch out for hairline cracks, since they can develop into a fracture. Chips are acceptable if they are unobtrusive.

Many pieces were broken and repaired over the years. Be sure that you are paying for a piece in good condition, not one that has been repaired. If a broken line is covered with a lead-based paint, it is likely to show up when viewed with an ultraviolet light. But many conservators do not use lead-based paint—a UV examination is not sufficient.

Hold a piece up to the sun, so that it is backlighted. This will reveal many repaired breaks. Rub your fingers over the entire surface of a piece. Often the material used for restoration will have a different conductance property than the original material, and it won't feel quite as cold. The pinprick method can also be useful. Gently poke at a piece with a pin. The original piece, fired in a kiln and protected with a hard glaze, will be impervious to a pin, but restored areas usually are not fired; they are softer than the original material. If you discover a soft spot, continue poking until you have determined the size of the repaired area.

Authentic factory marks add value to a piece, because most people prefer a factory attribution rather than the vague description "English porcelain." Note the style and color of a mark—you might see some reasonable-looking marks in the wrong color. Ask yourself whether the style of the piece is consistent with the mark. For instance, there is something wrong if you discover a 1770s-type mark on a piece whose style suggests an 1805–10 date.

Like silver, some porcelain bears marks relating to the original buyer. A full coat of arms can be beautiful. Initials aren't particularly interesting, and they may detract from the value of a piece.

Small factories that produced exceptionally fine pieces command a rarity premium. For instance, Billingsley's Nantgarw pieces can exceed $1,000.

For More Information

In *English Porcelain, 1745–1850* (London: Ernest Benn, 1965), R. J. Charleston gathered together articles about the major English factories. Good overview.

Bernard and Therle Hughes, in *English Porcelain and Bone China, 1743–1850* (New York: Praeger, 1968), provide somewhat more detail, including illustrations of factory marks.

Encyclopedia of British Pottery and Porcelain Marks, by Geoffrey A. Godden (New York: Bonanza, 1964), shows you the marks of all factories, not just the majors.

If you should decide to go whole hog for the wares of a specific factory, here are some sources you might consult:

Franklin A. Barrett, *Worcester Porcelain and Lund's Bristol.* London: Faber & Faber, 1966.

——— and Arthur Thorpe, *Derby Porcelain.* London: Faber & Faber, 1971.

Robert Copeland, *Spode's Willow Pattern and Other Designs After the Chinese.* New York: Rizzoli, 1980.

Geoffrey A. Godden, *Coalport and Coalbrookdale Porcelain.* London: Antique Collectors Club, 1981.

———, *Minton Pottery and Porcelain of the First Period, 1793–1850.* London: Barrie & Jacobs, 1968.

Dennis G. Rice, *Rockingham Pottery and Porcelain.* New York: Praeger, 1971.

Henry Sandon, *Flight & Barr Worcester Porcelain, 1783–1840.* London: Antique Collectors Club, 1978.

Museums

BOSTON
Boston Museum of Fine Arts
Huntington Avenue
Boston, MA 02115
(617) 267-9300

CHICAGO
Art Institute of Chicago
Michigan Avenue and Adams Street
Chicago, IL 60603
(312) 443-3600

FARMINGTON, CONN.
Hill-Steed Museum
671 Farmington Avenue
Farmington, CT 06032
(203) 677-9064

HARTFORD
Wadsworth Atheneum
600 Main Street
Hartford, CT 06103
(203) 278-2670

INDIANAPOLIS
Indianapolis Museum of Art
1200 West 38th Street
Indianapolis, IN 46208
(317) 923-1331

LOS ANGELES
Los Angeles County Museum of Art
5905 Wilshire Boulevard
Los Angeles, CA 90036
(213) 937-4250

MINNEAPOLIS
Minneapolis Institute of Arts
2400 Third Avenue South
Minneapolis, MI 55405
(612) 870-3046

MEMPHIS, TENN.
Dixon Gallery and Gardens
4339 Park Avenue
Memphis, TN 38117
(901) 761-5250

NEW YORK
Frick Collection
1 East 70th Street
New York, NY 10021
(212) 288-0700

Metropolitan Museum of Art
5th Avenue at 82nd Street
New York, NY 10028
(212) 879-5500

PALM BEACH, FLA.
Henry M. Flagler Museum
Whitehall Way
Palm Beach, FL 33480
(305) 655-2833

PHILADELPHIA
Philadelphia Museum of Art
26th Street and Benjamin Franklin Parkway
Philadelphia, PA 19101
(215) 763-8100

A. S. W. Rosenbach Foundation Museum
2010 Delancy Place
Philadelphia, PA 19103
(215) 732-1600

PROVIDENCE
Museum of Art
Rhode Island School of Design
224 Benefit Street
Providence, RI 02903
(401) 331-3511

SAGINAW, MICH.
Saginaw Art Museum
1126 North Michigan Avenue
Saginaw, MI 48602
(517) 754-2491

ST. PETERSBURG, FLA.
Museum of Fine Arts
255 Beach Drive North
St. Petersburg, FL 33701
(813) 896-2667

SAN FRANCISCO
M. H. de Young Museum
Golden Gate Park
San Francisco, CA 94118
(415) 751-4432

SAN MARINO, CALIF.
Huntington Library, Art Gallery and Botanical Gardens
1151 Oxford Road
San Marino, CA 91108
(213) 681-6601

SANTA CLARA, CALIF.
de Saisset Art Gallery and Museum
University of Santa Clara
Santa Clara, CA 95053
(408) 984-4528

SARASOTA, FLA.
John and Mabel Ringling Museum of Art
501 Bayshore Road
Sarasota, FL 33580
(813) 355-5101

Where to Buy

New York auction houses holding regular sales that include English porcelain, of which Sotheby's and Christie's do the most volume:

Christie's
502 Park Avenue
New York, NY 10022
(212) 570-4733

William Doyle
175 East 87th Street
New York, NY 10028
(212) 427-2730

Phillips
406 East 79th Street
New York, NY 10021
(212) 570-4653

Sotheby's
1334 York Avenue
New York, NY 10021
(212) 472-3517

Among dealers with English porcelain:

ATLANTA
William Word Antiques
3107 Early Street, NW
Atlanta, GA 30342
(404) 233-6890

AURORA, COL.
Europa Antiques
1405 Florence Street
Aurora, CO 80010
(303) 344-3142

BALTIMORE
London Shop
1500 Bolton Street
Baltimore, MD 21217
(301) 669-5400

BOSTON
Shreve, Crump & Low
330 Boylston Street
Boston, MA 02116
(617) 267-9100

CARMEL, CALIF.
Davis-Holdship
Mission Street near 6th
Carmel, CA 93921
(408) 624-5757

DALLAS
Rose Driver Antiques
2916 Sale Street
Dallas, TX 75219
(214) 521-7012

Heirloom House
2521 Fairmont
Dallas, TX 75201
(214) 748-2087

ESSEX, CONN.
James Elliott Antiques
8 North Main Street
Essex, CT 06426
(203) 767-1600

HOUSTON
Jennie's Antiques
2039 Gray Street
Houston, TX 77019
(713) 528-2767

LAKE FOREST, ILL.
Cat & Fiddle Inc.
270 Market Square
Lake Forest, IL 60045
(312) 234-0160

NEW YORK

Earle D. Vandekar
15 East 57th Street
New York, NY 10022
(212) 308-2022

La Ganke
1093 Second Avenue
New York, NY 10022
(212) 688-9312

James Robinson
15 East 57th Street
New York, NY 10022
(212) 752-6166

PALM BEACH, FLA.

Meissen Shop
343 Worth Avenue
Palm Beach, FL 33480
(305) 832-2504

PHILADELPHIA

Alfred Bullard/Helen McGehee
1604 Pine Street
Philadelphia, PA 19103
(215) 735-1879

Florence Hocksten Antiques
138 South 17th Street
Philadelphia, PA 19103
(215) 567-6663

Harry A. Eberhardt & Son
2010 Walnut Street
Philadelphia, PA 19103
(215) 568-4144

SAN FRANCISCO

Ronald James
Sacramento
(415) 567-7888

Red Anchor
872 North Point
San Francisco, CA 94109
(415) 673-3436

WASHINGTON

Antony Childs Associates
1670 Wisconsin Avenue, NW
Washington, DC 20007
(202) 337-1100

5

AMERICAN ARTS AND CRAFTS FURNITURE

"I TRIED TO MAKE FURNITURE THAT WOULD BE SIMPLE, DURABLE, COMfortable and fitted for the place it was to occupy and the work it had to do," declared Gustav Stickley, a restless, resourceful immigrant cabinetmaker who helped revolutionize American design around the turn of the century.

Inspired by the English cultural writers John Ruskin and William Morris, Stickley threw up his hands at industrialization and spearheaded what became known as the American Arts and Crafts movement. Embracing artisans in many fields besides furniture, it stood for a revival of sturdy, old-fashioned craftsmanship.

Stickley selected humble oak as his material rather than flashy Victorian woods. He developed largely rectilinear designs instead of the elaborate curves then in vogue. He all but banished decoration—no carving, inlay or paint is found in his mature work. He made functional construction beautiful, and it became popularly known as mission oak. Merchandisers like Sears Roebuck began producing cheaper versions referred to, more simply, as Grand Rapids oak.

It was passing out of fashion by the 1920s, and even now a Stickley piece can turn up at the Salvation Army. Though prices have climbed as collectors learned more about this neglected field, it still sells for less than the sinuous Art Nouveau furniture made in the same period. It is less than almost any other major type of furniture, and you can do exceptionally well for several thousand dollars. Just about all the pieces you'd need to furnish a home are available in the Arts and Crafts styles: armchairs, easy chairs, dining-room tables, tables, desks, cabinets, bookcases, dressers, even wastebaskets.

Chairs

As you would expect, more Arts and Crafts chairs were made than any other form. Side chairs come in both slat-back and ladder-back varieties. Seats are leather, rush or straight wood. Height: 36–46 inches. Width: 16–19 inches. Depth: 14–16 inches. They can be had for $500–$700.

Good armchairs are scarce in traditional styles, but they abound in Arts and Crafts styles. Best known perhaps is the so-called Morris chair, named after William Morris. It is a reclining chair with an adjustable back and a wood or upholstered seat and back. Height: 36–40 inches. Width: 22–32 inches. Depth: 25–30 inches. Simple, open-arm designs can be bought for $500–$700, but more formidable designs, with closely spaced slats under the arms, run $1,000–$2,000. A few unusually fine designs can bring twice as much.

Armchairs without a reclining back are available for $500–$700. Height: 36–49 inches. Width: 21–28 inches. Depth: 19–21 inches. They include ladder backs, slat backs or upholstered backs.

You can find nice slat-back rocking chairs, with and without arms. Height: 34–36 inches. Width: 16–20 inches. Depth: 14–18 inches. Prices range from $300 to $700.

Rarest is the Eastwood chair, a particularly spacious design fashioned from large beams with ladder back, open arms, upholstered seat. Height: 36–38 inches. Width: 36–38 inches. Depth: 30–32 inches. An Eastwood chair has not appeared on the market in several years, so it is difficult to price, but dealers figure it might be in the $4,000–$5,000 range.

Mission settles, a type of sofa, are quite handsome. They are likely to have slat backs, an upholstered seat and open arms. Height: 32–40 inches. Width: 45–75 inches. Depth: 20–28 inches. Prices are $800–$1,200.

A now-scarce variety is the high-back hall seat or fireplace settle, with solid back and arms. Height: 55–62 inches. Width: 68–72 inches. Depth: 21–23 inches. It sells for $3,000–$5,000.

Tables, Servers and Sideboards

Dining tables are solid, practical and easy to find. Most tops are round. Pedestal-base tables are single-piece. Four-leg tables, with a center support, are two-piece. Legs do not get in the way. Height: 28–30 inches. Diameter: 55-60 inches. These are worth $800–$3,000.

A lot of library tables appear on the market. Many have drawers beneath the rectangular top, and a wide lengthwise stretcher, connecting the legs, which can serve as a shelf. Height: 30–32 inches. Width: 40–65 inches. Depth: 28–30 inches. They sell for $500–$1,000.

Small tables come in a variety of designs—side tables, plant tables, drink tables, tea tables—square-top or round-top. Height: 20–30 inches. Width, depth or diameter: 16–20 inches. These bring $300–$600.

Servers are tables with a backboard raised several inches above the top, drawers beneath the front of the top, and a shelf below. Height: 36–40 inches. Width: 40–44 inches. Depth: 18–22 inches. Prices are from $500 to $1,000.

Sideboards are much more massive. The backboard is higher, and there might be four drawers in front, flanked by cabinet doors. Height: 38–50 inches. Width: 50–60 inches. Depth: 20–22 inches. They can be bought for $1,000–$4,000.

Desks and Bookcases

There are three kinds of Stickley desks: fall-front, rolltop and flattop. Fall-fronts, as the name suggests, have a writing surface that hinges upward to conceal drawers and pigeonholes. Simple versions are essentially a desk-on-stand, with a single drawer below the writing surface, a shelf connecting the legs. Height: 28–30 inches. Width: 28–30 inches. Depth: 18–20 inches. These might sell for $500–$1,000.

More formidable fall-fronts have two or three drawers below the writing surface, and perhaps a couple of cabinet doors as well. Height: 45–52 inches. Width: 24–33 inches. Depth closed: 7–12 inches. Prices range from $1,000 to $3,000.

Rolltops are among the most friendly reminders of yesteryear—Thomas Edison and Henry Ford each had one. Height: 40–50 inches. Width: 50–60 inches. Depth: 25–30 inches. They sell for $500–$1,500.

Flattops are the most familiar designs, an open central area for your feet, flanked by two or three drawers on either side. Height: 28–30 inches. Width: 40–50 inches. Depth: 25–30 inches. These are worth from $300 to $600.

Bookcases have one or two doors with eight to twelve square glass panes in each. The top is a usable space, molded on back and sides. Height: 55–65 inches. Width: 30–60 inches. Depth: 12–15 inches. Prices are from $1,000 to $3,000.

Corner cupboards are similar to bookcases, but they will have angled, glass-paneled sides, a single glass-paneled door. They are taller too. Height: 60–65 inches. Width: 45–50 inches. Depth: 26–28 inches. They can be $1,000–$3,000.

Chests

These might have two to six half-drawers, three to five wide drawers. Drawer pulls are likely to be wood knobs or copper rings secured to hammered-copper plates. Height: 40–50 inches. Width: 40–50 inches. Depth: 20–22 inches. Prices go from $500 to $1,500.

Potpourri

Besides these major pieces, you will find a surprising and delightful variety of smaller, inexpensive pieces like oak umbrella stands decorated with one or two hammered copper bands, coat racks, plate-display racks, table lamps, three-panel screens, music cabinets or magazine stands. These pieces can be had for several hundred dollars each.

Names to Look for

Gustav Stickley is the most important name, because he not only pioneered high-quality designs but also promoted himself through his catalogs and other publications. His work tends to sell for more than other designs of Arts and Crafts furniture—sometimes twice as much as pieces by his brothers Lee and George Stickley, who worked for him a few years before striking out on their own in 1900. Gustav Stickley's work also commands a premium over Arts and Crafts furniture made at the Roycroft shops or at Charles Limbert Company, though they did very fine work in similar styles.

Gustav Stickley's work passed through several phases from its beginning until 1916, when his overextended firm went bankrupt. Until 1900, he experimented, looking for a style. His structural elements, like chair legs and backs, were heavier than those he used later. His hardware was cast brass or iron. By 1902, Stickley had switched to handwrought hardware. He also began using wooden knobs and square drawer pulls. He exposed the joints to relieve the plain areas of wood.

Stickley hired a brooding, ingenious designer named Harvey Ellis in 1903. Ellis introduced pieces with light-colored woods as well as pewter and copper inlay. Many of his designs had rounded corners. They were not commercially successful, and Ellis, an alcoholic, died after about a year. These pieces, bearing Stickley's mark, are rare. Collectors pay over $10,000 for Ellis furniture when it appears on the market.

Stickley was most productive between 1904 and 1910. He introduced veneer, and he often used V-shaped and circular drawer pulls. After 1910 he simplified his designs, brought out fewer new ones and discontinued some of his most distinctive ones from earlier years.

In general, Stickley took more pains than other furniture-makers of his time. He used wooden pegs to secure joints because they were more aesthetically pleasing. Competitors, including his brothers, chose screws or nails, which took less time to put in. Sometimes they would insert a little plug on top of the screw, to conceal it. Most competitors continued using cast hardware after Stickley switched to more elegant and durable wrought hardware. Stickley used quarter-sawed wood, a wasteful process that yielded the most spectacular wood grain. Most competitors opted for cheaper straight-sawed wood.

Stickley was versatile. Each of his almost-annual catalogs described an average of 150 different designs. Most of Gustav Stickley's work is marked, the early pieces mainly by a red decal. After 1908, he used a brand or paper label. These show his emblem, the joiner's compass and the motto *Als ik kan*—Flemish for "As I can," a rallying cry of sorts for craftsmen who worked with their hands rather than with machines.

Lee and J. George Stickley started the Onondaga Shops, Fayetteville, New York, in 1902. Their designs as well as their catalogs were modeled after those of Gustav's, though details don't always equal his. They might be just massive enough to be clunky, for instance, or have a curve that seems out of step with dominant rectilinear lines. Nonetheless, their best work can represent a superb buy.

They remained in operation until 1917, when they joined Gustav and another brother, Albert, to form Stickley Associated Cabinetmakers. Lee and J. George Stickley marked their furniture with several decals. Initially they read: "The Onondaga Shops. L. & J. G. Stickley, Fayetteville, N.Y." Between 1906 and 1910: "L. & J. G. Stickley Handcraft." Then: "The Work of L. & J. G. Stickley."

The Roycroft Shops were launched by the flamboyant businessman and popular writer Elbert Hubbard, best known for his book *Message to García,* a parable about loyalty. Started in East Aurora, New York, in 1893 as high-quality printers, Roycroft had expanded into handcrafted furniture by 1896, before Gustav Stickley. The idea, apparently, was to furnish Hubbard's nearby inn. The robust designs proved popular, and he began selling them.

Whereas Stickley relied on oak, making only a few pieces in mahogany, Roycroft turned out many pieces in mahogany, ash, maple and walnut. Designs featured unusual (for the Arts and Crafts style) touches like tapered legs and shaped feet. But since Roycroft was a small shop, seldom more than ten craftsmen at a time, it did not become a major influence.

Its furniture is marked with either "Roycroft" or a double cross and circle enclosing a capital *R*. These marks appear in conspicuous places like a chair back, the side of a table, or a cabinet door.

In a special class is custom-designed, often one-of-a-kind Arts and Crafts furniture. For instance, many clients of architect Frank Lloyd Wright asked him to design furniture that would complement his homes. Wright was not in the furniture-making business, so these pieces are scarce, but his furniture does come up from time to time. Note that he also designed furniture for the Hendredon Company during the 1950s. Examples of his work:

- Cypress settee and room divider, *circa* 1940, the backrest fitted with two white-painted bookshelves, $500–$1,000. Length: 10 feet. Width: 40 inches.
- Pair of hexagonal cypress stools, *circa* 1940, slip seat in salmon vinyl, $800–$1,000. Height: 15 inches.
- Mahogany extension dining-room table, circular top edged with a fretwork-stamped copper band, the four X-shaped feet with matching carved banding, a 12-inch extension leaf, $2,500–$3,500. Diameter without extension: 54 inches. Height: 24½ inches.

Much rarer and more expensive is furniture by Green & Green, California woodworkers who designed furnishings for the spectacular Gamble House in Pasadena. A single one of their mahogany side chairs with ebony pegging and Japanese inlay could be worth $25,000, and a similarly styled vitrine in less than perfect condition, $40,000.

How to Evaluate Arts and Crafts Furniture

Proportions are the most important factor influencing value. A lot of Arts and Crafts furniture imitating Gustav Stickley's styles has a boring, institutional look.

Wood grain varies tremendously from one piece to another. The showier, the better as far as most collectors are concerned.

Hardware like hinges and drawer pulls—usually made of hammered copper—provide the most interesting decoration. Pieces with particularly beautiful hardware bring more money.

Rare forms mean extra money. For instance, while there are many good library tables around, music cabinets are unusually rare. They can be worth as much as $15,000.

During the decades that Arts and Crafts furniture was utterly out of fashion, many people left it out on porches and other places vulnerable to the elements. That is why so much Arts and Crafts furniture has an unappealing pitted look. Over the years, too, quite a few pieces were

1

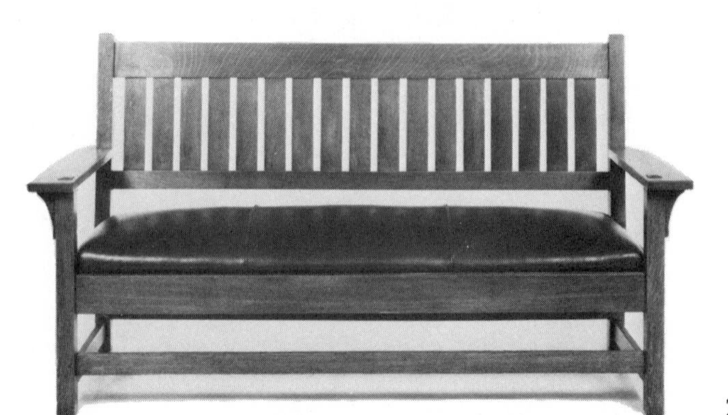

2

Handsome oak pieces in the turn-of-the-century American Arts and Crafts style. The finest examples were fashioned with meticulous hand craftsmanship. (1) Oak china cabinet, circa 1910, by Gustav Stickley, who pioneered the style. 63 inches high; $2,500–$3,500. *Sotheby Parke Bernet.* (2) Stickley oak settle, circa 1910. 39 inches high × 72 inches wide; $1,500–$2,000. *Christie's, New York.*

3

4

(3) Stickley oak sideboard, circa 1910, with hammered black-painted hardware. 50 inches high × 70¼ inches wide; $4,500–$5,500. *Christie's, New York.* (4) Stickley oak dining table, circa 1910. 48 inches in diameter; $2,000–$3,000. *Sotheby Parke Bernet.*

coated with paint, shellac, or other finishes. Do not compound the felony by taking a piece to a professional stripper—the harsh chemicals that strippers use could make the problem worse. The only solution is elbow grease, removal of the finish with a mild solvent and a small brush.

For More Information

David M. Cathers, *Furniture of the American Arts and Crafts Movement.* New York: New American Library, 1981.

Robert Judson Clark, ed., *The Arts and Crafts Movement in America, 1876–1916.* Princeton, N.J.: Princeton University Press, 1972.

Gustav Stickley, *Craftsman Homes, Architecture and Furnishings of the American Arts and Crafts Movement.* New York: Dover, 1979, reprinted from 1909 edition.

Stickley Craftsman Furniture Catalogs. New York: Dover, 1979. A reprint in one volume of *Craftsman Furniture Made by Gustav Stickley* and *The Work of L. & J. G. Stickley,* catalogs.

Museums

ALLENTOWN, PA.
Allentown Art Museum
Fifth and Court Streets
Allentown, PA 18105
(*215*) *432-4333*

BUFFALO, N.Y.
Albright-Knox Art Gallery
1285 Elmwood Avenue
Buffalo, NY 14222
(*716*) *882-8700*

CHICAGO
Art Institute of Chicago
Michigan Avenue and Adams Street
Chicago, IL 60603
(*312*) *443-3600*

DETROIT
Detroit Institute of Arts
5200 Woodward Avenue
Detroit, MI 48202
(*313*) *833-7900*

EAST AURORA, N.Y.
Elbert Hubbard Library-Museum
Village Hall
571 Main Street
East Aurora, NY 14052
(*716*) *652-6000*

HOUSTON
Museum of Fine Arts
1001 Bissonnet
Houston, TX 77005
(*713*) *526-1361*

LOS ANGELES
Los Angeles County Museum of Art
5905 Wilshire Boulevard
Los Angeles, CA 90036
(*213*) *937-4250*

NEWARK, N.J.
New Jersey Historical Society
230 Broadway
Newark, NJ 07104
(201) 483-3939

Newark Museum
49 Washington Street
Newark, NJ 07101
(201) 733-6600

NEW YORK
Brooklyn Museum
188 Eastern Parkway
Brooklyn, NY 11238
(212) 638-5000

Metropolitan Museum of Art
Fifth Avenue at 82nd Street
New York, NY 10028
(212) 879-5500

OAK PARK, ILL.
Frank Lloyd Wright Home and Studio
Chicago and Forest Avenues
Oak Park, IL 60302
(312) 848-1976

PASADENA, CALIF.
Gamble House
4 Westmoreland Place
Pasadena, CA 91103
(213) 793-3334

RICHMOND, VA.
Virginia Museum of Fine Arts
Boulevard and Grove Avenues
Richmond, VA 23221
(804) 257-0844

ROCHESTER, N.Y.
Strong Museum
700 Allen Creek Road
Rochester, NY 14618
(716) 381-1818

ST. LOUIS
St. Louis Art Museum
Forest Park
St. Louis, MO 63110
(314) 721-0067

SYRACUSE, N.Y.
Everson Museum of Art of Syracuse and Onondaga County
401 Harrison Street
Syracuse, NY 13202
(315) 474-6064

WILMINGTON, DEL.
Delaware Art Museum
2301 Kentmere Parkway
Wilmington, DE 19806
(302) 571-9590

Where to Buy

Auction houses offering Arts and Crafts furniture:

BOLTON, MASS.
Robert W. Skinner
Route 117
Bolton, MA 01740
(617) 779-5528

NEW YORK
Christie's
502 Park Avenue
New York, NY 10022
(212) 546-1025

Phillips
406 East 79th Street
New York, NY 10021
(212) 570-4849

Sotheby's
1334 York Avenue
New York, NY 10021
(212) 472-3508

There are plenty of dealers, especially in the Northeast and the West, who offer turn-of-the-century American oak furniture. Little of it, though, is likely to be good quality. Dealers:

NEW HAVEN
ARK Antiques
266 Alden Avenue
New Haven, CT 06515
(203) 387-3754

NEW YORK
Michael Carey American Arts and Crafts
107 Spring Street
New York, NY 10003
(212) 226-3710

Jordan-Volpe Gallery
457 West Broadway
New York, NY 10012
(212) 533-3900

WESTWOOD, N.J.
Oak and Stuff
187 Fairview Avenue
Westwood, NJ 07675
(201) 666-2261

6

CLASSIC FLOWER AND FRUIT PRINTS

PERHAPS NOWHERE ELSE IN THE ART MARKET CAN YOU FIND AS MUCH BEAUTY for so little money as with fine vintage flower and fruit prints. "Throughout the ages," observed collector Wilfred Blunt, "the flower-painter has been tossed like a shuttlecock between the scientist on the one hand and the lover of the beautiful on the other."

The golden age of flower and fruit prints began during the mid-eighteenth century. With growing world trade and exploration, each ship landing in London, Paris and other centers seemed to bring intriguing new plant species. This stimulated tremendous enthusiasm for horticulture.

Wealthy amateurs backed flower artists who used improved printing processes to produce lavish color-illustrated books, frequently hand-finished. The outpouring of magnificent flower and fruit books continued for almost a century, until the wealthy found other diversions. Incredibly, fine prints by the most important flower and fruit artists—prints removed from damaged or odd volumes—can be had today for under $2,000. You can buy beauties for half that.

Magnificent Herbals

Growing interest in medicine during the seventeenth century led to some of the most spectacular early illustrated books. They depicted medicinal plants known as herbals, showing roots, seeds, flowers, everything about a plant in glorious detail. The better artists created pleasing designs, too.

Some of the most striking herbal illustrations are by Basil Besler (1561–1629), a Nuremberg druggist hired to oversee the gardens of the Prince Bishop of Eichstätt. For sixteen years, Besler made drawings of what he discovered in those gardens. He depicted now-familiar varieties like crocus, narcissus, hyacinth, daisy, sage and mint as well as things strange to us. Together with at least ten artists and engravers, he published *Hortus Eystettensis* (1613). It contains 374 plates depicting over 1,000 flowers, 667 species. Most were published in black and white, but a few were hand-colored. Plates average 21¼ by 17 inches. Hand-colored illustrations sell for $1,000–$2,000, black-and-white perhaps a quarter as much.

One of the earliest color flower books was by the resourceful Elizabeth Blackwell, a London woman who wanted to get her husband out of debtors' prison. She heard about the need for a new illustrated book on medicinal plants, and, though she lacked formal training, she plunged ahead, producing *A Curious Herbal, Containing Five Hundred Cuts of the Most Useful Plants Which Are Now Used in the Practice of Physick.* The graceful, hand-colored illustrations were published from 1737 to 1739, reprinted two decades later. Her husband was freed. Each illustration shows key parts of a plant such as stem, leaves, flowers, seeds, roots. Dimensions: 7⅛ by 12 inches. Prices range from $75 to $250.

The wandering naturalist Mark Catesby (1683–1749) created vigorous images of flowers, many combined with birds. Displaying a playful disregard for precision, he juggled with proportions to enhance his design. For instance, a majestic flamingo shown against a tree-size branching coral which is, in real life, just a few inches high. Catesby's work resulted from his travels gathering specimens through the American Southeast. Most of his prints appeared in *The Natural History of the Carolinas, Florida and Bahamas,* published between 1731 and 1743. Two editions appeared after his death, 1748–56 and 1771. The images are about 14 by 19 inches. They sell for $500–$1,000.

Flowers as Fine Art

A rigorous self-taught German botanist, the inventive George Ehret (1710–70), created robust, sculptural designs, suffused with delicate, glowing colors. He prided himself on meticulous detail. His flowers seem to take on a life of their own, inviting you to reach out and touch them.

Ehret grew up at a time when many aristocrats were eager plant collectors, paying steep premiums for specimens that arrived from Asia, Africa and the New World. The aristocrats were curious to learn about these wonders, and they wanted to show off a little. So when Ehret, a gardener's son, revealed his talent for drawing, he soon had an income. He traveled from castle to castle, making watercolors of flowers.

He also illustrated books for explorers and scholars, including the revolutionary system of plant classification devised by the Swedish botanist Carl Linnaeus. Ehret moved to London, where wealthy horticulturists paid him to immortalize their most-prized blooms. Often he liked to add a butterfly as a playful touch. Over three thousand of his drawings survive.

Ehret was the first really great master of flower illustration. He made eighteen engravings for *Plantae et Papiliones Rariores* (1748–62). One of his patrons, a Nuremberg doctor named Christoph Trew, commissioned a skilled engraver to produce *Plantae Selectae* (1750–71), a book based on a hundred of Ehret's drawings. There's an emphasis on exotic plants like guava, banana, pawpaw and pineapple. Dimensions: 11½ by 17 inches, 12 by 19 inches. They are worth $325–$850.

Rose King

The most prolific flower painter was the Frenchman Pierre-Joseph Redouté (1759–1840), who endowed each sprig of leaves and flowers with personality. Some are flamboyant, some dainty, some elegant. He also popularized stipple engraving, a technique in which the engraver uses a needle or a spiky wheel to cut tiny indentations in a metal plate. These hold ink, which is tranferred to paper, creating subtle tonal qualities not possible with conventional etching.

The overpowering beauty of Redouté's images enabled him to prosper during turbulent times. He gave drawing lessons to Queen Marie Antoinette, and after she was beheaded in the Revolution he did work for Napoleon's Empress Josephine. When she was banished, Napoleon's second Empress, Marie Louise, became Redouté's patron, too. He illustrated flowers for the royal family when it regained power after Napoleon's downfall. "I have given all my love," he reportedly uttered on his deathbed, "in exchange for a measure of glory."

Redouté illustrated more than fifty books with 2,300 images. Among them: *Plantes grasses* (185 stipple engravings, 8 by 11 inches, 1799), *Traité des arbres et arbustes* (494 stipple engravings, 8⅞ by 11⅞ inches, 1801–19), *Choix des plus belles fleurs* (144 stipple engravings, 8½ by 11 inches, 1827). Many collectors rate *Les Liliacées* (Lilies) as Redouté's best work. Issued between 1802 and 1816, its 486 stipple engravings depict not just lilies, but also irises, amaryllis, gladiolas, tulips, and related species. Dimensions: 14 by 20 inches. The most famous Redouté work is *Les Roses,* 168 stipple engravings issued between 1817 and 1824. Dimensions: 10 by 14 inches. Most Redouté prints you'll see were printed in color, finished by hand. Typical prices range from $400 to $800, with rarities going as high as $2,000.

Fruit Wizard

The Englishman George Brookshaw created the most spectacular fruit prints. He was as interested in appealing composition as in scientific accuracy. His images are bold, sometimes accented with sinuous leaves and flowers. He achieved dramatic effects by placing his designs on a beige or brown background.

He devoted his major energies to illustrating fruit growing around London. His great work, *Pomona Britannica* (1812), contains ninety aquatint, hand-colored images, each about 8¼ by 10¼ inches. Included are strawberries, raspberries, cherries, currants, plums, apricots, peaches, pineapples, grapes, melons, figs and pears. These sell for $800–$2,500. The highest prices are for the largest, most striking images such as his pineapples or cantaloupes. Less expensive are designs featuring small fruit like gooseberries, though a few of his marvelous raspberries and strawberries sell in the high end of the price range.

Flowers and Romance

The Englishman John Robert Thornton (*c.*1765–1837) brought high romance to flower prints. He was consumed by an ambition to top every flower illustrator who went before him. He wanted his prints to be bigger, brassier, even a little melodramatic.

From 1799 to 1807, he threw his inherited fortune into an ambitious project with a windy title, *A New Illustration of the Sexual System of Carolus von Linneaus: comprehending an elucidation of the several parts of the fructification; a prize dissertation on the sexes of plants; a full explanation of the classes and orders, of the sexual system; and the Temple of Flora, or Garden of Nature, being picturesque, botanical, coloured plates, of select plants, illustrative of the same, with descriptions.* Thornton ended up penniless, but part of this project, *Temple of Flora,* secured his fame. It contains thirty-two plates which are a hefty 15 by 20 inches. The flowers are depicted up close. Thornton was the first to use landscape backgrounds—craggy mountains, lush jungles, stormy skies and ancient Roman architecture. These backdrops don't necessarily represent the actual habitat for the flowers, but they provide quite an atmosphere. To achieve extraordinary effects, Thornton combined four techniques in his images: copper engraving, mezzotint, aquatint and hand coloring. Collectors do not mind that Thornton himself drew only one of the images, working instead as a director who conceived designs, selected artists and approved production.

His prints sell for $1,500–$4,000. On the high end are "A Group of Carnations," "Sacred Egyptian Bean," "White Lily" and "Tulips." On

1

2

3

Flower and fruit prints are beautiful, hand-colored images and they are now less expensive than most other graphic arts. (1) A shimmering lily by the greatest French flower painter, Pierre-Joseph Redouté, whose patrons included Louis XVI and Napoleon. 14 × 20½ inches; under $1,500. *W. Graham Arader III.* (2) A dramatic Nodding Renealmia by Englishman Robert Thornton, the most expensive botanical artist because of his lush backgrounds and use of different printing techniques to add extra richness. 15½ × 20½ inches; $3,000–$4,000. *W. Graham Arader III.* (3) Hand-colored aquatint pineapple by Englishman George Brookshaw, considered to have done the finest fruit prints. 10⅝ × 13⅜ inches; $2,000–$2,500. *W. Graham Arader III.*

the low end: "Snowdrop," "Persian Cyclamen," "Pitcher Plant" and "Quadrangular Passion Flower."

How to Evaluate Flower and Fruit Prints

Once you have decided that you enjoy a particular print, and it has a desirable composition, check its technical qualities. In the event you want to sell a print later, you can be sure prospective buyers will be very picky, and you will pay for any oversight then.

Since classic flower prints came from books, you can become familiar with authentic examples by looking through the books. A surprising number of city and university libraries have some of them; see the listing at the end of this chapter.

Before you buy a flower print, remove it from its frame and note the following:

Printing process. Learn what process was used to make an original and how to recognize it. If an original print is an engraving, any example you consider should have the inky look of an engraving, not the lighter, penciled look of a lithograph, or the even lighter look of a modern offset reproduction.

Watermark. Many books used watermarked paper through the early nineteenth century. Check whether an original print was watermarked. If so, do not buy a print alleged to be original unless it has the right watermark.

Quality of strike. The plates used to strike an image on paper gradually wear out as more prints are made. Consequently, sharp lines become fuzzy, and an image loses its crispness. Avoid a later, less desirable strike.

Original hand-coloring. Collectors want color that passed the artist's inspection, so check to see that it is original. Suspect added color if the paper is faded, the colors fresh. An easy test: hold a print against the light and view it at a low angle. Added color has a different sheen from original color, and any hand coloring has a different sheen from uncolored areas. By contrast, an offset reproduction with machine-produced color has the same sheen all over.

Color quality. As with any handwork, hand coloring varies widely in quality. See that you get a print with good rich color, not something washed out. See if the color was applied evenly. Notice whether colors stay within the printed lines, or whether the colorist was sloppy.

Full margins. Big white margins not only may be very appealing, but often include a watermark or a revealing legend. Avoid a print that has been trimmed down.

Condition. Collectors want a print that is clean, so try to avoid one with tears, stains, creases or other marks on the paper. Avoid a print that has faded in the sun.

For More Information

Handasyde Buchanan, *Nature into Art.* New York: Mayflower Books, 1979.

Gerta Calmann, *Ehret, Flower Painter Extraordinary.* Boston: New York Graphic Society, 1977.

Alice M. Coats, *The Book of Flowers.* London: Phaidon Press, 1973.

Gordon Dunthorne, *Flower and Fruit Prints of the 18th and Early 19th Centuries.* Washington, D.C.: Dunthorne, 1938, reprinted 1970.

Flowers in Books and Drawings, c.940–1840. New York: Pierpont Morgan Library, 1980.

Paul Hulton and Lawrence Smith, *Flowers in Art from East and West.* London: British Museum Publications, 1979.

Ronald King, *Botanical Illustration.* New York: Clarkson Potter, 1978.

P. J. Redouté, *Roses.* Miller Graphics, undated reprint.

Martyn Rix, *The Art of the Plant World.* Woodstock: Overlook Press, 1982.

Robert Thornton, *The Temple of Flora.* Boston: New York Graphic Society, 1981.

Museums

CAMBRIDGE
Botanical Museum of Harvard University
Oxford Street
Cambridge, MA 02138
(617) 495-2326

CHICAGO
Field Museum of Natural History
Roosevelt Road at Lake Shore Drive
Chicago, IL 60605
(312) 922-9410

ITHACA, N.Y.
L. H. Bailey Hortorium and Library
Cornell University
Ithaca, NY 14853
(607) 256-2131

Rare Book Collection and History of Science Collection, Olin Library
Cornell University
Ithaca, NY 14853
(607) 256-4144

LAWRENCE, KANS.
Spencer Research Library
University of Kansas
Lawrence, KS 66045
(913) 864-4710

NEW HAVEN
Beinecke Rare Book Library
Yale University
120 Howe Street
New Haven, CT 06504
(203) 436-8438

NEW YORK
American Museum of Natural History
79th Street and Central Park West
New York, NY 10024
(212) 873-1300

New York Public Library
Fifth Avenue and 42nd Street
New York, NY 10018
(212) 790-6262

Pierpont Morgan Library
29 East 36th Street
New York, NY 10016
(212) 685-0008

SAN MARINO, CALIF.
Huntington Library, Art Gallery and Botanical Gardens
1151 Oxford Road
San Marino, CA 91108
(213) 681-6601

ST. LOUIS
Missouri Botanical Garden
2101 Tower Grove Avenue
St. Louis, MO 63110
(314) 577-5100

WASHINGTON
Smithsonian Institution
1000 Jefferson Drive, SW
Washington, DC 20560
(202) 357-1300

Where to Buy

Flower and fruit prints appear in sales of low-priced prints (individual sheets) as well as in book sales at these auction houses:

NEW YORK
Christie's
502 Park Avenue
New York, NY 10022
(212) 546-1195

Sotheby's
1334 York Avenue
New York, NY 10021
(212) 472-3593

Swann Galleries
104 East 25th Street
New York, NY 10010
(212) 254-4710

SAN FRANCISCO
California Book Auction Galleries
358 Golden Gate Avenue
San Francisco, CA 94102
(415) 775-0424

Dealers:

KING OF PRUSSIA, PA.
W. Graham Arader III
1000 Boxwood Court
King of Prussia, PA 19406
(215) 825-6570

NEW ORLEANS
Didier Inc.
3439 Magazine Street
New Orleans, LA 70115
(504) 899-7749

NEW YORK
Old Print Shop
150 Lexington Avenue
New York, NY 10016
(212) 683-3950

SPARTANBURG, S.C.
Musgrove Mill
509 East St. John Street
Spartanburg, SC 29302
(803) 583-9847

WASHINGTON
Old Print Gallery
1220 31st Street, NW
Washington, DC 20007
(202) 965-1818

7

AMERICAN BRILLIANT CUT GLASS

ITS FACETS SPARKLE IN THE LIGHT LIKE RARE JEWELS, AND IT HAS A SOLID HEFT in your hand. During the late nineteenth and early twentieth centuries, it was a luxury only the wealthy could afford. The White House used it to serve foreign dignitaries. The Prince of Wales, the President of Mexico and the Crown Prince of Sweden ordered complete services of it: American brilliant cut glass.

Cut glass goes back to the ancient world, but it was reintroduced on a grand scale at the 1876 Centennial Exposition in Philadelphia. The hit of the show was a massive, deeply faceted wine decanter from Christian Dorflinger's Glassworks, White Mills, Pennsylvania. Included were thirty-eight matching glasses, each engraved to commemorate a state of the Union.

During the next several decades, cut glass was distinguished by elaborate geometric patterns such as Harvard, Russian, Honeycomb and Strawberry-Diamond. These, in turn, were fashioned from motifs bearing names like pinwheel, rosette, fan, step, blaze. Star motifs were the most popular: hobstar, flashed star, pyramidal star, shooting star. Different patterns might use many of the same motifs.

Good brilliant cut glass began with quality material. The harder the glass, the sharper the edges, the more dazzling the light effects and the more expensive. Lead is usually a key ingredient, 35–50 percent of the formula. Large glass blanks were needed, because this style involved deep cutting.

Master craftsmen created the desired patterns by pressing the glass against a sharp-edged steam-powered wheel. Since cutting produces a smoky or white area on the glass, it had to be polished. Dipping the glass in an acid bath was the quickest polishing method, but hand polishing yielded still greater brilliance.

By the 1880s, an Art Nouveau variation with swirling lines and plant forms was introduced by Thomas Webb, an English firm, and popularized by Thomas Hawkes of Corning, New York. Geometric styles, though, remained popular. Brilliant cut glass peaked by about 1910. It was made after that, and it is still being made now. Now American brilliant cut glass is a staple of flea markets and antiques shows: inexpensive, largely ignored by collectors. Certain rarities have sold for several thousand dollars, but most is under $500.

Dishes and Bowls

Dishes less than 12 inches in diameter were made mainly for use, and they are readily available. They sell for $200–$300. Larger plates are more desirable, because they were made more for decoration. A good 15–18-inch-diameter plate might bring $700–$800.

A good plate will always bring more than a bowl, since large plates are rarer than large bowls. Punch bowls tend to have similar patterns, usually a hobstar or pinwheel and fan pattern. Punch bowls range from $500 to $2,500, depending on quality.

Punch bowls 10–14 inches in diameter can be worth $600–$800. Really big ones, with a 25-inch diameter, come in two pieces with an inverted trumpet-form base. If they are in good condition with deep cutting, the price could run $3,000–$4,000. A punch bowl is more desirable when a set of cups, 8 minimum, is included.

Smaller than punch bowls are salad bowls with straight sides, or fruit bowls with flaring sides. They might be worth $100–$150 apiece.

An individual compote, 10–14 inches high, can bring $350–$500. With a large, nicely shaped bowl and a flaring base, heavily cut, a compote can bring more. A pair, $1,000–$1,500.

Trays

Celery trays, 11–14 inches long, sell for $30–$50. Bread trays, 11–14 inches long and 5–7 inches wide (several inches wider than a celery tray), $30–$50. Super examples might bring $100–$200.

Two-handled trays, such as tea trays, 15–20 inches long, are rare. They might be worth $1,000–$2,000.

Tumblers and Stemware

Water tumblers, water goblets, whiskey glasses, wine glasses, sherry glasses and champagne glasses are all available. Individually, they're worth $25–$30 apiece.

Prices climb for sets. In an extreme case, sixteen place settings with nine different stems per setting, the price could be $100 a stem.

Pitchers, Bottles and Jugs

Pitchers for water, milk or lemonade, 8–12 inches high, were made in comparatively large quantities, and they sell for $100–$400. Champagne pitchers, 16–18 inches high, are $200–$400.

Bitters bottles, 6–9 inches high, bring $100–$150. A whiskey jug, 5–7 inches high, is $300–$400. A whiskey bottle, 8–10 inches, or a whiskey decanter, 8–12 inches, may be $100–$200. Carafes are about the same—$200 tops for a typical one.

Vases

A plain tubular vase, 8–14 inches high, can be had for $30–$70. Add a foot and a scalloped rim, and the price may climb to $200–$300.

Other common shapes include flaring and baluster. Often worth more money are unusual shapes such as cornucopia and jack-in-the-pulpit, which can be worth $400–$600.

Lamps and Candlesticks

Lamps tend to be large pieces, and like any large pieces they command premium prices. A shade by itself, 12–14 inches in diameter, would be worth $200–$250. If you have shade, stem and base, all brilliant cut, 18–25 inches high, the price could climb to $1,000–$2,000.

Candlesticks, 9–11 inches, are available for $200–$400 per pair. Add perhaps $100 per stick if it has a silver base, more if the base is unusually heavy or ornate. A five-stick candelabra is $200–$400, more if it is hung with prisms.

Brilliant Cut Miscellany

Small pieces were made in substantial quantities, and very few are over $100. Included here are powder boxes, cologne bottles, bells, inkwells, $30–$50 apiece. A pair of cruets with silver stoppers might be $75–$100. A tobacco humidor, 8 inches high, $50–$100.

Two-handled baskets, the ones with overhead handles, are a com-

1

2

Brilliant cut glass was the choice of royalty and industrial tycoons from the 1880s through the 1920s, but now it is surprisingly inexpensive. The more facets a piece has, the more brilliant it is, and the more appealing to collectors. (1) Part of a dessert service including 12 plates; $750–$1,000. *Sotheby Parke Bernet.* (2) Gone With the Wind lamp by L. Straus & Sons. Large, elaborate lamps like this are rare. 18½ inches high × 12 inches in diameter; $6,000–$8,000. *Robert W. Skinner, Inc.*

3

4

(3) Punch bowl on stand, T. G. Hawkes & Company, circa 1900. 15 inches in diameter; $1,500–$2,000. *Sotheby Parke Bernet*. (4) (left to right) Glass cologne bottle attributed to Dorflinger & Sons, circa 1890, 7¾ inches high, $400–$500; one of 8 plates, attributed to Dorflinger & Sons, circa 1900, 7½ inches in diameter, $400–$500; one of a pair of stoppered cologne bottles attributed to T. G. Hawkes & Company, circa 1890, 6 inches high, $350–$450. *Robert W. Skinner Inc.*

mon form—they look like little flower baskets. They are vulnerable to chipping, but if you find a good-condition basket, it could be worth $150–$200.

How to Evaluate Brilliant Cut Glass

Collectors insist on glass that is really brilliant cut, not pressed. After about 1900, machines that turned out a convincing brilliant cut look-alike were introduced. Usually, though, you can tell the difference with your fingers. Feel a good pressed piece with one hand and a brilliant cut piece with the other. The brilliant piece is almost sharp enough to cut you.

Discerning collectors want brilliant cut glass that was made during the nineteenth century, because it was of a better quality. The patterns tend to be more intricate, resulting in more brilliance. After 1900, patterns became simpler, with less reflected light. A sure sign of later manufacture: floral patterns. Earlier brilliant cut glass relied on geometric patterns for brilliance. Often, however, experts are "winging it" when they declare that a piece of glass was made in 1890 as opposed to 1910. They have only style and cutting technique to go on. Glass doesn't go through physical changes, like wood, that can help pinpoint age. In any event, nobody will reject a spectacular piece from 1910 because it is ten years too late.

The larger a piece, the scarcer it is likely to be, and the more valuable. The more elaborate the pattern, the more collectors will pay.

Collectors also pay a premium for unusual features, pieces on a pedestal—cruets, compote dishes, decanters and others. Add legs to a butter dish or basket that normally didn't have them, and it is worth perhaps 50 percent more.

Unusual shapes such as an S-shaped celery dish have increased value. An unusual honeycomb handle means that a pitcher is worth more. A piece with a properly marked silver liner is scarce and commands a premium.

Rare patterns can command a premium, too. For instance, a rare Oxford-pattern dinner plate would be worth $600–$800; a common Russian-pattern dinner plate, half as much.

Colored brilliant cut glass can be interesting. Because of its high production cost, it was not made for very long, so it is scarce now. It is priced about the same as clear glass, because the color reduces brilliance, which is the primary appeal. Available colors: yellow, red, blue, green.

Collectors like to know that a piece was made by a firm associated with high quality. The best were:

- C. Dorflinger & Sons, White Mills, Pennsylvania.
- New England Glass Company (which became Libbey Glass), Toledo, Ohio.
- Hobbs Glass Company, Wheeling, West Virginia.
- Gillinder & Sons, Philadelphia, Pennsylvania.
- J. Hoare & Company, Corning, New York.
- T. G. Hawkes & Company, Corning, New York.

A signature from a desirable firm can transform a $200 vase into a $2,000 vase. A piece may be signed almost anyplace where there is enough room. Check the inside center of a foot, under the foot near the rim, on a base near the outside edge, the flat of a handle. To see a signature, hold a piece against the light until there is a mirrorlike reflection, and keep your eye out for something that interrupts the reflection. In some cases, you will need a magnifying glass.

You aren't likely to find outright fakes, but forged signatures do occur. Generally, they are made with an electric needle which creates a raised surface, unlike an authentic etched signature which cuts into the glass. Consequently, you can see such a signature more easily than an etched signature, and the forgery can be felt with your fingernail. Most brilliant cut glass is unsigned, so a signature should be viewed as a plus, not a must. Lack of a signature does not diminish the desirability of high-quality glass.

Sets of anything mean more money, including dishes, cruets and candlesticks. Dealers keep their eyes out for attractive available patterns, so that they can assemble sets and thereby increase the value of each piece. Check details very carefully, because it is easy to confuse similar patterns and buy a mismatched set. This goes for things that involve more than one piece. For instance, a butter dish and top, punch bowl and its base, bottle and stopper. If two pieces that are meant to fit together precisely do not, suspect trouble.

Since condition problems have a drastic impact on value, you should inspect a piece carefully before buying. Look for chips, flakes and cracks. Check under a silver rim to see that it does not conceal a condition problem. See if a vulnerable area like the lip of a pitcher appears odd—a sign that a chip may have been cut away. A cloudy area, due to repeated abrasion, can become quite a distraction. Sometimes vinegar in a cruet or salt in a salt shaker can discolor glass if it was not formulated right.

Many badly damaged pieces were modified by skilled cutters. Broken handles or feet can be removed, chipped tall glasses recut down to smaller glasses, a carafe with a broken neck converted into a bowl. Give a supposedly rare piece a skeptical, hard look.

To clean brilliant cut glass, wash in ordinary soap and water. Scrub away dirt with a soft brush like an old toothbrush. Denture cleaners can remove many stubborn deposits. Avoid ammonia and bleach, since they can discolor glass. Do not place cut glass in a dishwasher, because of the extremes of heat and cold involved.

For More Information

The most helpful book is *American Brilliant Cut Glass,* by Bill and Louise Boggess (New York: Crown, 1971). It has over six hundred illustrations and includes facsimile signatures of thirty-seven noteworthy glassmakers.

Several chapters in Robert E. Di Bartolomeo, ed., *American Glass* (New York: Weathervane Books, 1974), Vol. 2, talk about brilliant cut glass. They appeared originally in *The Magazine Antiques.*

Harder to find but containing some useful material is Dorothy Daniel, *Cut and Engraved Glass, 1771–1905* (New York: William Morrow, 1967).

Museums

CORNING, N.Y.
The Corning Museum of Glass
Corning Glass Center
Corning, NY 14830
(607) 937-5371

NEW YORK
Metropolitan Museum of Art
Fifth Avenue at 82nd Street
New York, NY 10028
(212) 879-5500

NORFOLK, VA.
Chrysler Museum at Norfolk
Olney Road and Mowbray Arch
Norfolk, VA 23510
(804) 622-1211

PHILADELPHIA
Philadelphia Museum of Art
26th Street and Benjamin Franklin Parkway
Philadelphia, PA 19101
(215) 763-8100

ST. AUGUSTINE, FLA.
Lightner Museum
City Hall–Museum Complex
King Street
St. Augustine, FL 32084
(904) 829-9677

TOLEDO, OHIO
Toledo Museum of Art
2445 Monroe Street
Toledo, OH 43697
(419) 255-8000

Where to Buy

Brilliant cut glass is included in Victoriana sales at the following auction houses:

BOLTON, MASS.
Robert W. Skinner
Route 117
Bolton, MA 01740
(617) 779-5528

DELAWARE, OHIO
Garth's Auctions
2690 Stratford Road
Delaware, OH 43105
(614) 362-4771

HILLSBORO, N.H.
Richard W. Withington
Hillsboro, NH 03244
(603) 464-3232

HYANNIS PORT, MASS.
Richard A. Bourne
Corporation Street, Route 28
Hyannis Port, MA 02647
(617) 775-0797

NEW YORK
Christie's
502 Park Avenue
New York, NY 10022
(212) 546-1181

William Doyle
175 East 87th Street
New York, NY 10028
(212) 427-2730

Phillips
406 East 79th Street
New York, NY 10021
(212) 570-4653

Sotheby's
1334 York Avenue
New York, NY 10021
(212) 472-3508

PHILADELPHIA
Samuel T. Freeman
1808 Chestnut Street
Philadelphia, PA 19103
(215) 563-9275

WASHINGTON
C. G. Sloan & Company
715 13th Street, NW
Washington, DC 20005
(202) 628-1468

Adam A. Wechsler & Sons
905–9 E Street, NW
Washington, DC 20004
(202) 628-1281

Dealers tend to be small, tucked into out-out-of-the-way places, particularly in the South and the West.

ATWATER, CALIF.
Bustemante Enterprises
5100 Crest Drive
Atwater, CA 95301
(209) 358-3134

BATH, N.Y.
Abbey's Antiques
12 Gansevoort
Bath, NY 14810
(607) 776-6719

CHARLESTON, S.C.
A'riga IV
204 King Street
Charleston, SC 29401
(803) 577-3075

DE LAND, FLA.
Angevine's Antiques
Highway 17–92 South
De Land, FL 32720
(904) 734-6347

GLENDALE, CALIF.
Nina's Antiques
454 West Colorado Street
Glendale, CA 91204
(213) 247-1805

GRANVILLE, MASS.
Carlyle and Charles Eubank Antiques
Route 57
Granville, MA 01034
(413) 357-6641

LAGUNA BEACH, CALIF.
Gallery One
1220 North Coast Highway
Laguna Beach, CA 92651
(714) 494-4444

Roberta Gauthey Antiques
1290 North Coast Highway
Laguna Beach, CA 92651
(714) 494-9925

LEMON GROVE, CALIF.
Lillian's Antiques
2046 Berry Street
Lemon Grove, CA 92045
(619) 469-1454

LITTLE ROCK, ARK.
Kaylin's Antique Galleries
2917 Kavanaugh
Little Rock, AK 72205
(501) 664-7379

LODI, CALIF.
Lakeside Antiques
1102 West Turner Road
Lodi, CA 95240
(209) 368-9400

MINEOLA, N.Y.
Time Was Antiques
315 Willis Avenue
Mineola, NY 11501
(516) 742-0195

MURPHYS, CALIF.
Carriage Trade Antiques
434 Main Street
Murphys, CA 95247
(209) 728-3688

NEW YORK
Lillian Nassau
220 East 57th Street
New York, NY 10022
(212) 759-6062

Ye Olde Treasure Shop
106-20 New York Boulevard
Jamaica, NY 11433
(212) 523-5765

PASADENA, CALIF.
Gisele's Antiques
256 South Rosemead Boulevard
Pasadena, CA 91107
(213) 795-7449

SACRAMENTO, CALIF.
Plunder Inn Antiques
2300 Capitol Avenue
Sacramento, CA 95816
(916) 446-1100

ST. LOUIS
Margo Antiques
4660 Maryland
St. Louis, MO 63108
(314) 367-1177

SAN DIEGO, CALIF.
Koehmstedt Antiques
4187 Fairmount Avenue
San Diego, CA 92105
(619) 284-9909

SAN JOSE, CALIF.
Classic Antiques
2210 Lincoln Avenue
San Jose, CA 95125
(408) 264-0604

SOLVANG, CALIF.
Chimney Sweep Antiques
530 Alisal Road
Solvang, CA 93463
(805) 688-3137

SOUTH MIAMI, FLA.
Antique Paradise
5828 Sunset Drive
South Miami, FL 33143
(305) 666-1135

8

CHINESE SNUFF BOTTLES

MINIATURE ART INSPIRES WONDER AT THE SMALL THINGS PEOPLE LAVISH THEIR talents on, exquisite things you can hold in the palm of your hand. One of the most surprising and delightful miniature arts is the carving of Chinese snuff bottles.

The Chinese acquired the habit of sniffing a pinch of powdered tobacco and spices, known as snuff, during the seventeenth century. Something was needed to put snuff into, and ingenious artisans began exploring exotic materials and techniques to transform these utilitarian objects, seldom more than a few inches long, into little treasures. Almost from the start, people began collecting snuff bottles, though they have never attained the status of other Chinese arts like porcelain wares. The finest snuff bottles you are likely to see were made during the nineteenth century. Most are under $1,000.

Glass Bottles

A remarkable variety of materials were used. We tend to look down on glass as common stuff, but the Chinese treated it as semiprecious material, and connoisseurs pay as much for a good glass bottle as for almost any other kind. Many of the most magnificent snuff bottles are glass.

Some glass bottles are a single color. For instance, a flattened pear-shape bottle, rich blue tone, stopper, is $125–$175. A circular bottle tapering sharply toward the base, waisted neck, rich yellow tone, 1780–1850, stopper, brings $500–$700. An octagonal-form bottle with a raised faceted pane on each side, turquoise tone with traces of black, 1780–1850, stopper, is priced at $800–$1,000.

Then there are bottles with a mottled tone, many different colors. They look like marble. For instance, a slender, pear-shaped bottle, mottled emerald green with flecks of gold, stopper, is worth $150–$250.

An unusual glass bottle, flattened disk shape, grayish tone with tiny colored chips, stopper, sells for $400–$600.

Overlay glass pieces were made by dipping a single-color glass bottle into another-color glass, or by applying different-color glasses—as many as a half-dozen—on the surface. Then a carver cut away overlay glass down to the bottle itself, creating an intricate pattern. The quality of carving has a tremendous impact on value—earlier pieces tend to be more meticulously carved. For example, a flattened ovoid bottle, pale turquoise overlaid in bright blue in front and reverse with a pair of dragons flanking a medallion, 1780–1850, stopper, is worth $800–$1,200. A fine five-color bottle, flattened ovoid form, a "snowflake" ground overlaid with a yellow bird perched amidst green leaves and branches of a flowering tree peony, pink and red blooms, springing from blue rocks, 1750–1830, stopper, brings $1,600–$2,000. A rare disk-shape bottle, dark blue overlaid with white lily sprays, broad stems, 1780–1850, stopper, may be worth $2,400–$3,200.

Inside-painted bottles are perhaps the most astounding, because through the top hole, perhaps a quarter inch wide, an artist inserted tiny brushes and created fantastically detailed images. Most inside painting was done during the late nineteenth and early twentieth centuries, but a few early, fabulous pieces survive, mainly from palace workshops. Prices for these vary tremendously. A good slender rectangular bottle inside-painted with autumn trees, pale-yellow leaves, the reverse with rocks and flowerpots, signed "Zhou Leyuan, 1888," stopper, sells for $500–$700. On the other hand, in 1980 a rectangular milk-glass bottle inside-painted with a girl in red, yellow and blue, ornate collar design, eighteenth century, stopper, sold at Sotheby's, New York, for $50,000—the record snuff-bottle price at auction.

Porcelain Bottles

With porcelain snuff bottles, enamel decoration is a key factor affecting value. Twentieth-century pieces tend to use brighter colors. Thanks to even, electrical firing, the glaze on twentieth-century pieces is smooth. Early porcelain bottles have a pitted glaze and other tiny irregularities.

For example, a fine rare disk-shaped bottle resting on a splayed base, decorated on one side with a circular panel enclosing a pair of quail beneath sprays of millet, flanked by chrysanthemums, against a background of clouds, decorated on the reverse with a similar panel enclosing two exotic birds perched on rocks and bamboo, eighteenth century, stopper, sells for $1,200–$1,500.

Some porcelain was molded into various shapes. For instance, a molded porcelain pear-shape bottle, a dignitary and attendants on an island, the reverse with two maidens in a boat surrounded by sea demons, 1800–1850, stopper, is worth $500–$700.

Reticulated porcelain involved overlaying the bottle with a colored layer which was carved into intricate patterns affording a contrast with the bottle underneath. These were made during the late eighteenth and early nineteenth centuries. For instance, a reticulated-porcelain bottle, ovoid form with waisted neck, decorated with eight Buddhist emblems on a cloud-scroll ground pierced to reveal the inner bottle, covered with creamy-white glaze, 1820–1850, stopper, brings $600–$800.

Jade Bottles

Carved jade, the popular name for two similar stones, Burmese jadeite and Chinese nephrite, came in several colors, the best known being white and green. But there's much more than that:

Pure white. Almost-pure white is much less desirable. A flattened spade-shape bottle with waisted neck, even white tone with a brown splash on one side, 1750–1820, stopper, is worth $600–$800.

Apple green, emerald green. An ovoid bottle with slightly concave mouth, bright apple-green color, 1780–1850, stopper, brings $1,400–$1,800.

Dark spinach green, the rage of the 1920s, is worth a fraction as much. An ovoid bottle, supported on a low foot, the shoulders carved in relief with mask and mock-ring handle, spinach-green color, stopper, sells for $200–$300.

Lavender. An ovoid bottle, one side carved as a leaf, lavender color, stopper, is worth $4,000–$6,000.

Yellow. A flattened body supported on neatly finished foot, yellow color, 1750–1850, stopper, is valued at $1,200–$1,600.

Occasionally you'll see intriguing sculptured shapes. For instance, a pale jade bottle carved as a melon on which two monkeys, riding on the back of a third, climb up the sides and grasp a ribbon, 1780–1860, stopper, is priced at $1,200–$1,500.

Since quartz can look like jade, you'd be well advised to have a high-priced bottle that is represented as jade tested by an independent laboratory. The standard test is specific gravity, the mass per unit volume. This is expressed as a ratio of the material being tested to water. Jadeite has a specific gravity of 3.34, nephrite 2.95 and quartz 2.66. For a test, which should cost maybe $10, contact:

Gemological Institute of America, 1660 Stewart Street, Santa Monica, CA 90404, (213) 829-2991, and 680 Fifth Avenue, New York, NY 10036, (212) 221-5858.

American Gemological Laboratories, 645 Fifth Avenue, New York, NY 10022, (212) 935-0060.

U.S. Gemological Services, 201 Civic Center Drive East, Santa Ana, CA 92701, (714) 547-5993.

Quartz Bottles

Quartz is a large family of gorgeous minerals including:

Rock crystal, a pure form that is clear. A crystal bottle of upright form and rounded section with indented base, carved with an overall wickerwork pattern, 1780–1860, stopper, may sell for $700–$900.

Hair crystal, quartz crystal with needlelike inclusions—embedded material—of tourmaline, chrysocolla, asbestos, molybdenite, rutile or other colorful minerals. A hair-crystal spade-shape bottle with slightly flared neck, tourmaline inclusions, the sides with ring handles, 1770–1860, stopper, might bring $800–$1,000.

Agate, formed from layers or bands of color-contrasting material. Ingenious carvers select a stone with possibilities, then create a design that takes advantage of the various colors. For instance, a rare agate bottle, natural pebble form, the banded white stone finely carved in front with a clump of lotus, the leaves and flowers skilfully highlighted using the translucent russet inclusions in the white stone to depict leaves and buds, the reverse with striking inclusions of crystalline gray, stopper, may be priced at $1,800–$2,500.

Chalcedony, a variety of agate formed by salts deposited in a cavity. A calcedony bottle of upright form with rounded shoulders, the honey-colored stone with green skin carved as two waterfowl perched on lotus leaves, 1780–1860, stopper, brings $1,200–$1,500.

Carnelian, a translucent chalcedony, usually red or brown. For instance, a carnelian bottle carved in the form of a melon enveloped by leafy stalks and smaller fruits, with tree squirrels climbing up the sides, mottled russet tone, stopper, is worth $500–$700.

Amethyst, quartz crystal whose purple, lilac, red or magenta colors are due to the presence of manganese. For instance, an amethyst bottle carved in the form of an eggplant, mottled deep-purple color, stopper, sells for $400–$500.

Rose quartz, ranging from light pink to a rich rose, was used mainly after the mid-nineteenth century. A rose-quartz bottle of flattened ovoid shape, indented base, carved in relief on front with a sage beneath a pine, the reverse with a seven-character inscription, flanked by seals, 1800–1870, stopper, is priced from $400 to $600.

Jasper, an opaque quartz that is red, yellow, green, brown or with bands of these. For instance, a jasper bottle of flattened pear shape resting on a neatly finished foot, the stone brightly mottled with inclusions of orange, black and ochre, 1800–1860, stopper, sells for $400–$600.

Assorted Semiprecious Materials

A lapis-lazuli bottle of flattened ovoid form with indented base, the rich blue stone mottled with gold specks, stopper, would be worth $800–$1,200.

A turquoise bottle of small size, flattened form, the greenish-blue stone suffused with black crystals resulting in a dappled effect, 1800–1860, is priced at $700–$900.

A rare topaz bottle, flattened upright form supported on a neat foot, even pale-blue color, stopper, brings $2,000–$3,000.

A rare beryl bottle of semicircular section supported on a well-carved base, vivid lime-green color, stopper, is worth $1,800–$2,500.

Exotica

The Chinese displayed extraordinary resourcefulness in selecting materials. For instance, a rare mammoth tooth bottle of flattened rounded form resting on a neat foot, the pale ochre-colored stone encircled by parallel crystalline bands of white suffused with a darker crackle, stopper, is $1,600–$2,200.

Or a Baltic amber bottle, 1780–1850, small size, supported on neatly finished foot, material a rich gold tone suffused with feathery clouds of paler tone, stopper, 1780–1850, for $700–$900.

Fossilized material made superb snuff bottles. For instance, a fossiliferous limestone bottle of slender pear shape with indented base, the black stone with an unusual crocodile-skin pattern, stopper, is worth $600–$800.

Volcanic rocks too. For example, a basalt bottle of flattened upright form with rounded shoulders, resting on a neat foot, the dark stone suffused with splashes of green and purple, 1780–1860, sells for $900–$1,200.

A coral bottle carved as a melon, sides enveloped by broad leaves, a beetle resting to one side, and a butterfly hovering above, pinkish stone, stopper, is $1,000–$1,400.

A rare tangerine-skin bottle, mottled brownish rind molded in upright form with splayed base, stopper, is $200–$300.

A double-gourd bottle, the body divided into eight flutes, set with an ivory collar, stopper, is priced at $700–$900.

A bamboo bottle of slender pod shape, carved in relief with two men in a boat and two more on land beneath a pine tree, stopper, is worth $500–$700.

A seedpod bottle of flattened form with a silver collar around the shoulders, stopper, is $150–$250.

How to Evaluate Snuff Bottles

Artistry is the primary factor affecting value. The better the carving or painting, the more valuable. In general, artistry is superior on older bottles.

Though a bottle may be fashioned from semiprecious material, it has a significant bearing on price only if exceptional. Usually quality of carving and painting in a less expensive material like glass will dwarf the value of a less well-executed bottle in a more glamorous material like jade.

Many materials, while exotic, are also comparatively common, because they were used during the twentieth century. For instance, opal snuff bottles were made during the 1960s and 1970s, since the discovery of large opal deposits in Australia. Aquamarine is a twentieth-century material. Most ivory and almost all hornbill snuff bottles are twentieth century (some early-nineteenth-century bottles were made for the Emperor). Lacquer on metal with mother-of-pearl inlay suggests Japanese origin during the late nineteenth or early twentieth century.

Great rarities can be very expensive. For example, a flattened rectangular enameled glass bottle, a European subject, a flower girl with flowing blue robes and red shawl, flower basket, landscape scenes, enclosed in yellow border painted over with red scrolling, elaborate red-and-blue collar design, eighteenth century, sells for $30,000–$50,000.

Do not put too much stock in signatures. Many signatures can be authenticated, but quite a few artists changed their style of signature, and even experts throw up their hands in confusion.

Snuff bottles can suffer such damage as chipping or abrasion. In an important area, damage can reduce the value of common bottles more than 75 percent. Collectors accept modest damage with rarities.

Chinese snuff bottles are miniature art, fashioned from an intriguing variety of materials. The best examples usually date from the 19th century. (1) Snuff bottles made of (top row, left to right) painted enamel, silver and enamel, braid inlaid with mother-of-pearl; (middle row) engraved bronze, enamel on copper, gilt-metal; (bottom row) inlaid enamel, Mongolian silver with brown quartz, enamel on copper. *Sotheby Parke Bernet.*

(2) Snuff bottles fashioned from (top row, left to right) soochow agate, striated agate, striped agate; (middle row) brown agate, "macaroni" agate, striped agate; (bottom row) brown agate, green and ocher jasper, brown agate. *Sotheby Parke Bernet*.

For More Information

Hugh Moss, *Snuff Bottles of China.* London: Bibelot Publishers, 1971.
Lilla S. Perry, *Chinese Snuff Bottles: The Adventures and Studies of a Collector.* Rutland, Vt.: Charles Tuttle, 1977.
Bob C. Stevens, *The Collector's Book of Snuff Bottles.* New York: Weatherhill, 1971.

Museums

CHICAGO
Field Museum of Natural History
Roosevelt Road at Lake Shore Drive
Chicago, IL 60605
(312) 922-9410

HONOLULU
Honolulu Academy of Arts
900 South Beretania
Honolulu, HI 96814
(808) 538-3693

KANSAS CITY
William Rockhill Nelson Gallery and Atkins Museum of Art
4525 Oak Street
Kansas City, MO 64111
(816) 561-4000

NEW YORK
American Museum of Natural History
79th Street and Central Park West
New York, NY 10024
(212) 873-1300

Metropolitan Museum of Art
Fifth Avenue at 82nd Street
New York, NY 10028
(212) 879-5500

PHILADELPHIA
Philadelphia Museum of Art
26th Street & Benjamin Franklin Parkway
Philadelphia, PA 19101
(215) 763-8100

SAN FRANCISCO
M. H. de Young Museum
Golden Gate Park
San Francisco, CA 94118
(415) 751-4432

SEATTLE
Seattle Art Museum
Volunteer Park
Seattle, WA 98112
(206) 447-4710

Where to Buy

Most market activity in snuff bottles seems to take place among collectors rather than through dealers or auctions. Contact:

International Chinese Snuff Bottle Society
2601 North Charles
Baltimore, MD 21218

First International Snuff Bottle Society
70 Marine Parade
Hythe, Kent, UK CT216AW

Chinese snuff bottles are auctioned regularly in the United States and England by:

LONDON
Sotheby's
34–35 New Bond Street
London, W1A2AA, UK
(01) 493-8080

NEW YORK
Sotheby's
1334 York Avenue
New York, NY 10021
(212) 472-3529

Christie's
502 Park Avenue
New York, NY 10022
(212) 546-1158

Among dealers in England as well as the United States:

LONDON
Hugh Moss Ltd.
23 Bruton Lane
London WIX7LD, UK
(01) 492-1835

Robert Hall
Studio 59
Clifton Hill
London, NW8, UK
(01) 624-2115

NEW YORK
Hartman Rare Art
980 Madison Avenue
New York, NY 10021
(212) 794-2800

Eugene Sung
3 Greenway Terrace
Forest Hills, NY 11375
(212) 261-2084

9

AMERICAN ILLUSTRATORS

POPULAR ILLUSTRATION CONJURES THE DREAMS OF AN AGE. BY AND LARGE, the great illustrators offer a virile, extroverted, sympathetic view of the world. The images they created were free of the tortured introspection that plagued modern art. Illustrators dealt with romance, adventure, style, things everybody likes to think about. If our lives are not as uncomplicated as illustrations might suggest, the illustrations serve as a gentle reminder of the good times. It is a wink of nostalgia that makes many people look at a good illustration and smile.

Illustration came into its own during the late nineteenth century when books, magazines and advertising that appealed to millions began paying top artists princely sums. Many achieved greater fame than the authors whose stories they illustrated. While marvelous illustrations are being done now, the golden age of illustration passed on as mass-circulation magazines relied more on photographs, then fell by the wayside, unable to compete with television.

"There have been disadvantages to being an illustrator," Norman Rockwell reflected. "Many who consider themselves serious painters look down their noses at us. We paint for money, against the deadlines, our subject matter often prescribed by an editor or an author. I have always felt comfortable working within these confines, however, and I suspect most of the truly great illustrators did, too. The only limit to my work, really, was the limit of my own imagination."

In recent years, a trickle of illustrators long scorned by the art establishment have gained new stature. Perhaps recognizing that some of our greatest artists, like Winslow Homer, John James Audubon and Edward Hopper, worked as illustrators, people are more willing to consider the quality of an illustration rather than dismissing it out of hand as commercial fluff. Norman Rockwell is grudgingly granted some scholarly respect for stylishly saluting small-town America. The Western subjects painted by Frederic Remington and Charles Marion Russell bring high five-figure prices at auction.

As you will see here, there is a tremendous range of material available. Splendid illustrations can be had for very reasonable prices, usually under $1,000. Only the most famous names bring prices over $5,000 or $10,000.

Family Fare

Family-type material dominated popular magazines such as *The Saturday Evening Post,* the largest-circulation magazine of the early twentieth century. The best illustrators did covers, because they played a key role in selling magazines. Norman Rockwell, most famous illustrator of all, is quite expensive—oil paintings over $50,000, charcoal drawings over $15,000. Maxfield Parrish, who portrayed the magical romance of yesteryear, is almost as steep. But there is plenty more to choose from in more modest price ranges.

For instance, John Legatta (1894–1977) did graceful, stylish images of pretty girls. He was prolific during the 1930s. His *The Dancers,* a graceful oil-painting vignette of a ballroom scene, 29 by 34 inches, would be worth $1,500–$2,000. His *Tea for Three,* oil-painting vignette of couples around a table, 25 by 31 inches, $1,300–$1,600.

Joseph Christian Leyendecker (1874–1951) did over three hundred subjects for *The Saturday Evening Post*—he inspired young Norman Rockwell. His *The Tuba Player,* 17 x 11¾ inches, study for a *Post* cover, illustrated in a book called *America's Great Illustrators,* is worth $4,000–$5,000. His *Portrait of a Young Girl,* oval oil on canvas board, 18½ by 13¾ inches, $3,500–$4,000. Snazzy, finished oil paintings for covers can run $16,000–$18,000, while nice figure drawings (studies) perhaps 11 by 8 inches can be had for $300–$400.

Steven Dohanos (1907–) did over one hundred for the *Post,* becoming popular for meticulous illustrations. His *Texas Wheels,* showing three boys ogling a gaudy motorcycle, appeared on a *Post* cover. It is an oil on masonite, 47½ by 35¼ inches, worth $8,000–$10,000. His *Birthday Party,* also a cover, oil on canvas, 42 by 33 inches, is $5,000–$6,000.

James Montgomery Flagg (1877–1960), best known for *I Want You,* his U.S. Army recruiting poster of Uncle Sam pointing at the viewer, had a flourishing career illustrating fiction. He liked humorists such as P. G. Wodehouse. He did a lot of pen-and-ink drawings as well as oil paintings. Something like his *Self-Portrait of Artist and His Model,* oil on canvas, 24 by 18 inches, would sell for $2,500–$3,000. *Blackbeard,* pen and ink, 28 by 22 inches, is a charming image of a woman seated perhaps on a train, flanked by people buried in their newspapers, dreaming about a story she read—Blackbeard looms overhead, making a fierce gesture. This kind of illustration can be had for $500–$700.

If you keep your eye out for work by Newell Convers Wyeth (1882–1945), founder of an art dynasty, you may find something reasonable, though his prices tend to be in the $10,000 range now. He illustrated a tremendous amount of magazine fiction. For *Anthony Adverse,* he created such images as *Anthony in a Tree,* oil, 30¼ by 46¼ inches, worth maybe $6,500–$8,500.

Saul Tepper (1899–), in the Illustrators' Hall of Fame, did a wide range of illustration for magazine fiction and advertising. A subject like *Toasting the Baby,* oil, 39½ by 38¼ inches, would sell for $3,000–$4,000. *Change of Heart,* showing a woman running off a ship at the last minute, presumably to her lover, oil, 24 by 40 inches, would sell for $2,000–$2,500. Some oil paintings, like *Old Barbershop,* illustrated in *American* magazine, 27¼ by 47 inches, can go as high as $6,000–$8,000.

Robert Fawcett (1903–67) was a fine draftsman who worked with colored inks, best known for his 1950s *Collier's* illustrations of Sherlock Holmes stories. He did appealing domestic scenes too. *Doctor and Patient,* showing a leering woman beneath a kaleidoscopic comforter, colored inks, 18 by 14 inches, would be worth $1,000–$1,500. *Gardener and the Gentleman,* a sympathetic portrayal of old age, colored inks, two panels, each 17 by 6½ inches, is $600–$800.

Amos Sewell (1901–) did covers for numerous magazines including the *Post.* He favored rural subjects. For instance, his *Valedictory,* pen and ink, 15 by 10 inches, would be worth $150–$200. A stronger image such as *An Ornery Kind of Kid,* casein, 24½ by 29 inches, sells for $1,500–$2,000.

Do you like *New Yorker* covers? Some appear on the market. For instance, *Softening the Blow,* by Garrett Price (1896–), pen and ink, 10 by 33 inches, is worth $300–$400.

John Held, Jr. (1889–1958), articulated the 1920s high-living-flapper style in cartoons for *The New Yorker, Vanity Fair* and other magazines. Featuring eye-popping horses, his *Polo Scene,* watercolor, 13 by 19 inches, would be worth $750–$1,000. *Sitting Pretty,* a *Life* cover of a chic woman gesturing at a churlish bulldog, watercolor, 14½ by 11¼ inches, would bring $4,000–$4,500.

David Levine (1926–) is a respected contemporary caricaturist of literary, political and celebrity figures. His drawings have appeared in major magazines as well as books. He works with pen and ink. For instance, his *Portrait of Emily Dickinson,* pen and ink, dated '75, 13½ by 11 inches, would be worth $400–$600.

Stylish Women

Early women's magazines like *Cosmopolitan* published illustrations of fashion and romance. Compared to family fare, which is a steady market, this is a volatile area where prices, like fashions, might vary widely from year to year.

Brandshaw Crandell (1896–1966), who worked mainly with pastels, did *Cosmopolitan* covers during the 1930s and 1940s. *Summer Fashions,* a head-and-shoulders shot of a woman, a cover illustration, pastel on board, 19 by 17 inches, would sell for $2,500–$3,500.

Coles Phillips (1880–1927) depicted beautiful women in a distinctive Art Deco manner. He did covers for *Life, The Saturday Evening Post* and *Good Housekeeping.* For instance, *April,* gouache, 26 by 17 inches, appeared as a *Good Housekeeping* cover and would be worth $2,500–$3,500.

Helen Dryden (1887–?) did numerous *Vogue* covers as well as designing posters, stage settings and theatrical costumes. Her *Lady in the Snow,* scarf blowing gracefully in the wind, watercolor, 17½ by 17½ inches, would be worth $500–$1,000.

Among the diverse work by Howard Chandler Christy (1873–1952) are portraits, done with élan, of attractive women. For instance, *Countess Theresa,* pastel, 31½ by 20 inches, is $1,000–$1,500. *Portrait of Mrs. Nancy Austin,* oil, 60½ by 40 inches, would bring $2,000–$3,000.

Charles Dana Gibson (1867–1944) created stylish women who became the rage around the turn of the century. Songs were sung about his Gibson Girl, and she had an impact on fashion. He depicted high society with a flourish, too. Until the 1930s, he did mainly pen drawings; after that, oil portraits. An image like *The Ball,* pen and ink, 14½ by 27 inches, would be worth $1,500–$2,000. *His First Love,* an amusing image of a boy in bed talking to his elegantly gowned mother, pencil on board, 18¼ by 26¼ inches, is $3,500–$4,500. A simple head-and-shoulders ink drawing of *Gibson Girl,* featuring her coiffed hair, 15½ by 15½ inches, sells for $1,200–$1,500.

Adventure

Men's magazines offered sports, hunting and other action illustrations. Sometimes these subjects appeared in family magazines as well.

Tom Lovell (1909–) is a versatile illustrator who tackled romance for women's magazines and adventure for men's magazines. For instance, his *Mountain Rescue,* oil, 25 by 17¼ inches, appeared in *True* and would be worth $3,500–$4,500 now. Also appearing in *True, Mutiny on the Dreadnought,* a less ambitious image, oil, 19 by 10¼ inches, would fetch $800–$1,000.

Frank McCarthy (1924-) illustrated crime melodrama, hunting, fishing and especially scenes from the Old West. An advertising illustration, his *Trout and Fishing Camp,* a hooked fish jumping into the foreground, tempera on board, 16 by 25½ inches, would be worth $2,500-$3,000. *Roping the Stag,* oil on board, 10¼ by 25¼ inches, is a wonderful image, $3,500-$4,500.

Though Henry Soulen (1888-1965) illustrated romance for *The Saturday Evening Post, Ladies' Home Journal* and *Country Gentleman,* he portrayed adventure too. He had a fine sense of design and favored bright colors. For instance, a World War I airborne battle called *The Dogfight,* oil, 25½ by 29½ inches, is worth $2,500-$3,500.

Mead Schaeffer (1898-) illustrated classics such as *Moby Dick* and *The Count of Monte Cristo,* and did numerous covers for *The Saturday Evening Post.* Among his adventure subjects are dramatic westerns like *Chisholm Trail,* oil, 21 by 29 inches, worth $3,000-$4,000.

J. F. Kernan (1878-1958) produced illustrations for *The Saturday Evening Post* and *Field & Stream,* particularly humorous outdoor scenes such as *What a Fish!,* oil, 24 by 21 inches, selling for $1,000-$1,500. Or *Hunter with His Dogs,* pencil drawing, 16¼ by 13¼ inches, for $500-$750.

After studying with Howard Pyle, one of the earliest and most influential illustrators, Frank Schoonover (1877-1972) turned out high-spirited work for *Country Gentleman, Boy's Life, Red Book* and other magazines. He illustrated such writers as Zane Grey and Jack London. His *A Hunt from the Ship,* hunters in the frozen North, charcoal, 9 by 27½ inches, is priced around $1,500-$2,000. *Man with His Dog,* oil, 28 by 36 inches, would bring $1,000-$1,500.

Mickey Mouse, Betty Boop and Friends

In a special category are celluloids—or cels, as they are called—from animated cartoons. A vast number were made—twenty-four for each second of running time. But since they had no value to the movie studios once the cartoons were filmed, untold numbers were destroyed. During World War II, when celluloid was difficult to obtain, much of it was cleaned and reused. The earliest cartoons, before about 1938, used a nitrate-based material which self-destructs and in certain conditions can self-ignite.

Far and away the most popular celluloids are from the Disney Studios. Collectors want examples from cartoons that broke new ground. The big three are *Snow White* (1938), the first full-length animated feature, *Pinocchio* (1939) which displayed a spectacular three-dimensional effect of the multiplane camera, and *Fantasia* (1941), the most extravagant of full-length animated films. "Snow White and the Witch," gouache (opaque watercolor) on celluloid, 7½ by 9½ inches, is worth $1,500–$2,000. "Pinocchio," gouache on celluloid, 8 by 7½ inches, brings $500–$700. Or "Pegasus and Family" (from *Fantasia*), 9½ by 13½ inches, priced at $700–$900.

Naturally, the most desirable celluloids feature lively renderings of key characters. The Mickey Mouse that people want, for instance, is from *Fantasia.* It is also attractive because it is on celluloid, whereas the early Disney cartoons were on nitrate. An image of "The Sorcerer's Apprentice" from *Fantasia,* Mickey Mouse in a red coat and a blue conical hat against a star-filled background, gouache on celluloid, 7½ by 10 inches, would be worth $1,500–$2,000.

By the late 1940s, the cost of making cartoons had soared, and Disney turned his attention to nature films, Disneyland and television. Fewer cartoons appeared, and they were less elaborate, though they are still quite wonderful. For instance, "Alice" from *Alice in Wonderland* (1951), gouache on celluloid, 9½ by 7½ inches, brings $200–$300.

A few characters from other studios excite interest now. Particularly Betty Boop and Popeye. Characters who reached a peak during the 1950s excite less interest now. For instance, Bugs Bunny. "Bugs and the Knight," pencil and red pencil on paper, 8 by 10 inches, sells for $150–$250.

How to Evaluate Illustrations

The most satisfying illustrations are self-contained. You understand immediately what they are about, as was essential for a magazine cover. Such illustrations bring the highest prices.

Other illustrations ran with captions, and they are hard to understand by themselves. For instance, a picture showing one man pointing at another raises more questions than it answers, and collectors tend to avoid this kind of scene. Consequently, a good self-explanatory cover from a minor magazine is likely to be worth more money than a puzzling stop-action picture by a fine artist.

Now collectors are willing to pay top dollar for illustrations they can identify with. This is why those that evoke nostalgia and humor do better than more abstract images.

The larger the illustration, the most valuable it is, generally speaking. Many collectors want "wall power," something that can convey impact from across a room. A large, good-quality illustration is likely to bring

1

2

3

American illustrators evoked adventure, romance, humor and nostalgia, usually for popular magazines. The images involve superb draftsmanship and are considerably less expensive than "fine art." (1) Pastel of Carole Lombard, cover of *Cosmopolitan* during the 1920s, by Bradshaw Crandall, well-known for his images of stylish women. 25½ × 22 inches; $3,000–$4,000. *Illustration House.* (2) "The Fast Gun," a gouache from the *Saturday Evening Post,* by Stan Galli. 17 × 24 inches; $3,500–$4,500. *Illustration House.* (3) Disney cartoon celluloid used in the making of *Dumbo,* 1941. 8 × 9 inches; $800–$1,000. *Phillips Auctioneers.*

4

5

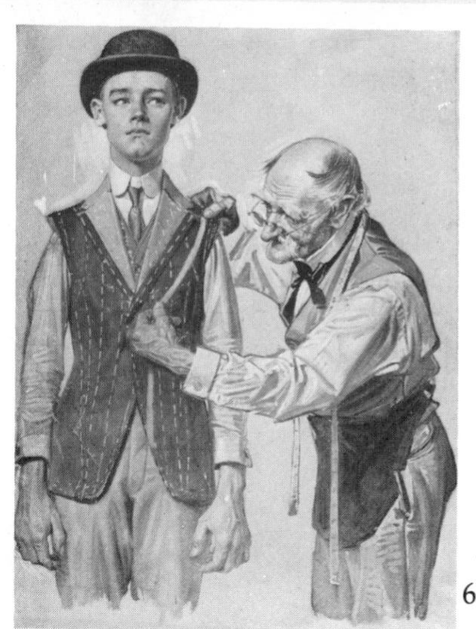

6

(4) "Chemical Experiments," a whimsical cover for *American Weekly* by Charles Dye. 19 × 17 inches; $1,500–$2,000. *Illustration House.* (5) "Hop in Neighbor" by Norman Rockwell, done for an American Oil Company billboard. 18 × 24 inches; $6,000–$7,000. *William Doyle Galleries.* (6) "His First Suit" by Joseph Leyendecker, published as a *Saturday Evening Post* cover. 16 × 12 inches; $5,500–$6,500. *Illustration House.*

several times more money than an intimate drawing that must be viewed up close. This means that if you are not concerned about wall power, you can make some terrific buys.

The lowest-priced area of illustration is early-twentieth-century work done in black and white. Collectors pay a substantial premium for color. Consequently, if you are interested in draftsmanship, you will find a large number of superb pen-and-ink drawings, pencil sketches and charcoal sketches for a few hundred dollars.

Since many fine illustrations are available, they must be in good condition to stir a collector's interest—no rips, tears, stains or distracting problems.

For More Information

Susan Meyer, *America's Great Illustrators.* New York: Harry Abrams, 1978.

Henry C. Pitz, *200 Years of American Illustration.* New York: Random House, 1977.

Walt Reed, *Great American Illustrators.* New York: Abbeyville Press, 1979.

Museums

CHADDS FORD, PA.
Brandywine River Museum
Box 141, U.S. Route 1
Chadds Ford, PA 19317
(215) 459-1900

FORT WORTH, TEXAS
Amon Carter Museum of Western Art
3501 Camp Bowie Boulevard
Forth Worth, TX 76113
(817) 738-1933

NEW BRITAIN, CONN.
New Britain Museum of American Art
56 Lexington Street
New Britain, CT 06052
(203) 229-0257

NEW HAVEN
Yale University Art Gallery
1111 Chapel Street
New Haven, CT 06520
(203) 436-0574

NEW YORK
Brooklyn Museum
188 Eastern Parkway
Brooklyn, NY 11238
(212) 638-5000

Museum of the City of New York
Fifth Avenue at 103rd Street
New York, NY 10029
(212) 534-1672

New-York Historical Society
170 Central Park West
New York, NY 10024
(212) 873-3400

New York Public Library
Fifth Avenue and 42nd Street
New York, NY 10018
(212) 790-6262

Society of Illustrators
Museum of American
Illustration
128 East 63rd Street
New York, NY 10021
(212) 838-2560

WILMINGTON, DEL.
Delaware Art Museum
2301 Kentmore Parkway
Wilmington, DE 19806
(302) 571-9590

Where to Buy

Among auction houses, Phillips, 406 East 79th Street, New York, NY 10021, (212) 570-4848, has done the most with American illustrations. Also auctioning them, usually in sales of middle-priced and twentieth-century American art:

Christie's
502 Park Avenue
New York, NY 10022
(212) 546-1179

Sotheby's
1334 York Avenue
New York, NY 10021
(212) 472-3551

Dealers to check:

NEW YORK
Judy Goffman Fine Arts
18 East 77th Street
New York, NY 10021
(212) 744-5190

PHILADELPHIA
Newman Galleries
1625 Walnut Street
Philadelphia, PA 19103
(215) 563-1779

SOUTH NORWALK, CONN.
Illustration House
53 Water Street
South Norwalk, CT 06854
(203) 838-0486

10

NINETEENTH-CENTURY FRENCH SCULPTURE

GERALDINE ROCKEFELLER DODGE, THE HEIRESS, WAS A SQUIRREL. AFTER SHE died in 1975, Sotheby's auctioned the contents of her New Jersey and New York City mansions. Among other things, she had acquired hundreds of nineteenth-century sculptures. The most interesting ones sold for around $5,000, and many for a few hundred dollars. Quite likely, this was the first real money realized by nineteenth-century sculpture since it passed out of fashion during the 1920s.

For decades until then, sculpture was one of the most-prized arts, and practically every chic nineteenth-century drawing room had some sculpture. At the end of this chapter, there is an unusually long listing of museums where you can see nineteenth-century sculpture—the industrial barons who endowed our museums and colleges considered sculpture an essential bequest. With their passing, taste shifted to paintings, which have commanded the top prices in the art market ever since.

The Dodge sale helped focus attention on sculpture again, and prices have advanced along with inflation. But with about 80 percent of the pieces selling for less than $1,500, nineteenth-century sculpture still offers a lot of art for your money.

Nineteenth-century sculpture was made for reproduction, like prints. Typically, a sculptor would create a life-size clay model and try to have it displayed at a prestigious exhibition such as the annual Paris Salon. If his work proved popular, the sculptor would pour plaster over his model and, after it hardened, scrape out the clay, leaving a mold. The sculptor would wash out the inside with an oily substance, then fill it with plaster. Once it had hardened, he would knock off the mold, then wait for somebody to order a piece. They could choose to have it done in marble, the most expensive material then, or in terra cotta or bronze. Moreover, thanks to an invention by Achille Callas, reproductions could be made in a wide range of sizes, typically 8 to 50 inches. It was like having a master key duplicated.

The sculptor turned his models over to a foundry for actual fabrication. Thus, quality depended as much on the foundry as on the sculptor. Happily, the best sculptors and foundries usually selected each other. One of the best-known foundries belonged to a meticulous, resourceful man named Ferdinand Barbédienne.

Animal Bronzes

Sculptures of horses, dogs, deer, lions, wild boars and other animals are appealing because of the subjects, but they offer more. They represent a jolt of realism—lively, muscular, rough-edged images. While they are not always pretty, fine animal bronzes convey tremendous energy.

Most popular, understandably, are bronzes of familiar animals such as horses and dogs. A well-executed horse and rider, for instance, 22 inches long, no special artist, would be worth $2,000–$3,000. A mastiff, 9 inches long, $500–$700.

Violent scenes, known as combat groups, are quite popular. For instance, two fighting stags, 21 inches long, again no special artist, brings $1,000–$1,500. A combat group tends to be worth more money than a bronze of a single wild animal.

The most important sculptor of animal bronzes was Antoine-Louis Barye (1796–1875). The son of a goldsmith, he studied at the École des Beaux-Arts and held a number of official positions, including director of plaster casting at the Louvre. He moved away from the prevailing notions of classical beauty, which emphasized smooth surfaces and graceful form, seeking gritty realism instead.

He established combat groups as a powerful means of expression. For instance, his panther seizing a stag, 21 inches long, is worth $1,200–$1,800. A bear attacked by hounds, 14 inches, brings $1,500–$2,000. An ocelot carrying off a heron, 12 inches, is $2,000–$3,000. A dog stealing eggs, 6 inches long, is priced at $800–$1,200. A tiger devouring a snake, 11 inches, is $1,000–$1,500. An eagle holding a heron, 13 inches high, sells for $1,200–$1,800. His more peaceful sculptures of individual animals tend to bring less money. For instance, a greyhound, 14 inches long, is $800–$1,200. An elephant, 8 inches, $500–$800.

Another fine animal sculptor was Jules Moignez (1835–1894), known for his quieter hunting scenes and birds. For instance, a pheasant, 13½ inches high, is $400–$600. An egret, 21½ inches high, sells for $1,800–$2,500. A horse, 15 inches long, brings $500–$800.

Pierre-Jules Mène (1810–1879) did horses, stags, dogs, bulls, rams, panthers and other animals with an elegant touch. For instance, a huntsman and hound, 18½ inches high, is worth $1,500–$2,000. Two whippets, 8¼ inches long, sells for $700–$900. Two horses nuzzling each other, 22 inches long, is $2,000–$3,000.

Isadore Bonheur (1827–1901) depicted wild as well as domestic animals. For instance, a standing bull, 15¼ inches long, is priced at $500–$800. A woman with a cow, 17 inches long, brings $800–$1,000.

Real People

Among private collectors, lovely and sentimental sculptures of domestic scenes are sought as pleasing decorations. For instance, a boy playing a violin, after Jean-Louis Grégoire, 27 inches high, is worth $1,000–$1,500. A man sowing seeds, after Ernest Wante, 19 inches high, brings $1,000–$1,500. An unusually large sculpture of a woman bather ready to dive, after Odoardo Tabbacchi, 32 inches high, sells for $4,000–$6,000. A young girl with flowers, inscribed "A. Levaseur," 35 inches high, is $2,000–$3,000.

Usually less expensive are portrait busts—many were made depicting famous people. One of French novelist Honoré de Balzac, after Jean-Alexandre-Joseph Falguière, 9⅞ inches high, would be worth $500–$700. Essayist Ralph Waldo Emerson, inscribed "H. Muller," 16 inches high, could be had for $400–$500. Beethoven, after Carl Kauba, 8 inches high, is $500–$700. Medical pioneer Louis Pasteur, after Paul Richer, 22¾ inches high, sells for $700–$900. Joan of Arc, after André Massoulle, a 26-inch-high bust, is $1,000–$1,500.

Gods and Goddesses

Steeped in the classical tradition, many nineteenth-century sculptors depicted gods and goddesses from Greek and Roman mythology. In part, this involved celebrating ideal beauty: smooth skin, pleasing proportions, a slender, gracefully muscled physique. Often, references to mythology such as Roman garb served to slip an erotic nude figure past the eye of a potentially bothersome censor. The best of these pieces are quite beautiful. The worst are static and repetitive attempts at sculpture.

Some private collectors buy sculptures of mythological subjects, but mostly they go to museums that want to illustrate a noteworthy phase of art history. Perhaps a pair of sculptures, *Diana* and *Apollo,* after Eutrope Bouret, each 22 inches high, would bring $1,500–$2,000. A nymph and a putto (winged baby), after Jean-Léon Gérôme, 13½ inches, is $2,000–$3,000.

Then there are nineteenth-century copies of famous ancient sculptures. For instance, *Apollo Belvedere,* after the highlight of the Vatican Collection, 36 inches high, is worth $800–$1,200. Or *Venus de Milo* after the famous lady of the Louvre, 42½ inches, brings $900–$1,200.

Similar to mythological sculptures are allegorical figures. For instance, *The Angel of Industry,* after Georges-Charles Coudray, 34¼ inches, sells for $2,000–$2,500. *Gloria Victis,* commemorating the defeat of France by Germany in 1870, after Marius-Jean-Antonin Mercie, 36 inches, is $1,800–$2,200. *Inspiration,* after Eugène Marioton, 37 inches high, brings $1,500–$2,000.

How to Evaluate Nineteenth-Century Sculpture

Most people who buy nineteenth-century sculpture specify bronze. Terra cotta and marble, though they can be quite beautiful, are less valuable, perhaps worth half as much as metal. Fashion plays a part here, and collectors also shy away from terra cotta and marble because they are breakable and more difficult to clean than bronze.

The quality of a sculpture is the most important factor affecting its value. This means the expressiveness of the pose, the skill of execution and casting. The better articulated the casting, the better.

Generally, the more figures in a sculpture, the more complex the composition, the more valuable it will be. *After the Hunt in Scotland,* a bronze of a horse, three dogs and a hunter holding a fox, 23¼ inches high, might be worth $15,000–$20,000, perhaps ten times more than good single-figure bronzes.

The most desirable sculptures were made by the artist or under the artist's direction. Many times, detailed areas like the face required hand finishing. Less sought after are sculptures made after the artist's death, perhaps a carefully supervised limited edition. The Impressionist Edgar Degas, for instance, created casts but never made sculptures himself. His work is all posthumous. Sculptures made after an artist is dead, with no supervision, are the least interesting. For instance, works by the great eighteenth-century sculptor Jean-Antoine Houdon were reproduced throughout the nineteenth century. A distressing amount of detail was lost along the way.

Serious collectors want the imprint of a respected artist, and signed sculptures command a premium. Some signatures, by artists whose work is rare, like François Rude, Jules Dalou and Antoine-Auguste Préault, are worth substantial sums. A life-size Dalou might fetch $100,000.

On the other hand, people looking for sculpture as decoration do not particularly care about signatures. The lack of a signature does not hurt the salability of an attractive piece.

Especially toward the end of the nineteenth century, casts were made from sculptures, and reproductions appeared on the market. Since they

1

2

3

The best buys in fine sculpture now are French bronzes from the 19th century. Look for any foundry marks, since the best sculptors were associated with highly skilled foundries capable of doing justice to their designs. (1) Florentine singer, after Paul Dubois. 24 inches high; $1,500–$2,000. *Sotheby Parke Bernet*. (2) Panther bringing down a stag, after Antoine-Louis Barye. 21 inches long; $1,500–$2,000. *Sotheby Parke Bernet*. (3) "Gloria Victis," after Marius-Jean-Antonin Mercie. 42½ inches high; $2,500–$3,500. *Sotheby Parke Bernet*.

were not cast from the original model, there is a significant loss of detail that is obvious when you compare objects or photographs. Look in areas normally full of detail, like a person's hair. Compare signatures. Also, the dimensions of a reproduction will be a little different from a piece cast from the original model.

Do not be put off by a good-quality piece with scratches or flecks of patina missing. Often you can acquire such a piece cheaply. A skilled restorer can mix up lacquer to match the patina, then remove the old lacquer and repatinate it. It will look splendid. For instance, Michael Dotzel, 402 East 63rd Street, New York, NY 10021, (212) 838-2890, quotes $100 for repatinating a small bronze about 10 inches high, as much as $350 for one several feet high, the exact cost depending on the amount of detail work.

Since bronze is tough, there are few condition problems. You might see a horse with a tail that fell off, but that is not a serious matter. Bronzes were cast in sections, and they can be resecured easily.

A puzzling problem is something called "bronze disease." It is an awful green fungus that seems to take hold when the patinizing process does not go quite right. It is poisonous and contagious. If you have another bronze in your home, it is likely to catch the disease from the infected piece. You can patch up an infected piece or send it to a founder, but bronze disease almost always comes back.

For More Information

Jeremy Cooper, *Romantic Bronzes.* Boston: New York Graphic Society, 1975.

Peter Fusco and H. W. Janson, eds., *The Romantics to Rodin.* Los Angeles: Los Angeles County Museum of Art, 1980. Exhibition catalog.

Maurice Rheims, *19th Century Sculpture.* New York: Abrams, 1972.

Sculpture from the David Daniels Collection. Minneapolis: Minneapolis Institute of Arts, 1979.

Jeanne L. Wasserman, ed., *Metamorphoses in Nineteenth Century Sculpture.* Cambridge: Fogg Art Museum, 1975.

Museums

ALBUQUERQUE, N.M.
Art Museum
University of New Mexico
Fine Arts Center
Albuquerque, NM 87131
(505) 277-4001

AMHERST, MASS.
Mead Art Museum
Amherst College
Amherst, MA 01002
(617) 542-2335

BALTIMORE
Baltimore Museum of Art
Art Museum Drive
Baltimore, MD 21218
(301) 396-7101

Walters Art Gallery
600 North Charles Street
Baltimore, MD 21201
(301) 547-9000

BOSTON
Museum of Fine Arts
Huntington Avenue
Boston, MA 02115
(617) 267-9300

CHAPEL HILL, N.C.
Ackland Art Museum
University of North Carolina
Columbia and Franklin Streets
Chapel Hill, NC 27514
(919) 966-5736

CHICAGO
Art Institute of Chicago
Michigan Avenue and Adams Street
Chicago, IL 60603
(312) 443-3600

David and Alfred Smart Gallery
University of Chicago
5550 South Greenwood Avenue
Chicago, IL 60637
(312) 753-2121

CLEVELAND
Cleveland Museum of Art
11150 East Boulevard
Cleveland, OH 44106
(216) 421-7340

DETROIT
Detroit Institute of Arts
5200 Woodward Avenue
Detroit, MI 48202
(313) 833-7900

GOLDENDALE, WASH.
Maryhill Museum of Fine Arts
Goldendale, WA 98620
(509) 773-4792

HARTFORD
Wadsworth Atheneum
600 Main Street
Hartford, CT 06103
(203) 278-2670

KANSAS CITY, MO.
William Rockhill Nelson Gallery and Atkins Museum of Fine Arts
4525 Oak Street
Kansas City, MO 64111
(816) 561-4000

LAWRENCE, KANS.
Spencer Museum of Art
University of Kansas
Lawrence, KA 66045
(913) 864-4710

LOS ANGELES
Los Angeles County Museum of Art
5905 Wilshire Boulevard
Los Angeles, CA 90036
(213) 937-4250

MEMPHIS
Dixon Gallery and Gardens
4339 Park Avenue
Memphis, TN 38117
(901) 761-5250

MINNEAPOLIS
Minneapolis Institute of Arts
2400 Third Avenue South
Minneapolis, MN 55404
(612) 870-3046

NEW HAVEN
Yale University Art Gallery
1111 Chapel Street
New Haven, CT 06520
(203) 436-0574

NEW YORK
American Museum of Immigration
Statue of Liberty
Liberty Island
New York, NY 10004
(212) 732-1236

Metropolitan Museum of Art
Fifth Avenue at 82nd Street
New York, NY 10028
(212) 879-5500

NORFOLK, VA.
Chrysler Museum at Norfolk
Olney Road and Mowbray
Arch
Norfolk, VA 23510
(804) 622–1211

PHILADELPHIA
Philadelphia Museum of Art
26th Street and Benjamin
Franklin Highway
Philadelphia, PA 19101
(215) 763-8100

PITTSBURGH
Museum of Art
Carnegie Institute
4400 Forbes Avenue
Pittsburgh, PA 15213
(412) 622-3131

PORTLAND, ORE.
Portland Art Museum
1219 Southwest Park Avenue
Portland, OR 97205
(503) 226-2811

PROVIDENCE
Museum of Art
Rhode Island School of Design
224 Benefit Street
Providence, RI 02903
(401) 331-3511

ST. PETERSBURG, FLA.
Museum of Fine Arts of St.
Petersburg
255 Beach Drive North
St. Petersburg, FL 33701
(813) 896-2667

SAN DIEGO, CALIF.
San Diego Museum of Art
Balboa Park
San Diego, CA 92101
(714) 232–7931

SAN FRANCISCO
M. H. de Young Museum
Golden Gate Park
San Francisco, CA 94118
(415) 751-4432

SARASOTA, FLA.
John and Mabel Ringling
Museum of Art
5401 Bayshore Road
Sarasota, FL 33580
(813) 355-5101

TOLEDO, OHIO
Toledo Museum of Art
2445 Monroe Street
Toledo, OH 43697
(419) 255-8000

WASHINGTON
Corcoran Gallery of Art
17th Street and New York
Avenue, NW
Washington, DC 20006
(202) 638-3211

Hirshhorn Museum and
Sculpture Garden
Independence Avenue at
Seventh Street, SW
Washington, DC 20560
(202) 357-3091

National Gallery of Art
Constitution Avenue at Sixth
Street, NW
Washington, DC 20565
(202) 737-4215

WELLESLEY, MASS.
Wellesley College Museum
Jewett Arts Center
Wellesley, MA 02181
(617) 235-0320

WILLIAMSTOWN, MASS.
Sterling and Francine Clark Art
Institute
225 South Street
Williamstown, MA 01267
(413) 458-8109

Where to Buy

Nineteenth-century French bronzes are offered in sales of Victoriana by these auction houses:

BOLTON, MASS.
Robert W. Skinner
Route 117
Bolton, MA 01740
(617) 779-5528

NEW ORLEANS
Morton's Auction Exchange
643 Magazine Street
New Orleans, LA 70190
(504) 561-1196

NEW YORK
Christie's
502 Park Avenue
New York, NY 10022
(212) 546-1148

William Doyle
175 East 87th Street
New York, NY 10028
(212) 427-2730

Phillips
406 East 79th Street
New York, NY 10021
(212) 570-4840

Sotheby's
1334 York Avenue
New York, NY 10021
(212) 472-3508

PHILADELPHIA
Samuel T. Freeman
1808 Chestnut Street
Philadelphia, PA 19103
(215) 563-9275

WASHINGTON
C. G. Sloan & Company
715 13th Street, NW
Washington, DC 20005
(202) 628-1468

Adam A. Wechsler & Sons
905–9 E Street, NW
Washington, DC 20005
(202) 628-1281

Dealers:

NEW ORLEANS
Manheim Galleries
409 Royal Street
New Orleans, LA 70130
(504) 568-1901

NEW YORK
Dalva Brothers
44 East 57th Street
New York, NY 10022
(212) 758-2297

F. Gorevic & Son
660 Lexington Avenue
New York, NY 10022
(212) 753-9319

Pfeifer Antiques
900 Madison Avenue
New York, NY 10021
(212) 249-4889

Paul Rosenberg & Company
20 East 79th Street
New York, NY 10021
(212) 472-1134

Rosenberg & Stiebel
32 East 57th Street
New York, NY 10022
(212) 753-4368

Shepherd Gallery
21 East 84th Street
New York, NY 10028
(212) 861-4050

SARATOGA, CALIF.
Corinthian Studios
20506 Saratoga-Los Gatos Road
Saratoga, CA 95070
(408) 867-4630

11

ENGLISH WATERCOLORS

IT IS AMAZING WHAT A LITTLE RECOGNITION CAN DO. UNTIL THE MID-eighteenth century, with few exceptions, watercolor was mainly a technique for jazzing up a drawing. An artist would create an image with a pencil, then fill in color afterward. Watercolor, referred to as stained drawing, was for minor subjects rather than for the major themes tackled by oil painters. It was a novelty in which the luminosity of white paper reflected through thin water-based pigments.

Then in 1769 the British Royal Academy invited watercolor submissions for its well-attended annual shows. Major talents began trying their hand at watercolors, and through the nineteenth century virtually every English artist of consequence left a legacy of watercolors.

English watercolorists explored a wide range of subjects and became best known for landscapes that celebrated the quiet beauty of their own countryside. They traveled around the world too, especially to Europe and the Middle East, making watercolors along the way. In so doing, they endeared themselves to people everywhere. Greeks go for English watercolors of Greece, Arabs buy English watercolors of brightly costumed Arabs, Italians buy Italian scenes, English and American collectors favor English scenes.

Encouraged by newfound attention, yet frustrated when the Royal Academy hung watercolors haphazardly and refused to admit pure watercolorists, as distinct from oil painters who also did watercolors, several artists launched the Society of Painters in Watercolours in 1804. It showcased the most magnificent watercolors, particularly landscapes, for a century.

Success spurred experiments to achieve new effects. Artists used different papers, applied multiple washes, dabbed freshly applied color with a sponge, scratched color out, achieving highlights via exposed fibers of the paper itself. As a serious medium, watercolor found its seven-league boots in England.

With English art largely out of fashion for over half a century, English watercolors are hard to find in the United States. Prices, mostly in the low thousands, are comparatively low. Only rare, major works by a few stars bring the high five-figure and six-figure prices now commonplace in twentieth-century European or American watercolors.

Graceful Landscapes

In many respects the father of the English watercolor was Paul Sandby (1725–1809). Trained as a military topographer, he recorded landscape all around England. He drew precise lines and applied muted colors to a gray base. Most common: blue, green, brown, a touch of red. He exhibited his work at the Society of Arts and the Royal Academy from 1760 to 1809, doing much to popularize watercolor. His was the dominant style for a half century. Sandby's watercolors can be had for $1,000–$5,000, with exceptional examples bringing several times as much.

Sandby's influence appears in the work of Thomas Hearne (1744–1812). He outlined his compositions with pencil, used greens, blues and gray wash to achieve charming effects. His skies and architectural rendering are particularly good. He made drawings in the West Indies as well as England. Most of Hearne's work too sells in the $1,000–$3,000 range.

Michael "Angelo" Rooker (1743–1801) achieved superb control, conveying a sense of light on surfaces like trees and walls. He did striking views of Essex, Norfolk, Suffolk, Somerset, Warwickshire, Worcestershire, Monmouthshire, Kent, Wales, with prices ranging from $1,000 to $3,000.

Edward Dayes (1763–1804) did appealing topographical views, particularly in northern England. He depicted picturesque ruins, a popular theme among romantics. Many of his images are blue monochromes accented with brown ink over pencil and are worth $1,000–$3,000.

The most popular of the early English watercolorists is John Robert Cozens (1752–97). He produced lovely, poetic landscapes, many from his travels around the Mediterranean, through Switzerland and Italy. His images are simply composed and involve few colors—mainly greens, blues, grays that convey a feeling of melancholy. Suffused with personality, Cozens' work can hit high five figures. It begins in the $5,000–$10,000 range.

Other fine English landscapists include Peter de Wint (1784–1849) who created rich, warm-toned panoramas based on his travels throughout northern England. He favored farm and river scenes. His early work tends to be precisely rendered, his later work more sketchy. He rarely signed his watercolors. Most are worth $1,000–$5,000.

John Sell Cotman (1782–1842) was a prolific artist whose early watercolors in the Yorkshire dales (1803–5) often have an intriguing abstract quality. Connoisseurs also seek the poetic images he did in Norfolk in 1841. Overall, he displayed great technical facility. Expect to pay $5,000–$10,000, though some images are as little as $1,000.

In his early work, John Varley (1778–1842) sought interesting topography, which he rendered faithfully. As he gained command of his technique, he concentrated more on composition, aiming to make watercolors rival oil paintings. "Nature wants cooking," he is reported to have said. He filled his images with contrasting colors, shapes and textures. Once he found his mature style, he stuck with it the rest of his life, and his works are priced from $1,000 to $4,000.

An Explosion of Color

Thomas Girtin (1775–1802) pushed English watercolor art toward bright colors. He used paper with a warm tone. He explored more varied color effects than his predecessors, and he created pictures with his brush rather than with a pencil. Color gained the upper hand over outline.

Girtin produced many exquisite city views, but his free manner hit its stride in wide-open spaces. Since he died at an early age, his work is particularly hard to find. His landscapes are among the most expensive, sometimes bringing over $150,000, but there is a decent selection of material priced in the low five figures.

Far more famous is Girtin's contemporary J. M. W. Turner (1775–1851), the greatest English artist. He and Girtin were friends. Each spurred the other to do more with pure color. The process took a while, though, because it wasn't until after about 1815 that Turner exploded with a burst of radiant color. Mountains, open vistas, sea scenes—the subject hardly seems to matter. Turner pursued dazzling light effects, anticipating Impressionism. Turner deserves mention as one of the greatest artists from any era, but he is hardly underpriced. His watercolors commonly sell in the high-five- and six-figures price range.

Richard Parkes Bonington (1802–28) created traditionally styled watercolors of English landscape, but he owes his good reputation more to bright images that sparkle with light. He spent much of his life in France, and he had a powerful impact on French Romantic artists, especially Eugène Delacroix. Because of his short career, Bonington had a relatively small output, and much of it was not signed. Be extra careful if you are considering a work supposedly by him. His prices can run into low five figures, but some things are available in the $5,000-$10,000 range.

Thomas Shotter Boys (1803–74), who virtually invented chromolithography, a hugely popular print medium, produced some dazzling watercolors during a brief career that petered out in the 1840s. He excelled at rendering buildings, but he was capable of strong landscapes as well. His rare, extraordinary images can hit six figures, but most are in the $2,000–$10,000 range.

Two Brooding Mystics

William Blake (1757–1827) achieved fame depicting figures instead of landscapes. He used color to conjure dreamlike visions. His numerous illustrations of religious medieval scenes appeal mainly to people interested in books rather than in decorative watercolors, but this does not mean they are cheap. Most sell for $5,000–$10,000.

Blake influenced Samuel Palmer (1805–81) who produced some mystical works before concentrating on landscape. He conveyed a sense of communion with nature. Palmer's best period: from 1825 to 1835, when he did dark, haunting watercolors. He favored opaque gold colors. His later work is more Romantic and flowing. An early, intensely Romantic so-called Shoreham-period landscape watercolor could bring a hefty six-figure price, but most of his work on the market sells for $5,000–$15,000.

World Travelers

With an eye for pleasing composition and precise control of his brush, William Callow (1812–1908) produced first-rate work early in his career. Over the years, he seemed to lose control as his watercolors became more mannered. He drew many of his subjects from his travels around southern England, southern France, Switzerland, Germany and Venice. Prices are from $500 to $6,000.

James Holland (1799–1870) visited Venice, Portugal, France, Holland and Austria, as well as traveling around England. Connoisseurs believe his best work was done before 1845, before he tried flashier color effects. Yet some of his later work worth $500–$4,000 was done with admirable verve.

David Cox (1783–1859) is noted for bright and airy scenes of Yorkshire, Derbyshire, Wales, Kent, Lancashire and Birmingham. You might also see work he did while visiting Belgium, Holland and France.

Watercolors done before 1820 tend to be subdued. From 1820 to 1840, he used a brighter palette, and in his late work he explored a freer, almost Impressionist style. Prices are from $1,000 to $5,000.

John Frederick Lewis (1805–76) started as an animal painter respected for his meticulous draftsmanship. He made watercolors around England but became best known for finely detailed, glistening watercolors made on his travels through France, Spain, Italy, Greece and Egypt—he remained in Egypt for a decade. He prided himself on getting everything just so, right down to a camel's eye. Toward the end of his career he gave up watercolors for oil painting, because he felt it was a much easier way to make money. His work sells for $1,000–$5,000.

Edward Lear (1812–88), who became famous for his nonsense rhymes, was a superb draftsman. He created elegant illustrations of birds for the London publisher John Gould. Lear traveled widely in Holland, Belgium, Germany, Switzerland, Italy, Greece, Malta, Palestine, Egypt, India and Ceylon, sketching as he went along. He was quite prolific, and a good many of his sleek watercolors are in the $1,000–$6,000 range.

How to Evaluate English Watercolors

Generally speaking, the brighter, nineteenth-century watercolors tend to be more valuable than rather somber, literal topographical watercolors of the eighteenth century.

The larger and more complex a watercolor, the more it is likely to be worth. Exhibition-size watercolors can command princely sums. They begin perhaps at 10 by 16 inches and can go up to 22 by 24 inches.

Most exhibition watercolors are signed, because they were meant to be displayed at the Royal Academy, the Watercolor Society or somewhere else. Attribution to a specific artist is usually straightforward. On the other hand, most sketches made in preparation for finished work were not signed. Works by hundreds of minor as well as some major artists were seldom signed. A signature is just one clue to attribution.

Forged signatures appear on authentic work, and of course forged signatures of high-priced artists are put on watercolors by lesser artists. You can anticipate more forged signatures as prices of these works rise.

Since attribution can have a big impact on value, you would be well advised to buy from a specialist, not someone who happens to have a few English watercolors around a shop. Have a dealer or auction-house attribution confirmed by an independent expert. Among the most highly recommended are scholars at:

1

2

During the great period of English watercolors from 1750 to 1850, almost every important English artist tried his hand at that medium. Only a few artists command steep prices. (1) "L'Hotel de Ville, St. Omer," by Thomas Shotter Boys. $12\frac{7}{8} \times 9\frac{3}{8}$ inches; $4,000–$5,000. *Christie's, London.* (2) Caricature by Thomas Rowlandson, "Providence the Protection of Drunken Men." $7\frac{1}{4} \times 9\frac{3}{4}$ inches; $1,500–$2,000. *Christie's, London.* (3) Watercolor of a locomotive by Reginald Marsh. $14 \times 19\frac{3}{4}$ inches; $9,000–$10,000. *Kennedy Galleries, New York.*

3

4

5

(3) Watercolor of a locomotive by Reginald Marsh. 14 × 19¾ inches; $9,000–$10,000. *Kennedy Galleries, New York.* (4) Pastoral landscape by John Faulkner, known primarily for his work in Ireland. 10 × 20⅜ inches; $1,000–$1,500. *Christie's, New York.* (5) "Resting in the Wood," a typical subject in impeccable condition by Myles Birket Foster. 14 × 10⅜ inches; $10,000–$12,000. *Christie's, London.*

- Yale University Center of British Art, 1080 Chapel Street, New Haven, CT 06520, (203) 432-4594.
- Huntington Library, 1151 Oxford Road, Los Angeles, CA 91108, (213) 681-6601.

These institutions will compare the style, subject and signature, if any, of your watercolor with other watercolors whose attribution is established beyond a reasonable doubt. What you will get is an opinion about the attribution of your watercolor, not an appraisal of value. Keep in mind that experts can disagree and change their mind from time to time. There is usually no charge for their service.

If you would like an expert's opinion, send an 8-by-10-inch black-and-white photograph together with a color transparency to the institution, explaining just what you want. They will tell you how far the question is worth pursuing. For instance, you might be told that your watercolor almost certainly is not a Palmer, or that it might be by a student of David Cox. Obviously, you are likely to get a stronger opinion if an expert can see the watercolor itself.

Since watercolors are vulnerable to fading, avoid exposure to bright light. Museums store watercolors in boxes and exhibit them in dimly lit rooms, no more than 5½ candles as measured by a photographic light meter. As an extra measure, it is a good idea to frame watercolors behind Plexiglas, which reflects some ultraviolet light.

For More Information

Derek Clifford, *Collecting English Watercolors.* Princeton, N.J.: Auerbach Publishers, 1971.

English Drawings and Watercolors 1550–1850 in the Collection of Mr. and Mrs. Paul Mellon. New York: Pierpont Morgan Library, 1972.

Lionel Lambourne and Jean Hamilton, *British Watercolours in the Victoria and Albert Museum, an Illustrated Summary Catalogue.* London: Sotheby's, 1980.

H. L. Mallalieu, *The Dictionary of British Watercolour Artists up to 1920,* 2 vols. Woodbridge, Suffolk, England: Antique Collectors Club, 1976.

Christopher White, *English Landscape 1630–1850: Drawings, Prints and Books from the Paul Mellon Collection.* New Haven: Yale Center for British Art, 1977.

Andrew Wilton, *British Watercolors 1750–1850.* New York: Dutton, 1977.

Museums

CAMBRIDGE
Fogg Art Museum
Harvard University
32 Quincy Street
Cambridge, MA 02138
(617) 495-7768

CLEVELAND
Cleveland Museum of Art
11150 East Boulevard
Cleveland, OH 44106
(216) 421-7340

NEW HAVEN
Yale Center for British Art
1080 Chapel Street
New Haven, CT 06520
(203) 432-4594

NEW YORK
Metropolitan Museum of Art
Fifth Avenue at 82nd Street
New York, NY 10028
(212) 879-5500

Pierpont Morgan Library
29 East 36th Street
New York, NY 10016
(212) 685-0008

PHILADELPHIA
Philadelphia Museum of Art
26th Street and Benjamin Franklin Parkway
Philadelphia, PA 19101
(215) 763-8100

PROVIDENCE
Museum of Art
Rhode Island School of Design
224 Benefit Street
Providence, RI 02903
(401) 331-3511

SAN MARINO, CALIF.
Huntington Library, Art Gallery and Botanical Gardens
1151 Oxford Road
San Marino, CA 91108
(213) 681-6601

Where to Buy

There are numerous English-watercolor auctions in London, but here in the United States watercolors are included only among spring and fall Old Master/nineteenth-century-drawings sales at these New York auction houses:

Christie's
502 Park Avenue
New York, NY 10022
(212) 546-1092

Sotheby's
1334 York Avenue
New York, NY 10021
(212) 472-8447

A few U.S. dealers maintain a regular stock of English watercolors:

Davis & Langdale
746 Madison Avenue
New York, NY 10021
(212) 861-2811

Shepherd Gallery
21 East 84th Street
New York, NY 10028
(212) 861-4050

If you ever travel to England, you will find watercolors in London at:

John Basket
173 New Bond Street
London W1, UK
(01) 629-1578

Martin Gregory
34 Bury Street
London SW1Y6AU, UK
(01) 839-3731

Morton Morris & Company Ltd.
32 Bury Street
St. James
London SW1Y6AU, UK
(01) 930-2825

Spink & Son Ltd.
5–7 King Street
St. James
London SW1, UK
(01) 930-7888

Andrew Wild & Anthony Reed
3 Court Street
London W1, UK
(01) 437-2741

12

AMERICAN PEWTER

PEWTER LACKS THE GLEAM OF SILVER, THE SPARKLE OF GLASS, THE BRIGHT colors of porcelain, yet Americana collectors love it. Fine pewter is solid, simple, unpretentious. An alloy of base metals that can be fashioned into stately shapes, pewter shows us the noble possibilities of humble things.

Henry J. Kauffman, a devoted pewter collector in Lancaster, Pennsylvania, affirmed his affection for the "warm, soft, unobtrusive quality of the metal which complements so ideally a simple pine mantel or an old walnut table. There's nothing quite like it—no similar objects are available in silver, brass, or copper. It's not too new and shiny, or too old and grimy. It's just right."

Made in America since the seventeenth century, pewter served people of modest means with conservative tastes. Styles evolved gradually. Pewter never became ornate like rococo or Victorian silver.

Consisting mainly of tin, pewter contains copper, antimony, bismuth and lead. The percentages vary. High-quality pewter might be about 95 percent tin, and it has a silverlike finish. Cheaper grades are as much as 40 percent lead, a soft metal easy for pewterers to work with. This resulted in a dull finish. The presence of toxic lead makes Early American pewter unsuitable for use as eating or drinking wares.

Pewter was cast in molds, usually brass, many of which came from England. Simple shapes like plates and basins, known as "sadware," were cast in a two-part hinged mold. More complicated articles such as teapots and tankards, called "holloware," involved several cast parts soldered together. Rough edges were eliminated by hand or on a lathe.

Throughout the eighteenth century, basic eating utensils were the primary pewter forms—plates, dishes, spoons, mugs, tankards. By the early nineteenth century, teapots, coffee pots and other forms originated by silversmiths and potters appeared in pewter.

With the advent of inexpensive silver-plated wares in the mid-nineteenth century, pewterers tried to remain competitive by devising a new formula that yielded shinier surfaces. Called Britannia, it is about

90 percent tin, 5 to 10 percent antimony and copper, and it has no lead.

Pewter is easy to find now, though pieces with decorative flourishes are scarce. Most pieces are in the low hundreds of dollars.

Plates

Plates 7–10 inches wide were used for eating, larger ones that were usually deep served as soup dishes. As you might expect, the larger and more sculptural the plate, the more desirable it is. For instance, a plate, 8-inch diameter, Nathaniel Austin, Charlestown, Massachusetts, 1763–1807, sells for $250–$350. A deep plate, 11–13 inches in diameter, would be worth $350–$450.

Most pewter plates you will see are plain, and they are the least expensive, as a rule. Add a reeded brim, molded brim or other decoration, and the value mounts. An eighteenth-century decorated deep plate could run as much as $500–$700.

Deeper than plates, basins have brims much narrower than plates. Basins range in capacity from a pint (5–6-inch diameter) to a gallon (14–15-inch diameter). A smaller basin, 7⅞-inch-diameter circular bowl with everted lip, Samuel Pierce, Greenfield, Massachusetts, 1792–1830, would be worth $200–$300. A bigger basin, not much more.

Porringers are small bowls with flat, usually pierced decorative handles, used apparently for eating as well as for drinking. The handle design provides the main interest. Rare ones have crown handles or dolphin handles, while most have various interlocking scroll designs, and the least interesting are solid and simply shaped. A porringer, 5¼ inches in diameter, circular bowl with everted lip, pierced and scrolling handle, Samuel Hamlin, Providence, Rhode Island, *circa* 1800, would be worth $300–$500.

Beakers, Mugs, Tankards and Chalices

A beaker, 3 inches, flaring lip and shaped handle, nineteenth century, might sell for $75–$150. Another, 5⅛ inches, flaring cylindrical body, incised banding and molded foot, Timothy Boardman & Company, New York, 1822–25, could be worth $400–$500.

A chalice, 8⅜ inches, conical cup with incised lip above a baluster stem on a domed and molded base, Peter Young, Albany, New York, 1775–95, is priced at $2,500–$3,500.

Mugs are tapering drinking vessels with a handle. They do not have a lid. They range in capacity from several ounces to a quart. The bigger the size, the more desirable the mug. Most have very straightforward designs and sell for several hundred dollars.

A thickened lip, a nice molded base and banded decoration around the body add value, as does a large, scrolled handle. Mugs that benefited from the full treatment, especially early ones, can be quite expensive. For instance, a pint mug, 4⅝ inches, tapering cylindrical body with molded lip, raised midbanding, scrolling handle with scrolled terminal, on a molded base, Jacob Whitmore, Middletown, Connecticut, 1758–90, would be worth $4,000–$5,000.

Being larger than mugs and having a hinged lid, tankards are more valuable. There is more opportunity for decoration on a tankard. Lids and thumbpieces lend themselves to intriguing variations that can raise the price. Good tankards tend to be over $1,000.

Again, a full-dress design will bring a top price. For instance, a covered quart tankard, 7¾ inches, domed, hinged and molded lid with pierced thumbpiece, above a tapering cylindrical body with molded banding, the scrolling thumbpiece with bud terminal, above a molded base, William Will, Philadelphia, 1764–98, might sell for $5,000–$7,000.

Flagons are taller, slimmer and scarcer than tankards. They also have a handle and a hinged lid, often with a spout. Originally they were used to bring drink to a table, but by the late eighteenth century they had fallen out of fashion. They played a part, though, in church communion services. A flagon, 13¾ inches, domed lid with urn-form finial and chair-back thumbpiece above a tapering cylindrical body with raised midbanding and double-scrolling handle, on a flaring base, Thomas Boardman, Hartford, Connecticut, *circa* 1820, would sell for about $1,200–$1,500.

Assorted Vessels

Measuring containers are similar in shape to drinking vessels. For instance, a quart measure, 7 inches, baluster form with molded lip, incised midbanding, scrolling handle and flaring base, Timothy Boardman & Company, 1827, is worth $1,200–$1,500.

Large pitchers held mainly water. Size, design of the body and handles are the chief factors affecting value. For example, a pitcher 7 inches, with scrolling handle and spout, Leonard, Reed and Barton, mid-19th century, sells for $100. A more shapely pitcher, 6½ inches, baluster body with scrolling handle and spout, Freeman Porter, Westbrook, Maine, 1835–65, is priced at $350–$450.

Coffee and Tea

Entire early coffee and tea services in pewter are hard to find, though pieces made after about 1820 are more available. You are more likely to find individual pieces—pots, creamers and sugar bowls.

During the eighteenth century, ball-shaped teapots were popular, although by 1800 Neoclassical drum shapes had taken over. Because they were made in comparatively large numbers, nineteenth-century pewter teapots are quite reasonable. For instance, a teapot, 8 inches, domed lid, scrolling handle and spout, George Richardson, Boston, *circa* 1825, sells for $250–$350.

Coffeepots are taller than teapots, and they tend to have a tapered cylindrical form. A coffeepot, 10¾ inches, domed lid, scrolling handle and spout, Freeman Porter, Westbrook, Maine, 1835–65, is priced at $250–$350.

A sugar bowl, 5¾ inches, domed lid above baluster body with scrolling handles, Boardman & Company, New York, 1825–27, would be worth $250–$350.

Pewter Miscellany

Most pewter candlesticks come in tall baluster shapes. The more shapely, the better. As with silver, collectors want pairs. For instance, a pair of candlesticks, 9¾ inches, each with a baluster stem on a domed base, nineteenth century, is worth $150–$250. A more shapely design would push the price up to $350 or more.

Oil lamps, while mostly utilitarian, sometimes have an appealing symphony of curves. For instance, a whale-oil lamp, 8¾ inches, the two-light font with bull's-eye glass, on a baluster stem on a domed base, nineteenth century, is worth $250–$350.

Good pewter craftsmen lavished care on little things like toilet articles. For instance, a soap dish, 4⅜-inch diameter, circular with incised midbanding, hinged lid, probably Ashbil Griswold, Meriden, Connecticut, 1807–35, sells for $250–$350.

How to Evaluate Pewter

The all-important element, as you would expect, is the beauty of a piece. Pleasing proportions are the starting point. A clunky shape is never likely to win many hearts.

1

2

3

4

American pewter offers robust, graceful shapes in lustrous metal. Small, plain forms like beakers are readily available and inexpensive, while larger, more sculptural forms command more money. (1) Covered sugar bowl by George Richardson, Boston and Cranston, Rhode Island, 1818–45. 5¾ inches high; $1,800–$2,000. *Christie's, New York.* (2) Baptismal bowl by Lorenzo L. Williams, Philadelphia, 1838–42. 4¾ inches high; $300–$400. *Christie's, New York.* (3) Pewter beaker with strap handle, 19th century. 3½ inches high; under $100. *Christie's, New York.* (4) A quart dome-top tankard in impeccable condition. Believed to have been made in Philadelphia, 1780–1800. $5,500–$7,500. *Christie's, New York.*

Collectors also want a bright, lustrous color, not a leaden look. But not too bright: little irregularities give pewter much of its solid charm.

American pewter can be worth as much as ten times more than British or French pewter. Since a lot of pewter pieces were brought into the colonies from other countries, you should satisfy yourself that you have got an American piece before you pay an American price. Styles are similar.

Most pewter has touch marks which can offer important clues to their origin. Typically, you will see some kind of emblem and a maker's initials. Particularly after the Revolution, many pewterers declared the American origin of their work by stamping it "Boston," "Middletown," "New York" and so on. Check any marks you see against the references cited below.

Be careful when making an identification, since a number of initials were shared by many pewterers. Wear has at least partially obscured the marks on perhaps 20 percent of the pieces you might encounter. Also, some marks were applied at a later date. To add a little confusion, an owner's two- or three-initial monogram might be stamped on the bottom of pieces to help identify them if they were lost or stolen. Do not be put off by an early piece stamped "London" on the bottom. In Colonial days, an English-made piece was considered more prestigious, and some American pewterers used such stamps to make their work more appealing. Of course, you want positive evidence that a piece was American.

Determining the maker and the approximate date of a piece requires examining details of construction and style. Early pewter has linen marks inside mugs, coffee pots and porringers, and opposite the joints, resulting from the molds they were cast in. Lathes left small concentric circles on the bottom of pieces. Sometimes marks from a region share similar qualities because one die-maker produced dies for a number of local pewterers.

Forgers made copies from plaster casts of authentic pieces, picking up marks in the process. If you familiarize yourself with the details of a pewterer's authentic pieces, you will notice that a cast forgery seems coarse, because the cast magnified imperfections. A pair of forged pieces from the same cast would be easy to spot, because you would see identical scratches, something that you would never find on authentic pieces.

Wear can add value if it suggests authenticity. A tankard should show wear around the handle and the thumb rest, for instance. Naturally, disfiguring wear detracts from the value of a piece.

Large pieces are rare and command a premium. Since they were more expensive to make originally, fewer people could afford them, and fewer were made. Many small pieces are also rare, because pewterers melted worn-out or discarded pieces to provide metal for new ones. Pewter firmly attributed to small-town craftsmen tends to be scarcer than work from cities, but not much of it is very interesting.

Unusual, attractive decoration can mean extra money. For instance, shell-shaped feet on a pitcher, a double or triple-curved handle, bold ribs around a tankard, a particularly graceful thumbpiece or molded dome lid are interesting features.

Pewter should be cleaned with a good metal polish, but do not buff it. Avoid steel wool or abrasive cleansing powder. They can destroy the soft patina that gives pewter so much charm.

For More Information

Henry J. Kauffman, *The American Pewterer: His Techniques and His Products.* Camden, N.J.: Nelson, 1970.

Ledlie Irwin Laughlin, *Pewter in America: Its Makers and Their Marks.* Barre, Mass.: Barre Publishers, 1970.

Charles F. Montgomery, *A History of American Pewter.* New York: Weathervane, 1973.

——— and Patricia E. Kane, *American Art: 1750–1800, Toward Independence.* New Haven: Yale University Art Gallery, 1976.

Museums

ALBANY, N.Y.
Albany Institute of History & Art
125 Washington Avenue
Albany, NY 12210
(518) 463-4478

BENNINGTON, VT.
Bennington Museum
West Main Street
Bennington, VT 05201
(802) 447-1571

BOSTON
Museum of Fine Arts
Huntington Avenue
Boston, MA 02115
(617) 267-9300

CONCORD, MASS.
Concord Antiquarian Society
200 Lexington Road
Concord, MA 07142
(617) 369-9609

CONCORD, N.H.
New Hampshire Historical Society
30 Park Street
Concord, NH 03301
(603) 225-3381

DEARBORN, MICH.
Greenfield Village and Henry Ford Museum
Oakwood Boulevard
Dearborn, MI 48121
(313) 565-3000

DEERFIELD, MASS.
Historic Deerfield
The Street
Deerfield, MA 01342
(413) 774-5581

DETROIT
Detroit Institute of Arts
5200 Woodward Avenue
Detroit, MI 48202
(313) 833-7900

HARTFORD
Antiquarian and Landmarks Society, Inc.
394 Main Street
Hartford, CT 06103
(203) 247-8996

Connecticut Historical Society
1 Elizabeth Street
Hartford, CT 06105
(203) 236-5621

HOUSTON
Museum of Fine Arts
1001 Bissonnet
Houston, TX 77005
(713) 526-1361

LANCASTER, PA.
Rock Ford
881 Rock Ford Road
Lancaster, PA 17603
(717) 392-7223

LITCHFIELD, CONN.
Litchfield Historical Society and Museum
On-the-Green
Litchfield, CT 06759
(203) 567-5862

MANCHESTER, N.H.
Currier Gallery of Art
192 Orange Street
Manchester, NH 03104
(603) 669-6144

NEW HAVEN
Yale University Art Gallery
1111 Chapel Street
New Haven, CT 06520
(203) 436-0574

NEWPORT, R.I.
Newport Historical Society
82 Touro Street
Newport, RI 02840
(401) 846-0813

NEW YORK
Brooklyn Museum
188 Eastern Parkway
Brooklyn, NY 11238
(212) 638-5000

Metropolitan Museum of Art
Fifth Avenue at 82nd Street
New York, NY 10028
(212) 879-5500

PHILADELPHIA
Historical Society of Pennsylvania
1300 Locust Street
Philadelphia, PA 19107
(215) 732-6200

Philadelphia Museum of Art
26th Street at Benjamin Franklin Highway
Philadelphia, PA 19101
(215) 763-8100

PROVIDENCE
Rhode Island Historical Society
57 Power Street
Providence, RI 02906
(401) 331-8575

SALEM, MASS.
Essex Institute
132 Essex Street
Salem, MA 01970
(617) 744-3390

SPRINGFIELD, VT.
Springfield Art and Historical Society
Elm Hill
Springfield, VT 05156
(802) 885-2415

STURBRIDGE, MASS.
Old Sturbridge Village
Sturbridge, MA 01566
(617) 347-3362

TRENTON, N.J.
New Jersey State Museum
205 West State Street
Trenton, NJ 08625
(609) 292-6300

WASHINGTON
Smithsonian Institution
1000 Jefferson Drive, SW
Washington, DC 20560
(202) 357-1300

WILLIAMSBURG, VA.
Colonial Williamsburg
Goodwin Building
Williamsburg, VA 23185
(804) 229-1000

WINTERTHUR, DEL.
Henry Francis du Pont Winterthur Museum
Winterthur, DE 19735
(302) 656-8591

WORCESTER, MASS.
Worcester Art Museum
55 Salisbury Street
Worcester, MA 01608
(617) 799-4406

Where to Buy

Auction houses selling pewter along with other American decorative arts include:

BOLTON, MASS.
Robert W. Skinner
Route 117
Bolton, MA 01740
(617) 779-5528

DELAWARE, OHIO
Garth's Auctions
2690 Stratford Road
Delaware, OH 43105
(614) 362-4771

HILLSBORO, N.H.
Richard W. Withington
Hillsboro, NH 03244
(603) 464-3232

HYANNIS PORT, MASS.
Richard A. Bourne Company
Corporation Street on Route 28
Hyannis Port, MA 02647
(617) 775-0797

NEW YORK
Christie's
502 Park Avenue
New York, NY 10022
(212) 546-1181

William Doyle
175 East 87th Street
New York, NY 10028
(212) 427-2730

Phillips
406 East 78th Street
New York, NY 10021
(212) 570-4849

Sotheby's
1334 York Avenue
New York, NY 10021
(212) 472-3511

PHILADELPHIA
Samuel T. Freeman
1808 Chestnut Street
Philadelphia, PA 19103
(215) 563-9275

SOUTH DEERFIELD, MASS.
Douglas Galleries
State Street
South Deerfield, MA 01373
(413) 665-2877

WASHINGTON
G. C. Sloan & Company
715 13th Street, NW
Washington, DC 20005
(202) 628-1468

Adam A. Wechsler & Sons
905–9 E Street, NW
Washington, DC 20004
(202) 628-1281

Dealers to check:

BARRINGTON, ILL.
The Silver Vault
Box 421
Barrington, IL 60010
(312) 381-7063

COLD SPRING HARBOR, N.Y.
Valdemar Jacobsen
5 Main Street
Cold Spring Harbor, NY 11724
(516) 692-7775

DOWNINGTON, PA.
Philip Bradley
East Lancaster Avenue,
Route 30
Downington, PA 19335
(215) 269-0427

ESSEX, CONN.
June and Ben Carde
Old Bull House
Main Street
Essex, CT 06409
(203) 767-0022

GRANBY, CONN.
Celia Jacobs Stevenson
25 Granville Road, Route 189
Granby, CT 06060
(203) 653-6125

HANOVER, CONN.
John Carl Thomas
Box 185
Salt Rock Road
Hanover, CT 06350
(203) 822-9260

NORFOLK, VA.
Family Tree Antiques
420 West Bute Street
Norfolk, VA 23510
(804) 625-6250

WESTPORT, CONN.
Guthman Americana
Box 392
Westport, CT 06881
(203) 259-9763

WOODSTOCK, N.Y.
Marianne Clark Antiques
Route 17
Woodstock, NY 10817
(815) 459-7524

13

NINETEENTH-CENTURY CHINESE HARDWOOD FURNITURE

PERHAPS GEORGE KATES, FORMER CURATOR OF ORIENTAL ART AT THE Brooklyn museum, put it best: "What has been evolved from China's long experience fits remarkably well with our needs of today. It can be summed up in a few words: balance, simplicity, and civilization."

Chinese craftsmen developed the sturdiest furniture in the world, intended to endure for generations, and they did it without a drop of glue. They designed furniture with pieces that fit together like a puzzle. They selected solid hardwoods; a six-foot-high cupboard, for instance, might tip the scales at over 175 pounds, virtually unheard of for a European or American piece. Many European craftsmen used comparatively fragile glue to hold things together, and some pieces had decorative flourishes like veneer, highly vulnerable to damage. Nobody really expected that this furniture would outlive the king it was intended for. The next king would usher in a new style, anyway.

Chinese hardwood furniture is supremely graceful. Craftsmen achieved beauty with pure lines and exquisitely grained exotic woods such as *hua mu* (flowery wood), *hong mu* (red wood), *zi tan* (purple sandalwood), *ji chi mu* (chicken-wing wood), *chang-mu* (camphor), *wu-mu* (ebony), *huang-yang-mu* (boxwood), *taso-mu* (datewood). Most prized of all: *huang huali* (a rosewood). With materials like these, there was little need for decoration.

Chinese hardwood-furniture design reached a peak during the seventeenth century, when Ming emperors reigned. Though the basic designs were continued, forests were exhausted, and some of the most spectacular woods ceased to be available by the end of the eighteenth century.

Nonetheless, very fine nineteenth-century Chinese hardwood furniture is available. Toward the end of that period, Chinese craftsmen absorbed the ornate Victorian taste and produced heavily carved pieces that are very different indeed. Most simple, elegant hardwood pieces can be had for under $3,000, less than you would pay for almost any other major type of antique furniture.

Chairs

You can sense a lot about a civilization by looking at its chairs. Most Western chairs are side chairs meant for eating. The Chinese sat on stools and dined at low tables.

What we think of as a side chair for dining, the Chinese might have used for playing games: a flat seat, usually hardwood but often rush, straight legs joined by stretchers, a back that curves slightly backward, perhaps topped with a yoke-shaped rail. Some backs have a single, shaped splat, while others have six or seven vertical spindles. These chairs allowed their users to move around easily, lean forward, lean back and pursue the game. They are not especially comfortable, but that did not matter, because the owners wanted to remain alert so that they could win.

Chinese students' chairs have arms, but they are not comfortable enough to fall asleep in. Students are supposed to sit up straight so that they can learn. These chairs can be found in sets of four, six and sometimes more.

You might also find single-piece horseshoe-shaped arms that swoop around and serve as the rail for the back. These were probably designed for contemplation. They are lush and sensuously comfortable.

A pair of nice nineteenth-century hardwood chairs without arms would sell for $1,500–$3,000. Armchairs command 25–30 percent more than side chairs.

A settee, a European form adopted by the Chinese, is about the closest thing you will find to a Chinese sofa. They usually had solid hardwood arms and a back with simple carved decoration. There might be a deep, shaped decorative apron. Width: 60–72 inches. Depth: 20–25 inches. They are worth $1,500–$3,000.

Tables

Side tables can be quite pleasing. One with a molded top, slender legs joined by a platform stretcher in a decorative fashion, such as a "cracked ice" pattern, 30–35 inches high, 40–60 inches wide, 15–20 inches deep, is priced at $800–$3,000. Smaller side tables are about half as big and sell for half as much.

Low Chinese tables can add a lot to a living room. The top might have a molded edge with in-curved legs. Height: 10–20 inches. Width: 30–70 inches. Depth: 30–40 inches. Most of those you will see are square. Prices are from $1,000 to $2,000. Elaborate scrollwork on each side might reduce value, since collectors tend to prefer simpler designs.

Then there are stools which can serve as side tables. These also have molded tops, occasionally a marble inset top, in-curved legs. There might be a little scrollwork. Height: 18–20 inches. Width and depth: 15–17 inches. They are worth $600–$1,500.

A good way to show off Chinese porcelain is on an urn stand which might have a molded top, a shaped apron, stretchers joining the in-curved legs. Height: 38–45 inches. Width and depth: 14–16 inches. They are priced at $600–$800 for a pair.

An altar coffer is a kind of sideboard, designed for Buddhist and Taoist rituals at home, which can complement a dining room beautifully. The top has scrolled ends, two or three drawers in front. Drawer hardware should contribute to the overall feeling of a piece. Height: 33–35 inches. Width: 60–70 inches. Depth: 18–20 inches. These sell for $1,000–$2,000.

A similar form is the altar table, without drawers. Slender legs are joined by shaped stretchers, perhaps with carved decoration below the top. Height: 34–42 inches. Width: 70–90 inches. Depth: 18–22 inches. Such a piece might be worth $2,000–$3,000.

Desks and Cabinets

Chinese scholars traveled quite a bit, so their desks—known as writing tables—are made with three pieces, enabling them to be taken apart and moved easily. There are two pedestals, each with several drawers, supporting a top section including two or three drawers. Height: 28–31 inches. Width: 50–65 inches. Depth: 25–30 inches. Prices range from $2,000 to $4,000. A desk without drawers along the top is worth less money, and a desk having extra touches, like well-carved open-latticework stretchers, sells for more.

Simple lines and a blending of fine-grained woods make case pieces like small cupboards especially handsome. Height: 40–45 inches. Width: 30–35 inches. Depth: 14–18 inches. These are worth $1,500–$2,500 for a pair.

Also available are low cupboards, with a pair of doors flanked by short drawers. Their understated, elegant metal hinges and latches can have a great impact. Height: 18–20 inches. Width: 50–60 inches. Depth: 15–18 inches. These can bring $2,000–$3,000.

If you are looking for a large piece to help establish the feeling of a room, consider a cabinet. Some feature an asymmetrical arrangement of open shelves that Chinese collectors used to display prized possessions. Hinges and latches are important features. Height: 65–80 inches.

1

2

3

Chinese 19th-century hardwood furniture has a surprisingly contemporary look and is priced below other major styles. The quality of wood counts more than decoration. (1) Side table, carved with ovals, scrolls and floral sprays. 41 inches high × 19½ inches deep × 6 feet, 11 inches long; $2,500–$3,500. *Sotheby Parke Bernet*. (2) A *hong mu* (dark rosewood) early 19th-century desk. 34 inches high × 62 inches long; $6,000–$8,000. *Vallin Galleries*. (3) A *hong mu* (dark rosewood) 19th-century gaming chair. 38 inches high; $2,000–$3,000. *Vallin Galleries*.

Width: 35–50 inches. Depth: 15–22 inches. Prices are from $4,000 to $6,000.

You will find the most extravagant expanse of wood on a clothes cupboard. It has a pair of molded doors, sometimes several drawers below. Height: 60–105 inches. Width: 35–55 inches. Depth: 16–22 inches. These sell for $2,000–$10,000 for a pair.

How to Evaluate Chinese Furniture

Generally, collectors pay a premium for Chinese hardwood furniture with elegant lines and little decoration. Ornately carved pieces are worth decidedly less.

The wood is of primary importance. The more spectacular the grain, the more valuable the piece will be. Dark, muddy grains are much less interesting.

On fine furniture, wood is selected so that the grain of different parts harmonizes to heighten the overall impact. When a cabinetmaker took shortcuts, cupboard doors might not quite mesh with each other, or the front of a piece would not be integrated with the sides. Naturally, such furniture sells at discount.

Pieces of obviously mismatched wood in Chinese furniture could be a tipoff that it was reassembled from remnants of different, damaged pieces—the top of one chest combined with sides of another, drawers of yet another. So-called "married" pieces have no value to collectors.

Look for signs of age. This means no glue, a recent addition to the art of Chinese furniture construction. The more beautiful the wood, the earlier a piece is likely to be. See if there is wear in logical places like the bottoms of feet. Joints absorb tremendous stress over the years, and you should see evidence of it. Also, as wood shrinks, the joints can become a bit loose, and craftsmen would retighten them by inserting tiny pieces of wood.

It is a plus if you find meticulous old repairs. When the wood became gouged or a knot popped out, a craftsman would carve a little filler wood of similar-grained wood and slip it into place.

Watch out for unusual dimensions. For instance, if you find an altar table that is 30 inches high, the legs were probably cut down from 34 inches so that the table would be a convenient height for Western dining. Collectors do not want it. If you are suspicious, have the legs removed and see if there is evidence that they were cut in recent times.

For More Information

The most useful books:

Michel Buerdeley, *Chinese Furniture.* New York: Kodansha International.
Gustav Ecke, *Chinese Domestic Furniture.* 1944; undated edition reprinted during the 1970s.
Robert Ellsworth, *Chinese Furniture: Hardwood Examples of the Ming and Early Ching Dynasties.* New York: Random House, 1970.
———, ed., *Chinese Furniture in Hawaiian Collections.* Honolulu: Honolulu Academy of Arts, 1982.
George Kates, *Chinese Household Furniture.* Dover, 1962, reprinted from the 1948 edition.

Museums

BOSTON
Museum of Fine Arts
Huntington Avenue
Boston, MA 02115
(617) 267-9300

CLEVELAND
Cleveland Museum of Art
11150 East Boulevard
Cleveland, OH 44106
(212) 421-7340

DENVER
Denver Art Museum
100 West 14th Avenue Parkway
Denver, CO 80204
(303) 575-2793

HONOLULU
Honolulu Academy of Arts
900 South Beretania Street
Honolulu, HI 96814
(808) 538-3693

KANSAS CITY, MO.
William Rockhill Nelson Gallery and Atkins Museum of Fine Arts
4525 Oak Street
Kansas City, MO 64111
(816) 561-4000

MILTON, MASS.
Museum of the American China Trade
215 Adams Street
Milton, MA 02186
(617) 696-1815

NEW HAVEN
Yale University Art Gallery
1111 Chapel Street
New Haven, CT 06520
(203) 436-0574

NEW YORK
Brooklyn Museum
188 Eastern Parkway
Brooklyn, NY 11238
(212) 638-5000

Metropolitan Museum of Art
Fifth Avenue at 82nd Street
New York, NY 10028
(212) 879-5500

PHILADELPHIA
Philadelphia Museum of Art
26th Street & Benjamin Franklin Parkway
Philadelphia, PA 19101
(215) 763-8100

SAN FRANCISCO
Asian Art Museum of San Francisco
Golden Gate Park
San Francisco, CA 94118
(415) 558-2993

Where to Buy

Chinese hardwood furniture is auctioned in New York by:

Christie's
502 Park Avenue
New York, NY 10022
(212) 546-1158

Phillips
406 East 79th Street
New York, NY 10021
(212) 570-4830

Sotheby's
1334 York Avenue
New York, NY 10021
(212) 472-3516

This is a market where the finest pieces tend to pass among dealers. The major ones:

BOSTON
Albert Langdon
126 Charles Street
Boston, MA 02114
(617) 523-5954

NEW YORK
Antaeus Gallery
962 Madison Avenue
New York, NY 10021
(212) 737-3220

Robert H. Ellsworth
960 Fifth Avenue
New York, NY 10021
(212) 535-5538

Charles Gracie & Sons Orientalia
979 Third Avenue
New York, NY 10022
(212) 753-5350

SAN FRANCISCO
Edward Hardy
855 Montgomery Street
San Francisco, CA 94133
(415) 981-5886

WASHINGTON
China Coast Oriental Art
3003 P Street, NW
Washington, DC 20007
(202) 338-5458

WILTON, CONN.
Vallin Gallery
516 Danbury Road
Wilton, CT 06897
(203) 762-7441

14

TWENTIETH-CENTURY AMERICAN DRAWINGS

PRICES FOR AMERICAN ART HAVE GONE SKY-HIGH DURING THE 1970S, AND IT is hard to find a single area that has not boomed already. Nineteenth-century paintings soared, as have twentieth-century paintings and watercolors. Even Western art—cowboy pictures—has experienced one of the most dramatic rises.

Yet most drawings—black-and-white works of art on paper, made with pencil, ink, charcoal—remain quite reasonable. Fine work by important artists can be had for a few thousand dollars. This is about a tenth the price of comparable quality paintings. Perhaps drawings have lagged in the market because most collectors prefer big, brassy, colorful works of art, something that can take over an entire wall.

Drawings have a more intimate appeal that beckons collectors ready for subtle pleasures. Maxim Karolik, for instance, a major benefactor to Boston's Museum of Fine Arts, assembled his spectacular collection of American drawings during the 1950s after he had had his fling with American paintings. Like fine drawings anywhere, American drawings have a spontaneous quality. They are tentative, leaving more to the imagination. They give you a peek into a creative process.

"Since drawings are easier to produce than paintings, they tend to be more adventurous," mused Paul Cumming, curator of American drawings and watercolors at the Whitney Museum. "By contrast, paintings tend to be more formal."

Our First Moderns

Artists of the "Ashcan School" were the first real moderns. They rejected academic discipline and pretty subjects. Because they advocated a more robust response to the world, Robert Henri (1865–1929), John Sloan (1871–1951), George Luks (1867–1933), William Glackens (1870–1938), Ernest Lawson (1873–1939), Arthur Davies (1862–1928) and Everett Shinn (1876–1953) are credited with helping to usher in the modern era. They depicted the rough texture of city life, mainly around

New York. More restful subjects like nudes appear, too.

You are most likely to find pastels by Henri and Shinn, though some pencil drawings by Sloan and Glackens appear on the market from time to time. As former newspaper illustrators, these artists were very much interested in linear qualities. Their drawings represent vivid graphic art. Generally, the best were done before World War I. Prices tend to be in the $2,000–$3,000 range.

George Bellows (1882–1925), inspired by Henri, developed a powerful graphic style that achieved dramatic effects depicting crowds. He liked to draw people dancing, fighting, moving through the streets. Through his prints, he became famous for sporting scenes that pulsate with energy. He also did good nudes. Bellows' black-and-white drawings fetch $2,000–$5,000.

Reginald Marsh (1898–1954) studied with Luks and Sloan, and became a prolific illustrator of teeming, crowded New York street scenes. Often his style tended toward caricature. Occasionally, he produced a poignant, finished drawing. He was interested in modeled forms more than color, and his images, for the most part, are subdued. Prices are in the $1,000–$5,000 range.

John Marin (1870–1953) spent six years in Paris, becoming an enthusiastic convert to abstract modern art. He created strong images with slashing, jagged brush strokes. Tilting planes and bizarre forms convey a feeling of monumentality. During his early career, he prowled New York and made numerous drawings of everything from skyscrapers to flying trapeze artists. "I see great forces at work," he wrote in a 1913 exhibition catalog, "great movements; the large buildings and the small buildings; the warring of the great and the small; influences of one mass on another greater or smaller mass. . . . While these powers are at work pushing, pulling, sideways, downwards, upwards, I can hear the sound of their strife and there is great music being played." He also did many fine images of Maine's craggy coast, and they are somewhat easier to find than his New York subjects, particularly the large (26 by 21 inches, for instance) watercolors of New York. His pencil drawings can be had for $2,000–$5,000.

Charles Demuth (1883–1935) is best known for his elegant images in evocative, translucent watercolors. He was fastidious. "John Marin and I draw our inspiration from the same source, French Modernism," Demuth mused. "He brought his up in buckets and spilt much along the way. I dipped mine out with a teaspoon, but I never spilled a drop." Deft at figure drawing, Demuth depicted nightclub dancers, circus acrobats, vaudeville performers. He illustrated characters from novels by Henry James and Émile Zola. His drawings of flowers are perhaps the most sought after. A lot of his work is available for $2,000–$5,000.

Brooding Abstractions

Marsden Hartley (1877–1943) made a restless search for a personal style, traveling through France and Germany, experimenting with the latest European ideas. He sought inspiration in Mexico, Bermuda, Massachusetts and especially Maine. "What do pictures mean anyhow?" Hartley exclaimed in apparent frustration. "I have been trying to find out for at least half a lifetime. I have no interest in the subject matter of a picture, not the slightest. A picture has but one meaning—it is well done, or it isn't—and if it is, it is surely to be a good picture whether the spectator likes it or not." Hartley's brooding mature work consists of abstractions noted for nervous lines and angular forms often derived from the mountains he loved. His crayon and charcoal drawings are the most readily available, though you will see some watercolors too. Most of his drawings are in the $1,000–$4,000 range.

Joseph Stella (1877–1946) was a facile draftsman who produced strong charcoal portraits of immigrants, miners, city people. He was attracted to the turbulent emotions of tragic scenes, and he was awed by towering urban structures. "Massive dark towers," he gushed about the Brooklyn Bridge, "dominating the surrounding tumult of the surging skyscrapers with their gothic majesty scaled in the purity of their arches, the cables, like divine messages from above, transmitted to the vibrating coils, cutting and dividing into innumerable musical spaces the nude immensity of the sky, it impressed me as the shrine containing all the efforts of the new civilization of AMERICA." As Stella grew older, he experimented with subtle effects. He did flowers and landscapes, using pencil, crayon, pastel, gouache or watercolor. He seems to have done more flowers than anything else, perhaps because they are the most readily available. His work can be bought for $3,000–$10,000.

Arthur Dove (1880–1946), a favorite of Washington, D.C., collector Duncan Phillips, saw the lyrical possibilities in abstract natural forms and bold colors. "I should like to take wind and water and sand as a motif and work with them, but it has to be simplified in most cases just as music has done with sound," he reflected. Dove found peace of mind on his Long Island houseboat. His poetic style changed little during his career. Much of his work has a surprisingly playful quality. His watercolors sell for $2,000–$5,000. Most tend to be rather small, in the 5-by-7-inch range.

Currents of Realism

Edward Hopper (1882–1967), a leading American realist who resisted the trend toward abstract art, created memorable images of loneliness.

He showed solitary contemplative figures, buildings, city streets, lighthouses and sailboats enveloped in silence. He described his work as "austere and simple, even to coldness, but at times not without a certain richness." His pen, pencil or charcoal drawings sell for $3,000–$20,000 depending on quality.

Many artists responded with anger and bitterness to the crises of the 1930s. The Lithuanian immigrant Ben Shahn (1898–1969), for instance, used a blunt, primitive technique to give us polemical portraits of people who suffered from injustice. During the 1940s, he turned to more lyrical subjects such as children playing. His images have the simplified look of posters, reflecting his experience as a muralist. He achieved dramatic effects with telling details. "There's a difference in the way a twelve-dollar coat wrinkles from the way a seventy-five-dollar coat wrinkles, and that has to be right," he snorted. "It's just as important esthetically as the difference in the light of the Ile de France and the Brittany Coast. Maybe it's more important." Shahn's drawings sell for $2,000–$4,000.

Some of the so-called American regionalists like Grant Wood (1892–1942), Thomas Hart Benton (1889–1975) and John Steuart Curry (1897–1946) created quite sophisticated images. During the 1930s, when much of their most effective work was done, they favored rural Midwestern subjects.

Feisty Benton was the most productive, and his work appears on the market regularly. He described his images as "compact, massive and rhythmical composition of forms." He belittled the intellectual establishment and modern art, declaring that his art "symbolized aesthetically what the majority of Americans had in mind—America itself." His simple pencil drawings sell for $4,000–$6,000.

Charles Burchfield (1893–1967) produced cityscape and landscape fantasies that seem to vibrate with energy. "It is the romantic side of the real world that I try to portray," he confided in his journal. "My things are poems (I hope)." He was a shy man who spent years designing wallpaper for a Buffalo company, but he had occasional bursts of enthusiasm. "Gosh I just love me," he exulted at an exhibition. "I love to bask in his glory. Burchfield's I mean." Burchfield's most prized images were done before 1920, when his style crystallized. His drawings sell for $3,000–$5,000.

If your taste runs to abstract expressionism, you might look at the allover drawings of Mark Tobey (1890–). He was a figure painter until 1940, when he threw himself into Modernism. Using gouache, he meshed small lines and created intricate patterns akin to Chinese calligraphy, which he revered. They beckon a viewer to contemplate mysterious space. Prices are from $1,500 to $5,000.

1

2

American 20th-century drawings, black-and-white images in pen, pencil, crayon or chalk on paper, are available for a fraction of the price of color images. (1) A striking crayon profile of a man by Joseph Stella. 11 × 8½; $1,000–$1,500. *Sotheby Parke Bernet*. (2) A drawing of Wall Street by John Marin, one of the first American moderns. New York was one of his favorite subjects. 9⅞ × 7½; $6,000–$7,000. *Kennedy Galleries, New York.*

3

4

(3) A pencil sketch of houses and trees by Charles Burchfield, whose experimental doodlings in the left border radiate as much energy as the image itself. 11 × 17; $1,500–$2,500. *Kennedy Galleries, New York.* 4) A charcoal sketch of two nudes by Edward Hopper. 17¾ × 12; $9,000–$10,000. *Kennedy Galleries, New York.*

Arshile Gorky (1904–48), a major Expressionist figure who avowed his artistic debt to Picasso and Kandinsky, was primarily interested in the magic of lines. His paintings consist of lines conjuring sensuous abstract forms to which color was added. His drawings—in pencil, crayon, pen, pastel—are usually on a smaller scale, and they sell for $3,000–$5,000.

Until recently, few drawings were known by David Smith (1906–65), a major American sculptor, and critics derided those as boring. But in 1979 the Whitney Museum mounted a revealing show. "Smith realized he had great graphic sensibility," noted the Whitney's Paul Cumming, "and he produced many drawings—20 or 30 a day—while standing at a work table. His drawings exploded with ideas, and later some appeared in his sculpture. Smith, like many artists, had his biggest adventures in drawings." They sell for $2,000–$5,000.

How to Evaluate Drawings

As you can see, twentieth-century American drawings and watercolors offer something for practically every taste. Happily, this is a field where it is still possible to form an important collection.

The most important part of a drawing is the expressive quality of the image. This helps assure interest regardless of who the artist was. A strong image by a lesser name is a better bet than crumbs from the table of a famous artist.

Pleasing subjects are easier to live with while you own them and easier to resell later than gruesome subjects. Bitter topical commentary, for instance, unless it is of a very high order, can become tiresome quickly.

Seek drawings by artists, like those we have mentioned, who did fine work in drawings. You are apt to see drawings by artists who never gave the medium their best efforts, but such artists are best bought in another medium or not at all. Though intimacy is an important appeal of drawings, larger size means more money.

Be wary of drawings with condition problems. Some artists like Reginald Marsh produced so many drawings that you should not settle for one in poor condition. On the other hand, do not be scared away from an exceptionally fine image or a rarity because of condition problems.

But before you buy a drawing with fading, tears, creases, stains, dog-eared corners or other problems, have it inspected by an experienced paper conservator. Know what problems can be eliminated before you buy a drawing. Ask a museum with a drawings collection to give you the names of some paper conservators.

Drawings are not as delicate as watercolors, but they still require some care. Backing should be acid-free board, and it helps to mount them behind Plexiglas which reflects some ultraviolet light. Keep away from strong light, especially if your drawing has any color.

For More Information

American Drawings. New York: National Academy of Design, 1980.

Donelson F. Hoopes, *American Watercolor Painting.* New York: Watson-Guptil Publications, 1977.

The Natural Image. New York: Richard York Gallery, 1982.

Theodore Stebbins, Jr., *American Master Drawings and Watercolors.* New York: Harper & Row, 1976. Most comprehensive survey of the field.

Museums

ANDOVER, MASS.
Addison Gallery of American Art
Phillips Academy
Andover, MA 01810
(617) 475-7515

ANN ARBOR, MICH.
University of Michigan Museum of Art
South State and South University Streets
Alumni Memorial Hall
Ann Arbor, MI 48109
(313) 764-0395

BALTIMORE
Baltimore Museum of Art
Art Museum Drive
Baltimore, MD 21218
(301) 396-7101

BERKELEY, CALIF.
University Art Museum
University of California
2626 Bancroft Way
Berkeley, CA 94720
(415) 642-1207

BOSTON
Museum of Fine Arts
Huntington Avenue
Boston, MA 02115
(617) 267-9300

CAMBRIDGE
Fogg Art Museum
Harvard University
32 Quincy Street
Cambridge, MA 02138
(617) 495-7768

CHICAGO
Art Institute of Chicago
Michigan Avenue and Adams Street
Chicago, IL 60603
(312) 443-3600

CINCINNATI
Cincinnati Art Museum
315 West Court Street
Cincinnati, OH 45202
(513) 621-5553

CLEVELAND
Cleveland Museum of Art
11150 East Boulevard
Cleveland, OH 44106
(216) 421-7340

COLUMBUS, OHIO
Columbus Galleries of Fine Art
Ohio State University
146 Hopkins Hall
128 North Oval Drive
Columbus, OH 43212
(614) 422-0330

DETROIT
Detroit Institute of Arts
5200 Woodward Avenue
Detroit, MI 48202
(313) 833-7900

LINCOLN, NEBR.
Sheldon Memorial Art Gallery
University of Nebraska
12th and R Streets
Lincoln, NE 68588
(402) 472-2461

LOS ANGELES
Grunwald Center for the Graphic Arts
University of California at Los Angeles
405 Hilgard Avenue
Los Angeles, CA 90024
(213) 825-3783

Los Angeles County Museum of Art
5905 Wilshire Boulevard
Los Angeles, CA 90036
(213) 937-4250

NEW BRITAIN, CONN.
New Britain Museum of American Art
56 Lexington Street
New Britain, CT 06052
(203) 229-0257

NEW HAVEN
Yale University Art Gallery
1111 Chapel Street
New Haven, CT 06520
(203) 436-0574

NEW YORK
Metropolitan Museum of Art
Fifth Avenue at 82nd Street
New York, NY 10028
(212) 879-5500

Whitney Museum of American Art
945 Madison Avenue
New York, NY 10021
(212) 570-3600

PHILADELPHIA
Philadelphia Museum of Art
26th Street and Benjamin Franklin Parkway
Philadelphia, PA 19101
(215) 763-8100

PITTSBURG, OHIO
Carnegie Institute
4400 Forbes Avenue
Pittsburg, OH 15213
(412) 622-3131

UTICA, N.Y.
Munson-Williams-Proctor Institute
310 Genesee Street
Utica, NY 13502
(315) 797-0000

WASHINGTON
Hirshhorn Museum and Sculpture Garden
Independence Avenue at Seventh Street, SW
Washington, DC 20560
(202) 357-3091

National Museum of American Art
8th and G Streets, NW
Washington, DC 20560
(202) 357-3176

WILLIAMSTOWN, MASS.
Sterling and Francine Clark Art Institute
225 South Street
Williamstown, MA 01267
(413) 458-8109

WORCESTER, MASS.
Worcester Art Museum
55 Salisbury Street
Worcester, MA 01608
(617) 799-4406

Where to Buy

New York auction houses selling twentieth-century American drawings:

Christie's
502 Park Avenue
New York, NY 10022
(212) 546-1179

William Doyle
175 East 87th Street
New York, NY 10028
(212) 427-2730

Phillips
406 East 79th Street
New York, NY 10021
(212) 570-4859

Sotheby's
1334 York Avenue
New York, NY 10021
(212) 472-3551

Dealers:

BOSTON
Vose Galleries
238 Newbury Street
Boston, MA 02116
(617) 536-6176

CHICAGO
Joseph Faulkner Mainstreet Gallery
620 North Michigan Avenue
Chicago, IL 60611
(312) 787-3301

HOUSTON
Meredith Long Gallery
2323 San Filipe Street
Houston, TX 77019
(713) 523-6671

LOS ANGELES
Jack Rutberg Fine Arts
357 North La Brea Avenue
Los Angeles, CA 90036
(213) 938-5222

NEW YORK
Berry-Hill Galleries
743 Fifth Avenue
New York, NY 10022
(212) 371-6777

Coe Kerr Gallery
49 East 82nd Street
New York, NY 10028
(212) 628-1340

Graham Gallery
1014 Madison Avenue
New York, NY 10021
(212) 535-5767

Hirschl & Adler
21 East 70th Street
New York, NY 10021
(212) 535-8810

Kennedy Galleries
40 West 57th Street
New York, NY 10019
(212) 541-9600

Ira Spanierman
50 East 78th Street
New York, NY 10021
(*212*) *879-7085*

Richard York
21 East 65th Street
New York, NY 10021
(*212*) *772-9155*

PHILADELPHIA

Frank Schwartz & Son
1806 Chestnut Street
Philadelphia, PA 19103
(*215*) *563-4887*

SANTA FE, N.M.

Santa Fe East
200 Old Santa Fe Trail
Santa Fe, NM 87501
(*505*) *988-3103*

WASHINGTON

Adams Davidson Gallery
3233 P Street, NW
Washington, DC 20007
(*202*) *965-3800*

15

AMERICAN ART POTTERY

DURING THE LATE NINETEENTH AND EARLY TWENTIETH CENTURIES, A BAND OF remarkable American potters created powerful new forms with bold, swirling, undulating lines, often in gemlike tones. This was Arts and Crafts pottery, meant more for thoughtful contemplation than for daily use.

Like those in the Arts and Crafts movement who worked with furniture and metalware, these potters rebelled against mass-produced, ornate Victorian styles. They celebrated the magic of things made with skilled hands. While these potters were scattered around the country, they were not rustic. They achieved sophisticated designs as well as decoration, a considerable advance from Early American rural artifacts like redware.

A few examples of Arts and Crafts pottery have reached sophisticated prices, but most fine pieces are under $1,000. Prices are much less than you would pay for the more fashionable Art Nouveau material of the same period.

Highly Finished, Realistic Pottery

American art pottery started with two enterprising Midwestern women, Mary Louise McLaughlin and Maria Longworth Nichols. Inspired by European and Japanese designs, they built a Cincinnati firm called Rookwood Pottery in 1880. The earliest pieces were plain within a matte glaze—a dull finish. Their mature style featured mostly straightforward, carefully molded forms with colorful underglaze decoration: flowers, seascapes, landscapes, birds, animals, human figures. They used a glossy so-called high glaze and achieved subtle gradations of color. Most pieces are vases or ewers. Rookwood won international acclaim and a gold medal at the 1889 World's Fair in Paris.

Rookwood attracted first-class pottery decorators from around the world. The factory produced work in almost a dozen styles simultaneously, and it is easily the best hand-painted pottery available.

Though Rookwood represents handcraftsmanship, its easy-to-understand realistic designs and meticulous finish have the widest appeal of any Arts and Crafts pottery. Rookwood is almost Victorian in style, and people who like it do not necessarily like other Arts and Crafts pottery.

Colorful, highly decorated pieces tend to bring more money than plain ones. Similarly, the glaze has an impact on price—a sea-green vase might bring twice the price of a brown glaze. A lightly decorated, 6-inch-high brown Rookwood jug, 1903, might sell for $150–$250.

Subject too makes a difference. Good portraits on the pottery sell for $4,000–$6,000. Indians are a popular subject, and some rare Indian designs have sold for more than $10,000. You will find some wonderful buys if you prefer flowers—vases decorated with them bring $1,000–$1,500.

Hard-core collectors seek the work of certain Rookwood artists who signed their pieces on the bottom. The most highly valued names include Indian painter Frederick Laurence; Albert Valentien, a meticulous flower painter; Edward Hurley, a landscape artist; and especially Kataro Shirayamadeni, esteemed for his striking clay bodies and floral decoration. A 12-inch vase floral-decorated by one of these could be worth $2,500–$3,500. A rare vase signed by Maria Longworth Nichols herself, 1882, could fetch $5,000–$7,000.

Artus Van Briggle worked at Rookwood, and after studying in Paris he moved to Colorado for his health and produced art pottery there. His work reflected the European Art Nouveau style, emphasizing shapely curved bodies rather than decoration as at Rookwood. He molded it in low relief—stylized flowers or figures covered with matte glazes. Included are various greens, turquoise and rose. A 13-inch cylindrical vase molded with flowers and decorated with turquoise glaze, *circa* 1906, would sell for $400–$600. A 7-inch-diameter bowl, molded with flowers and decorated with a dark-green glaze, *circa* 1905, brings $400–$600.

Pieces from the Weller Company, Zanesville, Ohio, are similar to Rookwood. However, the pieces are signed "Weller" on the bottom, so it is easy to distinguish them. A 15-inch shouldered cylindrical Weller vase with dark-red flowers against a gray ground, *circa* 1905, would be worth $400–$600. An unusual 36-inch bulbous vase having a tall waisted cylindrical neck, painted with flowers and foliage against a brown ground, might bring $800–$1,200.

The Wildest Shapes

George Ohr, the "Mad Potter" of Biloxi, Mississippi, worked from 1883 to 1909 creating strange ruffled shapes, imaginative variations of traditional forms. Even his handles are unusual. His work exploded with color. His repertoire included a bright palette of pinks, reds and yellows along with olive, khaki and black.

A painstaking craftsman, the white-bearded Ohr involved himself in the whole process. He began by gathering his own clay around the Tchoutibuffe River. He threw pots, fired them, glazed them and sold them. He had just one assistant. By contrast, Rookwood was a factory where some people designed the pieces, others prepared the clays, still others molded them, and a separate crew attended to firing and finishing. Thus Ohr's work reflects greater unity between the decorator and the pot. He never lets you forget that clay is his medium. He punched out wild shapes that are virtually impossible with a molded process. They bear his personality, sometimes even his fingerprints. Ohr's work has a timeless appeal that extends to collectors of contemporary art, whereas most other Arts and Crafts pottery collectors tend to be absorbed in the style of that period.

Very few of Ohr's large pieces come on the market. Most are smaller than what you will find from other potters. For instance, a 6-inch mug with two bulging sections, a crimped handle and a streaky olive-mustard and dark-brown glaze, *circa* 1900, which would sell for $500–$800. Or a 9-inch bulbous vase with a waisted neck, double handles, an olive-green glaze flecked with gray, *circa* 1900, which brings $2,500–$3,500. A ruffled 7-inch-diameter bowl, brown and green glaze flecked with brown, *circa* 1900, is worth $250–$400.

Elegant Organic Forms

William Grueby, Revere, Massachusetts, produced what some collectors consider the most elegantly designed Arts and Crafts pottery. It has clean, formal lines and is decorated with a matte glaze—mostly green with some yellow, tan and brown.

Grueby formed his own company in 1892 and won honors at expositions in France, Italy and Russia as well as the United States. His production of wares seems to have stopped around 1911, when he ran out of money. While he did have a factory, it was closer to the Arts and Crafts ideal than was Rookwood. At most, three people worked on a Grueby pot, compared to about fifteen on a Rookwood pot.

Grueby's potters understood they were dealing with clay, and they exploited the plasticity of clay in their designs. Thrown on a wheel, the clay was fashioned into flowing plant forms. A fine Grueby pot looks just as if it were picked from your garden.

Among his appealing works is a 7-inch-diameter bowl, 1893–1903, the sides modeled with broad tapering leaves, matte green glaze, worth about $400–$600. Or an ovoid 17-inch vase covered with orange crackle glaze, *circa* 1915, which sells for $400–$600. A 10-inch bulbous vase modeled with flat overlapping leaves, decorated in a matte green glaze, *circa* 1900, brings $1,000–$1,500. A 12-inch-high, 8-inch-wide lamp base, wide molded rim on swelled body, modeled leaf decoration, green matte glaze, might sell for $1,200–$1,600.

A Wide Range of Glazes

In 1909, a potter named William Fulper, of Flemington, New Jersey, introduced crystalline glazes quite different from the other major American potters'. Fulper colors tend to be light blues, beige, green. These, a greater variety than most other potters offered, were applied to comparatively straightforward molded forms. Fulper was interested in greater output than what was possible with hand-thrown pottery production.

His factory won numerous awards before his death in 1928, but by then he had long since adopted gaudier, more commercial wares like porcelain figures. Most desirable: Fulper pottery from their "Vase Kraft" period, 1909–10. Collectors are especially enthusiastic about Fulper pieces made in the Arts and Crafts style before about 1915.

You buy shape and glaze with Fulper pieces, for there is no painted decoration. A 13-inch ovoid vase, four handles, covered with blue crystals over a tan ground, *circa* 1910, is worth $800–$1,200. A pair of 16-inch cylindrical candlesticks on bulbous bases, covered in a brown glaze with pink and green shading, *circa* 1910, goes for $400–$600.

Louisiana Flowers

Directed by Mary Sheerer and Joseph Meyer, Newcomb Pottery opened in New Orleans, 1895, and used green, blue, black and yellow to decorate their graceful wares, which come in a handful of distinctive Newcomb shapes. Often these colors were painted over incised designs derived from magnolias, jasmine, palm trees, wild roses, water lilies and other natural forms seen around New Orleans. Entire plants were depicted, not just the blossoms. The factory reached a high point when

1

2

American Art Pottery embraces a remarkable variety of handcrafted expressive forms that appeared in the 1870s and flourished until the 1920s. While some styles were highly sophisticated, others reflected wild eccentricity. (1) An assortment of vases from Rookwood of Cincinnati, the first major American art potters. Certain painters like Kataro Shirayamadani command a premium price; he decorated the second from the left, and it is the most expensive piece shown. *Christie's, New York.* (2) Some of the eccentric designs created by George Orr of Biloxi, Mississippi. Prices range from $200 for the simple bowl on the right to $1,800 for the two-handled vase. *Christie's, New York.*

3

(3) A sampling of the abstract renderings based on natural forms, favored by potters at Newcombe College near New Orleans. Most expensive is the tallest piece in the center. 5 to 9 inches high; $500–$2,000. *Christie's, New York.*

it won Grand Prize at the Panama-Pacific International Exposition in 1915. Pottery production slowly died out during the 1920s.

A 5-inch Newcomb bowl, four handles, carved with yellow-and-white jonquils against a blue ground, *circa* 1915, would be worth $400–$600. A 6-inch cylindrical vase with a tapering neck, carved with stylized flowers, light- and dark-blue matte glaze, brings $350–$450. An 8¼-inch-high cylindrical vase with tall blue-green leaves and yellow-centered pink flowers on a blue ground sells for $350–$450.

How to Evaluate American Art Pottery

Highly finished, realistic Rookwood pottery, as noted earlier, has the broadest appeal and commands the highest prices. A glossy finish brings more money than a comparable design in matte finish. Popular subjects by esteemed artists bring the highest prices of all, as much as $20,000. The name alone excites some collector interest.

The importance of condition varies with the potter. Since Rookwood buyers are attracted to the meticulous look, they tend to be picky about chips, flakes and cracks. A little damage here can result in a 20–50 percent loss of value.

Newcomb buyers are less concerned about condition, Grueby and Ohr buyers least of all. It is hard to find Ohr pottery in mint condition, and while this does not impair its salability, it does limit the price somewhat.

Rarity accounts for some high prices, notably the one-of-a-kind work of Adelaide Alsop Robineau. Though ranked with Arts and Crafts potters, she worked with porcelain, used dazzling crystalline glazes, and is said to have spent as much as ten thousand hours carving a single piece. She had a small output, most of which is at the Everson Museum, Syracuse, New York. Her pieces might come on the market several times a decade and sell for $15,000–$30,000. Happily, wonderful work by the potters covered here is not rare or expensive.

For More Information

Garth Clark and Margie Hughes, *Century of Ceramics in the United States, 1878–1978.* New York: Dutton, 1979.

Robert Judson Clark, *The Arts and Crafts Movement in America, 1876–1916.* Princeton, N.J.: Princeton University Press, 1972.

Paul F. Evans, *Art Pottery of the United States.* New York: Scribner's, 1974.

Ralph and Terry Kovel, *The Kovels' Collector's Guide to American Art Pottery.* New York: Crown, 1974. Generously illustrated in black and white, helpful for ceramic marks shown.

Museums

BOSTON
Museum of Fine Arts
Huntington Avenue
Boston, MA 02115
(617) 267-9300

CINCINNATI
Cincinnati Art Museum
Eden Park
Cincinnati, OH 45202
(513) 721-5204

JACKSON, MISS.
Mississippi State Historical Museum
North State and Capitol Streets
Jackson, MS 39205
(601) 354-6222

NEWARK, N.J.
Newark Museum
49 Washington Street
Newark, NJ 07101
(201) 733-6600

NEW YORK
Brooklyn Museum
188 Eastern Parkway
Brooklyn, NY 11238
(212) 638-5000

Metropolitan Museum of Art
Fifth Avenue at 82nd Street
New York, NY 10028
(212) 879-5500

PRINCETON, N.J.
Art Museum, Princeton University
Princeton, NJ 08544
(609) 452-3788

RICHMOND, VA.
Virginia Museum of Fine Arts
Boulevard and Grove Avenue
Richmond, VA 23221
(804) 257-0844

SYRACUSE, N.Y.
Everson Museum
401 Harrison Street
Syracuse, NY 13202
(315) 474-6064

WASHINGTON
Smithsonian Institution
1000 Jefferson Drive, SW
Washington, DC 20560
(202) 357-1300

WINTER PARK, FLA.
Morse Gallery of Art
133 East Welbourne Avenue
Winter Park, FL 32789
(305) 644-3686

Where to Buy

Auctions which include American art pottery are held at:

BOLTON, MASS.
Robert W. Skinner
Route 117
Bolton, MA 01740
(617) 779-5528

NEW YORK
Christie's
502 Park Avenue
New York, NY 10022
(212) 546-1181

Phillips
406 East 79th Street
New York, NY 10021
(212) 570-4830

Sotheby's
1334 York Avenue
New York, NY 10021
(212) 472-3508

Dealers who handle American art pottery:

BAYONNE, N.J.
William Clark
708 Avenue C
Bayonne, NJ 07002
(201) 858-1133

CINCINNATI
Don Treadway
Box 8924
Cincinnati, OH 45208
(513) 321-6742

LARCHMONT, N.Y.
Antonia Antiques
2078 Boston Post Road
Larchmont, NY 10538
(914) 834-4326

NEW HAVEN
ARK Antiques
266 Alden Avenue
New Haven, CT 06515
(203) 387-3754

NEW YORK
Gem Antiques
1088 Madison Avenue
New York, NY 10028
(212) 535-7399

Jordan-Volpe Gallery
457 West Broadway
New York, NY 10012
(212) 533-3900

Macklowe Gallery
982 Madison Avenue
New York, NY 10021
(212) 288-1124

Pascoe and Solomon
1122 Madison Avenue
New York, NY 10028
(212) 535-5200

Fichera & Perkins Antiques
50 University Place
New York, NY 10003
(212) 533-1430

16

ANTIQUE MAPS

MAPS CHRONICLE ROMANCE, DISCOVERY AND CONQUEST THROUGH THE ages. They help us appreciate how people gained an understanding about the world. Fine old maps can be sensational wall decorations as well, embellished with bright hand coloring and bold designs.

Oftentimes maps have influenced events. Probably Christopher Columbus would not have sailed for the New World if he had known how far away it really was—those early maps were misleading. Later maps depicted a vast, wide-open continent, dazzling visions of fame and fortune, luring untold numbers of immigrants to America.

Maps emerged bit by bit from reports by sailors, camel drivers, trappers or soldiers. Many lives were lost in the pursuit of geographical knowledge, and still more because of mistaken maps. If errors appear obvious to us now, it is intriguing to see how long ago mapmakers grasped the broad outline of things.

Great trading powers learned about new geographical discoveries first, and that is where the most advanced maps were made. The earliest Western maps were from Rome and Venice. By the late sixteenth century Antwerp was a map center, and when it was crushed under Spanish rule Amsterdam became the hub of the Dutch commercial empire. It produced the most desirable maps throughout the seventeenth century. Then we begin to see maps from France, England and America.

As a collecting field, maps are just beginning to arouse widespread interest. Nice maps are available for $500. The rarest and most important maps seldom exceed $15,000—real money, to be sure, but low compared to other major collecting fields.

Maps of America

Among the comparatively inexpensive pieces is Johann Homann's amusing get-rich-in-America map, "Nova Anglia Septentrionali Americanae implantata Anglorumque coloniis florentissima" (1759). It is a not particularly accurate rendering of the Northeast from New Jersey to the St. Lawrence River. It shows abundant land and lakes. Decoration includes deer, an Indian, a European holding a beaver pelt, tools, ships' masts. It is 19¾ by 23¾ inches and sells for $750–$1,500.

John Reid's handsome "Connecticut from the best Authorities" (1796) is an example of a map appealing to more local interest. Shown is an area called Oblong, disputed between Connecticut and New York. Colored with pastel, the map is 15 by 18 inches and is worth $300–$500.

Or there is "A New Map of Mississippi" (1850), published by Thomas, Cowperthwait & Company, a 17-by-21½-inch lithograph that shows the growth of the area—steamboat routes, canals, railroads, towns. It is worth $100–$200.

S. Augustus Mitchell was the first commercial mapmaker to publish maps of the Western United States. They are lithographs that appeared during the Gold Rush period and are generally inexpensive. For instance, "Oregon and Upper California" (1845), 15⅜ inches by 12½ inches, $400–$500. Or: "A New Map Of The State Of California, The Territories Of Oregon, Washington, Utah & New Mexico" (1856), 16 by 12¾ inches, $200–$300. In the same price range is his "Map of the States of Texas" (1852), 8⅛ by 10 inches.

Some town plans are surprisingly inexpensive. William Faden's "A Plan of the Town of Boston" (1777), for instance. It shows where English soldiers were entrenched. It is 17⅜ by 12 inches and is worth $700–$800.

But if you want the first printed plan of Washington, D.C., you will have to pay more. Pierre Charles L'Enfant's "Plan of the City of Washington" (1792), 8¾ by 11¾ inches, sells for $2,500–$3,500.

A map that reflected the fantastic search for a Northwest Passage to China was "North America," by H. Briggs, London, 1625. It shows considerable oceangoing experience with the East Coast and Mexico, no knowledge about the interior, and the prevailing theory that California was an island. This is 11¼ by 11¼ inches, black and white, and is worth $2,000–$3,000.

Dutch cartographers made beautiful maps. The first map depicting exclusively the Western Hemisphere was Sebastian Münster's "Novae Insulae" (1544). It shows a distorted but recognizable profile of South America, a rough approximation of North America's East Coast, and the Gulf of Mexico. People had no idea of the vast North American interior, as the map shows. Münster speculated that India was just a stone's throw away from North America. This is a woodcut, 10 by 13¼ inches, worth $5,000–$6,000. Later French and German editions can be had for $2,000–$3,000.

Spanish explorers penetrated Florida, Central America and South

America, and the Dutchman Ortelius (Abraham Oertel) gained access to the findings. They are depicted in "Americae sive Novi Orbis," a map of the Americas published in his *Theatrum Orbis Terrarum* (1570–75), the first modern world atlas. The North American interior was unknown, but its vastness was beginning to be appreciated. The map is a hand-colored engraving 15½ by 21½ inches, worth $6,500–$7,500. Subsequent editions, issued until 1612, introduce new details, particularly about South America, and there is somewhat more decoration. They are worth about as much as the original edition.

By the end of the seventeenth century, France had become a major power, and French cartographers were coming into their own. For instance, there are maps by Guillaume Delisle that reveal discoveries by French explorers in the Mississippi Valley. A first state (print parlance for first edition) of such works as "Carte du Méxique et de la Floride des Terres Angloises" (1703) and "Carte de la Louisiane de Cours de Mississippi" (1718), 19 by 26 inches, is quite rare, and if you stumble upon one you will pay $9,000–$10,000 for it. Second states are very nearly as beautiful, fetching $4,000–$6,000.

As France and England struggled for control of North America, mapmakers were enlisted to press the claims of their side. An Edinburgh-trained botanist and physician named John Mitchell produced "A Map of the British and French Dominions in North America" (1755) which tilted things toward the English and in the process became perhaps the most important map of America. It consists of thirty-two sections which form a whole 53 by 76 inches. It would be worth $8,000–$10,000.

European and Asian Maps

Since people are most interested in their own locality, maps depicting foreign countries tend to be good buys in the United States.

For instance, the Dutchman Jodocus Hondius bought plates from the heirs of Gerard Mercator, who, during the late sixteenth century, had established the convention of depicting longitude lines as parallel. Mercator's famous maps were based on a grid of squares. This resulted in tremendous distortion of large areas like a world map, but not small areas. Jodocus reprinted Mercator's atlas many times during the early seventeenth century—initially in Latin, then in French, German, Dutch and English. The maps are detailed and attractive. His map of "Asia" (1611), 14⅞ by 18⅜ inches, is worth $900–$1,200. Remarkably detailed, it extends from Japan to the Mediterranean, from the North Pole to Australia.

For $400–$600 there are numerous maps of specific regions like

"Gallaecia Regnum" (1611), Spain's northwest coast. It is 14⅜ by 16⅜ inches. Or "Lucerner See" (1611), showing northeast Switzerland, 14 by 18¾ inches. Or "Bourbonois Borbonium Ducatus" (1611), which depicts central France near Moulins and Vichy, with castles, churches and towns.

There is a charming map of the Holy Land by the Dutchman Willem Blaeu, illustrating events from the Old Testament, with good contemporary color, 1629, 15 by 19½ inches, worth $1,000–$1,500.

World Maps

World maps provided spectacular openings for atlases. Since everybody can find some interest in world maps, they are the most popular and expensive.

While Gerard Mercator's famous world map (1569) is extremely rare—only four survivors known—you can find copies of appealing maps by his friend and traveling companion Ortelius. For instance, there is one from the first modern world atlas, Ortelius' "Typus Orbis Terrarum" (1570, 1587). It is an ornately decorated oval projection 13½ by 20 inches, black and white or color, worth $6,000–$9,000.

Or there is the Dutchman Jan Jansson's "Nova Totius Terrarum" (1641), 15¼ by 21½ inches, color, selling for $6,000–$8,000. This reflects Dutch exploration of the East Indies and what appears to be Australia. It is lavishly decorated, the four corners filled with portraits of ancients Julius Caesar and Claudius Ptolemy and mapmaking pioneers Gerard Mercator and Jodocus Hondius. In the seventeenth century, people believed there were only four elements—earth, air, fire and water—and they are represented along with an allegory about Indians and pictures of flowers.

Frederick de Wit created magnificent maps. An exquisitely detailed double-projection world map, "Nova Orbis Tabula" (1666), 19 by 22¼ inches, would be worth $3,000–$4,000. It is a color extravaganza decorated with scenes depicting battles, farming, ships and cavorting gods.

French refinement in mapmaking, by the late seventeenth century, can be seen in the work of Nicolas Sanson, royal mapmaker, and his son-in-law Hubert Jaillot. They did "Mappe-Monde" (1691), an engraved, colored double-projection map that reflects flamboyant French taste. It is an unusually large map for the time at 25 by 36¼ inches, worth $7,000–$9,000.

Louis Renard's "Nova Totius Terrarum Obris Tabula" (1739) is a double-projection map decorated in the corners with images of war,

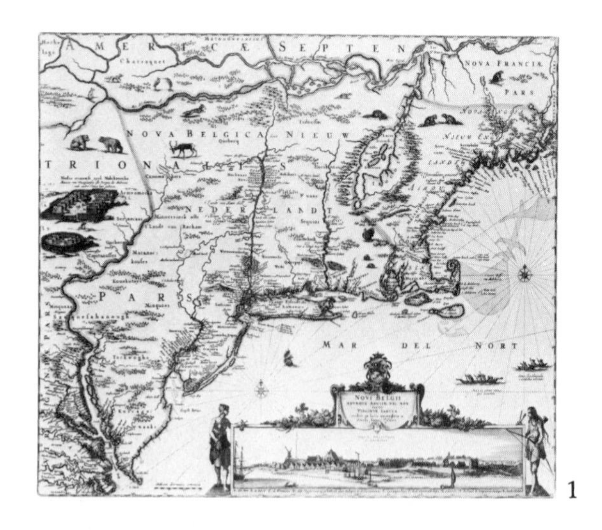

1

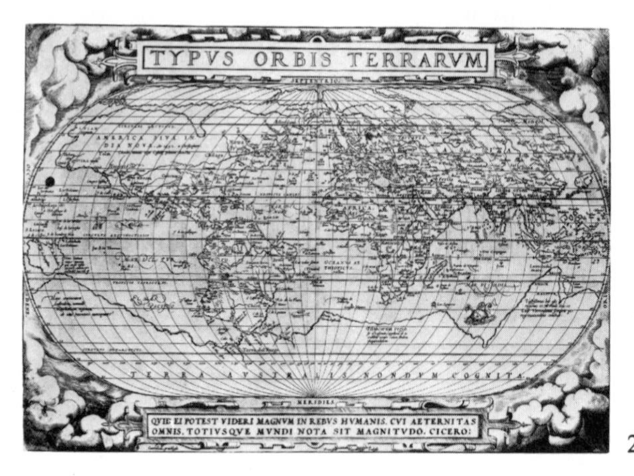

2

There is romance, adventure and beauty in fine antique maps. Since comparatively few collectors have discovered the often slavishly decorated maps still available, prices are surprisingly low. (1) One of the early maps of New England by the Dutch cartographer Justus Danckers, first issued in 1655. 18⅜ × 21¼; $1,500–$2,000. *W. Graham Arader III.* (2) A world map by the Dutch cartographer Abraham Ortelius, issued in 1570 and reissued many times. This is from 1587, the earliest world atlas published with an English text. 14¼ × 19½; $6,000–$8,000. *W. Graham Arader III.*

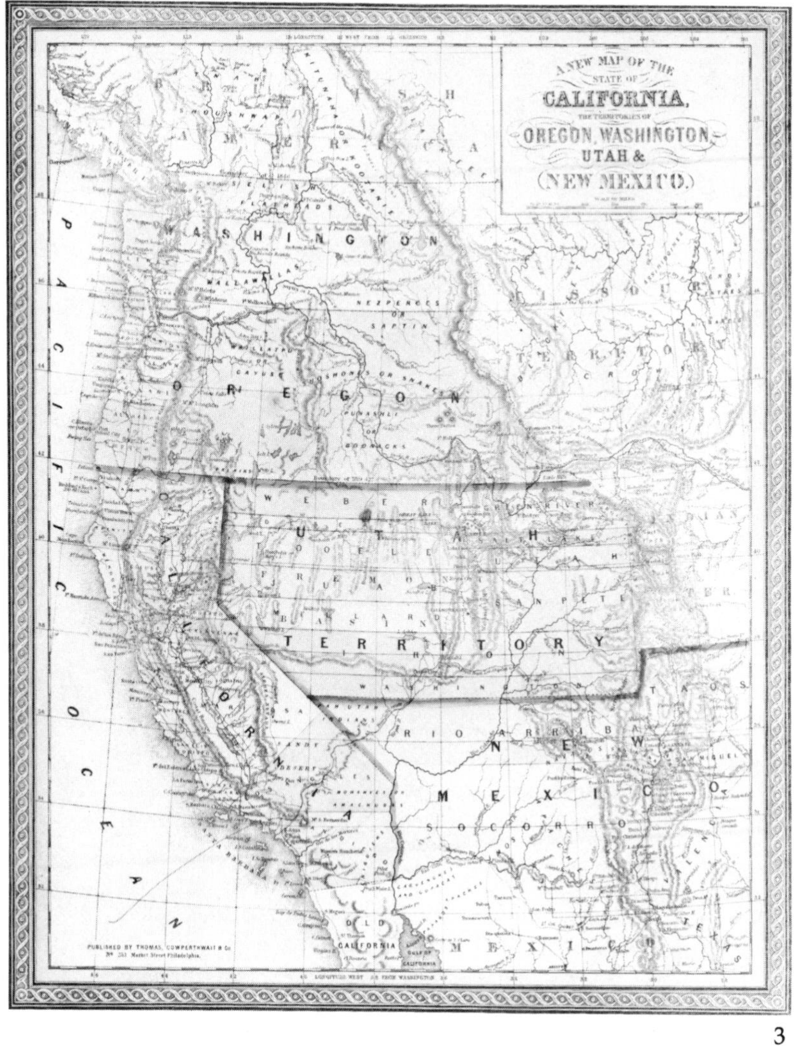

3

(3) A map of the American West, circa 1850, by S. Augustus Mitchell, a prolific Philadelphia cartographer. 16 × 12½; $300–$500. *W. Graham Arader III.*

agriculture and commerce. It is 19 by 22 inches and sells for $3,000–$4,000.

How to Evaluate Maps

The story a map tells is the most important single factor affecting value—perhaps 50 to 80 percent of the price. Collectors pay a premium for maps that reflect the latest knowledge gained from traders, explorers and surveyors. A map might be old, say seventeenth century, but if it was fifty years out of date when it was made collectors would be inclined to pass it by. Early world maps, the first map of America, maps that track the rise and fall of empires, maps about the opening of the American West—these are the ones collectors covet.

As you might expect, they favor maps with national or local interest. English collectors go for maps of England, West German collectors for maps of Germany, Americans for maps of America. Consequently, currency fluctuations affect the interest of English collectors, for instance, in maps offered by American dealers.

Many people trade off some historical importance for decorative features such as elaborate borders, a title enclosed in a scrolled cartouche, handsome calligraphy or bright colors.

Some condition problems like fading cannot be fixed. Others, like tears, foxing (mold discoloration) and stains, are repairable. Since there are many variables involved, the outcome depends on the individual case and who works on it. Some paper conservators are magicians, while others can make the problems worse. Until you have seen firsthand what a particular conservator can do, avoid maps with obtrusive condition problems.

Other things being equal, rarity means more money. The older the map, the more of its kind were lost, and thus it is worth more. Oddly enough, many nineteenth-century maps are rarer than seventeenth-century maps, and you can find rarities with little historical or decorative value.

For More Information

Tony Campbell, *Early Maps.* New York: Abbeville Press, 1981. Folio-size, mostly spectacular illustrations.

Seymour I. Schwartz and Ralph E. Ehrenberg, *The Mapping of America.* New York: Harry Abrams, 1980. Most comprehensive single book on the subject.

R. V. Tooley, *Maps and Map-Makers*. New York: Crown, 1978. Hard to use, but still a basic reference on early mapmakers.

———, *Landmarks of Mapmaking*. New York: Abbeyville Press, 1976. Good folio-size history of mapmaking, with 350 illustrations.

Richard Van de Gohm, *Antique Maps for the Collector*. New York: Macmillan, 1972. Good overview, limited amount of specific information.

John Noble Wilford, *The Mapmakers*. New York: Knopf, 1981.

Museums

Maps tend to be found at libraries rather than at art museums. The Special Libraries Association publishes *Map Collections of the United States and Canada* (third edition 1978), 745 listings. For a copy, send $19.75 to the association at 1035 Park Avenue South, New York, NY 10003. Phone: (212) 477-9250. Meanwhile, here are some major collections:

ARLINGTON, TEXAS
Cartographic Collection
University of Texas Library
Box 19497
Arlington, TX 76019
(817) 273-3391

BERKELEY, CALIF.
Bancroft Library
University of California
Berkeley, CA 94720
(415) 642-3781

CHICAGO
Newbury Library
60 West Walton Street
Chicago, IL 60610
(312) 943-9090

DENVER
Denver Public Library
1357 Broadway
Denver, CO 80203
(303) 571-2000

MILWAUKEE
University of Wisconsin Library
2311 East Hartford Avenue
Milwaukee, WI 53211
(414) 963-4785

NEW HAVEN
Beinecke Rare Book Library
Yale University
120 Howe Street
New Haven, CT 06504
(203) 436-8438

NEW YORK
New York Public Library
Fifth Avenue and 42nd Street
New York, NY 10018
(212) 930-0800

WASHINGTON
Library of Congress
10 First Street, SE
Washington, DC 20540
(202) 287-5000

Where to Buy

Maps are auctioned by (in New York):

Christie's
502 Park Avenue
New York, NY 10022
(212) 546-1195

Phillips
406 East 79th Street
New York, NY 10021
(212) 570-4845

Sotheby's
1334 York Avenue
New York, NY 10021
(212) 472-3593

Swann Galleries
104 East 25th Street
New York, NY 10010
(212) 254-4710

Mainly, though, this is a dealer's market. Among the most active dealers:

CHICAGO

Kenneth Nebenzahl
333 North Michigan Avenue
Chicago, IL 60601
(312) 641-2711

George Ritzlin
1216 West Altgeld
Chicago, IL 60614
(312) 528-6228

Harry Stern
620 North Michigan Avenue
Chicago, IL 60611
(312) 787-4433

FORT WORTH, TEXAS

Preston Figley
2417 Winton Terrace West
Fort Worth, TX 76109
(817) 923-4535

KING OF PRUSSIA, PA.

W. Graham Arader III
1000 Boxwood Court
King of Prussia, PA 19406
(215) 825-6570

LANCASTER, VA.

Paul Roberts Stony
Route 2, Box 521
Lancaster, VA 22503
(804) 462-5741

NEW YORK

Argosy Books
116 East 59th Street
New York, NY 10022
(212) 753-4455

Old Print Shop
150 Lexington Avenue
New York, NY 10016
(212) 683-3950

Richard B. Arkway
131 Fifth Avenue
New York, NY 10003
(212) 475-6777

NORTH STONINGTON, CONN.

Jon Rosenthal
Box 67
North Stonington, CT 06359
(203) 535-3152

SAN FRANCISCO

John Howell, Bookseller
434 Post Street
San Francisco, CA 94102
(415) 781-7795

SANTA FE, N.M.
Richard Fitch
2324 Calle Halcon
Santa Fe, NM 87501
(505) 982-2939

STAMFORD, CONN.
Rocky and Avis Gardiner
60 Mill Road
Stamford, CT 06903
(203) 322-1198

TAOS, N.M.
George Robinson
Box 1231
Taos, NM 87571
(505) 758-2278

WADING RIVER, N.Y.
Richard and Jo-Anne Casten
Route 1, Little Bay Road
Wading River, NY 11792
(516) 929-6820

WEEHAWKEN, N.J.
Lou Straight
101 Maple Street
Weehawken, NJ 07087
(201) 863-9115

17

AMERICAN QUILTS

"MY WHOLE LIFE IS IN THAT QUILT," MARGUERITE ICKIS, A DEVOTED QUILT collector, recalls her great-grandmother saying. "All my joys and all my sorrows are stitched into those little pieces. When I was proud of the boys and when I was downright provoked and angry with them. When the girls annoyed me or when they gave me a warm feeling around my heart. And John too. He was stitched into that quilt and all the thirty years we were married. I tremble sometimes when I remember what that quilt knows about me."

American women expressed a lot of personality while they were making humble things to keep their families warm. These quilts reflect great resourcefulness, transforming rags into kaleidoscopic displays of color. Or the intricate sewn patterns that made plain white fabric come to life. There are whimsical designs in crazy quilts, celebrations of everyday pleasures in all kinds of quilts. You might find a touching appliqué quilt signed simply with cut-up rags, "From your friend."

You can see pride and fierce independence too. Many American women broke away from the European tradition of enclosed, formal designs where individual elements were an insignificant part of the whole. They created more open and informal designs with individual elements that stood out. These women expressed the spirit of the New World.

Quilts are hardly an unknown field anymore, but you can still buy beautiful ones for $250 to several thousand dollars. It is hard to imagine comparable dramatic wall decoration for so little money.

Patchwork Quilts

Perhaps the best-known quilts are patchwork, made by cutting odds and ends of fabric into squares, diamonds and other geometric shapes, then sewing them together to form a large design. Some patchwork quilts depicted events related to social movements, political campaigns or the opening of the West. There are stripes, overlapping circles, latticework patterns, concentric diamonds, fans. Patchwork quilts have as many as four thousand pieces—an incredible amount of workmanship. The heyday of patchwork quilting was 1775–1875.

A pieced cotton "Star of Bethlehem" quilt composed of purple, lavender, rose, green and pink patches mounted on a deep-blue background quilted with flowers and wreaths, 80 by 80 inches, sells for $600–$800. Or a pieced calico quilt, probably Pennsylvania, late nineteenth century, dark green, yellow and pink printed and solid calico patches formed into a Double Irish Chain pattern, 88 by 84 inches, is worth $800–$1,000.

Appliqué Quilts

With appliqué quilts, fabric is cut into flowers, leaves, vines and other design elements—hundreds of them—and sewn into a background fabric. Because appliqué involves curves as well as straight lines, it is more complicated than patchwork. It requires more skill and tends to be of a higher quality. Appliqué quilts were made as presents to newlyweds, family members and ministers.

An appliquéd cotton quilt, nineteenth century, a white cotton field heightened with floral quilting and appliquéd with trapunto red and green blossoms, 76 by 76 inches, would be worth $500–$700.

A fancier example: a pieced and appliquéd quilt, probably New York State, nineteenth century, with a white cotton field heightened with flower and circle quilting and mounted with trapunto red, yellow and pink flowers with green stems and leaves, the whole within a red and white sawtooth border, 83 by 80 inches, would sell for $1,500–$2,500.

Linsey-Woolsey Quilts

The so-called linsey-woolsey quilts are made of heavy wool—typically a dark color like indigo blue that will not show dirt. Designs are created by sewing directly into the wool, in a sort of sculptural relief. Since these quilts are heavy and warm, they were made mainly in cold northern areas. Many Pennsylvania German linsey-woolsey quilts were made on small looms, so two or three sections were sewn together.

A linsey-woolsey quilt, *circa* 1930, composed of rust and green patches arranged in a bar pattern, the borders in brown, the field with diamond and feather quilting, 80 by 76 inches, brings $500–$700. Or a linsey-woolsey coverlet, late nineteenth century, red, green, black, beige, pink and orange against a brown background in a Star of Bethlehem pattern, 76 by 76 inches, is priced at $1,000–$1,500.

White-Work Quilts

If you like sculptural relief, you might consider white-work quilts, known also as trapunto quilts. Two pieces of fabric were sewn together—cotton on top and cotton or linen on the bottom. Then fine stitching created designs like cornucopias, flowers, plumes, which were filled in with cotton, creating a sculptural effect. These quilts are scarce, but, since cotton is more durable than wool or silk, they tend to be in good condition.

A white quilt, the white cotton field heightened with quilting in the form of large leaves on a cube-quilted background, 80 by 80 inches, brings $200–$300. An all-white bride's coverlet, probably New Jersey, *circa* 1820, white cotton field stitched with a center star outlined with a border of flowerheads and scrolls bordered with tulips and swags, fringe border, 78 by 76 inches, sells for $500–$700.

Embroidered Quilts

Embroidered quilts are available in a rich variety of delicate designs, thanks to the many techniques of crewel, cross-stitch and needlepoint. These can be quite valuable, particularly if they are older.

A rare crewel-embroidered bed cover, probably Connecticut, early nineteenth century, the white linen ground elaborately covered with yellow, blue, red, pink, green and rose wool vine, bud and floral motifs, at center a large yellow basket filled with various garden flowers within a circular border of flowers, the corners similarly stitched with baskets of flowers, the whole within a broad border of flowers, 76 by 84 inches, is priced at $3,000–$4,000.

Crazy Quilts

Crazy quilts are among the best known and most readily available types. They are made by sewing pieces of fabric together in a helter-skelter pattern. They are the most primitive kinds of quilts, yet these probably have the most modern feeling because of their abstract masses of color. They were particularly popular during the Victorian period.

A patchwork crazy quilt signed "Sopha Voilleau, Middletown,

Maryland," dated 1890, pink, blue, maroon, black, yellow and green satin and velvet patches, embroidered with flowers, birds, insects, children, 72 by 84 inches, sells for $600–$800.

Jacquard Quilts

Probably the least expensive quilts and perhaps the least interesting are those with woven intricate repeat patterns. They are made in one, two or three colors. The weavers used a device invented around 1820 by a Frenchman named Joseph Jacquard. It fit onto a hand loom and programmed a desired pattern. Some featured a primitive rendering of objects like animals or houses. The Jacquard quilts represented a step toward mechanization.

A blue-and-white Jacquard woven coverlet, dated 1841, woven with an allover pattern of flowers and stars within an American eagle border dated in two corners, 76 by 84 inches, is worth $400–$600. A fine blue-and-white Jacquard woven coverlet, initialed "MVH," probably Pennsylvania, dated "Feb. 21, 1832," a double-woven coverlet with center seam, woven with roses and stars, border with birds perched on leaves, 88 by 80 inches, $1,000–$1,500.

Amish Quilts

Because of their distinctive dark colors and bold designs, Amish quilts, made by various techniques, are in a class by themselves. Most good ones were made in the early twentieth century through the 1930s. New ones produced for the tourist trade are not nearly as satisfying. Amish quilts tend to be of abstract design in rich dark colors.

An Amish bar quilt, *circa* 1930, composed of purple, olive green, gray and maroon synthetic fabric, quilted with tulips, cubes and wreaths, 96 by 80 inches, is worth $500–$700. Unusually early Amish quilts are worth much more: a pieced wool and cotton Amish quilt, Ohio, *circa* 1880, red, black, purple and green patches forming Double Irish Chain pattern, 80 by 80 inches, sells for $1,000–$1,500.

How to Evaluate Quilts and Coverlets

Collectors want attractive, meticulously made quilts intended for home use. They avoid the generally lower-quality quilts made for a commercial market. And while you will find many beautiful examples

1

2

Antique American quilts make stunning wall decorations, and despite rising prices during the 1970s, they remain less expensive than almost any other kind of handcrafted textile. (1) An eagle quilt pieced and appliqued from calico patches. 80 × 88; $400–$500. *Sotheby Parke Bernet*. (2) A pieced and appliqued quilt, 19th century, probably from New York State. 83 × 80; $1,500–$2,500. *Sotheby Parke Bernet*.

of twentieth-century quilts, earlier ones tend to be more inventive. Later examples, by comparison, are often more repetitive, less interesting and less valuable.

Since collectors crave any documentation that links a quilt to its maker and surroundings, a signature can multiply the price manyfold. A pieced silk signature quilt, "Adeline Harris Sears, Providence Rhode Island," *circa* 1860, with silk patches bearing the names of several dozen notable Americans would be worth over $20,000.

Of course rarity adds considerable value. A documented, good-condition eighteenth-century quilt, for instance, is rare, and good nineteenth-century signed quilts are scarce.

A quilt stored out of harm's way in a chest will bring several times more than a comparable stained quilt. Collectors, though, are willing to forgive wear in a rare older piece. You might not be able to give away a badly damaged twentieth-century quilt.

For More Information

Robert Bishop, *Quilts, Coverlets, Rugs and Samplers.* New York: Knopf, 1982.

——— and Patricia Coblentz, *New Discoveries in American Quilts.* New York: Dutton, 1975.

Phyllis Haders, *American Quilts.* New York: Warner Books, 1981.

———, *Sunshine and Shadow: The Amish and Their Quilts.* New York: Universe Books, 1976.

Marilyn Lithgow, *Quiltmaking and Quiltmakers.* New York: Crowell, 1974.

Thelma Newman, *Quilting, Patchwork, Appliqué, and Trapunto: Traditional Methods and Original Designs.* New York: Crown, 1974.

Carleton L. Safford and Robert Bishop, *America's Quilts and Coverlets.* New York: Weathervane Books, 1974.

Museums

AMBRIDGE, PA.
Old Economy Village
14th and Church Streets
Ambridge, PA 17120
(412) 266-4500

BALTIMORE
Peale Museum
225 Holiday Street
Baltimore, MD 21202
(301) 396-3523

BEDFORD, N.Y.
Museum of the Bedford Historical Society
Village Green
Bedford, NY 10506
(914) 234-9328

BOSTON
Museum of Fine Arts
Huntington Avenue
Boston, MA 02115
(617) 267-9300

CHARLESTON, S.C.
Old Slave Mart Museum
6 Chalmers Street
Charleston, SC 29401
(803) 722-0079

CINCINNATI
Cincinnati Art Museum
Eden Park
Cincinnati, Ohio 45202
(513) 721-5204

CLEVELAND
Cleveland Museum of Art
11150 East Boulevard
Cleveland, OH 44106
(216) 421-7340

CONCORD, N.H.
New Hampshire Historical Society
30 Park Street
Concord, NH 03301
(603) 225-3381

DEARBORN, MICH.
Greenfield Village and Henry Ford Museum
Oakwood Boulevard
Dearborn, MI 48121
(313) 271-1620

DEERFIELD, MASS.
Historic Deerfield
The Street
Deerfield, MA 01342
(413) 774-5581

DETROIT
Detroit Historical Museum
5401 Woodward Avenue
Detroit, MI 48202
(313) 833-1805

HARTFORD
Wadsworth Atheneum
600 Main Street
Hartford, CT 06103
(203) 278-2670

HONOLULU
Honolulu Academy of Arts
900 South Beretania Street
Honolulu, HI 96814
(808) 538-3693

LANCASTER, PA.
Pennsylvania Farm Museum of Landis Valley
2451 Kissel Hill Road
Lancaster, PA 17601
(717) 299-7556

Rock Ford
881 Rock Ford Road
Lancaster, PA 17603
(717) 392-7223

MUMFORD, N.Y.
Genesee Country Museum
Flint Hill Road
Mumford, NY 14511
(716) 538-6822

NEW LONDON, CONN.
Lyman Alyn Museum
625 Williams Street
New London, CT 06320
(203) 443-2545

NEWARK, N.J.
Newark Museum
49 Washington Street
Newark, NJ 07101
(201) 733-6600

NEW YORK
Brooklyn Museum
188 Eastern Parkway
Brooklyn, NY 11238
(212) *638-5000*

Metropolitan Museum of Art
Fifth Avenue at 82nd Street
New York, NY 10028
(212) *879-5500*

Museum of American Folk Art
49 West 53rd Street
New York, NY 10019
(212) *581-2474*

New-York Historical Society
170 Central Park West
New York, NY 10024
(212) *873-3400*

ST. LOUIS
St. Louis Art Museum
Forest Park
St. Louis, MO 63110
(314) *721-0067*

SHELBURNE, VT.
Shelburne Museum
US Route 7
Shelburne, VT 05482
(802) *985-3346*

STURBRIDGE, MASS.
Old Sturbridge Village
Sturbridge, MA 01566
(617) *347-3362*

TRENTON, N.J.
New Jersey State Museum
205 West State Street
Trenton, NJ 08625
(609) *292-6300*

WASHINGTON
Smithsonian Institution
1000 Jefferson Drive, SW
Washington, DC 20560
(202) *357-1300*

WILLIAMSBURG, VA.
Abby Aldrich Rockefeller Folk
Art Center
307 South England Street
Williamsburg, VA 23185
(804) *229-1000*

Colonial Williamsburg
Goodwin Building
Williamsburg, VA 23185
(804) *229-1000*

WILMINGTON, DEL.
Historical Society of Delaware
505 Market Street
Wilmington, DE 19801
(302) *655-7161*

WINTERTHUR, DEL.
Henry Francis du Pont
Winterthur Museum
Winterthur, DE 19735
(302) *656-8591*

Where to Buy

Auction houses offering quilts:

BOLTON, MASS.
Robert W. Skinner
Route 117
Bolton, MA 01740
(617) *779-5528*

DELAWARE, OHIO
Garth's Auctions
2690 Stratford Road
Delaware, OH 43105
(614) *362-4771*

HILLSBORO, N.H.
Richard W. Withington
Hillsboro, NH 03244
(603) 464-3232

HYANNIS PORT, MASS.
Richard A. Bourne Co.
Corporation Street on Route 28
Hyannis Port, MA 02647
(617) 775-0797

NEW YORK
Christie's
502 Park Avenue
New York, NY 10022
(212) 546-1181

William Doyle
175 East 87th Street
New York, NY 10028
(212) 427-2730

Phillips
406 East 79th Street
New York, NY 10021
(212) 570-4849

Sotheby's
1334 York Avenue
New York, NY 10021
(212) 472-3512

PHILADELPHIA
Samuel T. Freeman
1808 Chestnut Street
Philadelphia, PA 19103
(215) 563-9275

SOUTH DEERFIELD, MASS.
Douglas Galleries
Route 5
South Deerfield, MA 01373
(413) 665-2877

WASHINGTON
C. G. Sloan & Co.
715 13th Street, NW
Washington, DC 20005
(202) 628-1468

Adam A. Wechsler & Sons
905–9 E Street, NW
Washington, DC 20004
(202) 628-1281

Dealers to check:

AUSTIN, TEXAS
Antedeluvian Antiques
1002 Rio Grande
Austin, TX 78701
(512) 476-5183

BALTIMORE
Armacost-Dorsey Antiques
837 North Howard Street
Baltimore, MD 21201
(301) 383-1616

CINCINNATI
Federation Antiques
2700 Observatory
Cincinnati, OH 45208
(513) 321-2671

LAKE WIRTH, FLA.
Americana in Florida
13 North H Street
Lake Wirth, FL 33460
(305) 562-8421

NEW YORK
America Hurrah Antiques
316 West 70th Street
New York, NY 10021
(212) 535-1930

Ruth Bigel Antiques
743 Madison Avenue
New York, NY 10022
(212) 988-3116

Benjamin Ginsburg Antiquary
815 Madison Avenue
New York, NY 10021
(212) 744-1352

Janos & Ross
110 East End Avenue
New York, NY 10028
(212) 988-0407

Kelter-Malcé Antiques
361 Bleecker Street
New York, NY 10014
(212) 989-6760

George Schoellkopf Gallery
1065 Madison Avenue
New York, NY 10028
(212) 879-3672

Thomas K. Woodward
835 Madison Avenue
New York, NY 10021
(212) 988-2906

OLD WICK, N.J.

Tewksbury Antiques
Crossroads
Old Wick, NJ 08858
(201) 439-2221

PRINCETON, MASS.

Antiques and Folk Art
Box 195
Princeton, MA 01541
(617) 464-5598

SAN FRANCISCO

Esprit de Corps
900 Minnesota Street
San Francisco, CA
(415) 648-6900

TUCSON, ARIZ.

Just Us
540 Speedway
Tucson, AZ 85705
(602) 622-3607

WEST BRANCH, IOWA

Main Street Antiques
110 West Main Street
West Branch, IO 52358
(319) 643-2065

WINNETKA, ILL.

Carrow & McNerney Country Antiques
566 Cedar Street
Winnetka, IL 60093
(312) 441-7137

18

OLD MASTER AND NINETEENTH-CENTURY PRINTS

FOR SURPRISINGLY LITTLE MONEY, YOUR HOME CAN DISPLAY BEAUTIFUL OLD master prints like those in the Metropolitan Museum of Art, the Louvre and Washington's National Gallery. In this survey, you will find sleepers—printmakers to watch, points to check, opportunities to buy great prints, some for as little as $300. By contrast, the most fashionable prints now sell for $20,000, $50,000, $100,000 or more.

I have not included modern and contemporary printmakers, because their work tends to be high compared to older prints. You will find here some of the most famous printmakers who ever lived. Their diverse styles offer something for almost every taste. And you will discover an astonishing range of subject matter from romantic landscapes to poignant characters and comic situations.

Old Master as well as nineteenth-century prints tend to be much better documented than modern prints. One and sometimes several scholarly catalogs are likely to be available. To that extent, they are safer to buy than work by many twentieth-century printmakers.

How Fine Prints Are Created

Before you reach for your checkbook, make sure you know exactly what an artist's authentic work is supposed to look like. If a particular artist made engravings, an example you are considering should look like an engraving, not an etching—which would reveal it immediately as a copy by somebody else. Here is a quick review of the major printmaking processes used by artists:

Lithography offers the spontaneity of drawings as well as a rich tonal scale and solid blacks. An artist uses a waxy crayon to draw on a limestone tablet. Then it is moistened and inked. Crayon attracts the grease-based ink, and water repels it. Paper, pressed against the stone, picks up the ink. If you examine it with a ten-power pocket magnifier, you will see that it lies flat on the paper—one sign that it is a lithograph.

Relief printing produces stark abstractions. Whether they are woodcuts, metal cuts or linoleum cuts, they are black and white—no gray tones in between. Relief printing begins with a design drawn on, say, wood. Everything but the artist's lines is cut away. Cutting curved lines is difficult, so you do not see many curves. Most woodcut lines are straight and rather thick compared to the lines typical of other printing processes, and they are sunk a little bit into the paper.

Intaglio printing makes possible different kinds of abstractions. There are several widely used types of intaglio, and each involves cutting a grooved design into a metal plate, inking the plate and wiping the surface clean. This leaves ink in the grooves. Paper is moistened to make it flexible, then set across the plate and subjected to strong pressure which forces paper into the grooves so that it can pick up the ink. On close examination, you will see that intaglio lines are raised a little from the surface of the paper.

The effects vary with the method used to cut the grooves. An engraver uses a tool called a burin which has a square or lozenge-shaped tip that is pushed into the metal plate. More muscle power produces a wider, deeper, swelling line. As pressure is relaxed, the line tapers off. Metal filings, known as burr, are scraped away.

Engraved lines tend to be more complex than relief-printed lines. You see many curves, for instance. Because engraving requires a disciplined hand to maintain strong, steady pressure against the metal plate, engraving developed a formal character. Pencil drawings are translated into systems of parallel lines. To suggest shading, engravers create weblike crosshatched lines. Thus engraving is not a technique for quick sketches!

Drypoint, a variation of engraving, makes possible a freer drawing style. An artist uses a steel or diamond-pointed tool to scratch lines into the metal plate. The burr is left so that it will catch ink and create lush velvety blacks. However, after about twenty prints are made, the burr wears off, and the special drypoint quality is lost.

Etching is easier, so the drawing style can be freer. You will see swirling lines and fine details. An etcher cuts through an acid-resistant coating on a metal plate. It is exposed to acid which bites grooves into the exposed metal. The edges and ends of an etched line are pitted—the work of acid. Shimmering light effects can result from the contrast between rich black lines and brilliant white paper.

Artists create soft-ground etchings to achieve the look of a crayon or pencil drawing. A metal plate is coated with a greasy, acid-resistant compound, and a sheet of paper is placed over that. Pressing down hard, an artist draws a design on the paper. When it is removed, it pulls away grease below the lines, exposing the plate. A subsequent acid bath bites grooves into it.

Smooth surfaces will not produce tones with the intaglio process, since surfaces are wiped clean of ink. But a pitted surface can reproduce tones; the more numerous and closer together the tiny indentations are, the darker the tone will be. This is the aquatint technique. A metal plate is coated with varying amounts of a porous resin, depending on the depth of tone desired. More resin translates to greater protection against acid, and lighter tones. Less resin, darker tones. Aquatints look somewhat like wash drawings or watercolors.

Silkscreen is the most impersonal process, concealing the artist's hand. A stencil is cut out, silk is secured across open areas, and ink pressed through the fabric onto print paper. Silkscreen lays down more ink than lithography, but otherwise images produced by the two processes can be confused. Silkscreen is favored by contemporary artists who work with simplified forms and large masses of color.

The First Great Printmaker

Albrecht Dürer (1471–1528) was the first great printmaker. Until he came along, the best-known prints were of men playing cards or simple religious images. Few important artists had given their major efforts to prints, because painting earned the big commissions. Though Dürer created some superb paintings, drawings and watercolors, he achieved fame with his prints, which displayed extraordinary virtuosity.

Born in Nuremberg, Dürer was the son of a goldsmith and from him acquired a disciplined hand. He apprenticed as an engraver decorating table silver. But inspired by certain prints he had seen, he resolved to pursue graphic art. He began creating woodcut book illustrations in 1486. For nearly a decade, he gained proficiency at small, flat religious book illustrations in the Gothic style.

Then his restless curiosity led him to Italy, where he learned perspective and figure modeling, the techniques of Renaissance realism. Suddenly, his woodcuts grew larger—up to about 16 by 11 inches. They became much more complex and vivid. They teemed with swine-faced devils, avenging angels, fierce knights, suffering saints and seven-headed monsters—grotesque nightmare visions that the medieval imagination seemed to thrive on.

Dürer reached a peak with his *Apocalypse* series (sixteen woodcuts), 15½ by 11⅛ inches, and *The Great Passion* (seven woodcuts), 15⅝ by 11⅛ inches, done during the years 1496–1500. After that, his name became a household word.

Individual prints from these series can run $2,000–$3,000. Crisp, clear early impressions—without the revisions an artist tends to introduce into later impressions—sell for as much as $5,000–$7,000. Also, collectors pay higher prices because Dürer both designed and cut the wood for these images, whereas in other woodcuts he turned over the actual cutting to assistants. Such prints are not really any less beautiful, though. He approved the work.

Altogether Dürer created about 250 woodcuts; the later ones were more finely drawn. By 1510 they looked like engravings, and although they were more sophisticated, they lost some of the stark abstract quality so appealing in his earlier work. Because woodcuts are more durable than engravings, more good woodcuts survive, and they are lower priced. You can buy an early-impression smaller woodcut, 5 by 4 inches, for under $1,000.

Meanwhile, Dürer created 105 engravings which tend to sell in the $3,000–$5,000 range if they are early impressions. These blossomed with lively detail. Since it is easy for an engraver to make crosshatched lines that simulate tone, Dürer's engravings became more realistic. They were no longer simply black lines against a white background.

Most of the engravings were about 4½ by 2¾ inches. His larger images—about 9⅞ by 7⅝ inches—include his most famous: *Adam and Eve* (1514), *Saint Jerome in His Study* (1514) and *Melencolia I* (1514). As comparatively secular subjects, these are among his most widely appealing, sought-after work, by no means underpriced, unless you are comparing them to the six-figure prices realized by Picasso, Edvard Munch and other twentieth-century printmakers. Early impressions can sell in the $10,000–$30,000 range.

Callot's Colorful Characters

In Jacques Callot's great etching *The Fair at Impruneta,* children play, women gossip, men fight, families feast, showmen display snakes, couples dance, beggars beg, and local officials conduct a hanging. Comedy goes with tragedy. Here, as in 1,428 other etchings, Callot (1592–1635) expressed tolerance and sympathy for a mixed-up, troubled world.

He was born in Nancy, France, amid pomp and ceremony. His father, Jean Callot, who was master of ceremonies for Charles III, Duke of Lorraine, staged pageants, tournaments, funerals and celebrations. It is no wonder that Jacques Callot became fascinated with dramatic gestures.

He apprenticed as an engraver for precious metals and learned how to create engravings. He reportedly ran away from home, joined some gypsies and traveled to Rome, then to Florence. He pored through its art treasures. Under Giulio Parigi, an artist who staged fireworks displays, Callot mastered engraving and etching. Before long the powerful Medici family became his patrons.

He introduced a technique that revolutionized etching. Until then, a waxy compound was used to coat metal plates, but it cracked and flaked off, often ruining plates before they were etched. This discouraged artists from attempting really ambitious etchings. Callot replaced wax with a hard varnish, freeing artists to create whatever they wanted.

He created scenes of everyday life around Florence (fifty etchings), 2¼ by 3½ inches, and a series of animated figures ranging from bandits to violinists (twenty-one etchings). He created the picturesque *Medici Landscapes* (ten etchings), 4⅜ by 9¾ inches, as well as *The Fair at Impruneta*, 16½ by 24¼ inches. *Impruneta*, one of his most popular images, can sell for $8,000–$12,000.

Callot was bewitched by the Italian improvisational street theater—*commedia del l'arte*. It involved satire, singing, juggling, dancing and gymnastics. Some of Callot's most memorable etchings recreate colorful characters from the *commedia del l'arte*—twenty-four altogether. With elongated noses, weird masks, baggy costumes and majestic hat plumes, they strut and posture as if on a great stage. A set of these, 2½ by 3⅜ inches each, can be had for $2,000–$3,000.

Natural death, assassination and mismanagement left Medici affairs in disarray, and Callot's patronage ended after nine years. He returned to Nancy in 1621 and found it impoverished by political infighting and war. This shocked him into producing *The Gypsies* (four etchings), 4¾ by 9¼ inches, $3,000–$4,000 for a good set. *The Beggars* (twenty-five etchings), 6 by 3¾ inches, sells for $3,000–$4,000. *Grotesque Dwarfs* (twenty-one etchings), 2½ by 3 inches, is priced at $2,000–$3,000. These characters do not begin to fulfill Renaissance notions of classical beauty, but they are marvelous, spirited creations. With an inspired line, Callot filled facial expressions, gestures and folds of fabric with captivating individuality.

In 1633 Callot created an eloquent antiwar broadside, *The Miseries of War* (eighteen etchings). They are about 3 by 7 inches and, in a fine early impression, can bring $8,000–$10,000 for the set, or $700–$1,000 individually. He did another *Miseries of War* (six etchings) in a smaller format, 2 by 4 inches, worth $1,500–$2,500 for the set. These etchings show soldiers plundering a farmhouse and burning a village. Trees choke with hanging bodies. A stagecoach is stopped, the passengers murdered. By choreographing his figures like an exquisite ballet, Callot underscored the horror of people kidnapped, raped, tortured and burned at the stake.

During his last years, Callot created little religious images like *The Life of the Virgin* (sixteen etchings), 1¾ by 2⅜ inches, *Small Apostles* (sixteen etchings), 2⅞ by 1⅞ inches, *Life of the Prodigal Son* (eleven etchings), 2⅜ by 3¼ inches, *The New Testament* (ten etchings), 2⅝ by 3¼ inches. These sets can sell for $500–$700.

His masterpiece was *The Temptation of Saint Anthony*, 7⅛ by 11¾ inches, showing a caldron of spiky, fire-breathing devils obsessed with inflicting pain. It seems to suggest where all the wars will lead. A fine early impression can sell for $10,000–$12,000.

Since Callot made etchings only, and they were enormously popular, large editions were printed. The plates became worn during his lifetime. Moreover, the plates survived into the eighteenth century, when more prints were made. A late impression of *The Temptation of Saint Anthony* might run $750, and it would not provide much of a thrill. Quality is crucial for your enjoyment of this gifted, versatile artist.

Dutch Treats

During the seventeenth century, English travelers were surprised to discover that Dutch butchers, bakers, blacksmiths and cobblers decorated their homes with art. Unparalleled prosperity, thanks largely to religious toleration and free enterprise, brought some beauty as well as comfort to the lives of ordinary people perhaps for the first time. The tiny Dutch Republic supported an incredible two thousand artists who created 200,000 paintings plus large numbers of drawings and prints.

Many Dutch people turned away from the melodramatic religious art favored by Catholic aristocrats and Church officials. The Dutch wanted a sympathetic view of the world around them. Among the most charming, intimate creations were landscape etchings. These began with direct observation, the empirical spirit that triggered a burst of Dutch discoveries in medicine, physics, astronomy. Dutch artists worked from sketches and often combined their observations into neat, tidy compositions that suited the Dutch character. Because much fine work is still available, and buyers pay a premium for famous names, you can acquire Dutch landscape etchings by lesser-known artists for under $1,000, sometimes as little as $200.

Early Dutch landscape etchings reflect the influence of Flemish art—a stylized look and interest in details. For instance, Claes Jansz Visscher (1587–1652) created some two hundred landscapes filled with people, buildings and animals. Many of his early etchings, before about 1610, were based on designs by other artists. Working around Haarlem and Amsterdam, Visscher used carefully drawn parallel lines to build his images. They have the formality of engravings. Visscher became an important publisher of prints, maps and topographical views too. His work, 4 by 6¼ inches, can be had for $100–$500.

With a detailed, formal engraving style, Jan van de Velde (1593–1641), a native of Rotterdam, achieved tonal effects like paintings. Both day and evening scenes feature dramatic shadows. Until around 1615 he executed his own designs, but increasingly after that he turned to the drawings of other artists. Altogether he etched about two hundred landscapes, available for $200–$1,000. His images were 5⅛ by 8 inches. The highest prices go for his series on the seasons, 10⅝ by 14 inches.

Herman van Swanevelt (1600–1655) was among the Dutch artists who sought inspiration abroad. Born in Woerden, he moved to Paris by age 23, and from 1629 to 1641 lived in Rome. Some of his picturesque scenes reveal the influence of the great French landscape artist Claude Lorrain, whom he met there. Swanevelt, in turn, achieved lighting effects and even a design or two that Claude adopted. Many of Swanevelt's 116 etchings are Italianate landscapes bathed in lovely, hazy light. Prices are $200–$500. They range from 3½ by 5¾ inches to 7 by 11¾ inches.

Jan Both (1615–52) also traveled to Rome for inspiration. He stayed there from 1635 to 1641 and made eighteen etchings, mostly idealized landscapes, perhaps 10½ by 8⅛ inches. His Italianate scenes capture a feeling of early-morning light, and some scenes are accented with picturesque ruins. While Claude Lorrain peopled his landscapes with Roman or Biblical figures, Both pictured contemporary figures such as travelers. These pieces sell for $200–$500.

Simon Jacobsz Vlieger (1601–53) excelled at seascape paintings that create an enchanting sense of space over water. Yet none of his twenty etchings depict the sea. They show animals, river scenes, forests, a village street, a beach. He liked tangled, towering masses, whether trees or buildings. His images range from 3¾ by 5¾ inches to 5⅜ by 6¼ inches and are priced at $400–$600.

Anthonie Waterloo (1610–90) made his reputation as an etcher who designed over a hundred beautifully balanced, interesting compositions with a rich variety of textures. There is a lot going on in dark areas, for instance. His wild, windswept trees alone can make his etchings worthwhile. He used people and buildings more sparingly than earlier artists. Sometimes he used drypoint and engraving to add depth in shadows. His images, 4 by 4⅝ inches, sell for $400–$600.

Karel Dujardin (1622–78) grew up in Amsterdam and traveled a good deal to Paris, Rome, Venice, Tangiers. His fifty-two etchings tend to be luminous pastoral Italianate scenes with shepherds, sheep and cows. He did most of his etchings in the Netherlands, and they project a sturdy Dutch feeling. They range from 4¾ by 6 inches to 7½ by 8¾ inches and sell for $100–$400.

Allart van Everdingen (1621–75) introduced northern air to Dutch art. He traveled through Sweden and Norway for four years, then returned to work out his ideas in Alkmaar, Haarlem and Amsterdam. His approximately 160 etchings abound with rugged Scandinavian mountains, rocks, pines and waterfalls. Many etchings have delightful subtle textures. Jacob van Ruisdael, the greatest Dutch landscape artist, probably adapted northern themes from Everdingen. His images, 4 by 4¼ inches to 4 by 5¾ inches, are worth $300–$500.

Paulus Potter (1625–54) established his name for superb renderings of animals. He made cattle, sheep and horses not just a prop but the main subjects in his eighteen etchings. They are convincing and sympathetic, and few animals artists have equaled Potter. His prints, 7¼ by 8 inches to 7⅛ by 10 inches, are worth $100–$300.

Roelant Roghman (1627–92) created about forty etchings of pleasant landscapes around many Dutch towns. He used picturesque techniques such as framing a composition with trees and using lines that draw your eyes toward a distant hazy horizon. Often he used strong side lighting. His most pleasing prints fill the sheet with gnarled foliage and dramatic clouds. Measuring 5⅛ by 6½ inches to 8¼ by 10½ inches, his images can be had for $200–$300.

Because these artists were so popular, prints were made from their plates well into the eighteenth century. It is quite possible that you will find unexciting late impressions. The paper provides clues. Seventeenth-century paper tends to be thinner and more even, with more of a cream color than eighteenth-century paper. The wire lines on later paper are more widely spaced. Later impressions tend to be more contrasty because of solid blacks and whiter paper, but fine detail has worn out.

These landscape etchings provide an inexpensive means to savor the pleasures of Dutch art. It radiates a serene, straightforward self-confidence that has virtually disappeared from modern art.

Quacks, Crooks and Crazies

A blind fiddler leads the mob. People beat each other with clubs, a bear scrounges around a garbage can, a fat politician tumbles out of his chair, and a monkey fires a gun—the usual hijinks after an election.

The image is vintage William Hogarth (1697–1764) from a series called *Four Prints of an Election* (1755–58). Until this wry Englishman came along, satire usually meant cheap quickie prints about religious or allegorical subjects. Hogarth lavished great care on his work, raising it to a high level, and he dealt with contemporary situations. He inspired other artists like Henry Fielding, author of the bawdy *Tom Jones.*

Hogarth's prints are inexpensive, under $300, because they are viewed as anecdotal moral illustrations rather than fine art. They abound with esoteric allusions that do not seem worth the effort to understand. Yet Hogarth's prints offer a marvelous zoo of characters. He took a poke at greedy politicians, hypocritical clergymen, scheming merchants, windy teachers and lazy sons, as well as drunks, whores and thieves. He drew his characters with appealing gusto, and he used symbols that were mundane enough to be amusing.

Born in London, Hogarth was apprenticed to a man who engraved coats of arms and wrote decorative designs on table silver, watchcases and bookplates—boring stuff for Hogarth. After he learned how to do it, he took the daring step of breaking his apprenticeship so that he could pursue more ambitious things. In 1720 he started his own business by engraving table silver, business cards and announcements.

Hogarth dreamed of becoming an artist, and his mind turned to satire. His father, Richard Hogarth, was an English and Latin teacher, so he grew up surrounded by books. Hogarth seems to have enjoyed satires such as Jonathan Swift's *Gulliver's Travels.* His ambitions must have acquired urgency from the four years the family spent in debtors' prison—Richard Hogarth had given up teaching, opened a coffeehouse and failed.

In 1720 Hogarth flexed his muscles by making seventeen illustrations for satirist Samuel Butler's *Hudibras,* a morality play about a religious hypocrite. The illustrations are copies of designs by previous artists. Hogarth gained confidence, and every project after *Hudibras* developed from his own designs. They are 10 by 13 inches, and the set would run $100–$200.

Hogarth searched for a satirical subject and decided on the South Sea Bubble, a feverish stock speculation that impoverished many people. Other artists had the same idea, producing such engravings as *Bubble's Mirrour, England's Folly* and *Bubbler's Medley.* Although Hogarth's *South Sea Scheme* appeared in 1721, after interest had peaked, he created the most memorable image. A mob fills the streets, a clergyman flirts with a prostitute, a pickpocket preys on a teacher, Villainy flogs Honesty, locals ride a merry-go-round wheel of fortune, women line up to select husbands by lottery. His print is about 10½ by 13 inches and is worth $75–$150.

Hogarth loved gossip. From it he concocted the tale of Moll Hackabout, a poor country girl who came to London, lived with a rich businessman, contracted venereal disease, went to live in a slum and became a prostitute, went to jail, tried quack cures for her disease, and died at twenty-three. Hogarth called this story *A Harlot's Progress* and painted six pictures to illustrate it. Then he made engravings of it in 1732. They approximated the texture of paintings and proved to be very popular. The engravings are about 12 by 14½ inches, and a set of six runs $400–$600.

Hogarth is believed to have made eighty-four guineas from selling the paintings, 1,240 guineas from the engravings. According to Ronald Paulson, the scholar who wrote the catalog of Hogarth's works, Hogarth reached a larger audience than any printmaker had before. He attracted both art buffs and plain folks. But as soon as Hogarth published an engraving, other people copied it and undercut him. There were knock-offs such as *Lure of Venus, Robin's Progress, Statesman's Progress.* Hogarth wrote a passionate broadside promoting the idea of a copyright law to protect printmakers, and it passed Parliament on June 25, 1734.

Soon afterward, Hogarth began his next picture story. Called *A Rake's Progress,* it chronicled the downfall of one Tom Rakewell, an heir who rejected his father's values—work, marriage and thrift. He made a girl pregnant, squandered money on lavish quarters, orgies and booze. His money running low, he married a rich widow and then gambled away her assets, landed in jail for debt and went mad in an insane asylum. Hogarth made eight paintings; then engravings followed in 1735. These images are about 12½ by 15½ inches, and they sell for $800–$1,000.

A decade later, in *Marriage à la Mode,* Hogarth showed parents arranging the wedding of their children, a simple middle-class girl and a vain young aristocrat who do not love each other. Husband and wife squander money, pursue lovers. He is killed in a duel, while she commits suicide. His sin was to go slumming; hers, aspiring to become something she was not, a sophisticated woman of the world. *Marriage à la Mode* prints, six altogether, are about 14 by 17½ inches, and they are worth $400–$600. Hogarth added touches he hoped would win a strong following among connoisseurs. For instance, the ill-advised wedding was negotiated in a room decorated with pictures depicting cruelty and death. The young couple had bawdy pictures for pleasure, religious pictures to atone for it. The vain aristocrat died in a harlot's room with a tapestry illustrating the Biblical story of King Solomon and two harlots who claimed the same baby.

By the 1740s, Hogarth still had not achieved the success he dreamed of. Disgusted, he decided to go all-out for a popular market: more dramatic images, simplified characters, fewer esoteric allusions.

Hogarth's longest series, *Industry and Idleness,* featured two apprentices, a lazy one named Tom Idle and the saintly, hard-working Goodchild. Idle was fired, while Goodchild earned promotions, rose to full partner and married the boss's daughter. Idle began living with a prostitute in a seedy flat. He turned to robbery and murder, gambled away the loot and was betrayed by his prostitute. Idle appeared for trial before Goodchild, who had become Alderman of London. Idle was executed. Goodchild rose further to Lord Mayor of London. Hogarth published twelve plates of *Industry and Idleness* in 1747. They are about 10¼ by 15 inches and sell for $750–$1,000.

He did several shorter series. Among them: *Before and After* (1736), two prints, each about 14¾ by 12 inches; *The Four Stages of Cruelty* (1750), about 14 by 11⅝ inches; *Four Prints of an Election* (1755–58), about 15¾ by 21⅛ inches. Prices here are $100–$150 per print.

Hogarth's single prints include *Scholars at a Lecture* (1736), about 8 by 7 inches, which shows jabbering or sleeping scholars listening to a boring lecturer. *The Company of Undertakers* (1736), about 8½ by 7 inches, is a mock coat of arms, showing fifteen dopy undertakers holding escutcheons, a symbol of death; beneath are two crossbones and the motto *Et plurima mortis imago*—"And many an image of death." *Strolling Actresses Dressing in a Barn* (1738), about 16¾ by 21¼ inches, provides a backstage view of bawdy actresses who played dignified roles. In *The March to Finchley* (1750), about 16¼ by 21¼ inches, supposedly disciplined soldiers become drunk and chase women. *Beer Street* (1750), about 14 by 11¾ inches, and *Gin Lane* (1750), about 14 by 11⅞, show working people making themselves drunk and silly. The prints can be had for $100–$200 apiece.

Hogarth's most popular etching was *Simon Lord Lovat* (1746), 13 by 8¾ inches, a full-length portrait of the wily rebel who tried to rally Scots around the Stuarts, pretenders to the English throne. He is said to have sold over ten thousand prints of this image, and it is worth $100–$200 now.

Despite Hogarth's tough satire, he was a typical human being—thin-skinned. A contemporary wrote: "Hogarth, who has all his life dealt in Satire in his way, is rendered extremely unhappy by the attack on him. . . ."

If Hogarth seemed like a stern schoolmaster warning against enjoyable things in life, Thomas Rowlandson (1756–1827) was an amiable companion having a boisterous good time. His friends called him "Old Rowly." As an artist, he was pure ham. His lines dance and twirl around, creating humorous characters almost effortlessly. Drawing unleashed a burst of energy, and he relished showing off his speed.

To be sure, Rowlandson learned a few tricks from Hogarth. For instance, *Strolling Actresses Dressing in a Barn* is crowded and chaotic; Hogarth intended these qualities to convey sober meaning. Rowlandson saw opportunity for comedy. He created crowded, chaotic, funny situations over and over again.

Some scholars have dismissed Rowlandson as frivolous, but he achieved an enduring appeal, and he remains popular now. His etchings, which average 7½ by 9 inches, sell for $250–$500.

Rowlandson was born in London. His father, a merchant, lost the modest family fortune in the wool and silk trade. Apparently Rowlandson's mother died young. Thanks to a friend whose father was an actor, they had ready access to the Drury Lane and Covent Garden theaters, and Rowlandson began drawing caricatures of people he saw: actors, stagehands, musicians, people in the audience. The elegant caricatures of John Hamilton Mortimer caught Rowlandson's eye, and he refined his style after Mortimer.

By the age seventeen he was off to France, which set the fashions in European art then. He pored through prints and drawings at the Louvre as well as at the Bibliothèque Nationale. He must have loved the exuberant Rococo styles of the leading French masters, François Boucher and Jean-Honoré Fragonard, because he acquired a very French facility with his drawing.

Back in London, Rowlandson began making formal portraits of aristocrats and beautiful women, but this didn't satisfy him. He switched to rapid-fire sketches of life around him: bumbling politicians, romantic couples, prizefights, prostitutes in jail, foxhunting, gamblers at gaming tables, a bustling fish market, delicate landscapes. He turned many designs into watercolors. Like a candid cameraman, Rowlandson relished comical, off-guard moments: leering expressions, pratfalls, exposed breasts, sagging bellies, stolen kisses. He excelled at dramatic flourishes.

As early as 1774, Rowlandson started etching designs from his drawings. He did both in a spontaneous, inventive style that changed little over the years. He added colors to almost all his prints.

Beginning in 1798, Rowlandson teamed up with publisher Rudolph Ackermann. Rowlandson made the etchings, and assistants added colors according to his instructions. His etchings appeared in series such as *Loyal Volunteers of London* (1799), *The Microcosm of London*

(1808–10), *The Three Tours of Doctor Syntax* (1812–21), *The English Dance of Death* (1815–16), *The Dance of Life* (1822), *The Vicar of Wakefield* (1817), *The World in Miniature* (1821–27), *The History of Johnny Qyae Genus* (1822). One writer remarked that Rowlandson "etched as much copper as would sheathe the British navy."

Perhaps Rowlandson's best-known subjects are sporting scenes, anti-Napoleon caricatures and erotic images. Sporting scenes appeared throughout his career; the anti-Napoleon caricatures, during the Napoleonic period; erotic images, after about 1815.

Much of Rowlandson's later work is slapdash. In his haste, he drew lines that did not project character, or his proportions were not quite right. So it is especially important to evaluate individual images in his work.

Since many prints were made by various etchers after Rowlandson's watercolors, you should double-check whether a print you are interested in is by Rowlandson or an "after" that is less valuable. Exception: *Vauxhall Gardens* (1785), his most famous single image, a rare etching-aquatint by R. Pollard and F. Jukes after his exhibition watercolor, 19 by 29½ inches, of a fashionable London pleasure spot. If one of these came on the market, it would be worth many times Rowlandson's other images.

Rowlandson achieved popularity for a predictable, immediately recognizable style. Yet thanks to his mischievous spirit, he can offer you some delightful surprises in almost every image.

Piranesi's Sublime Dreams

From crumbling, overgrown ruins, Giovanni Battista Piranesi (1720–78) conjured a sublime vision: the vast, heroic, remote world of ancient Rome. Its grandeur lives through Piranesi's approximately one thousand etchings.

One of Piranesi's earliest fans was the eighteenth-century English art collector Horace Walpole. He expressed awe for

> the sublime dreams of Piranesi who seems to have conceived visions of Rome beyond what it boasted even in the meridian of its splendor. Savage as Salvator Rosa, fierce as Michael Angelo, and exuberant as Rubens, he has imagined scenes that would startle geometry, and exhaust the Indes to realize. He piles palaces on bridges, and temples on palaces, and scales Heaven with mountains of edifices. Yet what taste in his boldness! What grandeur in his wildness! What labour and thought both in his rashness and details!

Though prices for Piranesi's etchings have advanced during the 1960s and 1970s, they are still inexpensive compared to those of many lesser artists. About 95 percent of Piranesi's etchings, fine impressions, sell for less than $2,500.

Born near Venice, Piranesi learned the art of architectural drawing and traveled to Rome. Rubbish had piled up around broken columns, goats nibbled the weeds, beggars stumbled where senators used to ponder the fate of the Empire. But Piranesi saw magic. He marveled at the "exact perfection of the architectural form of the buildings, the rarity and the immeasurable quantity of marbles which are to be seen on every side in the enormous areas which were once occupied by the Circuses, the Fora and the imperial palaces. . . . These eloquent ruins filled my mind with images which no drawings, however accurate, could have expressed."

He learned etching, and at age twenty-three published a dozen etchings depicting imaginary temples, palaces, ruins and a prison. The images are competent and straightforward. Titled *Prima parte di architetture e prospettive,* the series did not sell many copies. Failure proved to be a blessing, because he landed a job with Giovanni Battista Tiepolo, the greatest Italian artist of the eighteenth century. Tiepolo created drawings, frescos and etchings with spirited lines. The experience transformed Piranesi's style, which became freer and more inventive.

Refreshed, he etched views of Rome—about one a day—for guidebooks. Included were all the tourist favorites such as St. Peter's, the Pope's Palace and the Colosseum. Piranesi scattered small, Callot-like figures around his images to help dramatize the large scale of the buildings. Fausto Amidei, a Roman bookseller, published 108 of Piranesi's etchings together with etchings by other artists in a volume called *Varie vedute di Roma antica e moderna.* They are about 4½ by 7 inches. Amidei republished this work three years later. A man named Jean Bouchard issued it again sometime afterward as *Raccolta di varie vedute di Roma,* and certain images appeared in other guidebooks until the plates wore out.

In 1748 Piranesi published twenty-five of his etchings in *Antichità romane de' tempi della repubblica, e de' primi imperatori.* Included were views of Rome and other sights he had encountered on his travels. To dramatize further the large scale of antiquities, Piranesi selected the lowest possible viewing angles. Often he dug a hole so that he could work below ground level. When Piranesi republished the series in 1765, he gave it a new title: *Alcune vedute di archi trionfali ed altri monumenti.* It is referred to as *Archi trionfali.* The images are about 10½ by 5 inches, and a complete set sells for about $7,500 ($300 per etching).

Piranesi's longest series was *Vedute di Roma,* 133 etchings issued over several years. In 1751 he published the first thirty-four in *Le magnficenze di Roma,* an omnibus volume that included etchings from *Archi trionfali,* enlarged etchings from *Prima parte,* four wild romantic images known as *Grotteschi,* and his etchings which depict vast imaginary prisons—*Carceri.* The book failed, because people preferred to select a few images of tourist attractions; they did not want a large number of them, and they didn't want Piranesi's imaginary scenes.

The *Vedute* themselves are an impressive size: about 21½ by 16 inches to 18¾ by 27⅝ inches. Later *Vedute,* issued during the 1760s, have deeper shadows, angular clouds. The popularity of a subject affects the price, which ranges from $1,000 to $2,000. People pay more for famous sights like St. Peter's.

The *Grotteschi* are an abstract tangle of bushes, vines, snakes, broken cornices, columns and sculpture. Stone heads have piercing eyes that seem to suggest the spirit of the Roman Empire surviving amidst the ruins. The *Grotteschi* etchings are 15⅜ by 21¼ inches. Prices range from $2,000 to $2,500.

Least wanted during Piranesi's lifetime were the fourteen etchings from *Invenzioni capric de carceri*—images of imaginary dungeons. First published in 1750, they have become his most famous, most expensive work. They show staircases that zigzag into the unknown, walkways that go nowhere, instruments of torture, immense stone walls and arches that dwarf the small figures wandering about aimlessly. The images suggest catacombs of Byzantine complexity. They look like spectacular movie sets that Cecil B. De Mille might have created. A decade later, Piranesi reworked the plates, making them darker and more forbidding. Compared to the scarce 1750 impressions which sell for $7,000–$10,000, fine impressions from his reworked plates run $3,000–$6,000. *Carceri* prints were made long after Piranesi's death, and worn nineteenth-century impressions are worth less than $1,000.

When Piranesi etched antiquities a second or third time, he moved closer, lower than before. He exaggerated perspective. His later images have a commanding presence. However, some later *Vedute* reflect haste perhaps resulting from pressures to satisfy brisk demand. During the 1770s, shadows, foliage and stone details did not always benefit from the same loving attention as in his earlier work.

Piranesi looked south for fresh inspiration, to the three Greek temples of Paestum, built in the fifth century B.C. about sixty miles below Naples. He did eighteen etchings of them, rich with lovely details, before he died. Two more etchings were finished and signed by his son, Francesco. The *Paestum* etchings are about 19 by 27 inches. Though they are gaining popularity, they can still be had for about $1,000.

Piranesi surprised many tourists, who discovered that his etchings were more appealing than real scenery because he provided an inspired interpretation. "I need to produce ideas on a grand scale," he wrote. "I think if someone asked me to design a new universe, I'd be mad enough to undertake the task."

Goya Fights Back

Sudden deafness transformed Francesco José de Goya y Lucientes (1746–1828) from a competent Spanish-royal-court painter to a great master. Deafness turned him inward, away from polite society. Like nobody else before, he looked the world in the eye and spoke his mind. He saw hypocrisy, cruelty and stupefying ignorance all around him, and he fought back with blistering prints. They were his banner of hope. When he saw people struggling to preserve their humanity, he celebrated their quiet heroism.

At forty-six, an age when most artists have settled into a comfortable routine, he injected fresh life into etching. He was the first to show what aquatint could really do, and when lithography came along he was the first to master it.

Major art movements like Impressionism, Expressionism and Surrealism thrived on scraps of his ideas. He expressed visceral feelings, discarding unessential details. He captured the malaise of the modern world with strange distorted symbols involving goblins, demons, witches.

Because Goya's images can be hard to understand, they are an acquired taste. Considering their importance and expressive power, they are remarkably inexpensive—less than $3,000 in most cases.

Goya was born near Saragossa, the son of a gilder. He apprenticed with a local painter for four years, then departed for Madrid. After several failures, he began painting church murals. By 1773 he had married a woman well connected in Spanish art circles and landed commissions creating tapestry designs for the Royal Tapestry Manufactory. With this lead, growing skill and a little luck, he was soon doing high-society portraits in a lively rococo style.

Deaf by 1799, he produced *Caprichos,* a set of eighty etchings with aquatint. They are a mixture of humor, horror and exquisite beauty, one of Goya's most appealing graphic works. A complete set, first edition, can bring $130,000–$140,000, less than $1,750 per plate. They were reissued through the nineteenth century, and prints pulled from worn plates are worth a tenth as much.

The series begins with a stern self-portrait: Goya in a top hat. The keynote: Plate 43, *The Sleep of Reason Produces Monsters;* here a man sleeps at a worktable while bats, owls and cats seem to spring out of his subconscious. Goya skewered those who he believed were perverting reason. He showed goblins dressed like monks, peasants cowering around a tree covered with a monk's habit, a group of monks worshiping a parrot. Goya's doctors are donkeys administering quack cures. He pictured the idle aristocracy as effeminate figures helpless in a strait-jacket emblazoned with their coat of arms. A fickle woman (the Duchess of Alba) is carried away by witches. Masqueraders try to see through each other's masks. A victim sits wearing a tall conical hat, head bowed, awaiting his fate from the Spanish Inquisition.

Spain did not have any print dealers, and Goya could not persuade a book dealer to stock his prints, so he ended up offering them through a liquor store in the building where he lived. Once on display, the images caused an outcry. It was considered poor taste for Goya, first painter to the King, to be ridiculing society. Consequently, he withdrew *Caprichos* after just two days, with twenty-seven sets sold. He did make money from the enterprise, because the King seemed to find the images amusing and, after the furor died down, bought the plates as well as most unsold sets.

Uncut images from *Caprichos* are about 12½ by 8¾ inches. Delicate aquatint tones wore off quickly, so fine early impressions are essential if you are to appreciate Goya. Many sell for less than $1,500–$2,500. The self-portrait and *Sleep of Reason* are somewhat more.

In 1808 Napoleon used French soldiers to install his brother Joseph as king of Spain, and this triggered rebellion, savagery and famine. Crisis spurred Goya to create horrifying images: hanging bodies, a beheading, people being torn apart, impaled on trees, cut in two, shot. Bodies are stripped and shoveled into a pit. These are close-ups and are not for the squeamish. They stand as perhaps the most potent antiwar images ever created. Yet amidst the horrors Goya provided a flicker of hope: Plate 7, *Que valor!* (*What courage!*), depicts a woman standing on dead bodies, lighting a cannon, fighting back.

Altogether Goya produced eighty-three images on war. He was afraid to publish them, and they remained unpublished until 1863, thirty-five years after his death. Then they appeared as *The Disasters of War*. The images are about 6 by 8 inches. Because of the gory subject, and because Goya did not print the images himself, they can be purchased for $1,000.

Goya was an aficionado of bullfighting, the Spanish ritual in which a skilled commoner defeats an enraged wild animal. Bullfighting symbolizes the struggle between reason and the irrational, life and death. In *La Tauromaquia*, Goya tackled bullfighting. He started to work out his ideas in 1804 but put the project aside during the civil war. Afterward, the series grew to thirty-three images, first published in 1816. About 9⅝ by 13⅞ inches, they were a popular success. Fine early impressions, which sell for $2,000–$3,000, convey the glare of the noonday sun. You can practically smell blood and dust in the bullring.

Goya's last and most mysterious etchings with aquatints were *Los Proverbios* (*Proverbs*), better known as *Los Disparates* (*Follies*). They were intended to portray pointless stupidities that created the dead-end existence of contemporary Spain, but it is anyone's guess exactly what some of the images mean. Nor does it matter. Goya's spooky, wild-eyed people achieve a surreal quality that strikes a modern chord.

The images are about 9⅝ by 14 inches. Since they were first printed long after Goya died, in 1864, they are less expensive than prints he pulled off the press himself. You will find prices in the $1,000-to-$1,500 range. Collectors pay more for Plate 4, *Bobalicón* (*Big Booby*) which shows a giant with a mad grin across his face and castanets in his hands, mad faces looming behind him. Plate 10, *El caballo raptor* (*The Kidnapping Horse*), a horse rearing up on its hind legs and grabbing a horrified woman with his teeth, commands a premium, too, as does Plate 12, *Disparate alegre* (*Merry Folly*), six people dancing around a circle in an empty space.

In 1819, at age seventy-three, Goya tried his hand at lithography. Before him, artists made pen lithographs that were scratchy and weak. Goya rolled up his sleeves and attacked lithographic stones like a young man eager to establish his reputation. He made a few strong images such as *The Duel* and *The Monk* before fleeing oppressive Spain for exile in France.

There, in 1824, he created four large masterpieces, 12 by 16 inches: *The Bulls of Bordeaux*. Returned to the bullfighting theme, his images have rich blacks, and they are full of light and dust. You can feel the surge of the crowd. It is no wonder that *The Bulls of Bordeaux* are Goya's most expensive graphic works. A fine early impression can sell for $20,000 to $25,000.

Goya's prints are probably his most satisfying creations. Because he did them to please himself rather than patrons, they provide exhilarating views of his free spirit and towering genius.

The Most Underrated Printmaker Today

To most people who have heard of Honoré Daumier (1808–79), his name means caricatures—amusing perhaps, but not the stuff of fine art. Only a handful of his nearly four thousand lithographs sell for more than several hundred dollars. Also, during his own time Daumier was known mainly as a newspaper caricaturist. He had great difficulty selling his paintings and sculptures, and he never made his living from them. But connoisseurs recognized Daumier's genius for creating an unforgettable character with a few strokes. His quivering lines project tremendous energy. He used many different drawing techniques, so he remained fresh throughout his long career. Almost all of his images offer something special.

The novelist Honoré de Balzac remarked, "That fellow has Michelangelo in his bones." The French Romantic artist Camille Corot, the landscapist Charles François Daubigny, the photographer Nadar and others made more than seventy portraits of Daumier. According to biographer Roger Passeron, the Neoclassical master Jean-Auguste-Dominique Ingres "used to sneak out behind his pupils' backs" and view Daumier's latest lithographs. The French romantic artist Eugène Delacroix wrote Daumier: "there is no man I love and admire more than you."

Daumier's incredibly expressive lines influenced later French artists like Édouard Manet, Edgar Degas and Henri de Toulouse-Lautrec. Vincent van Gogh confessed: "I remember being so very much impressed at the time by something so strong and manly in Daumier's conception that I thought it might be a good thing to feel in that way. . . ." American artists reflected Daumier's influence: Robert Henri, John Sloan, William Glackens, Everett Shinn, George Bellows. Daumier cast a long shadow.

He portrayed ordinary people struggling through everyday situations. For instance, *En Chemin de fer—un voisin agréable* (1862), a shot of a woman suffering a man's cigar smoke in a train car, 8¼ by 10¼ inches, early impression, sells for $2,000–$3,000. Or *Le Pipelet du lendemain* (1866), a man interrupting his newspaper reading to chat with a passerby, 9¼ by 8⅜ inches, early impression, is worth $1,500–$1,800. *Baissez le rideau, la farce est jouée* (1834), a clown on stage gesturing with a baton, 7⅜ by 11 inches, brings $1,000–$1,500. *Ayant eu la fâcheuse idée d'aller faire la sieste au bord de l'eau* (1856), two aggravated picnickers trying to keep flies away, 7½ by 10½ inches, is worth $800–$1,000.

Lawyers and judges provided some of Daumier's favorite targets. In a series of thirty-nine lithographs called *Gens de Justice*, Daumier skewered sleeping judges, long-winded judges, rude lawyers, pompous lawyers, hypocritical lawyers. A typical example in this series, *Dites donc, confrère, vous allez soutenir* (1846), 7⅝ by 10¼ inches, might be priced at $800–$1,000.

As a political satirist, Daumier wielded a wicked pen. While it is hard to become involved with old political controversies now, the sheer power of his drawing lifts many images beyond satire to memorable works of art. He caused a sensation with *Le Ventre Législatif* (*Legislative Belly*), which caricatured the supporters of King Louis-Philippe in 1830. They are fat, sour-faced and deformed. This is one of Daumier's most famous images. It is 11⅛ by 17⅛ inches and is worth $8,000–$12,000.

Rue Transnonain, 15 avril 1834, 12 by 18⅛ inches, selling for $6,000–$10,000, depicts several people murdered in their bedroom by French soldiers. It renders the victims with stark dignity. This image secured Daumier's reputation, and it is still considered one of the greatest lithographs ever made.

Born in Marseilles, Daumier grew up in Paris, and that is where he spent most of his life. His father was a glazier who wanted to be a poet but never fulfilled his dream; he imbued his son with knowledge of poetry and the theater, and this was as close to a formal education as Daumier ever got. For the most part, he taught himself. At the Louvre he soaked up Michelangelo, Rubens, Rembrandt and Goya. He observed people in Paris streets. He became fascinated with mischief revealed through facial expressions, gestures and posturing.

After a stint as errand boy and clerk, the teenage Daumier declared his ambition to become an artist. His parents relented, and Daumier joined the studio of a genial academic painter. Before long, Daumier was bored with the dry academic regimen of drawing statues. Meanwhile, he browsed around print stalls. Since he could not afford to paint, he decided to try the then new printmaking process of lithography. At fourteen he made his first lithographs, and soon he was apprenticed to a Paris print publisher.

Daumier began frequenting the offices of republican newspapers that protested against the oppressive French monarchy. He met many artists, writers and the publishers of dissenting publications like *La Silhouette, La Caricature* and *La Charivari.* One or another of them published his work over the years—he averaged two new lithographs a week.

Daumier announced his arrival as a major talent with a lithograph called *Gargantua.* It showed a fat, pearheaded king in a high chair, and taxpayers carrying loads of food up a ramp and dumping it into his mouth.

Periodically censorship was relaxed, and Daumier poured out political caricatures—over a hundred on legislators. He targeted Prussian militarism and British colonialism, championed Irish independence. He attacked the Pope for his doctrine of papal infallibility. If officials cracked down, Daumier turned to social commentary. He did thirty images about bathers, twenty-eight about beggars, thirty-four about philanthropists, twenty about foreigners in Paris, thirty-two about teachers and students, thirty-two about landlords and a deluxe variety assortment of one hundred everyday situations, which sell in the $500–$1,000 range.

During his last years, eyesight failing, Daumier drew with bolder strokes. His late lithographs, after the newspaper images, became a sort of shorthand version of his earlier style.

Reflecting on Daumier's achievements, the twentieth-century American printmaker Will Barnet recalled: "Even in [Daumier's] smallest works there is a draftsmanship of bigness, which taught me the lesson that one didn't have to paint the Sistine Chapel to achieve monumentality."

Most Daumier prints you will see are on newsprint, and they sell for $50 to $200. Collectors, however, want the images on white paper—*en blanc,* as the sales catalogs say.

Inside a Print Catalog

Perhaps the trickiest area of print collecting is analyzing the different states of an image, an indicator of value. Whenever an artist changed a plate and pulled some more prints from it, reflecting the changes, those prints are referred to as a new state. The changes might be trivial or far-reaching enough to create a whole new feeling. Some images exist in a single state, while others might have a dozen states.

Generally speaking, the earlier the state, the more desirable the image. This is partially because collectors prize the original conception of a visual idea. Also, the later the state, the more prints were pulled, the more worn and less expressive a plate is likely to be. To be sure, with some states, only a few prints were pulled, and images from the first and second states might sell for virtually the same price. But usually there is enough wear to result in a 20 percent or greater price drop with each additional state.

How do you tell one state from another? Consult the catalog raisonné, a scholar's analysis of all the known images and states an artist produced. Many contemporary artists do not have a catalog raisonné, so buying their work is tricky. On the other hand, the work of some Old Masters, including a few covered in this chapter, was analyzed by more than one scholar, and there is abundant reference material for a collector to lean on.

To see how you can take advantage of a catalog raisonné, consider *Ponte del Piovan,* an image by the nineteenth-century American expatriate James Abbott McNeill Whistler. He is a good example because he made more changes on his plates than most artists, and if you can keep

1

2

There are plenty of surprisingly affordable fine prints by established artists who are currently out of fashion. now the best buys are found among Old Master and 19th-century prints rather than modern prints. (1) A lively, sympathetic scene of everyday life by the Frenchman Honore Daumier, one of the greatest draftsmen who ever lived. $750–$1,500. *Paul McCarron Fine Prints & Drawings.* (2) An animated image of gypsies by the French etcher Jacques Callot. The original set of 4, called *Les Bohemiens,* was created in about 1621. 4¾ × 9³⁄₁₆; $2,500–$3,500. *Kennedy Galleries, New York.*

3

4

(3) An imaginary, eerie dungeon by Giovanni Battista Piranesi, from his series of 14 etchings called *Invenzioni Capric de Carceri,* first published in 1750 and reworked to be much more haunting, like this one, a decade later. 12¾ × 9½; $3,000–$6,000. *Kennedy Galleries, New York.* (4) "General Folly" from *Los Proverbios,* a mysterious set of 22 etchings with aquatint by the great Spanish painter and printmaker José de Goya y Lucientes. 9⅝ × 14; $1,000–$2,000. *Kennedy Galleries, New York.*

Whistler straight you can probably handle anybody. *Ponte del Piovan* depicts an arched footbridge over water, with buildings in the background. A Sotheby's auction catalog, New York, November 13, 1981, described a print as follows:

> *Ponte del Piovan* (K. 209, M. 206)
> Etching, c. 1880, sixth (final) state, a fine impression, printed in dark brown ink, with plate tone, signed on the tab with the butterfly and inscribed 'imp.,' on an old laid paper, in good condition except for a fox mark in the right hand edge, 9 by 6⅛ inches.

Those capital letters "K" and "M" refer to Whistler's catalogs raisonnés. If you do not know their titles, just ask. In this case, Sotheby's print specialists will tell you the "K" stands for Edward G. Kennedy, *The Etched Work of Whistler: Illustrated by Reproductions in Collotype of the Different States of the Plates* (New York: Grolier Club, 1910). Do not be put off by this ancient date. Cataloguing an artist's work can be a herculean task that few scholars have the stomach for, and unless a catalog is flawed seriously it will remain the standard for years. Despite the date, this catalog should not be hard to find. Art libraries have scholarly catalogs, and many were reprinted. Da Capo, a New York publisher, reprinted the Kennedy catalog in 1975.

Though Sotheby's and most Whistler collectors rely mainly on Kennedy, Sotheby's referred to a second catalog as well: Howard Mansfield, *Catalog of Whistler's Etchings and Drypoints* (New York: Caxton: 1896). Sotheby's point was to enhance the legitimacy of the print by showing that both scholars accepted it as Whistler's.

The numbers (K. 209, M. 206) were assigned to the image by the respective scholars. As best as Kennedy could tell, *Ponte del Piovan* was the 209th etching Whistler made. Apparently Kennedy determined it was a little later than did Mansfield, who listed it as the 206th etching. The exact number does not matter much. It is simply a handy reference. If a print is an authentic *Ponte del Piovan,* the details had better jibe with Kennedy 209.

Sotheby's described our *Ponte del Piovan* as a sixth state. How could they tell, and how could you? Here are the distinctions between the states, according to Kennedy:

> Height—9 inches. Width—6 inches.
> I. Before cloud in the sky; before any shading on the doorway, etc., under the bridge; the roof, under the balcony above the bridge, is only partly drawn. The late Otto H. Bacher.
> II. There are clouds in the sky, the roof under the balcony is completed, and there are indications of a tall third figure to the left

of two already on the center of the bridge. New work all over the plate.

III. There is more shading in the water at lower right; a small boy is now in the center of the bridge, instead of the tall figure. H. L. Quick.

IV. There are a number of short horizontal lines in the sky; there is new work on the top of the parapet of the bridge; vertical lines are on the lower part of it, and also on the supporting timbers. Short lines shade the top of the window-frame just above the bridge at left. W. Dowdeswell.

V. The horizontal lines in the sky and in the water at lower right have been removed; also the figure of the small boy, and part of the lines on the corner of the window mentioned in IV.

VI. There are longer lines on the corner of the window mentioned in V, and new vertical lines, at center and right, in the direction of the arch.

You will note that Sotheby's described its *Ponte del Piovan* print as a "fine impression." This refers to the amount of ink, whether the print is a delicate, light impression, a rich and heavily inked impression or a fresh impression—just right. Impression quality refers to sharpness as well.

The meaning of the terms used varies considerably. A "fine impression of the sixth state" of *Ponte del Piovan* is not as fine as a "fine impression of the first state." This might not be as fine as a fine impression of the first state of another image, or it might be better. You have to compare and see for yourself.

Yet these terms help place a print on a relative scale of desirability. Here are some of the terms you are likely to come across, from most desirable to least:

Superb, rich, early impression
Superb impression
Very fine impression
Fine, fresh impression
Fine, sharp and bright impression
Fine, rich impression
Fine, delicate impression
Fine impression
Very good, strong and bright impression
Very good, exceptionally clear impression
Very good, clear impression
Good, unusually even impression
Good, though showing some wear
Fairly good impression
Later impression
(No comment)

Thus, in the opinion of Sotheby's print specialists, this *Ponte del Piovan* is not the best, but it is respectable. Only you can decide whether it is good enough for you. The answer emerges after you have made many comparisons.

Most dealers and auction houses tend to describe a print as being "in good condition except for . . ." It is the "except" you must keep an eye on. Sotheby's noted that the *Ponte del Piovan* had a fox mark—a brown stain due to mildew—in the right-hand corner. It might not be much, but it could be quite a distraction. Again, there is no substitute for a firsthand look and making up your mind.

These are some more, self-explanatory condition problems you will encounter:

Small tears
Stains
Water stains
Thin spots
Horizontal center fold
Traces of horizontal crease
Touches of gray wash
Lightly soiled
Soiled
Pencil scratches
Pen scratches
Nicked edges
Holes
Pinholes
Restored paper loss
Split along platemark
Reinforced split
Hinge stains on verso

If a condition problem deserves a comment, probably it is serious. Since most prints have some condition problem, you should expect to find something when you examine a print. If you do not, somebody else will, in the event you try to sell the print later.

Generally, the bigger the margins, the better. They provide some protection for the image itself, and they can include watermarks or collectors' marks that might help verify the authenticity of the print. A catalog notation "large margins" is preferable to "small margins," which is better than "thread margins." Sotheby's did not say anything about the margins, so until you see the work, assume they are small.

Okay, you have a good idea about the quality of this *Ponte del Piovan.* How do you estimate its value?

Gordon's Print Price Annual, a comprehensive reference work, does not record any sales during 1980, but two occurred the year before, both at Sotheby's, New York. Here is the shorthand from *Gordon's* about one of them:

> *Ponte del Piovan*—etching—225 x 150—
> K209I—M209—Large margins
> SPBNY—11/13/79—#662......$1,980

The dimensions appear in millimeters, followed by the Kennedy and Mansfield numbers, an abbreviation for the auction house and the city, the date, the auction lot number and the price. The Roman numeral "I" next to the Kennedy number signifies first state, the most desirable. If we look up the Sotheby's print catalog for November 13, 1979, this is what we find:

> *Ponte del Piovan* (K. 209, M. 206)
> Etching, a fine proof impression of the first state of six, on thin white laid paper ("India proof"), with large margins, traces of foxing, pinholes, two thin spots (one reinforced) in the upper edge, and a few printers' creases in the upper portion of the sky, 8⅞ by 5⅞ inches.

From the description here, the impression quality seems better than that of the print we have been considering, but there might be more condition problems. It is slightly smaller than the November 1981 print.

The other print is described in Sotheby's print catalog for February 15, 1979, Lot 497 (it realized $1,210):

> *Ponte del Piovan* (K. 209, M. 206)
> Etching and drypoint, sixth (final) state, printed in sepia, signed in pencil with the butterfly on the tab, on thin laid paper, in good condition apart from slight thin spots in the top edge, 8⅞ by 5⅞ inches.

Going back one more year, *Gordon's* reports a sale on November 10, 1978, again at Sotheby's, New York, Lot 380:

> *Ponte del Piovan* (K. 209, M. 206)
> Etching and drypoint, fifth state of six, printed in sepia, signed in pencil with the butterfly on the tab, on fine laid paper, in good condition apart from a slight crease, and a few tiny nicks in the top edge, framed, 8¾ by 5⅞ inches.

This print realized $1,500, higher than the sixth state which appeared on the market the following year, the one we have described. We cannot conclude from just two examples that the market declined, especially since we did not see the two prints firsthand. An enthusiastic bidder may have walked in during the first sale and missed the second. You never know. At least these three sales seem to establish a ballpark: $1,000 to $2,000.

Since inflation has helped push up art prices generally, you might expect *Ponte del Piovan* to exceed $2,000 now. If you estimate 10 percent increase in each of the years since the 1979 sales, the price would be under $2,000. By checking with dealers who might have a print, you might narrow the estimate further. Sotheby's estimated $2,200 to $2,800. This seems aggressive considering known precedents, but it is not outrageous. The print sold for $2,300.

The details that affect prices can vary from artist to artist. In some cases, signatures are highly important, and in other cases the paper used poses possible pitfalls. Once you garner needed information from a scholarly catalog, you will be able to read between the lines and judge the relative desirability of a print.

For More Information

Theodore Donson, *Prints and the Print Market.* New York: Crowell, 1977.

Frank and Dorothy Getlein, *The Bite of the Print.* New York: Bramhall House, 1968.

Gordon's Print Price Annual. Martin Gordon, Inc., 25 East 83rd Street, New York, NY 10028.

Arthur M. Hind, *A History of Engraving and Etching.* New York: Dover, 1963, reprint of 1923 edition.

William Ivins, *How Prints Look.* Boston: Beacon, 1943.

———, *Prints and Visual Communication.* Cambridge, Mass.: MIT Press, 1980.

A. Hyatt Mayor, *Prints and People.* New York: Metropolitan Museum of Art, 1971.

Paul J. Sachs, *Modern Prints and Drawings.* New York: Knopf, 1954.

Ralph E. Shikes, *The Indignant Eye, the Artist as Social Critic in Prints and Drawings from the Fifteenth Century to Picasso.* Boston: Beacon Press, 1969.

Here are scholarly references for the artists covered in this chapter:

Callot:

Jules Lieure, *Jacques Callot, la vie artistique et catalogue raisonné.* Paris, 1924–29, reprinted 1970.

Daumier:

Loys Delteil, ed., *Honoré Daumier, le peintre-graveur illustre,* 11 vols. Paris, 1926–30.

Dürer:

Albrecht Dürer: Master Printmaker. Boston: Museum of Fine Arts, 1971.

Karel G. Boon and Robert W. Scheller, *The Graphic Art of Albrecht Dürer, Hans Dürer and the Dürer School.* Amsterdam, 1971.

Joseph Meder, *Dürer-Katalog: ein Handbuch über Albrecht Dürers Stiche, Radierungen, Holzschnitte, deren Zustände, Ausgaben und Wasserzeichen.* Vienna, 1932, reprinted 1971.

Dutch Etchers:
Clifford S. Ackley, *Printmaking in the Age of Rembrandt.* Boston: Museum of Fine Arts, 1981.
Irene de Groot, *Landscape Etchings by the Dutch Masters of the Seventeenth Century.* Maarssen, Netherlands: Uitgeverij Gary Schwartz, 1979, distributed by Viking.

Goya:
Loys Delteil, ed., *Le Peintre-graveur illustre: Goya,* 2 vols. Paris, 1922, reprinted 1969.
Thomas Harris, *Goya: Engravings and Lithographs,* 2 vols. Oxford: Oxford University Press, 1964.

Hogarth:
Ronald Paulson, *Hogarth's Graphic Works,* 2 vols. New Haven: Yale University Press, 1970.

Piranesi:
Arthur Hind, *Giovanni Battista Piranesi: A Critical Study, with a List of All His Published Works of the Prisons and the Views of Rome.* London, 1922, reprinted by Da Capo Press, New York, 1967.

Rowlandson:
Bernard Falk, *Thomas Rowlandson: His Life and Art.* London, 1949.
Joseph Grego, *Rowlandson the Caricaturist.* London, 1880, reprinted since.

Museums

ATLANTA
High Museum of Art
1280 Peachtree Street, NE
Atlanta, GA 30309
(404) 892-3600

BOSTON
Museum of Fine Arts
Huntington Avenue
Boston, MA 02115
(617) 267-9300

CAMBRIDGE
Fogg Art Museum
Harvard University
32 Quincy Street
Cambridge, MA 02138
(617) 495-7768

CHICAGO
Art Institute of Chicago
Michigan Avenue and Adams Street
Chicago, IL 60603
(312) 443-3600

CINCINNATI
Cincinnati Art Museum
Eden Park
Cincinnati, OH 45202
(513) 721-5204

LOS ANGELES
Grunwald Center for the Graphic Arts
University of California
405 Hilgard Avenue
Los Angeles, CA 90024
(213) 825-3783

Los Angeles County Museum of Art
5905 Wilshire Boulevard
Los Angeles, CA 90036
(213) 937-4250

NEW HAVEN
Yale Center for British Art
2120 Yale Station
New Haven, CT 06520
(203) 432-4594

Yale University Art Gallery
1111 Chapel Street
New Haven, CT 06520
(203) 436-0574

NEW YORK
Brooklyn Museum
188 Eastern Parkway
Brooklyn, NY 11238
(212) 638-5000

Metropolitan Museum of Art
Fifth Avenue at 82nd Street
New York, NY 10028
(212) 879-5500

Pierpont Morgan Library
29 East 36th Street
New York, NY 10016
(212) 685-0008

PHILADELPHIA
Philadelphia Museum of Art
26th Street & Benjamin Franklin Parkway
Philadelphia, PA 19101
(215) 763-8100

SAN FRANCISCO
M. H. de Young Museum
Golden Gate Park
San Francisco, CA 94118
(415) 751-4432

SAN MARINO, CALIF.
Huntington Library, Art Gallery and Botanical Gardens
1151 Oxford Road
San Marino, CA 91108
(213) 681-6601

WASHINGTON
National Gallery of Art
Fourth and Constitution Avenue, NW
Washington, DC 20565
(202) 737-4215

Where to Buy

New York auction houses offering fine prints regularly:

Christie's
502 Park Avenue
New York, NY 10022
(212) 546-1181

Phillips
406 East 79th Street
New York, NY 10021
(212) 570-4845

Sotheby's
1334 York Avenue
New York, NY 10021
(212) 472-3437

Dealers:

CHICAGO

R. S. Johnson International
645 North Michigan Avenue
Chicago, IL 60611
(312) 943-1661

LOS ANGELES

O. P. Reed, Jr.
521 North La Cienega Boulevard
Los Angeles, CA 90048
(213) 652-5500

NEW YORK CITY

Associated American Artists
663 Fifth Avenue
New York, NY 10022
(212) 755-4211

Theodore B. Donson Ltd.
38 East 57th Street
New York, NY 10022
(212) 355-6970

Lucien Goldschmidt, Inc.
1117 Madison Avenue
New York, NY 10028
(212) 879-0070

James Goodfriend
61 East 77th Street
New York, NY 10021
(212) 725-3571

Martin Gordon
25 East 83rd Street
New York, NY 10028
(212) 249-7350

Paul McCarron Fine Prints
1014 Madison Avenue
New York, NY 10021
(212) 772-1181

William H. Schab Gallery
37 West 57th Street
New York, NY 10019
(212) 758-0327

David Tunick Inc.
12 East 81st Street
New York, NY 10028
(212) 570-0090

SANTA BARBARA, CALIF.

Robert Light & Co.
Box 5597
Santa Barbara, CA 93108
(805) 969-0257

19

HOW TO SELL ART AND ANTIQUES FOR TOP DOLLAR

ON MAY 18 AND 19, 1981, COLLECTOR SAUL STEINBERG OFFERED HIS MULTI-million-dollar collection of modern European paintings and drawings at a Christie's auction in New York. About 35 percent failed to sell. "Big Art Goes Begging," screamed a newspaper headline. Yet during the next two days, May 20 and 21, Sotheby's sold 86 percent of similar artworks, some for record prices. "The two-day depression is over," exulted John Marion, Sotheby's chairman. Observers attributed Steinberg's disappointing results to a botched sales strategy. He reportedly had demanded terms such as steep minimum prices which discouraged bidders. Sotheby's, with a freer hand from its consignors, could be more realistic.

As this case shows, how much money you realize for your art and antiques depends very much on how you handle a sale. Happily, there are straightforward, commonsense steps you can take to realize good prices for your property.

What Is It Worth?

The process begins with determining what your property is worth. This will help you decide whether the time is ripe to dispose of your property and how best to do it. You will gain a basis for evaluating appraisers as well as offers. The more homework you do, the more in control of the outcome you are likely to be.

First, you will need a thorough description of your property if you do not have one already. It should include type of object, style, approximate age, materials used, dimensions, nature of decoration, where made, maker's name if known, any restorations and repairs.

Keep your eye out for seemingly small distinguishing features that can have a big impact on price: some inlay, for instance, the amount of detail in the inlay, original paint, delicate carvings or the presence of a maker's label. Any of these things could increase the value of an antique 20 percent, 50 percent, even more.

With this information in hand, you can see what similar objects are selling for. If you happen to live near an art center like New York, Boston or Los Angeles, you can visit dealers. Inspecting comparable material firsthand will give you confidence when the time comes to negotiate a sale.

But if your property is scarce, you will have difficulty making direct comparisons even in New York. It would be better to consult priced, illustrated auction catalogs available from major international houses like Sotheby's, Christie's and Phillips as well as regional houses such as Skinner's in Boston, Morton's in New Orleans, Clement's in Dallas or Butterfield's in San Francisco. Generally, you can buy catalogs from previous sales for a few dollars apiece. Or you can peruse them at a major art library—most large museums and universities have one. Unlike dealers, who rarely reveal the price an object sold for, auction houses give you a window on the market. Prices are public. Auctions afford your only opportunity to see what art and antiques brought in the past. You can trace a trend by following prices over time.

Auction prices are meaningful for the place where a sale was held. If you happen to have fine French furniture, and you live in Kansas City and want the simplest possible sale, do not expect a New York price. Many French-furniture dealers and collectors monitor New York sales, so prices are usually higher.

If property is worth more than about $2,000, and it can be shipped without undue risk of damage, it is probably worth arranging for a New York sale. Use a professional art packer—ask an auction house or a museum if you need a referral.

With many items such as paintings by regional artists, the best prices tend to be realized locally. For example, art of the American West does particularly well in places like Texas, Arizona and New Mexico. Here you should seek catalogs from the nearest sales.

At the very least, after reviewing hundreds of items, you will find a few similar enough to yours so you can establish a price range. Keep in mind that auction catalogs say little about condition. Usually there is some damage. If the catalog comments about it, you know it is serious. Moreover, fine points like color cannot be conveyed well in a catalog. It gives you a broad view.

As you might anticipate, there are trade-offs to consider. For example, your property might not seem rare, so you would not expect an unusually high price. But it might have pluses: perhaps decorative touches that other examples lack, or it might be a more desirable size.

When reading an auction catalog, note whether objects similar to yours did not sell. They are omitted from the after-sale price list issued by the auction house. For instance, if you see prices for Lots 27, 28 and

30, you know that Lot 29 did not sell. Such an object will not help you estimate the value of your property. But if you see many similar things that did not sell, you know the market is weaker than the auction house and the consignors anticipated.

The more unusual your property, the further back you will have to go before finding an auction catalog with comparable material. Obviously, you should interpret prices that go back several years in light of market ups and downs that have occurred since. With eighteenth-century French porcelain, a flat market for more than a decade, a four-year-old price would still be pertinent. On the other hand, in the volatile gem market, a month-old price might be lower than you would expect now.

If your property is worth more than about $500, you will want a formal appraisal from somebody with specific experience in that type of object. This should alert you to fine points you may have overlooked and strengthen your position when you negotiate a deal.

What You Should Know About Appraisals

There are three kinds of appraisers: independent appraisers, dealers and auction-house specialists. Each offers advantages.

Some people prefer to use the services of a full-time appraiser who has no vested interest in an auction house or in an art or antiques gallery. An independent appraiser should be able to give you whatever type of value you want. From highest to lowest: retail value for insurance; values as a tax-deductible donation or at sale to another collector; liquidation value at auction; liquidation value at a dealer. For a referral, ask a local museum curator or collector. Or contact one of the following appraisers' associations:

- Appraisers Association of America, 60 East 42nd Street, New York, NY 10165, (212) 867-9775. Over 1,100 members in some eighty areas of art, antiques, jewelry, coins, stamps.
- American Society of Appraisers, Dulles International Airport, P.O. Box 17265, Washington, DC 20041, (703) 620-3838. Four hundred members in over thirty areas of art, antiques, jewelry, coins, stamps.
- International Society of Appraisers, P.O. Box 726, Hoffman Estates, IL 60195, (312) 885-2480. Thirteen hundred members in over eighty areas of art, antiques, jewelry, coins, stamps.

Many collectors prefer a dealer who specializes in a particular field. Often such a dealer is more knowledgeable than anybody else around.

Quite a few have published good books, so your familiarity with the literature can give you a starting point.

Your best referral, of course, would come from a satisfied collector. You can reach them through collectors' societies and publications; even the most obscure field has several. Or you can get referrals from:

- Art Dealers Association of America, 575 Madison Avenue, New York, NY 10022, (212) 940-8652. One hundred thirteen members.
- Antiquarian Booksellers Association of America, 50 Rockefeller Plaza, New York, NY 10020, (212) 757-9395. Over four hundred members.
- National Antique and Art Dealers Association of America, 49 East 53rd Street, New York, NY 10022, (212) 355-0636. Forty-two members.

Make it clear that you will not be offering the appraised property to the dealer, so that you do not tempt him or her to give you an unduly low appraisal. It is considered unethical for a dealer to give an appraisal and then make an offer based on it.

Many sellers feel comfortable with an auction-house specialist, because an auction house, like a seller, stands to gain from realizing the highest possible sale prices. Be wary, though, of unrealistically high estimates, a tactic used sometimes to attract consignments. The appraisal should reflect what has actually sold at auction.

If you have doubts about an auction-house appraisal, check their buy-in rates—the percentage of property offered which did not sell. While good general-estate auctioneers report buy-in rates under 5 percent, buy-in rates of 10 to 20 percent are common at the international houses. Statements from a specialist who has assembled numerous sales with buy-in rates over 20 percent should be viewed with skepticism.

An appraisal should provide a detailed description of your property and explain how the appraisal was arrived at. For instance, how recent were the sales that the appraisal was based on? How were these sales interpreted? What features of your property are most noteworthy in the current market?

An appraiser should charge a fee based on the amount of time involved to do the job. Avoid one who charges a percentage of appraised value, since this creates an incentive for an unrealistically high appraisal. Auction houses offer free oral appraisals. The charge for a written appraisal may be waived if you consign the property to that auction house.

You might pay $150 for a letter appraisal of a single antique or work of art. If the appraiser must visit your home, travel expenses are involved. For an assortment of property, you might be quoted $50 an hour by a Midwestern appraiser, $200 an hour or $1,000 a day in an art center like New York. New York auctioneer William Doyle did a $15,000 appraisal for a $2.2 million estate of more than ten thousand items.

When to Sell

If you need cash and have a choice of things to sell, dispose of the ones facing a strong market and try to avoid selling in a weak market. Your own investigation or an appraiser's report should tell you the state of the markets.

With a collection, it is probably worth your while to follow market activity via publications such as *Art and Auction* (250 West 57th Street, New York, NY 10019, $30 for ten issues a year) or *Art Newsletter* (122 East 42nd Street, New York, NY 10168, $92 for twenty-six issues a year). They report on auction sales, noteworthy private sales and other events that can suggest trends.

Keep your eye open for events that might create unusual selling opportunities. For example, the publicity that surrounds an exhibition at one of the nation's major museums can stimulate new buying. The Museum of Modern Art's huge Picasso show, to name one case, stimulated tremendous interest in that artist's work. Prices surged upward, particularly for his prints. An early painting sold for a hefty $3 million during the exhibition period. But if you want to time a sale with an exhibition, make arrangements when it is announced, because by the time it opens, many dealers will be selling the stock they accumulated, and they will not be buying much.

Political problems can provide a sell signal. If a revolution occurs in a country whose collectors lead your market, there may be significant emigration of individuals who suddenly need to sell their works of art for cash. The market can become glutted. This happened to Oriental rugs after Khomeini's revolution in Iran, for instance. If you are interested in selling, better do it fast, because a market can remain depressed for several years.

Selling to Collectors

You can net the most amount of money selling direct to a collector. This is quite commonplace among stamp and coin collectors, for example. In some fields such as antique Navajo textiles, the most desirable material tends to change hands among collectors rather than through dealers or auctions.

How do you find collectors? Your best bet is a collectors' society. *The Encyclopedia of Associations* (Detroit: Gale Research Company, 1979) has a category for hobbies. This volume is a standard library reference. Most collectors' societies publish some kind of periodical, in which case you might find helpful listings in *Ulrich's International Periodicals Directory* (New York: R. R. Bowker Company, 1981), also available at a library reference shelf.

You can talk to collectors who attend shows or advertise in an appropriate publication. Advertising is suitable for low-priced antiques and assorted items. Few advertised items exceed several hundred dollars, and fewer are graphic works like paintings or prints. Serious collectors do not look for masterpieces in the classified ads.

A simple way to learn about prospective buyers, whether collectors or dealers, is to attend auctions and kibbitz with other auction-goers. Ask who they are, where they come from, when they come to town, what they are interested in, what publications they read.

Selling to Dealers

You may not want to seek collectors, because it means dealing with strangers. Or perhaps you have a hard time locating interested buyers. Also, there is concern about security and the time involved in showing your material to casual lookers.

Selling to a dealer, on the other hand, offers several advantages. A dealer handles the marketing on his or her premises. You know what the price will be before you agree to it, and you can get immediate cash.

By contrast, property must be consigned several months in advance of a major auction. You never know how much your property will sell for at auction or whether it will sell at all. Auction houses take up to 45 days to pay after a sale, so you can wait a long time for your money.

Moreover, a dealer can handle a sale in confidence. This is a benefit for people who do not want friends, relatives or the public to know they are disposing of certain material. You can request that an auction house keep your name confidential. But it is always possible that somebody will recognize your property.

Works of art that attract attention, perhaps because of their rarity, can be hard to sell after they have failed at auction, because many people assume there is something wrong with the property. When a dealer handles the sale, less is known about how many prospects may have turned your property down.

The chief drawback of dealers is that generally you will get the least amount of money through them. Certainly this is true when the dealer acquires your property for stock and does not have a ready buyer. Dealers, like most retailers, need about a 100 percent markup, so expect half to a third of retail.

Private dealers can offer more, because they do not carry the overhead of a shop, and they hold little stock. Working out of their homes, they buy what they can sell quickly. If what you are offering is being sought by one of their clients, you might get 75 percent of retail.

Where can you find a dealer near you who handles the kind of property you would like to sell? The aforementioned dealer associations will tell you where their members are located. You can consult the following sources too, though the large number of dealers they cover means at best a ten-word description of stock:

Patricia Bayer and Michael Goldman, *Antiques World Travel Guide to America*. New York: Doubleday, 1982.

Joseph Derum, ed., *Antiques Shops and Dealers U.S.A.* New York: Crown, 1982.

You can see who is advertising currently in arts and antiques publications such as

Americana, 475 Park Avenue, New York, NY 10016, $12 for 12 monthly issues. Slick magazine, broad service coverage, national advertisers.

Antiques and the Arts Weekly, Newtown, CT 06470, $15 for 52 weekly issues. Tabloid that publishes press releases on shows and sales plus a ton of advertising.

Antiques Monthly, 2320 Seventh Avenue, Box 2274, Birmingham, AL 35201, $14 for 12 monthly issues. Upbeat color tabloid.

Art and Antiques, 1515 Broadway, New York, NY 10036, $21 for 12 monthly issues. Slick magazine publishing scholarly, practical articles relating to Americana. National advertisers.

Art News, Box 969, Farmingdale, NY 11737, $22 for 23 monthly issues. Slick magazine focusing on contemporary art scene. National advertisers.

Connoisseur, 959 Eighth Avenue, New York, NY 10019, $19.95 for 12 monthly issues. Slick monthly magazine catering to broad, expensive tastes. Advertisers from England as well as the U.S.

The Magazine Antiques, 551 Fifth Avenue, New York, NY 10176, $38 for 12 monthly issues. Lushest of the antiques magazines. It publishes a dealer directory in its pages from time to time.

Maine Antiques Digest, Box 358, Waldoboro, ME 04572, $24 for 12 monthly issues. Tabloid that publishes the only investigative reporting in the art press. *MAD* provides superb critical coverage of major auctions relating to Americana, and it attracts advertisers all along the East Coast.

Portfolio, 271 Madison Avenue, New York, NY 10016, $18 for 6 bimonthly issues. Slick magazine covering fine arts of the past as well as current activity. National advertisers.

There are innumerable specialized magazines in such areas as Oriental art, American Indian art, textiles. Consult an art library or periodicals directory.

Selling at Auction

Auction houses have gained about half the art-and-antiques market, because typically they charge a 10–15 percent commission which is deducted from the sale price. A dealer can be expected to pay you only half to a third of the current retail value.

Auction houses are the most efficient means of reaching large numbers of prospective buyers. Auction catalogs are distributed around the world, therefore many bids can come from afar. This is an important benefit if you have material, such as Old Master prints, that enjoys an international market. When it is advantageous, an international auction house can ship your property for sale to its branch in another country.

Often the services of an auction house cannot be matched by dealers. For example, some auction houses handle all the headaches of an estate: remove property from a house, broom-clean it, deliver what the heirs wish to keep, sell as much as possible at auction, take less valuable items to secondhand dealers and help dispose of the remainder as you wish—perhaps to your favorite tax-deductible charity.

Some auctioneers are known as the best source for certain material, and property offered there brings top prices. For example, collectors and dealers seeking Victorian Belter furniture regularly turn to Morton's Auction Exchange, New Orleans. Those seeking New England antiques subscribe to catalogs from Robert W. Skinner, Inc., Bolton, Massachusetts.

For a pretty good listing of auction houses, see Daniel J. and Katharine Kyes Leab, *The Auction Companion* (New York: Harper & Row, 1981). Curiously, this is stronger on international listings than on auction houses in the United States.

Tax-Deductible Donation?

In many cases, it is advantageous to donate your art or antique rather than try selling it. For instance, during a recession, offering prices plummet, because dealers conserve cash. They are reluctant to add inventory unless they are confident they can move a particular property quickly. Yet even in tough times dealers try to hold their selling prices as high as before a downturn. They do not like to cut prices, undermine their price structure and jeopardize future profits. Faced with a high retail valuation and meager offers, you might be better off if you donated your property to an interested institution.

Your tax situation also might favor a donation over other ways to dispose of your property, though reduced tax rates make donation a less obvious choice than it was a few years ago. The higher your bracket, the more likely you will gain financially from a donation. The amount of your potential capital gain will affect the calculations, too.

If you do not need cash, and your tax situation is not affected much one way or the other, you might prefer a donation which can bring you a little of the recognition and goodwill that can accompany a donation.

How do you go about making a donation? Unless you have an important rarity, a major museum probably will not be interested. Perhaps a local museum, library or college would. You might start with your alma mater. For more ideas, check *The Official Museum Directory,* published for the American Association of Museums by the National Register Publishing Company, 20 East 46th Street, New York, NY 10017. This reference book lists about six thousand American museums, and it costs $60.

Whatever your choice, your property must be an outright gift; loans or exchanges are not deductible. Furthermore, the Internal Revenue Service's Valuation Branch will allow your tax deduction only if the gift is related to the purpose of the institution. Decorating the halls is not good enough.

Your property must be valued by a recognized appraiser, preferably a specialist in the field. A dealer in American antiques is not likely to be accepted as an authority on the subtleties of Chinese porcelain, for instance.

Fair market value is the IRS standard. That means, in IRS parlance:

> the price that property would sell for on the open market. It is that price that would be agreed on between a willing buyer and a willing seller, with neither being required to act, and both having reasonable knowledge of the facts. It takes into account many factors that affect the value of property on the date of contribution.

The institution must keep your property. If it turns around and sells your gift because it wants to raise cash, all you can deduct is what you paid for the art or antique—not its current retail value.

For the text of IRS policy on donations, see their Publication 561, *Determining the Valuation of Donated Property*. Revised November 1982, it is available through a local IRS office.

Preparing Your Property for Sale

Most art and antiques are bought for their decorative value, but some are meant to be used. Private buyers may be deterred by a distracting condition problem, because it means that the object cannot be used right away. And a private buyer may not know where to have conservation work done right.

If a table has wobbly legs, or a desk has loose veneer, or a canvas is a little torn, seek a competent conservator who can fix them. Taking care of these headaches means that more people are likely to bid on your property, and it is likely to bring considerably more money—perhaps 25–50 percent more. To be sure, a repaired antique will not bring as much money as a comparable example in fine original condition. But repaired decorative objects are sure to do better than those offered "as is."

Usually works of art costing many thousands of dollars are bought by sophisticated collectors and dealers, and to them superficial appearance is not so important. With a painting, for instance, all you need is to have a restorer remove gross dirt. Do not order a thorough cleaning which involves stripping away yellowed varnish. Buyers like to think they are making a discovery, and they are particularly enticed by property out of an estate, long off the market. If you restore such a painting with new varnish, it will look as if a dealer showed it around the trade and could not sell it—tainted goods.

Nor should you worry about dirty, damaged upholstery on high-quality antique furniture. If it can be documented as original eighteenth-century needlework, for instance, it is best left on the furniture, because it will add value. Most upholstery is not original, and prospective buyers rip it away from joints so they can inspect the wood, which is what they are paying for.

Be extremely careful before having anybody work on a surface. If valuable antique furniture is refinished and the mellow old color destroyed, you have probably lost half your money. The surface texture of a print can be altered just enough that collectors do not want it anymore. Overzealous restoration to a painting can leave thin spots, a distressing deformity called skinning.

When in doubt, do not have restoration done. Show your property to an auction-house specialist, for instance, and ask if some restoration would more than pay for itself, and if so what kind of restoration, or whether an object is best offered as is.

Never try making repairs yourself, because quite a few jobs are more complicated than they seem, and if you goof you have no recourse. If restoration is indicated, ask a private collector, a museum, a dealer or an auction house for references. A top restorer is a specialist. Somebody who regilds furniture, for instance, will not touch paintings. Within a category, like paintings restoration, you will find subspecialties—experts who resecure a new backing, inpainters who simulate the artist's style, filling in areas of missing paint.

Keep in mind that a collector and a museum tend to value the soundest restoration. Understandably, a collector is somewhat more concerned about cost, since the money comes out of his or her own pocket. A museum might spend more money on restoration than an object is worth, because the curator's eye is on art history. A dealer or an auction house, on the other hand, might be tempted to order cosmetic restoration, making property look good enough to sell. When talking to a restorer, ask not only the cost but also how long the work can be expected to last.

Ask, too, whether a restorer proposes using techniques that are reversible in case they discolor, glue does not hold, or you want certain work undone. Reversibility is a cardinal principle of restoration, but many widely used procedures leave permanent scars. For example, a startling number of American restorers use wax to bind fresh canvas to the back of a weak old canvas. Wax is a poor adhesive, and, as an oily substance, it is absorbed by canvas. It cannot be removed entirely.

How much can restoration cost? Here are some examples:

Furniture restoration might be figured on the basis of $40 an hour. Fixing a wobbly leg could mean opening a joint, squeezing in some glue and clamping the pieces in place—an hour's work. But if a tongue is broken, it has to be replaced, and the repair becomes a two-hour job, $80.

A new leather top on a partner's desk costs about $30–$35 per square foot. Old leather must be stripped away and the surface cleaned. This is easy if a water-based glue was used, but shellac takes more time. If removing the leather reveals cracked wood, cabinet repairs would be called for. Little strips of wood might have to be placed into the split. Then the top must be prepared to take the new leather. The total cost can approach $400.

Repairing loose veneer: If it is just a single strip, an hour's work might be involved. Any missing pieces must be replaced. This means finding mahogany, rosewood, tulipwood, burl walnut or other woods to match the surrounding pieces. Some veneered furniture, though, is quite battered and might require fifty or sixty hours. The cost would exceed $2,000.

Removing stains from a print: If it is a small, hand-size print, and the job can be done by dipping the entire sheet into a special bleach, the cost might be $20. Larger prints—for instance, 20 by 30 inches—can run the cost up to $75. If a print surface has numerous small stains better removed individually, the cost might be $150. If a particular solution does not work, several others have to be tested. A restorer doesn't want to remove a brown spot if it means leaving a new white one. Such complications can turn a $20 job into a $50 job and so on.

Surface cleaning of a nineteenth-century pre-Impressionist painting, 20 by 24 inches, might run $100. Old Masters (work done before 1800) involve more grime, prior restoration and other problems, so a surface cleaning can cost several times more. Contemporary artists use comparatively less stable paints, and they do not use protective varnish on top of the paint, so cleaning a contemporary work can be surprisingly complicated—as much as $1,000.

Beyond taking care of distracting problems, there may be additional steps you can take to help your property bring more money. The right frame can make a decorative painting more salable to the general public. For instance, a busy painting will look best in a quiet frame. A still-life painting might be enhanced by an elaborate frame. Dutch seventeenth-century paintings look stunning in a simple black frame with a gold stripe running around the border. An old frame can cost $400–$500.

How to Negotiate with a Prospective Buyer

Offer your property to a prospective buyer only after you know about how much it is worth. Do not depend on a prospect's goodwill. Nobody is obliged to pay you fair market value. Having estimated that on your own or with the help of an appraiser, decide how badly you need immediate cash, the lowest price you are willing to accept.

Try to find out how much prospects are willing to pay. Once they have named a price, it is hard for them to offer less. They are more likely to go higher. Savvy dealers push you to name a price, because that means you do not need to be offered anything higher. On the contrary, they will haggle to batter your price lower.

Expect a prospective buyer to pick on real as well as imagined faults in your property. Prepare answers to those objections by familiarizing yourself with faults in similar material a dealer has sold, so that you can relate price to what are apparently acceptable faults. Notice the faults in material displayed at a major museum—for instance, porcelain whose rarity and beauty make it important despite a number of small cracks.

To conserve cash, a dealer may decline a purchase but offer to accept your property on consignment. This is a bad deal. Typically, a dealer takes about 20 percent in commission yet has no inventory risk. In most businesses, a 10 percent sales commission is standard. The 20 percent dealer consignment commission is double what most major auction houses charge, and for their 10 percent an auction house can give your property considerably more exposure.

Even that 20 percent is less than dealers stand to make on property they own outright, so the incentive is always to promote their own property and offer yours only when a prospect happens to ask for something like it. "Your property can gather dust until you lose patience," groused a New York collector. He described one personal experience:

A seascape painting by the French nineteenth-century master Eugène Boudin sat in a fashionable art gallery on New York's Madison Avenue for two years, consigned at $16,000. Then the consignor had his entire estate reappraised and was told that his painting was highly marketable for much more. Eventually the owner pulled his painting out of the shop and prepared to consign it to auction. The gallery owner protested that the consigner was receiving terrible advice, and some unpleasant phone calls followed. The painting sold at William Doyle's, New York, for $43,000.

How to Negotiate with an Auction House

An auction usually involves a sales commission, and the terms vary. The three international auction firms generally charge a 10 percent sales commission. In San Francisco, Butterfield & Butterfield charges a 25 percent commission for lots selling for less than $100, 15 percent for lots selling for $100–$500, 10 percent for lots that exceed $500. Garth's Auctions, in Delaware, Ohio, charges 25 percent for lots fetching less than $50, and 20 percent for lots that exceed $50. Doyle's, New York, charges 15 percent for lots selling for less than $1,000 and 10 percent for everything else.

If your property has a high enough value, you may be able to negotiate the sales commission before agreeing to sell through that auctioneer. In many cases, it is sliced to 8 or 5 percent, and every once in a while, reportedly, to zero—the auction house making its money from the 10 percent buyer's premium added to the price realized.

Another expense is the "buy-in" charge. Ranging from about 2.5 percent to 5 percent of your "reserve" (the minimum price below which the auction house agrees not to sell your property), the buy-in charge is incurred when your properety does not sell. It covers the cost of processing your property and returning it to you. Sometimes the auction house will waive the buy-in charge during negotiations.

Many sellers become greedy and think they can dictate the price at which their property will sell, so they insist on a high reserve. But the higher the reserve price, the greater the risk your property will not sell, leaving you to swallow the buy-in charges and take the property back a bit shopworn.

Some auction houses are overeager for consignments, and they give in to demands for high reserves. This is the main reason why property does not sell at auction. Other auction houses have established a reputation for largely unreserved sales. Property goes to the top bidder. For example, in a recent Americana sale at William Doyle's in New York, just thirty of the 793 lots had reserve prices. This policy attracts swarms of bargain hunters, who, ironically, tend to push prices high. About 99 percent of what Doyle offers actually sells. Remember this when you negotiate a reserve price.

Try to place your property in the most desirable sale. For example, you do not want an important work of art offered in a September warm-up sale that starts the auction season. Prime buyers are accustomed to looking for the most important works in the October and November sales.

Some sales take advantage of another event, such as a collectors' convention or show that brings prospective buyers into town. The most important Americana sales are scheduled in New York for the last week of January, the same time as the prestigious Winter Antiques Show.

If there is a week-long series of sales in your field, and major auction houses are offering similar terms, consider consigning your property to the auction house that will schedule the early sale. Serious collectors and dealers will sit through hours of auction selling, but more casual buyers become weary, spend their budgets and don't stay through the Friday-afternoon sales. Prices can go lower as a result.

Be sure that the sale date you agree upon is specified in the written agreement. You do not want the auction house deciding that for their convenience your property will appear in a different, perhaps less advantageous sale. A competent auction house would not knowingly harm the chances of important property, but with more commonplace items logistics can affect scheduling.

Since many people arrive late at a sale, you do not want your property offered early. Allow people perhaps twenty minutes to make their way through traffic jams. You can figure the pace of an auction like this: With more inexpensive items, usually about two are sold every minute, so you don't want your property among the first forty lots. With expensive paintings, the pace may be one lot per minute; offered after Lot 20, your property will be presented to as large a group of bidders as are likely to appear.

Similarly, people will begin drifting away from a sale before all bidding is completed. There will be background chatter as buyers settle their accounts. Try to avoid having your property offered during the last twenty or thirty minutes.

Expect charges for catalog photographs—perhaps $100 for full-page black-and-white photos, $800 for color, proportionately less for smaller sizes. Some auction houses waive these charges.

Although you can request a color illustration, you may be turned down. Color photographs connote importance that may not be warranted. To maintain credibility, an auction house tends to approve such illustrations only when they believe the property has enough merit.

If your property is superb, request a prominent illustration. The best positions in the catalog are front cover, frontispiece and back cover. You also might ask about the possibility of your property's being used for advertisements of the upcoming sale. There is no guarantee your property will sell with such extra exposure, but it is bound to help.

Generally, the more information the catalog provides about your property, the more appealing it is likely to be. The auction-house specialists will describe it in their customary style, but you must provide historical information such as any prior owners of note, exhibitions where the work was shown, any book or magazine that mentions the work, respected dealers or auctions where it was sold. This information helps assure uncertain buyers that your property is desirable.

A different psychology can work with dealers and some sophisticated collectors. If you withhold some favorable information, the prospect might check the usual references, discover that a painting has an interesting historical association, figure that the work is a discovery and become more determined to buy it.

Expect to pay about .05 percent of your property's value for insurance (again the fee varies). And there will be fees for any shipping and any conservation work you order from the auction house.

Once you finish negotiating with an auction house and sign a contract, keep tabs on your property as it proceeds to the sale. Visit when the presale exhibition is being set up. Examine the condition, making sure your property has not been damaged in the handling. If you spot new damage, let the specialist you deal with know about it. Document the damage and try to rectify the problem before prospective buyers see it.

Notice how and where your property is displayed. At large sales with several exhibition galleries, some will get more traffic than others. Some may have dark corners. Usually the best location is near the podium where the auctioneer will gavel the sale. If you arrive at the auction house as the exhibition is being set up, and you are courteous, you can often persuade the specialist to display your property more advantageously.

Try to sell some of your property every year. The experience will give you valuable firsthand knowledge of the markets that interest you, and you will sharpen your ability to realize top dollar for your property.

While you cannot do much about economic conditions or art-market fashions, there are, as you can see, many ways to help your property realize top dollar. They can cancel out any buying mistakes and, with a little luck, add to your nest egg.

ACKNOWLEDGMENTS

A LOT OF PEOPLE HAVE SHARED THEIR KNOWLEDGE AND EXPERIENCE WITH ME, and I appreciate it.

At Sotheby's, New York: Kevin Tierney on English silver; Mike Grogan on flatweaves; Letitia Roberts on English porcelain; Barbara Deisroth on nineteenth-century sculpture; Harold Stevens on snuff bottles; Nancy Druckman on American quilts; Thomas Lloyd on American pewter; Peter Rathbone on American drawings; Eric Silver on Arts and Crafts pottery; Marc Rosen and Susan Pinsky on Old Master and nineteenth-century prints; Liz Robbins, Debbie Nadler, Batya Knapp and Marcie Stuchin in public relations; John Marion on buying and selling at auction.

At Christie's, New York: Anthony Phillips on English silver; Victor Bernreuther on English porcelain; Jay Cantor on American drawings; Anthony Derham on Chinese snuff bottles; Noel Ainsley and Kathleen Harwood on English watercolors; Dean Failey on American pewter; Alice Levi on nineteenth-century sculpture; Nicholas Stogdon on Old Master and nineteenth-century prints; Elizabeth Shaw, Polly Peabody, Lele Friend and Marjolaine Williams in public relations; David Bathurst on buying and selling at auction.

Phillips, New York: Nicholas Dawes on American cut glass; David Dunham on American illustrators; Cintra Huber in public relations.

William Doyle Galleries, New York: Lee Keeno on American pewter; Helen Kippax in public relations; William Doyle on buying and selling at auction.

John Edelmann Galleries, New York: John Edelmann and Meg Seligman.

Dealers: Edward Munves and Eric Shrubsole on English silver; Ulrich Schurmann, Mark Keshishian and Dennis Dodds on flatweaves; Michele Beiny, La Ganke, Price Glover and Philip Suval on English porcelain; David Rego, Beth and David Cathers on American Arts and Crafts furniture and pottery; Eugene Sung on Chinese snuff bottles; Lawrence Fleischman and Richard York on American drawings; Robert Ellsworth,

Peter Rosenberg, Albert Langdon and Edward Hardy on Chinese furniture; Lucien Goldschmidt, Robert Light, Theodore Donson, Martin Gordon and Jim Goodfriend on Old Master and nineteenth-century prints; Graham Arader, Kenneth Nebenzahl, George Robinson and Kenneth Newman on maps and botanical prints; Bert Melina, who can sniff out almost anything of value.

Scholars and museum people: Charles Grant Ellis, Jenny Housego, Louise Mackie, Walter Denny and Jon Thompson on flatweaves; Nancy Richardson on American furniture; H. J. Janson on sculpture; Patrick Noon on English watercolors; Theodore Stebbins, Paul Cummings, Michael Quick and John Dobkin on American drawings; Robert Bishop on American quilts; Seymour Schwartz on maps; Eleanor Sayre on Old Master and nineteenth-century prints; Richard Hilsop, who compiles the most comprehensive art-market indexes.

Collectors: Richard and Julie Rush have shared their years of experience buying and selling art across the United States as well as Europe. Also Arthur Jenkins, Russell Pickering and Sally Sherrill on flatweaves; Gordon Dunthorne on botanical prints; Henry Kauffman on American pewter and quilts; Paul Magriel on American drawings; Edward Carter on connoisseurship generally.

I have learned a great deal about art conservation talking with John Brealey, Gustav and Mira Berger.

I talked with countless more people in fields ranging from antiquities to drawings, folk art, furniture, gems, paintings, porcelain, primitive art, Russian enamels and antique watches before selecting the fields recommended in this book. To those people and anybody I may have overlooked, my thanks.

INDEX

Ackerman, Rudolph, 211
Adams, Ansel, 18
Adventure illustrations, 117–18
American art and antiques, 17
  Arts and Crafts furniture, 74–84
  brilliant cut glass, 94–103
  illustrations, 114–23
  maps, 180–82
  pewter, 143–52
  pottery, 171–79
  quilts, 190–99
  twentieth-century drawings, 160–70
American Association of Museums, 239
American Gemological Laboratories, 107
American Society of Appraisers, 233
Amidei, Fausto, 213
Amish quilts, 193
Anatolian flatweaves, 46–47
Animal bronzes, 125–26
Antiquarian Booksellers Association of America, 234
Appliqué quilts, 191
Appraisers, 233–35
Appraisers Association of America, 233
Aquatints, 202
Art and Auction, 235
Art Dealers Association of America, 234
Art Newsletter, 235
Art Nouveau, 11, 74, 94, 172
Art Sales Index Ltd., 25
Arts and Crafts movement
  furniture, 74–84
  pottery, 171–79
"Ashcan School," 160
Asian maps, 182–83
Auction houses
  buying at, 22–29
  catalogs of, 19–22
  negotiations with, 243–46
  pre-sale exhibits at, 18–19
  selling at, 238
Audubon, John James, 114
Austin, Nathaniel, 144
Authentication, 16

Baluch flatweaves, 53
Balzac, Honoré de, 126, 218
Barbédienne, Ferdinand, 125
Barnes & Noble, 22
Barnet, Will, 220
Barr, Martin, 66
Barye, Antoine-Louis, 125
Basins, pewter, 144
Baskets
  cut glass, 96, 99
  porcelain, 62
  silver, 35
Bateman, Hester, 37
Beaded Edge flatware, 31
Beakers
  pewter, 144
  silver, 35
Beethoven, Ludwig van, 126
Bellini, Giovanni, 20
Bellows, George, 161
Benton, Thomas Hart, 163
Besler, Basil, 85–86
Bidding
  establishing limits on, 25–26
  strategy for, 26–28
Bijar flatweaves, 49–50
Billingsley procelain, 69

Blackwell, Elizabeth, 86
Blaeu, Willem, 183
Blake, William, 136
Blunt, Wilfred, 85
Boardman, Thomas, 145
Boardman, Timothy, 144, 145
Boardman & Company, 146
Bokhara flatweaves, 50
Bone china, 58–59
Bonheur, Isadore, 126
Bonington, Richard Parkes, 135–36
Bookcases, Arts and Crafts, 76
Boston Museum of Fine Arts, 160
Both, Jan, 206
Bottles
  cut glass, 96
  See also Snuff bottles
Bouchard, Jean, 213
Boudin, Eugène, 243
Bouret, Eutrope, 126
Bowls, cut glass, 95
Boys, Thomas Shotter, 136
Briggs, H., 181
Brilliant cut glass, 94–103
Britannia pewter, 143–44
Bronzes
  nineteenth-century French, 124–32
  Renaissance, 11
Brookshaw, George, 88
Burchfield, Charles, 163
Bury St. Edmunds Cross, 15
Butler, Samuel, 208
Butterfield & Butterfield, 243

C. Dorflinger & Sons, 100
Cabinets, Chinese, 155–57
Callas, Achille, 124
Callot, Jacques, 203–5
Callow, William, 136
Candlesticks
  cut glass, 96
  pewter, 146
  silver, 34–35
Carter, Edward, 14
Carter-Hawley-Hale Stores, 14
Cartoon cels, 118–19
Case, Paul, 49
Catalogs, 19–22
  print, 220–27
Catesby, Mark, 86
Caucasian flatweaves, 47–49
Caughley porcelain, 66, 67
Celluloids, cartoon, 118–19
Chairs
  Arts and Crafts, 74–75
  Chinese, 154
Chalices, pewter, 144
Chamberlain, Robert, 61, 66
Chambersticks, porcelain, 62
Charles Limbert Company, 77
Chests, Arts and Crafts, 77
Chinese art and antiques, 18
  nineteenth-century hardwood furniture, 153–59
  snuff bottles, 104–13
Chippendale, Thomas, 20
Chippendale furniture, 19–20
Chocolate pots, 32, 33
Christie's, 21–23, 231
Christy, Howard Chandler, 117
Coalport procelain, 58, 59, 62, 66–67
Coffee services
  pewter, 146
  porcelain, 60
  silver, 32–33
Collectors, selling to, 235–36
Columbus, Christopher, 180
Copeland porcelain, 63
Corner cupboards, 76
Corot, Camille, 218
Cotman, John Sell, 135
Coudray, Georges-Charles, 127
Coverlets, *see* Quilts
Cox, David, 136–37
Cozens, John Robert, 134
Crandell, Brandshaw, 117
Crazy quilts, 192–93
Cumming, Paul, 160, 166
Cups, two-handled, 34
Curry, John Steuart, 163
Cut glass, 94–103

Da Capo, 223
Dalou, Jules, 127
Daubigny, François, 218
Daumier, Honoré, 217–20
Davies, Arthur, 160
Dayes, Edward, 134
Dealers, 22
  selling to, 236–38

Degas, Edgar, 127, 218
Delacroix, Eugène, 135, 218
Delisle, Guillaume, 182
Demuth, Charles, 161
Derby porcelain, 60–62, 65
Desks
  Arts and Crafts, 76
  Chinese, 155
de Wint, Peter, 134
deWit, Frederick, 183
Dishes
  cut glass, 95
  porcelain, 59–60
  silver, 33
Disney Studios, 118–19
Dodge, Geraldine Rockefeller, 124
Donahos, Steven, 115
Donations of objects, 239–40
Dorflinger, Christian, 94, 100
Dotzel, Michael, 129
Double Irish Chain quilts, 191, 193
Dove, Arthur, 162
Doyle, William, 235
Doyle's, 243, 244
Drawings
  American, 11, 160–70
  Old Master, 16
Dryden, Helen, 117
Drypoint, 201
Dujardin, Karl, 207
Dürer, Albrecht, 202–3
Dutch prints, 205–7

Eastwood chairs, 75
Éditions Mayer, 25–26
Edwards, A. Cecil, 51
Ehret, George, 86–87
Ellis, Harvey, 77
Embroidered quilts, 192
Emerson, Ralph Waldo, 126
Encyclopedia of Associations, 236
English art and antiques
  pewter, 148
  porcelain, 58–73
  prints, 207–12
  silver, 30–44
  watercolors, 133–42
Engraving, 201
Epergne, 35
Etchings, 201–2
European maps, 182–83
Everdingen, Allart van, 207
Everson Museum, 177
Ewers, silver, 34

Faden, William, 181
Fakes, 16
  English silver, 38–39
Falguière, Jean-Alexandre-Joseph, 126
"Famille-Verte" procelain, 61
Family-type illustrations, 115–16
Fashion illustrations, 117
Fawcett, Robert, 116
Feather Edge flatware, 31
Flagg, James Montgomery, 115
Flagons, pewter, 145
Flatware, 31–32
Flatweaves, 45–57
Flight, Joseph, 66
Flight, Thomas, 65–66
Flower prints, 85–93
Ford, Henry, II, 23
Forgeries, 16
  of pewter, 148
Fragonard, Jean-Honoré, 21
French art and antiques
  nineteenth-century sculpture, 124–32
  pewter, 148
  prints, 203–5, 217–20
Fruit prints, 85–93
Fulper, William, 174
Furniture, 13
  Arts and Crafts, 74–84
  Chinese, 153–59
  Chippendale, 19–20
  Victorian, 11

Gamble House, 79
Garbisch, Edgar and Bernice Chrysler, 23
Gashgai flatweaves, 50
Gemological Institute of America, 107
Gérôme, Jean-Léon, 126
Gibson, Charles Dana, 117
Gillinder & Sons, 100
Girtin, Thomas, 135
Glackens, William, 160, 161, 218

Glass
  brilliant cut, 94–103
  snuff bottles, 104–5
Goblets, silver, 35
Godden, Geoffrey, 64
Gordon's Print Price Annual, 225–26
Gorky, Arshile, 166
Gould, John, 137
Gowans, Alan, 11
Goya, 215–17
Grand Rapids oak, 74
Green & Green, 79
Grégoire, Jean-Louis, 126
Grey, Zane, 118
Griswold, Ashbil, 146
Grueby, William, 173–74, 177
Guest, Winston, 30

Hallmarks, 39–41
Hamlin, Samuel, 144
Hartley, Marsden, 162
Harvard cut glass, 94
Hawkes, Thomas, 94, 100
Hearne, Thomas, 134
Held, John, Jr., 116
Henderson Company, 79
Henri, Robert, 160, 161, 218
Herbals, 85–86
Hobbs Glass Company, 100
Hogarth, Richard, 208–10
Holland, James, 136
Homann, Johann, 180
Homer, Winslow, 114
Hondius, Jodocus, 182, 183
Honeycomb cut glass, 94
Hopper, Edward, 114, 162–63
Houdon, Jean-Antoine, 127
Hoving, Thomas, 15
Hubbard, Elbert, 78
Huntington Library, 140
Hurley, Edward, 172

Ickis, Marguerite, 190
Illustrations, 114–23
Indexes, auction-sales, 25–26
Industrial Revolution, 30
Ingres, Jean-Auguste-Dominique, 218
Intaglio printing, 201
Internal Revenue Service, 239–40
International Auction Records, 25–26
International Society of Appraisers, 233

J. Hoare & Company, 100
Jacquard quilts, 193
Jade snuff bottles, 106–7
Jaillot, Hubert, 183
James, Henry, 161
"Japan"-pattern porcelain, 59–62, 66, 67
Jenkins, Arthur, 53
Joan of Arc, 126
Josephine, Empress, 87
Jugs
  cut glass, 96
  silver, 34
Jukes, F., 212

Karaman flatweaves, 47
Karolik, Maxim, 160
Kauba, Carl, 126
Kauffman, Henry J., 143
Kennedy, Edward G., 223
Kernan, J. F., 118
Kettles, 32–33
Konya flatweaves, 46
Kuba flatweaves, 48
Kurdish flatweaves, 49

Ladik flatweaves, 47
Lamps
  cut glass, 96
  pewter, 146
Landscapes, watercolor, 134–35
Laurence, Frederick, 172
Lawson, Ernest, 160
Leab, Daniel J. and Katherine Kyes, 238
Lear, Edward, 137
Legatta, John, 115
L'Enfant, Pierre Charles, 181
Leonard, Reed and Barton, 145
Leonard's Annual Art Index of Art Auctions, 26
Levaseur, A., 126
Levine, David, 116
Lewis, John Frederick, 137
Leyendecker, Joseph Christian, 115
Linnaeus, Carl, 87
Linsey-woolsey quilts, 191–92

Lithography, 200–1
London, Jack, 118
London Goldsmith's Company, 39, 40
Lorrain, Claude, 206
Louvre, 200
Lovell, Tom, 117
Luks, George, 160, 161

Macaulay, Thomas, 58
McCarthy, Frank, 118
McLaughlin, Mary Louise, 171
Magriel, Paul, 11
Manet, Édouard, 218
Mansfield, Howard, 223
Maps, 180–89
Marie Antoinette, 87
Marie Louise, Empress, 87
Marin, John, 161
Marion, John, 231
Marioton, Eugène, 127
Marsh, Reginald, 161, 166
Massoulle, André, 126
Meissen porcelain, 20
Mellon, Mrs. Andrew, 11
Mène, Pierre-Jules, 125
Men's magazine illustrations, 117–18
Mercator, Gerard, 182, 183
Mercie, Marius-Jean-Antoine, 127
Metropolitan Museum of Art, 15, 17, 18, 30, 200
Meyer, Joseph, 174
Minton, Thomas, 63–64, 66
Mission oak furniture, 74, 75
Mitchell, John, 182
Mitchell, S. Augustus, 181
Moignez, Jules, 125
Morris, William, 74, 75
Morris chairs, 75
Morton's Auction Exchange, 238
Mugs
  pewter, 144–45
  porcelain, 62
Muller, H., 126
Munster, Sebastian, 181
Museum of Modern Art, 17–18
Museums, 14–15
  markets and, 17–18
Mythological sculptures, 126–27

Nadar, 218
Napoleon, 87, 216
National Antique and Art Dealers Association of America, 234
National Gallery, London, 21
National Gallery, Washington, 200
Neoclassical silver, 30–44
New England Glass Company, 100
New Hall porcelain, 60
Newcomb Pottery, 174, 177
Nichols, Maria Longworth, 171, 172

Oertel, Abraham, 182
Ohr, George, 173, 177
Old English flatware, 31
Old Master artworks
  drawings and paintings, 16, 20
  prints, 202–7, 212–15
Onondaga Shops, 78
Oriental rugs, 11, 13, 17
  flatweaves, 45–57
Oxford-pattern cut glass, 99

Paintings
  nineteenth-century American, 17
  Old Master, 20
  still-life, 11
  watercolor, 133–42
Palmer, Samuel, 136
Parigi, Giulio, 204
Parrish, Maxfield, 115
Passerson, Roger, 218
Pasteur, Louis, 126
Patchwork quilts, 190–91
Paulson, Ronald, 209
Persian flatweaves, 49
Pewter, 143–52
Phillips, Coles, 117
Phillips, Duncan, 162
Photographs, 11, 18
Photography Art Market, 26
Picasso, Pablo, 235
Pierce, Samuel, 144
Piranesi, Giovanni Battista, 212–15
Pitchers
  cut glass, 96
  pewter, 145
Plates, pewter, 144
Platters, porcelain, 59–60
Pollard, R., 212

Porcelain, 12
  Chinese, 104–6
  English, 58–73
  Meissen, 20
Porringers, 144
Porter, Freeman, 145, 146
Portrait busts, 126
Pots, porcelain, 62
Potter, Paulus, 207
Pottery, American art, 171–79
Prayer rugs, 47
Pre-Columbian art, 16
Préault, Antoine-Auguste, 127
Price, Garrett, 116
Prints, 12, 200–30
  flower and fruit, 85–93
Pyle, Howard, 118

Qashqai flatweaves, 50
Quality, learning to look for, 14–16
Quartz snuff bottles, 107–8
Quilts, 190–99

Rashwan flatweaves, 46–47
Redouté, Pierre-Joseph, 87
Regency silver, 30–44
Regent's China, 66
Reid, John, 181
Relief printing, 201
Remington, Frederic, 114
Renaissance bronzes, 11
Renard, Louis, 183
Restoration, 240–42
Richardson, George, 146
Richer, Paul, 126
Robert W. Skinner, Inc., 238
Robineau, Adelaide Alsop, 177
Rockefeller, Mrs. John D., 11
Rockingham porcelain, 67
Rockwell, Norman, 114, 115
Roghman, Roelant, 207
Rooker, Michael "Angelo," 134
Rookwood Pottery, 171–72, 177
Rose, John, 66
Rothschild collections, 23
Rowlandson, Thomas, 211–12
Royal Academy, 133, 134
Royal Worcester, *see* Worcester porcelain
Roycroft furniture, 77–79
Rude, François, 127
Rugs, Oriental, 11, 13, 17
  flatweaves, 45–57
Rundell & Bridge, 38
Ruskin, John, 74
Russell, Charles Marion, 114
Russian cut glass, 94

Salvers, 33
Sandby, Paul, 134
Sanson, Nicholas, 183
Schaeffer, Mead, 118
Schoonover, Frank, 118
Sculpture, nineteenth-century French, 124–32
Sears, Adeline Harris, 195
Sears Roebuck, 74
Selling
  at auction, 238, 243–46
  to collectors, 235–36
  to dealers, 236–38
  negotiating in, 242–43
  preparation of property for, 240–42
  timing of, 235
Senna flatweaves, 49
Servers, Arts and Crafts, 76
Serving dishes, porcelain, 61
Settees, Chinese, 154
Settles, 75
Sèvres porcelain, 64
Sewell, Amos, 116
Shahn, Ben, 163
Sheerer, Mary, 174
Shinn, Everett, 160, 161, 218
Shirayamadeni, Kataro, 172
Shirvan flatweaves, 48
Sideboards, Arts and Crafts, 76
Sileh rugs, 48–49
Silkscreen, 202
Silver, 12–13
  English, 30–44
Sloan, John, 160, 161, 218
Smith, David, 166
Snuff bottles, 104–13
Society of Arts, 134
Society of Painters in Watercolors, 133
Sotheby's, 21–23, 105, 223–26
Soulen, Henry, 118
Soumak rugs, 48
Special Libraries Association, 187

Spode, Josiah, 63
Spode porcelain, 58–60
Staffordshire porcelain, 60
Star of Bethlehem quilts, 191, 192
Steinberg, Saul, 231
Stella, Joseph, 162
Stemware, cut glass, 95–96
Stickley, Gustav, 74, 76–79
Stickley, J. George, 77, 78
Stickley, Lee, 77, 78
Storr, Paul, 38
Strawberry-Diamond cut glass, 94
Suzani embroideries, 51
Swanevelt, Herman van, 206
Swansea porcelain, 61

Tabbacchi, Odoardo, 126
Tables
  Arts and Crafts, 75–76
  Chinese, 154–55
Tankards, silver, 35
Tax-deductible donations, 239–40
Tea services
  pewter, 146
  porcelain, 60
  silver, 32–33
Tepper, Saul, 116
Textile Museum, 53
Thomas, Cowperthwait & Company, 181
Thornton, John, 88–90
Tiepolo, Giovanni Battista, 213
Tobey, Mark, 163
Toulouse-Lautrec, Henri de, 218
Trapunto quilts, 192
Trays
  cut glass, 95
  silver, 33
Trew, Christopher, 87
Tumblers, cut glass, 95–96
Tureens, silver, 33–34
Turkoman flatweaves, 50–51
Turner, J. M. W., 135
Two-handled cups, 34

Ulrich's International Periodicals Directory, 236
Untermeyer, Irwin, 30
Urns, 33
U.S. Gemological Service, 107

Valentien, Albert, 172
Valuation of objects, 231–33
Van Briggle, Artus, 172
van Gogh, Vincent, 218
Van Loo, Carle, 21
Varley, John, 135
Vases
  cut glass, 96
  porcelain, 62
Velde, Jan van de, 206
Veramin flatweaves, 50
Verneh flatweaves, 48
Victorian antiques, 11, 30, 66
Visscher, Claes Jansz, 205–6
Vlieger, Simon Jacobsz, 206
Voilleau, Sopha, 192
Von Hirsch, Robert, 23

Wall, John, 65
Walpole, Horace, 212
Wante, Ernest, 126
Watercolors, English, 133–42
Waterloo, Anthonie, 206
Webb, Thomas, 94
Weller Company, 172
Whistler, James Abbott McNeill, 220, 223
White-work quilts, 192
Whitmore, Jacob, 145
Whitney Museum, 160, 166
Will, William, 145
William IV, King of England, 67
Willow pattern porcelain, 63
Wine coolers, 34
Wodehouse, P. G., 115
Women's magazine illustrations, 117
Wood, Grant, 163
Worcester porcelain, 58, 60–62, 65–66
World maps, 183, 186
Wright, Frank Lloyd, 79
Wyeth, Newell Convers, 116

Yale University Center of British Art, 140
Yomud flatweaves, 51
Young, Peter, 144

Zhou Leyuan, 105
Zola, Emile, 161